Birds
New to Norfolk

The accounts of their discovery and identification

Keith Dye, Mick Fiszer & Peter Allard

Wren

This book is dedicated to the memory of

Michael Seago
(1926 – 1999)

Birdwatcher, naturalist, writer and author of *Birds of Norfolk* (1967 and 1977)
and co-author of *The Birds of Norfolk* (1999)

A friend and inspiration to all three authors of this book

Cover illustration – Red-breasted Nuthatch & Black-throated Thrush by Robert Gillmor

ISBN 978-0-9542545-3-7
First published 2009 by Wren Publishing, 4 Heath Road, Sheringham, Norfolk, NR26 8JH
Design by Nik Taylor
Printed in Great Britain by Crowes Complete Print of Norwich, Norfolk

Contents

Acknowledgements

Although the three authors will be credited with writing this book, without the willing help and assistance of many other individuals along the way it would never have been published and we owe a great deal to all of them.

We are indebted to Moss Taylor and Wren Publishing for having the belief in our project and Moss's willingness and commitment to be involved once we had approached him. His guidance, drive and enthusiasm, coupled with his extensive knowledge and advice, were the major influences in ensuring that this publication came to fruition.

We are extremely grateful to Bryan Bland for taking time out from his busy schedule to write the detailed and fascinating Foreword, for bringing to our attention some important additional early references and for correcting errors in the text, to Nik Taylor for his impressive work in designing the book, to Chris Taylor for taking the excellent photographs of the specimens at the Castle Museum, Norwich and to Dawn A. Balmer, Julian Bhalerao, Neil Bowman, Jon Clatworthy, David Cottridge, Dave Curtis, Steve Gantlett, Barry Jarvis, Mike Lawrence, Iain Leach, Pete Morris, Pete Wheeler, and Steve Young, who willingly allowed us to use the pictures we already had, or provided alternative copies of their photographs.

A special thanks goes to artists Norman Arlott, Robert Gillmor and Gary Wright for providing their superb vignettes to complement the species' accounts, and additional thanks must go to Robert Gillmor for designing and creating the most attractive and evocative linocut for the dust jacket.

A special thanks to Keith Naylor who allowed us to use his extensive archive of Norfolk rarity records and histories, without which our research would have been so much more arduous.

We are also very grateful to Dr. Chris Brookings who generously donated all of his volumes of *British Birds* to Keith Dye, when he moved house on his retirement from medical practice, providing us with valuable on-hand reference material and to Doug Mayes and Guy Oxborough, who allowed us to use particular volumes in their *British Birds* collections for our research (all before the advent of British Birds *interactive*).

We are indebted to Roger Riddington (Editor) who gave advice and permission to quote from *British Birds* and allowed us access to the BBRC archive, Colin Bradshaw (former Chairman), Adam Rowlands (current Chairman) and Nigel Hudson (Secretary) of the BBRC for their willingness to research and give advice on the rarity records we were having difficulty tracking down and Andrew Harrop of the BOURC for his advice and guidance regarding some older, perhaps contentious records. We really would have struggled with some species without their very important input.

Special thanks must also go to John Marchant for his thorough research into the BBRC archive on our behalf, looking for, and finding, unpublished information on some older, little-referenced records, and for putting us in contact with several finders of county firsts.

Our grateful thanks to Dr. Tony Irwin of the Castle Museum, Norwich for arranging and providing access to the museum's collection of birds for them to be photographed, and to both he and David Waterhouse for their willingness to give us all the background information on the specimens we were writing about. In the course of our research we also contacted several other museums around the country regarding important specimens in their collections and our gratitude is extended to Sarah Kenyon of Saffron Walden Museum, Dr. Gerald Legg and Jeremy Adams of the Booth Museum, Brighton, Phil Watson of the City of Birmingham Museum, Nigel Cleere of the Natural History Museum, Tring, Tim Thorpe of King's Lynn Museum and Jonathan Clatworthy of Birmingham University (where some important collections were stored).

We would like to thank Mark Grantham, Population Biologist at the BTO, for his speedy response to our requests for details on certain ringing records, and for drawing our attention to other important facts, and Aevar Petersen of the Iceland Bird Ringing Scheme for his quick response and willingness to assist in providing information requested.

Between us we spent many hours at Great Yarmouth Library and wish to thank Michael Bean and the staff there for their advice and willing assistance in making available to us the library's full set of the *Transactions of the Norfolk and Norwich Naturalists' Society*. Thanks also to the British Library at Wetherby, West Yorkshire and Cambridge University Library for providing us with many of the *Zoologist* references we requested.

Special thank you must also go to Sylvia Seago for allowing us access to her late husband's, Michael's, personal diaries and notebooks, which considerably helped in our research.

Mark Hawkes and Bruce Martin of the Cambridge Bird Club were a great help and our thanks to them for their efforts in gaining permission for us to quote from CBC Reports, and their willingness to provide all the CBC records we requested, particularly those concerning Wisbech Sewage Farm. Thanks also to Steve Gantlett and Richard Millington for their advice on some older records, and for permission to quote from *Birding World*, Bernard Bishop for giving permission for us to quote Billy Bishop from *Cley Marsh and its Birds* (1983) and for offering any help he could, Bill Oddie for granting us permission to quote from *Gone Birding* (1983), Tim Sparks and John Lines for their permission to quote from *Chapters in the Life of Robert Marsham Esq. F.R.S. of Stratton Strawless, Norfolk* (2008), Percy Trett for permission to quote him from the *Eastern Daily Press* and *Bird Watching* magazine for publishing our appeal for information regarding certain little-referenced records.

Thanks also to Peter Cranswick and Carl Mitchell of the Wildfowl and Wetlands Trust for their help in researching the Trust's archive material, Don Dorling for assistance with Norfolk Wildlife Trust archive material and Dave Holman for information on and providing accounts of some little-referenced records. All provided us with important missing details.

We are grateful to Giles Dunmore for his willingness to help in any way he could and for giving his permission, as editor of the *Norfolk Bird Report,* to use material from the reports, and Jim Scott of the RSPB for providing the dates of certain records.

Several clubs and associations within the county are owed our thanks: Norfolk Bird Cub for permission to quote from *NBC Bulletins*, Great Yarmouth Bird Club for permission to quote from their *Newsletters*, Sheringham Bird Observatory for permission to use their archive material and Norfolk Ornithologists' Association for permission to use, and for providing details of, certain records in their logbooks. We would also like to extend our thanks to Peter Clarke, former warden of Holme NOA Reserve, for his help with background details to some records.

We also wish to take this opportunity to thank the following for helping with historical research and locating people from whom we needed information: Andrew Bloomfield, Cley Bird

Club, Dave and Jacquie Bridges, John Burton, Judy Dunmore, Andrew Easton, John Eaton, Lee Evans, Jean Gaffney, Jeremy Gaskell, John Gooders, Allan Hale, Stephen Halliwell, Barry Jarvis, Eddie Jones, Maurice Jones, Colin Kirtland, Linda Larkowsky, Alan Leitch, Tony Marr, Derek Moore, Phillip Palmer, Malcolm Perch, Andy Musgrove, John Oates, Richard Porter, Peter Ransome, John Redshaw, Andrew Stoddart, Haley Thompson, Colin Tooke, Margaret Watson, Nicola Wingfield, John Williamson and Robert Wilton.

The authors wish to acknowledge and especially to thank all the individuals who provided us with their unpublished accounts or gave us permission to use their accounts published elsewhere. We could not have written this book without you. We very much appreciate how co-operative and helpful everyone was that we approached during the course of this project, we could not have done it without their very valuable and unique contributions. After all a first for Norfolk can only be found once, or can it?! Our sincere apologies to anyone we might have inadvertently omitted, it is entirely the fault of the authors.

Finally, Keith wishes to thank his partner Sue and son Robert for their encouragement and understanding during the endless hours he spent in his study at his desk and laptop, and at various libraries and museums researching material for this book.

Mick would like to thank his long-suffering wife Rada, daughters Nicola and Karen and granddaughter Angelina for their patience in understanding his passion for birds, and finally his old school teacher Mr. Breeze who first encouraged his interest in the natural world.

Peter would like to thank his wife Susan for her understanding and patience during the period this book was being written and researched, also his grandsons Matthew and Ethan, who wondered why 'grandad' was spending such long hours in his study and paying little attention to them.

Thank you all!

8

Foreword

In September 1986 most of the clients on my week's residential birding course had been to me many times during the previous ten years and were united on one front: 'This year you are not persuading us to trek out to Blakeney Point yet again'. But by the Friday we had cleaned up on all the known attractions, having explored the north coast, the Brecks, and the Broads. So I opted to lead them on a low-water walk to Scolt Head island. Long before we reached the dunes the mutterings had started: 'It's a con... this is Blakeney Point in disguise... how much further?' I realised that their effort had to be justified. I was desperate to pull something out of the hat. Anxiously scanning the sea I spotted a Velvet Scoter. At least that was something. Then I found an eclipse drake King Eider. That would do. It was the first I had seen in Norfolk. Nor could I recall having missed any. It transpired that it was indeed the first 20th century record... a Norfolk lifer for everyone. But it wasn't a Bird New to Norfolk. There had been three a hundred years before. That's the thing about Norfolk. Written bird records go back over a thousand years. From the Blickling Homilies, medieval falconry records, inventories of wedding feasts, and the House-hold and Privy Purse Accounts of the L'Estranges of Hunstanton 1519-1578, to the Accounts of Birds found in Norfolk by Sir Thomas Browne in the mid-17th century, the various bird calendars of the 18th century (notably Sir Robert Marsham's Indications), and an overwhelming proliferation of ornithological publications throughout the 19th century - to say nothing of the magnificent county bird books of the 20th century - Norfolk has documented its birdlife more than any other 2000 square miles on earth (and this does not even begin to take into account the more tenuous circumstantial evidence implied by the wealth of birds accurately depicted in the margins of so many East Anglian illustrated manuscripts of the 13th and 14th century, presumably observed locally by the monks who drew them: Bullfinch, Goldfinch, Coal Tit, Wood Pigeon, Jay, Crane, Spoonbill, Goshawk, and even - arguably - Common Gull, Chough, and Capercaillie.) So tracing a first for Norfolk means endless research into diverse source material not always in print. The authors have been commendably thorough and have even unearthed some errors in previously published records. Where there is room for doubt they have helpfully quoted from different sources with enough information for the reader to appreciate the situation. When was the first Cetti's Warbler, for instance? Or the first Thrush Nightingale? Or Marsh Sandpiper? Moreover, all taxa are included. Not only is this sensible in these days of escalating splitting when so many former races are being promoted to full species status but also it is actually interesting to learn that although long suspected, the first confirmed county record of *coburni* Redwing was not until November 2008 (a dead bird carrying an Icelandic ring).

But this is no mere checklist of dates. The subtitle of this book is significant and the accounts of the discovery and identification of the various species make fascinating reading. The generous quotations from all these historic references allow us to enter so many other worlds. The past is indeed a different country. Not only is the name of the bird often different but so is the focus of attention. 'Mr Wigg has had two specimens of the Castaneous (Ferruginous) Duck, both killed at different times in the neighbourhood of Yarmouth. One of them was preserved by Mr Youell; the flavour of the other was said to have been excellent'. Even more surprising is T. E. Gunn's comment on a White's (Scaly) Thrush in the Zoologist 1871: 'I had the breast cooked, and found the flesh firm and the flavour not unlike that of a woodcock'. Coincidentally Thomas Southwell writing of the same bird in Stevenson's The Birds of Norfolk vol III 1890 observes 'Mr Borrett confirms the statement of the other fortunate observers of this rare bird, that its appearance on the wing was so like that of a woodcock as to lead them to mistake it for one'. No recent description of White's Thrush mentions that it looked and tasted like a Woodcock. Fascinating also is the fact that the first Yellow-browed Warbler was 'shot with a 10-bore gun and very large shot... the man who shot it fired off his battered old muzzle loader at the first bird he saw rather than take it home loaded'. Similarly the first Mediterranean Gull was 'shot purely by accident with a cartridge the shooter could not extract... he was simply wanting any bird that might come'. And what could evoke an earlier era in ornithology more immediately than the fact that the first Pectoral Sandpiper (1830) was identified by Audubon who was staying in England at the time? The same applies to the first Savi's Warbler which was examined by Temminck on a visit to England (1819). The specimen was the only one known to science. The species obviously was problematic as a cased Thrush Nightingale presented to Mr L .A. C. Edwards in 1908 was labelled 'Savi's Warbler, Norwich, 1845'. These examples of firsts for Norfolk also happen to be firsts for Britain and it comes as no surprise that this applies to over 30 species, as diverse as Bearded Tit and European Roller in the 17th century, Wallcreeper and European Bee-eater in the 18th century, Macaronesian (Little) Shearwater and Flat-billed (Broad-billed) Sandpiper in the 19th century, and Rock Sparrow and Red-breasted Nuthatch in the 20th century. And surely it is time that the unringed first-winter 2001 Ross's Goose is allowed to continue the tradition in the 21st century? (Happily, the authors include it in their category D appendix.)

This sense of history, this connection with the past, can be reinforced beyond the mere reading of all these contemporary accounts as the authors reveal where we can examine as many as 54 firsts for Norfolk which are still intact around the country in various collections - at least 32 in the Norwich Castle Museum, at least 13 in the City of Birmingham Museum, and others in Great Yarmouth, King's Lynn, and Holkham Hall.

But where do historical records cease and modern accounts begin? The 1934 Cream-coloured Courser (still on display in the Norwich Castle Museum) or the 1969 individual (coincidentally at Morston where the first was seen in 1847)? The 1955 Collared Doves? The 1922 Eversmann's (Arctic) Warbler? If 'within the living memory of any reader' is the criterion then the more recent accounts are just as fascinating as the historical ones and the authors are to be congratulated in amassing a full set of first-hand anecdotes either specially penned by the finders or taken from the unpublished files of BBRC archives - as invaluable as the out-of-print historical records which they have gathered together in this one place. These 20th century records provide constant opportunities for nostalgia and will revive many happy memories for every reader. Take the 1976 Zitting Cisticola. I recall Nick Dymond bursting into my kitchen at Cley as I was cooking breakfast for my group with the news that he had just found a Fan-tailed Warbler. In true Francis Drake tradition I finished the cooking and was still able to show the group the bird - five days later at Holme. Or the 1981 River Warbler. In an attempt at semi-suppression I was driven to that blindfolded - having been told neither the species nor the location though I guessed the identity of the mystery bird en route and naturally identified the location immediately on arrival. For the record, the farmer dismissed the 'widening' of the footpath as negligible compared to the damage done by rabbits every year (but thanked us for the apology).

Nevertheless, thanks to a TV crew who stood in the crop to film the crowd, a cartoon appeared in The Daily Telegraph captioned 'They do say that the appearance of the River Warbler heralds a bad harvest'.

(Ah yes, suppression. Some accounts will revive memories that are not so happy. But surely the story told here of last year's White-crowned Sparrow at Cley proves that, given goodwill and organisation, suppression is never the necessary option. And as for the very occasional bad behaviour of today's desperate twitcher which has occasioned news to be withheld 'in the best interests of the reserve'- that, though reprehensible is put into perspective by reading of the bush-bashing of Victorian times when 'every sort of device was tried to induce the birds to show themselves, including the dragging of chains and ropes through the bushes' - before the bird was shot. That quotation comes from a lengthy article by Clifford Borrer - reproduced in full - occasioned by the 'securing' of the first British Pallas's Barred Willow-Warbler in 1896.)

One date which will surely ring the most bells is 30th May 1993 when it was possible to see three Birds New to Norfolk in one day: Oriental Pratincole, Asian Desert Warbler, and Pacific (Fork-tailed) Swift. For me it was the first day of a residential course and joining us were a journalist commissioned to write an article on birdwatching for Country Life and his beautiful actress wife Ciaran Madden - complete beginners, though Ciaran had played Linnet, the leading lady in the feature film The Green Knight. I don't think they fully appreciated the significance of this triplewhammy and I'm sure they found the Goldfinches and Greenshanks just as exciting.

Every reader will have his own memories: the 1989/90 Red-breasted Nuthatch, the 1992 Rüppell's Warbler, the 1993 Lanceolated and Paddyfield Warblers, the 1996 Blyth's Reed Warbler... And still they come. In the opening five months of 2008 there were another three county firsts.

As the authors observe in their Preface '…the old adage of What's hit is history, what's missed is mystery has been replaced by Always expect the unexpected.' That must surely have been adopted as the motto of the ringers at Croxton, a small village outside Thetford in south-west Norfolk (ie an inland site in the east of England), when a Grey-cheeked Thrush appeared in their nets in 2004. When the first British Little Whimbrel appeared in Mid Glamorgan I had to choose, on my one day off, between heading south-west to Wales or north-east to Cleveland for the Long-toed Stint. On the grounds that there would be plenty more Long-toed Stints but I would never see another Little Whimbrel I opted for the former. Three years later Little Whimbrel was a Cley window-tick for me. I still haven't seen a Long-toed Stint.

The story of Birds New to Norfolk is the story of birds and birding in Britain. It combines an academic historical perspective with stories encapsulating the excitement of modern birdwatching. Every page contains fascinating facts and evocative anecdotes. We owe a great debt to the three authors for bringing together so much archive and original material to conjure up not only all our yesterdays but also the yesterdays of our ancestors.

Bryan Bland
Cley next the Sea, Norfolk

Introduction

Norfolk is the third largest English county with a maximum length from east to west of 105km and a width from north to south of 65km. The coastline stretches for over 130km and this together with the Fenland rivers to the south-west and the Rivers Little Ouse and Waveney which make the southern boundary, create a virtual island.

Henry Stevenson in *The Birds of Norfolk* (1866-1890) divided the county into six geographical areas of habitat namely, 'Broad', 'Cliff', 'Meal', 'Breck', 'Fen' and the 'Enclosed' regions. These subdivisions remain largely relevant today although obviously changes to the habitat and species' use of them will have altered to a lesser or greater degree.

By dividing the county roughly into four sections those regions can be considered to cover the following areas today: 'Broad' takes in the south eastern area, 'Breck or Breckland' is an area of 94,000ha to the south west of the county; 'Fen' to the north-west and the 'Enclosed or Farm-land' district covers all the agricultural central and northern parts of the county. The 'Coast' speaks for itself, but we are very fortunate to have two excellent and ornithologically famous estuarine habitats in Norfolk: The Wash in the north-west and Breydon Water in the south-east. Almost the whole of the north Norfolk coastline from Holme to Salthouse is a wonderful habitat of saltmarsh and tidal creeks and that area, which includes the famed Scolt Head Island, Holkham Pines, Wells Woods and Blakeney Point, is renowned for turning up rare birds.

With such a diverse range of habitats within the county it is no wonder the range of species attracted to it is so great, earning it a reputation as one of the best areas in Britain for birds and birdwatching. All that we lack is fast flowing water, large lakes, rocky cliffs and coastline, high hills and mountainous areas. The current Norfolk List stands at 428 full species out of a British List of 583 full species (March 2009). In south-east Norfolk in particular there are differing opinions between Suffolk and Norfolk recorders regarding the actual Norfolk/Suffolk County Boundary. Suffolk tends to follow the old Watsonian vice county system and Norfolk goes with the administrative changes that occurred in 1974. As a result of these differences of opinion there is a considerable overlap covering distances of up to five miles, where records are claimed and recorded by both counties and can appear in both counties' annual Bird Reports. For any firsts that occurred in these areas prior to 1974, we have added a notation to that effect.

Research reveals that for bird species that were numerous or well known in the county in the 17th, 18th and 19th centuries when records were first being published, it is impossible to obtain details of all first occurrences in Norfolk. Obviously with many of the commoner species and the less common, there will be fossil records and earlier dated records of recoveries from excavations within the county, but in many cases it is not possible to determine with absolute accuracy whether they arrived at that site by accident or design, or indeed when. These are not included in the scope of this book. In the case of written records prior to the 18th century, some, as in the case of the unpublished diaries and journals of Robert Marsham (1708-1797) of Stratton Strawless have been lost or at best scattered. This book includes, where known, details of all known firsts for Norfolk, including where possible, written accounts by the original finder(s). Recognised races are also included. If it has proved impossible to find details of the first published dated record, the first published dated reference has been used. The species categories and nomenclature follow that of the BOU List for English and scientific names, which includes the now agreed international English name as published in "*Birds of the World – Recommended English Names*" by Gill and Wright (2006) on behalf of the International Ornithological Congress. The more regularly used and recognised English vernacular names, if markedly different, are shown in brackets.

Finding a first for the county is something most birders only dream about. But for those very fortunate individuals, whose dream becomes a reality, it brings on at the time feelings ranging through nervousness and disbelief to elation. All three authors have found birds that were new for Norfolk and have experienced these emotions - Peter an incredible 10 times, Mick twice and Keith once. As will be seen in the species' accounts there are several individuals who have been involved in the finding and/or identification of more than one first for the county. Besides Peter's 11 and Mick's two, at least two individuals have been involved with six, two with five, three with four, five with three and nine with two firsts. Most if not all are, or were, dedicated 'patch workers'.

Obviously most of the earlier dated accounts in this book may not convey that special feeling in any detail, as many are not related first hand, but in many of the more recent personal accounts this comes across extremely well. When quoting the actual finders' accounts, the grammar and spelling within the original has been followed, both for the older records from earlier publications as well as the recent ones, in order to retain the 'feel' of the occasion.

References are made in the species' accounts to various documents and publications, not all of which are still in print. A number of the more important pre-20th century publications are extensively referred to in the text and some of these references require a more detailed explanation.

"Extracts from the Household and Privy Purse Accounts of the L'Estranges, of Hunstanton, from 1519 to 1578". (Published by D. Gurney Esq. in the *Transactions of the Royal Society of Antiquaries,* for 1833).

Henry Stevenson in the preface to *The Birds of Norfolk* Vol. l. (1866) adequately describes the importance of these ledgers. 'That the "items" in this "private ledger" would assume, in the after years, a literary importance, was of course, never contemplated by its compilers, but from many of its quaint entries an insight is obtained, not only into the habits and customs of the period, but also as to the scarcity or abundance of certain birds in this county, and their use at that time for the table or sporting purposes.'

An Account of Birds found in Norfolk by Sir Thomas Browne, but not published until after his death in 1682. (Wilkin's edition of his works, vol iv 1835-36).

Stevenson again adequately describes this work 'This short but most valuable list of species, which dates only a century later than the L'Estrange accounts, affords the means of comparing, with singular accuracy, the present state of the county with its ornithological condition about two hundred years ago. In some few instances, also, we get glimpses of a still earlier period, in the "hearsay" evidence of that most enquiring and universal genius.'

Notes and Letters on the Natural History of Norfolk more especially the Birds and Fishes - from the manuscript of Sir Thomas Browne, M.D. (1605-1682) in the Sloane Collection in the Library of the British Museum and in the Bodleian Library, Oxford with notes by Thomas Southwell, F.Z.S. (Jarrold 1902).

This consists of very interesting accounts by Browne of the birds and fishes he encountered and his letters to Dr. Christopher Merrett among others, which gives a real insight into Browne's interest and passion to get the information on record. Not an easy task for Southwell to first decipher Browne's handwriting (of which there is a photograph of a page of a letter to Merrett) and then translate that into the species being described as accurately as possible.

"Indications of Spring" by Robert Marsham (1736-1789) was published *in extenso* in the Royal Society's *Philosophical Transactions* for 1789, extracts of which appeared in the *Transactions of the Norfolk and Norwich Naturalists' Society* 1874-1875: 31-45.

These were Marsham's annual records of first occurrences of seasonal events in the Stratton Strawless area, an activity known as phenology. He kept important records of weather and temperature, tree foliation, crop progress and migrating birds. In 1736 he commenced the series of records that developed into 27 "Indications of Spring". On his death in 1897, the indications of spring were continued by successive members of the same family until 1958, representing the longest, unbroken set of such records in the United Kingdom and they have been inspirational in the recording of phenology during the 19th, 20th and 21st centuries.

British Ornithology by John Hunt. (Norwich 1815).

Stevenson states 'Next in point of date, though after a long interval, this work, compiled and illustrated by the late Mr. Hunt, anengraver and bird preserver in Norwich, but unfortunately never completed, contains many valuable notes on Norfolk Birds, and in both the drawing, colouring, and engraving of itsnumerous plates, exhibits a very considerable amount of talent in the artist.'

"A Catalogue of the Norfolk and Suffolk Birds, with Remarks" by the Rev. R. Sheppard and the Rev. W. Whitear. *Transactions of the Linnean Society* (1826).

Stevenson writes 'This admirable paper, the first part of which was read before the Society in 1824, contains a complete list, to that date, of the birds of both counties, and was evidently the result of a gradual awakening interest in Natural History subjects. Arranged in a scientific form, its ample details supply many interesting particulars at a time when certain species, now no longer resident, were gradually becoming scarce.' A limited edition of 25 hardback facsimile copies was reprinted from the original paper by St Ann's Books (Malvern 1995).

"Extracts from the Calendar of the Rev. William Whitear 1809-1826" by the Rev. William Whitear. *Transaction of the Norfolk and Norwich Naturalists' Society* (1881-1882).

This little known diary of Whitear's observations during the period given mainly covers the Starston area. But it also includes his visits elsewhere and includes many early and important references to the county's avifauna.

"A List of Birds", contributed by Mr. Hunt to *Stacey's History of Norfolk* (1829).

Stevenson states 'This contribution to the general history of the county contains notices of many rare specimens either in the possession of the author or other local individuals, and here, again, the gradual decrease in the numbers of certain species is specially noticed.'

Sketch of the Natural History of Yarmouth by C.J. and James Paget (1834).

Stevenson remarks 'Confined exclusively to the fauna of Yarmouth and its neighbourhood, the ornithologicalportion, of course, forms a prominent feature in such a district, and though the remarks on each species are extremely brief, yet the carefully written introduction contains many curious facts with reference to the amount of wild fowl and other shore birds then visiting our coast.'

Observations on the Fauna of Norfolk by the Rev. R. Lubbock (1845).

Stevenson comments 'This deservedly popular work, and the one with which our local naturalists are best acquainted, professes only to treat of the rarer kinds among our land birds; but of such species as are found in the "Broads District," – of the peculiar features of that portion of the county, and of the formation and working of decoys, the author's descriptions leave nothing to be desired. Both for its felicity of style and abundant information, it must rank as one of those happy efforts of the "out-door" naturalist, for which White's Selbourne, as the first example, created a fresh demand.'

A new and enlarged edition of this book appeared in 1879. Edited by Thomas Southwell, it had additional information and contained unpublished manuscripts of the author as well as notes added by Southwell himself.

"An Account of the Birds found in Norfolk" by Messrs. J. H. Gurney and W. R. Fisher. (Published in the *Zoologist* for 1846).

Stevenson states 'It is greatly to be regretted that this, the latest and most perfect list of the "Birds of Norfolk," has never been re-published for general circulation. With the exception of a few subscribers to the "Zoologist" at the time, scarcely any of our local naturalists are aware of its existence. Indeed, with the exception of Lubbock's "Fauna," the same may be said of nearly all the rest, whilst both Mr. Hunt's and the Messrs. Paget's works are out of print, and extremely scarce. With this catalogue, comprising short notes on each species, and including many rarities not hitherto recorded, was also given a very valuable introductory paper, in which the natural attractions of the county for the feathered tribe, the local changes that have of late years affected our residents, and the chief causes of the predominance of migratory visitants to our coast, are all briefly discussed in a manner which established the reputation of its authors as sound naturalists.'

The Birds of Norfolk by Henry Stevenson (1866-1890).

This extremely important book, the first major work on the county's avifauna, was published in three volumes, in 1866, 1870 and 1890. Originally intended to be in two, the third volume was completed, from page 161 to the end, by Thomas Southwell in 1890, following Stevenson's death in August 1888. It was the first publication to include in detail all birds recorded in the county, and is an invaluable historical reference to anyone researching the county's birds.

Catalogue of the Birds of Suffolk by Churchill Babington (1884-1886).

The Rev. Churchill Babington published his *Catalogue* in the *Proceedings of the Suffolk institute of Archaeology and Natural History* which was issued to members in two parts in 1884 and 1886. These were reprinted and compiled into a book, which was an extraordinary publication for that period, and included a detailed list of specimens of birds killed in Suffolk and their current whereabouts in the collections scattered around the county and elsewhere, together with a brief summary on distribution and status. The book included many interesting Yarmouth and Breydon area records and publications.

Hopefully the above references will give the reader a better understanding of the contents of those publications and some insight into their authors and the comments of Stevenson, which were written in 1866 or earlier. Without those learned gentleman our knowledge of the natural history of Norfolk would be far less than it is now and the details of that period lost to us forever. We are indeed indebted to them and others.

The Le Estrange family ancestral home, Hunstanton Hall, for which the above mentioned 'Household and Privy Purse Accounts' were kept, was at Old Hunstanton, and the Le Strange family have been connected to Hunstanton for almost 1,000 years; in fact the present Squire still lives in the town. In the 16th century Hunstanton, as we know it today, did not exist. But for the imagination of Henry Styleman Le Strange, the town may never have existed in its present form. In 1840 there was very little to be found between Old Hunstanton and Heacham. Sea bathing had, however, become the latest fashion and in 1845 Le Strange issued a prospectus for a coastal holiday village on a hitherto undeveloped part of his estate. The focal point was to be a triangular green sloping down to the sea. The Golden Lion Hotel, which is still in business today, was the first building in 1846 but he made little further progress in constructing the 78 dwellings planned. Development remained slow until the Great Eastern Railway decided to build the line from King's Lynn to Hunstanton at a cost of £80,000. This opened in 1862, the same year Le Strange died. Under the patronage of his son Hamon Le Strange and spurred on by the investment boom between 1850 and 1870, Hunstanton soon expanded beyond the original planned coastal village to become a fully fledged Victorian seaside resort.

The Le Strange Estate still owns the majority of land in the Hunstanton area but Hunstanton Hall was sold in 1948 and converted into flats. The present Le Strange Arms Hotel in Old Hunstanton, although standing on land that was part of the original Estate, has no connection to the Le Strange family or the Estate.

Sir Thomas Browne, who is mentioned in many early references, was born in London on 19th October 1605, was educated at Winchester School and went up to Broadgates Hall (Pembroke College), Oxford in 1623. He graduated B.A. on 31st January 1627 and was awarded his M.A. on 11th June 1629. About the year 1633 he was created Doctor of Physick at Leydon. In 1636 he took up his residence in Norwich and in 1637 was incorporated Doctor of Physic in Oxford. In 1665 he was elected an Honorary Fellow of the College of Physicians. He was knighted at Norwich by Charles ll. After a rewarding and honourable career he died on his seventy-sixth birthday, 19th October 1682. He was buried in the church of St Peter Mancroft, Norwich. Browne in early life travelled much and was a prodigious writer; he made many friendships with men celebrated in his day, and his advice and assistance were sought and gratefully acknowledged by Dugdale, Evelyn, Ray and Willughby, Merrett, Sir Robert Paston (afterwards Earl of Yarmouth), Ashmole, Aubrey and others. His notes and letters were first published by Simon Wilkins in his Edition to Sir Thomas Browne's Works in 1835 but they were not treated from a naturalist's point of view, and in some places not correctly transcribed (see Thomas Southwell's Introduction to *Notes and Letters on the Natural History of Norfolk*, 1902).

His correspondent Dr. Christopher Merrett was born at Winchcomb in Gloucestershire on 16th February 1614. He graduated B.A. from Oriel College, Oxford in about the year 1635, before qualifying M.B. in 1636 and being awarded his M.D. in 1643. He was elected Fellow of the Royal College of Physicians in 1651 and was made first Keeper of the Library and Museum. He was Censor of the College seven times. He died in London in 1681. Merrett was the author of several works on various subjects, as well as of the *Pinax Rerum Naturalium Britannicarum*, said to have been brought out in 1666, containing the earliest list of British birds ever published, but it was little more than a bare list. Merrett was contemplating a new and improved edition when "in an auspicious moment" as Wilkin put it, he sought the assistance of Browne, whose liberal response is evident in the drafts of the letters, but the *Pinax* never attained an enlarged edition.

Had Browne published his own 'Natural History of Norfolk' he might have set the precedent for other writers of County Natural Histories. But he seems to have preferred contributing to the labours of those whom he considered better naturalists than himself and in his third attempt to render his observations useful, having originally prepared his observations for an unnamed friend prior to assisting Merrett, he had somewhat better success. He placed his materials, including a number of coloured drawings at the disposal of Ray, the father of systematic natural history in Great Britain, who acknowledged the assistance he obtained from him in his editions of Willughby's 'Ornithology' and 'Ichthyology', especially in the former.

Southwell (1901) writes 'It may be truly said of Sir Thomas Browne that a prophet hath no honour in his own country; the writings of this remarkable man are little known in the city of his adoption, and a recent movement to erect a monument to his memory has hitherto met with feeble support.'

This was put right in 1905 when a statue to Browne was erected on Hay Hill, Norwich to mark the tercentenary of his birth. The sculpture captures Browne contemplating a broken urn. Prior to 2007 Norwich City Council commissioned the artists Anne and Patrick Poirier to produce a 'Homage to Thomas Browne' which features a marble eye and brain, and various seats and benches have been located in front of his statue.

To quote Sir Thomas Browne from his fifth letter to Merrett in *Notes and Letters on the Natural History of Norfolk more especially on the Fishes* from the manuscript of Sir Thomas Browne, M.D. (1605-1682) – In the Sloane Collection of the Library of the British Museum and in the Bodleian Library of Oxford, with notes by Thomas Southwell, F.Z.S. published in (1902), to which we will refer in this book: 'I confess for such little birds I am much unsatisfied on the names given to many by countrymen, and uncertain what to give them myself, or what classes to authors cleerly to reduce them. Surely there are many found among us whch are not described; & therefore such whch you cannot well reduce if at all bee set down after the exacter nomination of small birds as yet of uncertain classe or knowledge.'

He clearly had great difficulty, as no doubt did others of that period, in identifying many of the smaller, regularly seen species, which would explain why many species that one would assume to have been common in his time were not mentioned by him and others.

An interesting article entitled 'Sir Thomas Browne as a Naturalist' appears in the *Transactions of the Norfolk and Norwich Naturalists' Society* 1899-1900: 72-89, written by the then Hon. Sec. W. A. Nicholson.

Brief mention should also be made of the three major works published during the 20th century relating to the history of the birds of Norfolk. In 1930 a major milestone appeared, this was B. B. Riviere's *A History of the Birds of Norfolk*. Bernard Beryl Riviere was a lifelong member of the Norfolk and Norwich Naturalists' Society and his research spanned a period which embraced the changeover from collecting to the early days of watching and studying birds. Without his observations and information, many important Norfolk bird records would have been lost. Mention should also be made of C. B. Ticehurst's *A History of the Birds of Suffolk* published two years later in 1932. This informative book also contains many fascinating Yarmouth and Breydon area records and compliments the earlier work of Riviere.

Michael Seago, the most important of modern day Norfolk ornithological compilers, published his first edition of the *Birds of Norfolk* in 1967 complete with colour photographs. A second edition followed in 1977. These brought all the county records up to date, Michael having been in instrumental in publishing the *Norfolk Bird Report* since its inception in 1953 and who for many years was both its editor and the county bird recorder.

Another major milestone was reached in 1999 with the publication of *The Birds of Norfolk* by Moss Taylor, Michael Seago, Peter Allard and Don Dorling. This mammoth task involved over 30 contributors with specialist experience, in order to bring the story of Norfolk's birds right up to date in the final year of the century.

The eagerly awaited *The Norfolk Bird Atlas – the Summer and Winter Distribution 1999-2007* by Moss Taylor and John Marchant will be a major publication on the county's birds. Another mammoth task involving several hundred fieldworkers, it will certainly be an important reference source for future researchers of the county avifauna.

Michaeal Seago covered the lives of most of the eminent Norfolk naturalists in the section entitled 'Ornithology in Norfolk: History and Personalities' in *The Birds of Norfolk* 1999: 22-43, many of whom are referred to in this book.

Another interesting article entitled 'The Lives of Riviere and Stevenson' whose works are referred to with some frequency in this book appeared in the *Norfolk Bird Club Bulletin* 31: 14-16, also written by Michael Seago.

Mention should also be made of the collections of mounted birds, within which, many of the county's first recorded specimens are, or were housed.

Undoubtedly the finest remaining collection in Norfolk is to be found in the Castle Museum at Norwich. It includes the collections formed by B. B. Riviere and by E. C. Arnold and comprises some of the best birds which were formerly in the Gurney and Stevenson collections. Among the historic specimens housed there are at least 32 which are 'firsts' for Norfolk.

The Tolhouse Museum at Yarmouth contains a small collection of birds, mainly those that survived the Second World War bombings in 1941. The majority of these specimens are extremely old and undated but include one of the first recognised Leach's Fork-tailed Petrels in England, dated 1823, and is the only known surviving specimen from the Girdlestone collection. At King's Lynn Museum, a small collection of specimens includes two Pallas's Sandgrouse, one of which is believed to be the first ever shot in this country. Another historic specimen housed there is the first Sooty Shearwater for Norfolk. A Sharp-tailed Sandpiper from January 1868 completes a trio of interesting specimens. Contained in the magnificent Holkham Hall is a fine collection of mostly locally-taken birds representing 220 species. Within this is Norfolk's first recognised Pink-footed Goose of 1841. Elsewhere in Norfolk notable collections remain at Sheringham Hall and at nearby Felbrigg Hall, whilst smaller collections exist at the Thetford Ancient House Museum and at Gresham Hall near Holt. Regrettably, Lord Hastings' large collection of birds and animals at Melton Constable was broken up many years ago. Sadly, small collections housed in many of Norfolk's country halls and manors, such a feature up until the middle of the 20th century, are now rare.

Outside the county, the finest known collection of Norfolk-killed birds is without doubt that housed at the City of Birmingham Museum, where the former Connop collection contained at its peak some 450 cases. To a greater extent still intact, a large percentage of specimens from this collection were on display until as recently as 2005, but due to a change of policy, were put into storage at Birmingham University. However, in 2007, the collection was returned to the City of Birmingham Museum where, unfortunately, it remains in storage. This collection contains at least 13 specimens which were 'firsts' for Norfolk. Also in storage at the City of Birmingham

Museum is the Robert Chase collection of over 5,000 specimens. Included in this wonderful collection are two 'firsts' for Norfolk, the Mediterranean Gull and the Serin. Both of these collections are, or soon will be, stored in the relatively new Museum Collection Centre, the home for all the collections not on public display in the City of Birmingham Museum. The eventual aim of the museum is to allow guided tours around these collections.

The famous Booth collection, at the Dyke Road Museum, Brighton, is still intact and contains many Norfolk specimens, including the notorious Cape Canary of 1904 which for many years was viewed as Britain's first ever Citril Finch. A large collection of Norfolk birds, over 450 specimens, formerly belonging to Clifford Borrer of Cley, was donated to Cambridge University in 1950. It contained the last known rare birds to be collected within the county: a Rose-coloured Starling shot at Cley in 1945, a Pectoral Sandpiper trapped at Cley in 1948 and a Mediterranean Gull, shot whilst following the plough in a field at Wiveton in 1949. The magnificent Ogilvie collection at Ipswich Museum contains a number of Norfolk birds including one 'first' for the county, the Red-breasted Flycatcher, and the collection at the Natural History Museum at Tring in Hertfordshire contains the first Coues's Arctic Redpolls.

Other collections outside the county and known to have housed a number of historic Norfolk specimens have probably ceased to exist. These include the one at Southend, which included the greater part of the John Hoy collection. Other large collections were at Lilford Hall, the home of Lord Lilford in Northamptonshire, and at the Gentlemen's Club at Spalding in Lincolnshire. Others remain, however, although much depleted, such as at Leicester Museum, which contains an undated Eagle Owl shot on Cley beach, mounted by H. N. Pashley. The collection at Bury St. Edmunds in Suffolk has recently been dismantled, but fortunately most of the Norfolk specimens were transferred to the Castle Museum, Norwich in 2007. A few Norfolk specimens remain at both Colchester and Saffron Walden Museums in Essex but, unfortunately, many others have been lost over the passage of time, and as Victorian stuffed birds became less fashionable. However, it is good to record that, as many as 54 specimens of 'firsts' for Norfolk remain intact at various museums around the country.

The localities and sites where many of the county firsts were discovered are well known to Norfolk birders and indeed many visitors from further afield, as they still exist today. One site that no longer exists is Wisbech Sewage Farm. Its former importance is shown by the fact that five county firsts were recorded there. Most modern-day birders will have heard of it but many will never have had the opportunity to birdwatch there as it closed down in 1985, having been a marvellous habitat for numerous species but especially migrant waders. Straddling the Norfolk/Lincolnshire boundary and also bordering Cambridgeshire, it was unique in that it was possible to get species on three county lists in basically the same area. Rumour has it that birders had been known to 'push' a bird around the site to get it on three county lists. John Moyes, who was one of the Wisbech Sewage Farm regulars in its heyday, wrote an excellent article in the 1983 *Norfolk Bird Report* and followed this up with an addendum in 1985, both of which are reproduced below.

Wisbech Sewage Farm – The End

'During the past thirty years Wisbech Sewage Farm maintained an international reputation for migrant waders. Its imminent closure has prompted this article. Readers will doubtless recall a succession of red-letter days at this once renowned locality. Many observations, particularly those of maritime species, are doubtless attributable to the Farm's special position: only six miles inland and beside the Nene which acts as a guiding line for many birds flying overland from The Wash.

Work on construction of the site – straddling the Lincolnshire/Norfolk boundary – began in 1874. The following is a passage from Gardiner's *History of Wisbech*: "In September 1871 after much negotiation the Corporation decided to purchase from Mr. John Spikings a farm of 217 acres opposite the Foul Anchor in Tydd St. Giles for £11,000 and subsequently appointed Mr. Easton engineer of the proposed irrigation scheme of sewerage". However, there were long and tedious delays and it was not until September 1874 that work actually commenced.

To the uninitiated the site consisted of a series of embanked fields which were periodically flooded with untreated sewage and factory effluent. It was bounded on the west by the tidal Nene and on the south-east by a row of Aspens planted prior to the First World War. Three pairs of tall pylons carrying power lines across the Nene provided a dominant landmark, visible for many miles around. Little is known of its early ornithological history. Infrequent visits were made by Cambridge Bird Club members from the mid 1940s onward, but it was not until 1955 that the true value of the Farm was realised when almost daily autumn counts were made by A. E. Vine and myself.

This increased observation fortunately coincided with a most remarkable return migration. Some observations included a flock of 40 Spotted Redshank and 100 Curlew Sandpipers (in a year notable elsewhere for small numbers of this species) are outstanding. The 1955 wader list was raised to 27 species by the current visits in November of Pectoral Sandpiper and White-rumped Sandpiper. At this time the fields when not under flood were used to grow a variety of crops including Spinach, Mangolds, Barley, Wheat and Potatoes. Consequently, the lagoons tended to remain flooded for long periods with perhaps only one lagoon at a time suitable for feeding wader flocks during migration times. Moreover, towards the end of the 1950s with the gradual build-up of toxic chemicals in the soil and the associated decline in crop quality, farming activities ceased with the exception of abortive attempts at growing tulips by local nurserymen.

The flooding of the lagoons was now regulated by a more casual regime, with the Farm Manager sympathetic to the requirements of both birds and bird-watchers. Additional shallow floods were made available to feeding waders during peak migration periods with spectacular results. The numbers of common species and some of the scarcer migrants visiting the Farm increased dramatically. This trend was maintained throughout the 1960s which became the best period ornithologically in the hundred year history of the Farm. It has long been realised that the state of the tides in The Wash greatly influenced both numbers and variety of birds at the site. Two visits on the same day separated by only a few hours often yielded completely different lists of birds. During periods of low tide in the adjoining Nene, if birds were disturbed on the Farm by human intrusion, they moved to the inter-tidal mud at Ferry Station some two miles down river. Here they remained until the incoming tide forced a return to the Farm to resume feeding.

A large commuter population of small waders became established in most years with birds flighting in from The Wash to feed on the Farm in the mornings and out again in late evenings, probably at times joining the larger roosting flocks on the fields behind the sea walls at Terrington. Yet on some bright moon-lit nights the Farm remained thronged with birds although the reasons for this behaviour are obscure (see C.B.C. Report for 1967 pages 40-41). Differences in soil texture also had a direct influence on species present. For example, up to 26 Bar-tailed Godwits at a time would only be found feeding when a particular lagoon became suitable. This field consisted of very fine silt reminiscent of the Wash mudflats from whence these birds had come. Vegetation also had a marked influence on the numbers of certain species. In years when plant growth became rank with Persicaria and *Rumex* dominating, the lagoons were less attractive to shore waders (including Dunlin, Curlew Sandpiper and Little Stint), but more favoured by Wood and Green Sandpipers with always the chance of a glimpse of Spotted Crake or very rarely Baillon's Crake. Some species delighted in searching the delta areas formed near outlet pipes. Ruffs, Curlew Sandpipers and Ringed Plovers were particularly fond of such areas and Turnstones became adept at flicking over pieces of hardened mud in search of prey in much the same way as they would search the tideline on the shore.

The breeding list was not extensive, but certain species became well established. The Shelduck colony raised 200 to 300 ducklings annually and became one of the largest concentrations in East Anglia. Half a dozen Mallard nests were recorded each spring. Single nests of Tufted Duck, Pochard, Shoveler and Gadwall were recorded in some years. The Black-headed Gull colony increased from two nests in 1957 to well over 200 pairs by the mid 1960s. About this period 2 or 3 attendant Little Gulls gave hope of nesting, especially in view of the breeding attempt on the Ouse Washes in 1975. Among waders, both Ringed Plover and Oystercatcher nested annually; Redshank and Snipe occasionally managed to raise young on the Farm. Three pairs of Avocets took up temporary residence at the northern end of the Farm in 1959. They gave hope of breeding as they mated and indulged in acts of aggression towards such potential predators as Carrion Crows and Herons. Reed and Sedge Warblers, Reed Buntings, Corn Buntings, Whitethroats and Yellow Wagtails were all abundant breeders with Blue-headed Wagtails nesting in 1978. The Poplar belt held breeding pairs of Little Owl, Kestrel, Stock Dove and Great Spotted Woodpecker.

It was the wealth and variety of migrants which made Wisbech famous. During spring, particularly after periods of easterly winds, one might expect Kentish Plover and Temminck's Stint as well as the more regular Ruff, Wood, Green and Common Sandpipers. A Broad-billed Sandpiper was present 18th/19th May 1959. Little Stint, although very scarce in spring, could sometimes be seen during the first week in June; a period favoured also by Avocets. Black Terns would often drop in at Wisbech en route to breeding grounds in Denmark or Holland. Ten or 20 became a usual number, but exceptionally as in May 1959 as many as 180 were gracefully feeding by picking insects from the water surface.

The period from mid-June until the second week in July, although quiet as regards migrants, often produced surprises. Up to 20 summering Spotted Redshank in full dusky breeding dress could sometimes be found at high tide. Post-breeding assemblies of Black-tailed Godwits often gathered at the Farm during this period. On one occasion 150 were counted. By mid-July a trickle of return passage migrants was the vanguard of the flood that was to follow. Green and Common Sandpipers were often first arrivals followed by adult Curlew Sandpipers still in superb chestnut-red nuptial dress. The events of 1971 make impressive reading: 34 Curlew Sandpipers arrived 31st July increasing to 100 by 3rd August and to a peak of 150 on the 7th; all were adults in breeding attire. Early Pectoral Sandpipers could sometimes be seen at this period often associating with the Curlew Sandpipers; one wonders at their origins as the two species nest as far west as the Taimyr Peninsular in arctic Siberia. Later Pectoral occurrences in the autumn may well be of birds of transatlantic origin.

By August migration through the Farm was well underway with the second week often producing the widest variety of species of the year. Green, Wood and Common Sandpipers would reach peak numbers by mid-month (as many as 31, 37 and 80 respectively) followed by Knot, Sanderling and up to 30 Turnstones during the third week of August.

Ruff totals could be as high as 200 or even 250, but the numbers of most of the larger waders was largely governed by the state of the tides in The Wash. High tide roosting groups of up to 50 or even 60 Spotted Redshank could be expected whilst flights of 20 or 30 Greenshank headed inland following the course of the Nene. Whimbrel provided a similar pattern.

The autumn migration during 1973 proved especially memorable and included five New World waders of three different species. First arrivals 18th July include 130 Black-tailed Godwits. Five days later a total of 19 species of waders could be found. First autumn rarity was a White-rumped Sandpiper 28th July. An evening tide 15th August brought an assembly of 50 Spotted Redshanks. A Red-necked Phalarope which arrived 8th September remained until 11th October. During a ten-day period of its stay it was in company with Temminck's Stint and Pectoral Sandpiper. By mid-September 24 wader species were on show in the lagoons. A fortnight later Little Stint numbers had built up to 80.

Under suitable conditions September produced peak numbers of Dunlin, Curlew Sandpiper and Little Stint, the combined flock often totalling over 2000 birds. As many as 150 curlew Sandpipers were present 9th September 1978. At the same time an unprecedented total of 130 Little Stints was reached. The Curlew Sandpiper count had in fact been eclipsed at the end of August 1969 when 400, mostly juveniles, were recorded.

Good numbers of Ringed Plovers could be found on the Farm on most days throughout autumn, but the Little Ringed Plover usually reached peak numbers during August; totals of 16 and 27 are on record. Golden Plover, although often abundant on surrounding arable fields, were only infrequent visitors often in the evenings for pre-roost bathing sessions. The usually maritime Grey Plover was a scarce visitor. Weed-grown lagoons were much favoured by Snipe with peak numbers of 800 on record. Unique numbers of Jack Snipe appeared in autumn 1966. Between October and December counts included 40 and 43 on 21st/22nd October and 50 on 5th November. By contrast, the rare Great Snipe would stay for periods in excess of ten days. Of the remaining palearctic and holarctic waders, Temminck's Stints were regular visitors, the trilling calls usually a first indication of their presence. Red-necked Phalaropes were regular too, mostly during August and September. Grey Phalarope, however, remained rare with just two observations of individuals in thirty years. Dotterel was added to the Farm list in September 1972 when one appeared among Golden Plovers. Bringing the story up to date, a Black-winged Stilt stayed a few days during April 1983.

Although not especially noted for its wealth of birds of prey, Wisbech Sewage Farm produced interesting records over the years. Marsh and Hen Harriers were regular and Montagu's Harrier could occasionally be seen in spring. Honey Buzzard, Osprey, Goshawk, Hobby and Peregrine were all recorded with Merlin a regular winter resident.

Wisbech gained a special reputation for sightings of rarities. Most bird-watchers came with the hope of seeing Nearctic waders. The least rare of the transatlantic wanderers was the Pectoral Sandpiper with a thirty-year total of nearly 50 birds. Wisbech became one of the most likely places in Britain to find them. Next in order of frequency was the White-rumped Sandpiper; since its first recorded visit in 1955 it has been recorded a further five times. A total of five Wilson's Phalaropes was recorded including two which remained for three weeks in 1967 and were readily photographed. Spotted Sandpiper and Lesser Yellowlegs totalled three each. Among other highlights were single Baird's Sandpiper (July/ August 1963), Semipalmated Sandpiper (November/December 1966), Long-billed Dowitcher (September/October 1963) and Lesser Golden Plover (August 1974). A star species in the history of Wisbech Sewage Farm is the Stilt Sandpiper: an adult in part summer plumage trapped and ringed in July 1963 was only the third record for Europe. Remarkably, another Stilt Sandpiper was present in August 1965. Other rarities at various times included Spoonbill in October 1970 and April 1974, Caspian Tern in July 1982, White-winged Black Terns (several immatures in autumn) and single Gull-billed and Whiskered Terns. Glossy Ibis in May 1976 remaining three days was remarkable. Among vagrant wildfowl Ferruginous Duck and 2 Blue-winged Teal are outstanding observations.

By the late 1970s the attractiveness of the Farm to the majority of wader species began declining. Until then, after flooding and subsequent draining, the lagoons were regularly ploughed and then re-flooded keeping plant growth to a minimum and maintaining a succession of suitable lagoons. Later policy encouraged flooding favoured lagoons repeatedly over a period and abandoning others.

The remaining lagoons at this former bird-watcher's paradise are expected to disappear by the end of 1984 followed by levelling and return of John Spikings Farm to agriculture. A unique ornithological era will have ended.'

Wisbech Sewage Farm – the final chapter

'The feature covering ornithological events at Wisbech Sewage Farm (strad-dling the Lincolnshire/Norfolk boundary) appearing in the 1983 Report was somewhat premature. However, during December 1985 work began draining the remaining water and levelling the banks thus bringing to an end its 110 year history.

The final autumn passage movements were at times on a spectacular scale commencing in July with a company of 57 Black-tailed Godwits, numerous Ruffs, Greenshank, Green Sandpipers and Spotted Redshanks still in superb breeding plumage. Pumping operations ceased in September. The resulting exposure of mud saw a dramatic build-up in numbers. Peaks of 200 Curlew Sandpipers and 36 Little Stints were attained with many other waders in support. Among the last highlights were Buff-breasted and Pectoral Sandpipers.

These final records illustrate the great loss to ornithology following the disappearance of the once extensive lagoons. Thanks to Agricultural Authority nothing but the name is left: its acres merged with those of the surrounding fens to grow their quotas of potatoes, wheat and sugar-beet.

Gone for ever are the flights of Curlew Sandpipers, Little Stints, Black-tailed Godwits, Spotted Redshanks and Wood Sandpipers. No more the likely encounter with rarities from places beyond our experience. We are all the poorer for its passing. The records speak for themselves. Yet observers fortunate enough to have known the farm during the most productive period of its life will always retain memories.'

Preface to the Systematic List

Norfolk with its long coastline, varied habitats and many wetlands is without doubt one of the richest counties for bird watching in the British Isles. The Norfolk list comprises at least 32 species which were the first for Great Britain. There are numerous 'seconds' and 'thirds' and so on, the list is almost endless. Britains' first Roller appeared as early as 1664. A Rose-coloured Starling was shot in 1747, but perhaps surprisingly was not the first for Britain. A Wallcreeper shot on the walls of a house in 1792 was the first, however, and this was followed the next year by Britain's first European Bee-eater. The interest in birds had begun.

The beginning of the 19th century saw many advances in bird identification and collecting became of age – it was an ornithological revolution. The works of Montagu, Macgillivray, Yarrell and Newton dominated British ornithological recording and the scene was set. The *Zoologist* began publishing birding articles in the first decade and other bird news appeared in *The Field* and *Ibis*. Lists were being formed for the first time. Improvements in gun manufacture and accuracy in the 1820s and 1830s led to a new intake of specimens.

Bird dealers and taxidermists appeared in both Norwich and Yarmouth. Game dealers' stalls were sought out for anything unusual and local gunners soon became aware of what to shoot. Taxidermist and bird dealer Isaac Harvey at Yarmouth, together with his Norwich contemporaries John Sayer and John Knights, were constantly busy. Indeed, Isaac Harvey used to send renowned ornithologist John Gould in London a basket of sandpipers and plovers each week from the Yarmouth area. He also supplied John Hoy, a very wealthy landowner at Stoke-by-Nayland, near Ipswich, with numerous specimens. In 1830 Harvey mounted the first British example of Pectoral Sandpiper. Six years later, Britain's first Broad-billed Sandpiper, shot at Breydon in May 1836, passed through his hands. John Sayer shot the first Whiskered Tern in the county in June 1847 as it flew over Hickling Broad. Thomas Knights set up Britain's first Sharp-tailed Sandpiper in 1848, little realising its great rarity at the time. Four years earlier, the first Nutcracker for Norfolk, shot at Rollesby, received his skills and attention. Yarmouth had exceptional opportunities for receiving rare birds, being close to Breydon Water and Broadland. Richard Lubbock, in his *Fauna of Norfolk* (1845), described Breydon Water as 'an emporium of the rarer Water Fowl'. Dealers, taxidermists and gunners became acutely aware of this.

George Smith of Yarmouth was one of the first rare bird dealers in Norfolk and was involved with a number of firsts for the county. Birds which passed through his hands were the first Iceland Gull, the infamous Mediterranean Gull, and both White Wagtail and Tawny Pipit. Other Yarmouth game and bird dealers and taxidermists followed suit as lucrative business could be done, often with rich collectors who paid high prices for prize specimens. Among them were George Watson, James Carter and Walter Lowne. In Norwich, John Cole set up business in 1864 and the best known taxidermist, Thomas Gunn, began trading two years later in

1866. The same year Thomas Roberts began trading as the third of the trio of city taxidermists. Others appeared in Attleborough, Holt, King's Lynn, Snettisham, Swaffham and Thetford. Business boomed as many choice specimens passed through all these dealers' hands. Wealthy collectors came from all corners of the country to purchase specimens. Whilst virtually all of them were content to purchase other people's specimens, E. T. Booth from Brighton would only keep birds he had shot himself. He regularly came to Yarmouth and Breydon and shot in the Broads at Hickling and Horsey. His collection remains intact at Brighton and contains many of his Norfolk-shot specimens. Among the avid local collectors were the Gurneys at Keswick Hall, the Rev. C. J. Lucas at Fleggburgh Hall, E. M. Connop at Rollesby Hall (later residing at Wroxham) and Robert Rising at Horsey Hall.

The extensive denes at Yarmouth, which stretched towards Caister, began to attract attention. The bird catchers soon became aware of anything unusual and as early as the 1840s Richard's Pipits were being shot and trapped. This led to interest in some of the smaller birds which frequented the coast and the many migrants that arrived here in the autumn. By the early 1880s the interest in obtaining small and rare migrant birds had extended to the north Norfolk coast. The Victorian passion for collecting was instrumental in the search for something unusual and it was an era when anyone, taking a little time and effort, could find a new bird for Britain. Brothers Frederick and George Power, doctors from London, were among the first of the gentle-man-gunners to shoot small migrant birds in the bushes at Cley and along Blakeney Point. Their efforts were rewarded and rare specimens obtained by them enabled Henry Nash Pashley to set up as a professional taxidermist at Cley. The first records of Icterine and Barred Warbler were obtained by Frederick Power in September 1884, and in 1890 the county's first Red-breasted Flycatcher was shot at Cley by F. M. Ogilvie. The first Yellow-browed Warbler soon followed in 1894. Two years later, Britain's first Pallas's Leaf Warbler was shot at Cley by Edward Ramm and the die had been cast for many years to come.

At Yarmouth, just before the turn of the century, E. C. Saunders began working as a profes-sional taxidermist and one of his first rare specimens was Norfolk's first Great Spotted Cuckoo, shot on the denes in October 1896. Durrant's game stall on Yarmouth Market Place was regularly checked for rare specimens and many were found, including several Great Snipe. The smaller common birds would be hung in bunches with the larger ones hung separately, whilst the rarer ones were placed conspicuously on fruit trays at the front of the stall. This practice continued for many years and even after Durrant had retired it was continued by game dealer Edmunds. However, by the outbreak of the First World War, the Victorian passion for collecting was becoming less fashionable and Lowne, the Yarmouth taxidermist, ceased trading in 1913. Others followed suit during this period or shortly afterwards; a few, however, continued to practice their skills as a side-line to other employment. The Great War itself was the final nail in the coffin for many taxidermy establishments as collectors dwindled by the year. E. C. Saunders closed his shop in Yarmouth in June 1926 and Frederick Gunn, the son of Thomas Gunn of Norwich, continued his father's profession until just after the outbreak of the Second World War. There was a distinct change in public taste, cases of birds and animals simply went out of fashion. The taxidermist and bird dealer were almost extinct.

The first half of the 20th century saw an increased knowledge of our birds and the magazine *British Birds* had developed from the *Zoologist*, reflecting the greater need for ornithological contributions. Although many birds were still being shot for their rarity value, the collecting era had virtually finished by the 1930s. Nature reserves were being established and birds were being studied with field glasses and later with binoculars and telescopes, and bird photography became more widespread. The first official ringing scheme began in Britain in 1909 and three years later Common Terns, Little Terns and Ringed Plovers were ringed at Blakeney Point using the *British Birds* marking scheme. One of the Common Terns was later reported as being taken on the Durham coast near Sunderland in September of that year. The same year, 1912, also saw the first Norfolk recovery of a foreign-ringed bird, a Common Black-headed Gull found at Terrington. It had been ringed in Germany as a nestling in July. Thus, bird ringing in Norfolk was born (see the excellent article entitled 'A History of Ringing in Norfolk' by Moss Taylor in *The Birds of Norfolk* (1999) which describes the excellent work done by Norfolk ringers). Richard Richardson will not be forgotten for his important and pioneering work at Cley in the 1950s and 1960s and Peter Clarke at Holme in the 1960s, 1970s and 1980s, both widely respected along with many other ringers around the county - their dedication to the task has given bird migration a whole new meaning and understanding.

Although the Second World War held up further interest, a new revolution was in the making. Cley and Blakeney Point were becoming *the* locations to see birds in Norfolk. The last of the rare birds to be trapped and shot in Norfolk for a collector, a Pectoral Sandpiper at Cley in 1948 and a Mediterranean Gull at Wiveton in 1949, ended the long tradition of collecting rarities. Birds were now being studied and admired. The county's first Subalpine Warbler was discovered at Cley in June 1951 and identified by a small band of enthusiasts. An Arctic Warbler soon followed on Blakeney Point later that autumn. More rarities followed almost annually and the north Norfolk coast became a 'Mecca' for birdwatchers. Nature reserves soon became established along the entire coastline and other rarities followed. The extensive woods at Wells and Holkham were now being regularly watched and it was no surprise that the first county record of Dusky Warbler appeared there in 1968. Holme was also becoming firmly established as another rarity hotspot and from there the first sightings of Collared Flycatcher and Western Bonelli's Warbler were recorded. To the west, the first Citrine Wagtail was identified at Welney in November 1980.

The east coast at Yarmouth, much neglected for several decades, was now turning up new birds again and at Breydon Water exciting birds were being discovered. Among the best were Terek Sandpiper and Greater Yellowlegs in 1975 and a Franklin's Gull in 1991. Yarmouth cemeteries, an easy site to work, became a popular locality to watch and record migrants and from there came the first records of Siberian Thrush in 1977 and a very popular Red-flanked Bluetail in 1994. A little further up the coast at Winterton Dunes the first records of Isabelline and Pied Wheatears in 1977 and 1978 respectively were unexpected additions. The Mundesley and Paston areas became increasingly watched and Bonaparte's Gull was added to the county list in 1967, followed by a Laughing Gull in 1991. The Sheringham area was not to be outdone. A Paddyfield Warbler and a Lanceolated Warbler, both trapped and ringed during a five-day period in September 1993, were county firsts, further highlighting the importance of ringing in the county during the last fifty years. At least ten birds new to the county were first found and identified having been caught in ringers' nets. Broadland was not forgotten either and a Great Egret graced Hickling Broad in 1979, followed by a Eurasian Penduline Tit in 1987. Unlikely birds were being found in the county: a Red-breasted Nuthatch from the high forests of Canada, at Holkham Meals in October 1989, was one of the ornithological events of the decade.

The 21st century saw a new era and the pleasure of watching birds had never been so popular. With increased leisure time, birdwatching was being enjoyed by thousands of people from all walks of life. It was a good and healthy hobby with few financial strings and people could watch birds anywhere. Information was being passed freely and identification skills had increased. A new collector of birds had already emerged, the 'twitcher', content to observe birds as opposed to shooting them, and with them came a different language and strange new terminology. The digital revolution changed and improved bird photography beyond peoples' wildest dreams. Bird information services sprang up and pager systems and mobile phones replaced postcards and telephone-box calls. New magazines came on the market, *Bird Watching, Birding World* and *Birdwatch* complemented the established *British Birds* and ornithological publications improved dramatically. As computers became a feature of many households, statistics and records became easier to collate and analyse and the internet presented many opportunities for the birding fraternity. Better technology provided numerous bird-related DVDs, CD-ROMs, iPods and other related software, all unthinkable a decade previously.

In Victorian times the collector's adage was '*What's hit is history, what's missed is mystery*'. It is now '*Always expect the unexpected*', the male Black Lark at Winterton in April 2008 surely being proof of this. The quality of the digital photographs of the county's birds is now quite exceptional; a Black Brant in flight at Titchwell in December 2008 will surely take some beating.

Systematic List of Category A, B and C Species

Mute Swan
Cygnus olor
The earliest dated reference we can find is of its presence in the park of Hugh de Bardolph at Wormegay in 1300. See the account of the Spoonbill.

Thomas Southwell writes in Henry Stevenson's *The Birds of Norfolk* Vol. lll. 1890: 102-111 where he discusses 'Norfolk Swan Marks', quoting local historian Blomefield:

> "…the city have three swan-marks on the narrow fresh water streams in Norfolk, one called Blake's mark, belonging to the manor of Rokele's in Trowse, another called Paston's, or the Hospital mark, which belonged to Margaret, widow of John Paston, Esq., daughter and heiress of John Mautby, Esq., which she gave to Edmund, her second son, and it was called Dawbeney's mark, and was late Robert Cutler's, clerk;"

He adds a footnote here:

> 'Mr. J. H. Gurney has kindly directed my attention to the will of the above Margaret Paston (communicated to "Norfolk Archaeology," vol. iii., p. 160, by the late Mr. Dawson Turner), from which it appears that Blomefield is not quite correct on this point since, as shown by the following extract, this lady bequeathed her swans to her grandson Robert, the son of her youngest son Edmund Paston.
> "It. I geve and gaute to Robt., son of the seid Edmund, all my Swannes, merken with a merke called Dawbeney's merk, and with the merke late Robt. Cutler, Clerk; to have hold, and enjoye the seid Swannes with the seid merkes to the seid Robt. and his heires for ev'more." This will was executed in 1481 and proved in 1484.
> John Dawbeney Esq., as Mr. Turner states in a footnote, was called by the Paston's "our cousin"; the Rev. Robt. Cutler was vicar of Caister St. Edmunds from 1453 to 1466, and was translated to Mautby in 1465 (vide Blomefield).'

Tundra (Bewick's) Swan
Cygnus columbianus
One was obtained at Yarmouth in the winter of 1827-28.

Thomas Southwell writes in Henry Stevenson's *The Birds of Norfolk* Vol. lll. 1890: 53:

'When the late Mr. Yarrell, in a paper read before the Linnean Society, in January, 1830, ("on a new species of wild swan taken in England and hitherto confounded with the whooper." – "*Linnean Transactions*," vol. xvi., p. 445.), pointed out the specific distinction between this smaller wild swan and the common whooper, he included amongst his specimens and anatomical preparations the sternum and trachea of one shot at Yarmouth in the winter of 1827-28, the skin of which was preserved in the collection of Mr. J. B. Baker, of Hardwicke Court. Further investigation and comparison, at the time, discovered several examples in private collections, and amongst others an adult bird in the possession of the late Mr. Lombe, of Melton, who in some MS notes in his copy of Montagu's Dictionary, thus identifies it with this county. "In addition to the common wild swan another has now been ascertained to exist; several specimens were killed in England in 1829, but prior to that I had one, now in my own collection, killed in Norfolk, and preserved by Leadbeater".'

In a footnote Southwell adds a reference to Mr. Lombe's collection:

'This fine collection, as has been elsewhere stated, is now at Wymondham in the possession of Mrs. E. P. Clarke.'

After his death, Mr. Lombe's collection was presented to the Castle Museum, Norwich by his daughter Mrs. E. P. Clarke (Southwell 1879).

Whooper Swan
Cygnus cygnus
Known as the Wild Swan by Sir Thomas Browne in his manuscripts, notes and letters written between 1605 and 1682, he is quoted in *Notes and Letters on the Natural History of Norfolk* 1902: 7:

'In hard winters elkes a kind of wild swan are seen in no small numbers'

In a footnote Thomas Southwell adds:

'The "Elke" is an obsolete name for the Wild Swan (*Cygnus musicus*), which occurs in the present day in the same numbers and under precisely similar circumstances as Browne describes; but of course this was the only species of wild swan known to him.'

Southwell writes in Henry Stevenson's *The Birds of Norfolk* Vol. lll. 1890: 45-53:

'The wild swan or Whooper is a winter visitant to our coast, rarely altogether absent, but its numbers depending mainly on the severity of the season.'

And in a footnote he adds:

'This name being derived from the perculiar trumpeting note of the species, I have preferred to spell it as in whooping-cough, the word "hooper" as it is more commonly written, having no special signification.'

Bean Goose
Anser fabalis
The Bean Goose and Pink-footed Goose were frequently confused by the early 19th century naturalists, not helped by the often inaccurate and contradictory identification criteria described by the acknowledged experts of the time (see under Pink-footed Goose).

Thomas Southwell writes in Henry Stevenson's *The Birds of Norfolk* Vol. lll. 1890: 21-31:

> 'Messrs. Sheppard and Whitear were evidently under a wrong impression when speaking of the bean goose in Norfolk as "met with particularly about Yarmouth." As Messrs. Paget describe it as "less frequently met with" than the grey-lag; and Mr.Lubbock, though referring to its abundance in West Norfolk, speaks of wild geese, generally, as "not very abundant on the Yarmouth side of the county." Occasionally, however, I have known this species killed in severe winters near Yarmouth, both at Hickling and Horsey, and stragglers also in spring when about to leave us for the north. From the extreme watchfulness of these birds I have rarely known any obtained, except in hard weather, when specimens have been sent to Norwich from the neighbourhood of Wells, Blakeney, and Lynn; but the winter of 1851-2, from its mildness both before and after Christmas, was remarkable for the unusual number and variety of wild geese killed in various parts of the county. At that time, on the 20th December, I saw no less than three couples of bean geese, two and a half couples of white-fronted, and two couples of bernacle geese, a rare species with us, hanging for sale at one time, having been killed at Hickling and other localities more immediately on the coast.'

It must be assumed that in the above account both Taiga *A. f. fabalis* and Tundra *A. f. rossicus* races were involved. But as *A. f. rossicus* was not described until 1933 they must remain as Bean Goose *Anser fabalis*.

Taiga Bean Goose
Anser fabalis fabalis
The first reference to Taiga Bean Goose in the county is in the *Norfolk Bird Report* 1984: 117 where it states:

> 'Following the virtual loss of the Taiga Bean Geese (*fabalis*) formerly winter-ing in the Dee valley in south-west Scotland, the East Norfolk flock is now of national importance being the last regular wintering population in Gt. Britain. In winter quarters *fabalis* favours grazing meadows, whereas the Tundra Bean Goose *rossicus* selects winter cereals, ploughed potato and sugar-beet fields and stubbles.'

Michael Seago writes in *The Birds of Norfolk* 1999: 141-143, of which he is co-author:

> 'Riviere considered the Bean Goose regular but only in small numbers and was apparently unaware of the mid-Yare Valley location during the 1920s when

many of the marshes flooded each winter. Fortunately Robin Harrison obtained details from Frank Ward, a marshman who occupied a cottage overlooking Buckenham Station Level until 1950. The first Bean Goose was shot by Ward in mid-December 1924 when between 200 and 300 fed regularly on Claxton and Langley Ham Marshes. Similar numbers arrived in 1925 and 1926. In the 1927-28 severe winter an exceptional total of over 5,000 Bean Geese put in an appearance. Very cold conditions commenced on 15th December 1927 "with continuous hard frosts… and the year closed with the country under deep snow and with the flooded river valleys vast sheets of ice" (Riviere 1928).'

It is reasonable to assume that the Yare Valley wintering population has always been *A. f. fabalis*.

Tundra Bean Goose
Anser fabalis rossicus

First described in 1933 and not mentioned in the *Norfolk Bird Report* until 1984, the Tundra Bean Goose *A. f. rossicus* was not recognised in Norfolk until a bird found dead by Peter Allard and Terry Boulton on California beach on 12th February 1976 was subsequently identified by them as being of this race. Although the record was mentioned in the *Norfolk Bird Report* 1976 it appeared under Bean Goose as the Tundra Bean Goose *A. f. rossicus* was not formerly recognized as a separate race in Britain at that time.

Peter Allard writes from his notes and recollections of the occasion:

'Following strong cold prevailing easterly winds, early February 1976 had brought an influx of continental birds into eastern England. A number of dead birds had been reported on local beaches and it was during this period that several observers were out recording birds washed up on the tideline. On February 12th, Terry Boulton and I covered over a mile of beach between Caister and California and recorded a total of 39 washed up birds including 9 Common Snipe, 11 Fieldfares and, unusually, a Bean Goose. Also noteworthy was an oiled Slavonian Grebe. The latter two birds were photographed and little else was thought about the photographs however, until a decade later the BOURC officially recognised two distinct races of the Bean Goose as occurring in Britain, the Taiga Bean Goose *A. f. fabalis* and the Tundra Bean Goose *A. f. rossicus*. The photograph of the Bean Goose at California beach was carefully examined and it showed enough of the head and bill features enabling it to be recorded as a bird of the Tundra *A. f. rossicus* race. The record appeared in *The Birds of Great Yarmouth* (1990). This appears to be the first recognised record of a Tundra Bean Goose for Norfolk, although it is now well known that virtually all Bean Goose sightings away from the Yare Valley are of this race. The Tundra Bean Goose is now recognised as an almost annual winter visitor in small numbers to both coastal and Broadland Norfolk and occasionally elsewhere, especially in the Fens at Welney. An examination of any existing old Bean Goose specimen shot in Norfolk away from the Yare Valley would surely result in a specimen of *A. f. rossicus* being identified and predate this 1976 California beach record.'

Pink-footed Goose
Anser brachyrhynchus
One was obtained at Holkham in January 1841. The cased specimen remains on display in the Bird Room at Holkham Hall.

First described as a distinct species by Baillon in 1833. Until Mr. A. D. Bartlett exhibited specimens at the Zoological Society on 8th January 1839 and published details of the distinction between them, all birds occurring in Britain were regarded as Bean Geese. Pink-footed Goose was not generally accepted in Britain as a distinct species from Bean Goose until the mid 1960s.

Thomas Southwell writes in Henry Stevenson's *The Birds of Norfolk* Vol. lll. 1890: 14-20:

> 'The earliest record of its identification in this county is apparently the notice by Yarrell of a specimen killed at Holkham, in January, 1841, by the present Earl of Leicester out of a flock of about twenty, since which time this goose has proved to be by far the most common species that frequents the Holkham marshes.'

He adds an interesting footnote:

> 'It is worthy of note, however, that the bird figured by Hunt in 1815, as the bean goose (*A. segetum*), and in all probability from a local specimen, represents, unquestionably, the pink-footed species, since the bill, though painted orange in the plate, is far to small for that of the bean, and the feet are coloured red as in the adult pink-footed goose. Mr Hunt moreover adds the provincial name of "small grey goose".'

Greater White-fronted Goose
Anser albifrons
The earliest reference we can find is in Sheppard and Whitear's *A Catalogue of the Norfolk and Suffolk Birds, with Remarks* 1826, where it is listed but not commented on. The Pagets in *Sketch of the Natural History of Yarmouth and its Neighbourhood* 1834: 10 write:

> '…occasionally shot on Breydon.'

Greenland White-fronted Goose
Anser albifrons flavirostris
One was at Cley from the 8th November to 4th December 1960 (finder apparently not known!).

The *Norfolk Bird Report* 1960 just states in the review of the year:

'November 8th… The same day a greenland white-fronted goose arrived among the feral grey-lags on Cley marshes…' and in the Systematic List it simply states 'Cley an adult of the Greenland race, *flavirostris*, Nov. 8th-Dec 4th.'

Interestingly, Michael Seago refers to this bird as an immature in *Birds of Norfolk* (1967 and 1977).

The Birds of Norfolk (Taylor *et al* 1999) incorrectly gives the year as 1966, presumably a misprint.

Lesser White-fronted Goose
Anser erythropus

An adult male was shot by Robert Porter close to Lockgate Mill on Breydon Marshes near Yarmouth on 24th January 1949. The specimen (Accession no. NWHCM: 1949.62) is on display in the bird gallery at the Castle Museum, Norwich where it remains on loan from the Porter family.

An interesting article, accompanied by a photograph of the dead bird, appeared in the *Yarmouth Mercury* newspaper on 28th January 1949:

> 'A fine specimen of a lesser white-fronted goose, a very rare visitor to this country from the Arctic, Siberia and Scandinavia, has been shot on Breydon Marshes, and will shortly be exhibited at Norwich Museum.
>
> It is the first time for 49 years – almost to the day – that a bird of this species has been taken, the last known record being of a female which was shot in the Wash on January 24th, 1900. Before then the only record was of a male bird which was secured at Fenham Flats (Northumberland) on September 16th, 1886.
>
> Four or five of the birds have been observed, however, by Peter Scott, son of the famous explorer, and England's recognised authority on wild geese, at the Severn Estuary during 1946 and 1947, but none has actually been taken.
>
> VERY RARE VISITOR
>
> The bird was shot by Mr. R. F. Porter, of 18, Windsor Avenue, on Sunday. It was identified by Mr. H. Davies, of 32, Regent Road, a member of Yarmouth Naturalists' Society, who devotes considerable study to bird life on Breydon.
>
> Mr. Davies says that the common white-fronted goose winters regularly in the British Isles, and many people may have seen large numbers of them flying in from the sea and over the coast in characteristic "V" formation.
>
> The lesser white-fronted goose is, however, a very rare visitor. It is slightly smaller than the common variety, its white forehead is more extensive, and its particular mark of identification is a swollen lemon ring round each eye.
>
> "It was this yellow ring that enabled me to identify it," Mr. Davies adds, "and the fact that a specimen has actually been taken helps to confirm the view that the lesser white-fronts are a distinct species and not a hybrid of the common variety.
>
> FOR NORWICH MUSEUM
>
> The bird weighs 3 lb. 8 and a half oz., its length is 24 in., single wing span 21 and a half in., and full span 4 ft. It has been accepted on temporary loan from the Porter family by the authorities at Norwich Museum, who are having it stuffed and displayed, possibly in the Breydon Room.
>
> Breyon Marshes and the Wash are favourite places for the common white-fronted geese," Mr. Davies points out, "and it seems that occasionally some of the lesser white-fronted variety come over with the others from the breeding grounds".'

Mr. H. Davies writes in *British Birds* 42: 295:

'It was coming in from the sea flying alone and was shot by R.F.Porter, one of a family of well-known sportsmen of Great Yarmouth who was mostly attracted by the high pitched call the bird was making.'

The 1900 Wash record of Lesser White-fronted Goose mentioned in the above newspaper article is referenced by B. B. Riviere in *A History of the Birds of Norfolk* (1930):

'An adult female of this species was killed in The Wash on 24th January 1900 (F. Coburn, *Zoologist*, 1901, p. 317. Gurney, *Ibis*, 1902, pp. 269-275).'

This bird was shot closer to the Lincolnshire coast than the Norfolk coast (*Transactions of the Norfolk and Norwich Naturalists Society* 1903-1904: 733), and based on this information cannot be considered as the first Norfolk record.

Lesser White-fronted Goose arriving at Breydon Water to join other grey geese January 1949. (*Gary Wright*)

Greylag Goose
Anser anser anser
The earliest dated reference we can find is in Henry Stevenson's *The Birds of Norfolk* Vol. lll. 1890: 1-14, where Thomas Southwell states:

'Mr. Lubbock particularly mentions the neglect of this county by the older writers on Natural History, with the exception only of Sir Thomas Browne. Lincolnshire, Cambridgeshire, and Holderness, as he says "were mentioned by all, but Norfolk, although perhaps richer than any of these, seemed consigned to total oblivion." Even Drayton in his *Polyolbion*, "occupies pages in the enumeration of different species of bird found in Lincolnshire, but dismisses poor Norfolk with a passing intimation that the open country around Brandon is admirably suited to hawking." It is thus that the local naturalist, though with little doubt in his own mind as to the fact, is unable to substantiate his belief that the true *Anser ferus* – the Grey Lag or fen goose, as distinguished from the bean or stubble goose – bred as regularly in former times in the Fens of Norfolk, as it is known to have done in other portions of the Eastern Counties. Sir Thomas Browne throws no light on this point, this class of wild fowl being dismissed by him with the bare enumeration of "wild geese, *Anser ferus*. Scotch goose *Anser scoticus*," the former probably including all the grey species and the latter the black or bernicles. There seems, however, no question that the following account of its habits in this country, as given by Pennant in 1776, applied as much to Norfolk as to Cambridgeshire and Lincolnshire, more particularly as no one county is specifically referred to. "This species resides in the fens the whole year; breeds there, and hatches about eight or nine young, which are often taken, easily made tame, and esteemed most excellent meat, superior to the domestic goose. The old geese which are shot, are plucked and sold in the market, as fine tame ones, and are readily bought, the purchaser being deceived by the size, but their flesh is coarse. Towards winter they collect in flocks, *but in all seasons live and feed in the fens*".'

A reference to this species by Robert Marsham (1708-1797) in Tim Sparks and John Lines' *Chapters in the Life of Robert Marsham Esq. F.R.S. of Stratton Strawless, Norfolk* 2008: 18 states:

> '...the commoner large wild goose breeds in vast numbers in the Marshes in the eastern part of Norfolk; then go in flocks in the later part of the Autumn to the large fields in the S & W part of Norfolk, & the N of Suffolk, where they stay all winter, & return to the Marshes in the Spring.'

Within the British Isles, there are now three quite separate populations: the native population, formerly much more widespread and now restricted to north and north-west Scotland, the Icelandic population which winters only in Scotland and the feral population (originating from Hebridean birds), which has expanded considerably throughout England since the first birds were released in the early 1930s. The native Scottish population is mainly sedentary, so it was with some surprise that two individuals bearing orange colour-marked collars appeared at Lound Waterworks on 21st December 2008, staying for three days before being seen at Strumpshaw Fen RSPB reserve on the 24th and at Buckenham Marshes around 22nd January 2009. Both were collared as almost fledged goslings at Loch of Hundland, Birsay, Orkney on 13th July 2008, one being last seen on 31st August and the other on 4th October. It is thought that both birds became caught up in gaggles of Pink-footed Geese migrating south. The local Lound Waterworks birds roost mainly at the RSPB Berney Marshes reserve, a major site for Pink-footed Geese, and having arrived there the Orkney birds are presumed to have teamed up with the local Broadland birds. This is an unprecedented and remarkable movement, however, and involves the first county record of truly wild Greylags in modern times. Both returned to Orkney.

Birds attracted to Pink-feet gaggles and possibly from the Icelandic population, have been seen in Norfolk on several occasions in recent years. Icelandic birds are almost identical in appearance to local birds and only sightings of ringed and marked individuals would prove their origin. None has been found to date.

Birds showing characteristics of the eastern race *A. a. rubrirostris* have been claimed in the county and mentioned in the *Norfolk Bird Report* with some regularity since 1977, but none have been fully authenticated. The first thought to be a genuine *rubrirostris* and recorded as such was one shot at Berney Arms, at the western end of Breydon Water, on 5th January 1998. It had been ringed as an adult female just north-east of Wroclaw, Poland on 29th May 1993. Research reveals that the Polish Greylag Goose population is intermediate between *A. a. anser* and *A. a. rubrirostris*, and as the Berney Arms bird is presumed to have been eaten by the wildfowler who shot it, there is unlikely to be any material for possible DNA analysis. Therefore, this record cannot be considered as the first *A. a. rubrirostris* for Norfolk, but it is probably the best candidate so far.

Lesser Snow Goose
Anser caerulescens caerulescens
A first-winter blue-phase which must surely have been a Lesser Snow Goose arrived at Buckenham with the first wave of 16 Bean Geese on 13th November 1973. It remained with the flock and departed with them on 26th February 1974. The Bean Geese during this period were always notoriously shy as they were regularly disturbed by shooting in the area, but it was noted that it was always the Snow Goose that was the first to be alert in the flock and one of the first to take flight. Taiga Bean Geese were considered an unlikely 'carrier' of any wild Snow Goose then as is the case today, but as the bird was unringed and exceptionally shy, together with it being a young bird, it was considered by many to be a genuinely wild individual.

Greater Snow Goose
Anser caerulescens atlanticus
A white-phase adult of this race in north-west Norfolk, mostly in the Docking area, from 17th November 1985 to14th January 1986, was given in the 1985 *Norfolk Bird Report* as '… considered wild as it arrived with Pink-feet and very few kept in captivity…'. It ranged widely with the Pink-footed Geese feeding on harvested sugar-beet tops.

This was the first racially identified Snow Goose to be published in the *Norfolk Bird Report*.

Snow Goose
Anser caerulescens caerulescens/atlanticus
Several earlier occurrences of Snow Geese in the county, either of the nominate western form *A. c. caerulescens* or the eastern race *A. c. atlanticus* but unspecified in the literature, could conceivably have related to genuinely wild birds. A flock of eight adults and four juveniles that arrived at Cley on 21st September 1982 following strong westerly winds, a first-winter intermediate bird with Pink-footed Geese at West Rudham in February 1984 and an adult white-phase with Pink-footed Geese at Holkham on 18th February 1984 all come into this category.

It is worth noting that blue-phase Greater Snow Geese are considered rare (Cramp *et al* 1977) or very rare (Madge & Burn 1988) while in Lesser Snow Goose, the form most commonly kept in collections, the blue-phase is common. The similar but smaller Ross's Goose *Anser rossii* cannot be entirely ruled out in some of the sightings. Although blue-phase Ross's are occasionally reported they are thought to relate to possible hybridisation with Lesser Snow Goose (Madge & Burn 1988).

Environmental Canada reports that the Snow Goose population, particularly Lesser Snow Goose, has tripled in the past 20 years and is increasing at a rate of 5% a year, to a 2008 figure of 4,500,000 birds. Ross's Goose, too, has shown a massive increase from just 6,000 in 1931 to over 1,000,000 in 1998.

There are no known feral flocks of Snow Geese in the county now.

Greater Canada Goose
Branta canadensis
Initially introduced into Britain in the 17th century, the earliest reference we can find is by the Rev. Richard Lubbock in *Observations on the Fauna of Norfolk* 1845, new edition by Southwell 1879: 166 where he writes:

> 'A very sharp look out should be kept for the well-known American species, the CANADA or CRAVAT GOOSE (*A. Canadensis*), as there is no doubt that this bird often occurs in England in a state completely wild.'

Henry Stevenson writes in *The Birds of Norfolk* Vol. lll. 1890: 43-44:

> 'On one occasion, when driving in the vicinity of Holt, early in the morning, three Canada geese flew over my head, low enough to have been touched by the whip; this was in the height of summer but a fine bird in my own collection was killed out of a flock of three or four at Hickling, in February, 1852, by a man "flight" shooting during very severe weather, and which had no doubt been either frozen, or starved out elsewhere.'

And in a footnote adds:

> 'The Rev. E. S. Dixon, late rector of Intwood with Keswick, near Norwich, in his useful little work on the "History and management of ornamental and domestic poultry," remarks of this species, that the want of a proper supply of corn in winter when the grass grows but little, is the chief cause of their restlessness. "It is no migratory impulse that sets them on the move, but over-crowding and under-feeding. They have been literally starved out".'

Lesser Canada Goose
Branta hutchinsii
The Lesser Canada Goose was given specific status as recently as 2006 when Canada Goose was 'split' into two species, Greater *B. canadensis* and Lesser *B. hutchinsii* by the British Ornithologists' Union. All earlier claims of Lesser Canada Goose in Britain are to be reviewed to see if any could be assigned to this species. Norfolk has several outstanding claims of what were then considered 'small race Canada Geese', some of which could come into this category.

To our knowledge three have been submitted to the BBRC, singles at Brancaster, West Rudham and Heacham from 16thJanuary to 3rd March 1984, Holkham 6th-23rd February 1999 and Holkham, Southwood and Brancaster 19th November 2005 to 21st January 2006. In early 2009 all claims for Lesser Canada Goose were being held by the BBRC awaiting the completion of an identification paper on the species.

Interestingly, the race *parvipes*, popularly known as Lesser Canada Goose prior to the split, has been assigned to the Greater Canada Goose complex.

Barnacle Goose
Branta leucopsis
The earliest dated reference we can find is by Sir Thomas Browne (1605-1682) in *Notes on the Natural History of Norfolk* 1902: 12 where it is only mentioned in passing:

'Barnacles Brants Branta are comon'

Sheppard and Whitear in *A Catalogue of the Norfolk and Suffolk Birds, with Remarks* (1826) just list it with no comments, and The Pagets in *Sketch of the Natural History of Yarmouth and its Neighbourhood* 1834: 10 considered it '…not uncommon'.

Brant (Brent) Goose
Branta bernicla
The earliest dated reference we can find is in Henry Stevenson's *The Birds of Norfolk* Vol. lll. 1890: 36-39, where Thomas Southwell writes:

> 'The young birds of this species are considered very good eating, and generally find a ready sale in our markets. In the L'Estrange (of Hunstanton 1519-1578) Household book it is once mentioned amongst articles purchased, as "Itm a brante, - - ii pence"; but the entry, "Itm a wyld goos kylled wt ye cros bowe" most probably referred to one of the larger species.'

Both Dark-bellied and Pale-bellied birds were noted at this time but as now the Dark-bellied *B. b. bernicla* were by far the more numerous. The Pale-bellied *B. b. hrota* were known as "stranger" Brents.

Black Brant
Branta bernicla nigricans
An adult was found by Gary Allport and Paul Batchelor at Cley Eye Field with the Dark-bellied Brent Geese flock on 7th November 1982. It stayed in the area until 13th March 1983.

Now residing in the U.S.A. Gary writes from his notes and recollections of the occasion:

> 'On 7th November 1982, Paul Batchelor and I headed for the North Norfolk coast. After two days of strong north-westerly winds there were plenty of birds arriving, including Little Auks and skuas on the sea. The news of such birds had reached many birders and there was a good arrival of regulars at Cley Coast-guards, including the familiar rusty van-full of Bryan Bland. I was, at the time, a budding undergraduate at University of East Anglia in Norwich, and about to embark upon what ultimately led to many years of studying the ecology of geese, so I set about grilling the large flock of newly arrived Brent Geese with gusto, searching through the flock with my 'scope as they were busily cropping the verdant early autumn sward on Eye Field. Within a few minutes I noticed a Brent Goose which was striking, to me, with more white on the flanks, a different tone to both the upperparts and underparts and a broader white necklace. I knew of Black Brant but was not fully familiar with the field characters and neither I nor anyone else that I met birding there that day had a field guide which described the subspecies. I pointed the bird out to a number of notable ornithologists, none of whom thought it was of particular interest, except Bryan. He studied the bird closely and at length, joining me in taking notes, but like me being unsure of the identity of the bird. He concluded ultimately that it was interesting but was probably just an oddly marked Dark-bellied Brent. Paul and I headed home and on looking up the subspecies in Birds of the Western Palaearctic we found

to our surprise that our bird was a perfect fit. I called Bryan who said that he had not been able to find the subspecies in any text that he had to hand – but then broke the news that there was an American Redstart at Gibraltar Point and offered me a lift in the rust bucket (his words) early the following morning. So, later that following day we found ourselves sitting in a transport café in southern Lincolnshire, pawing BoWP and clashing mugs in celebration of the addition of an American sprite to our British lists, and a less dazzling American interloper to the Norfolk list.'

Red-breasted Goose
Branta ruficollis
One was found by Peter Allard on the Halvergate Marshes in company with Greater White-fronted Geese on 2nd January 1962, which remained until the 28th.

Peter Allard writes from his notes taken at the time:

'January 2nd 1962 was a very cold day with part overcast skies and snow on the marshes. There was a light northerly wind blowing. Wild geese wintering on these marshes were becoming a thing of the past and as a young lad, I was very keen to become acquainted with the remaining gaggles. Usually my visits to the Halvergate marshes west of Yarmouth were by bicycle via the Acle New Road and then left along the branch road to Halvergate village area and to the extensive marshes bordering this road. However, with the roads being very slippery on this particular morning, my father offered me a lift in his car during a lunch break to an area south of the Stracey Arms public house. Very fortunately before he dropped me off along the Halvergate branch road, a large gaggle of some 250 White-fronted Geese were noted feeding on the east side of the road and at a reasonable distance to easily 'scope' them. The 250 or so were an increase since my last visit and as I viewed through them, a very distinctive red coloured goose became strikingly obvious amongst them. I knew straight away that this was a Red-breasted Goose, a species I had seen in various bird books in my collection. My notes began unusually stating the bird carried no obvious ring so I must have been aware at that time of this bird being a possible escapee. The very conspicuous red coloured breast and white wing bar were noted (the white wing bar obviously referring to the white flank stripe) together with its small size and black belly. Other features written in my notes include white undertail coverts, black tail, white spot between bill and eye, white band around the lower breast and red patch behind the eye. I noted the red colouration initially as reed red, but after 45 years or so, I simply cannot recall why! The small bill was black and the legs noted as of blackish colouration. My father was also watching the bird when for no apparent reason the whole gaggle suddenly took wing and landed a considerable distance away. As my father had to return to work in town, he left me to take the opportunity to see the goose again. Walking across the marshes and creeping along dyke edges with difficulty enabled me to obtain further views of the Red-breasted Goose. The bird was now asleep and my notes state that it was the size of a Brent Goose and the red colouration had changed in my notes from reed red to deep red. I eventually made my way back to Great Yarmouth via the Acle New Road and joined the Breydon wall towards the council cottages for the last mile to town.

I had already realized the enormity of this find and on arrival home phoned Michael Seago. Michael could not take the following day off, but had let one of my early birding mentors Robin South know of the discovery. The following morning both Robin and I were out early on the Halvergate levels and quickly located the feeding gaggle of White-fronted Geese. Again by careful approach and scanning of the feeding birds, the Red-breasted Goose was located with reasonable ease. When in flight, both Robin and I noted the much faster wing-beats compared with those of the White-fronts. The weather was not too kind on this particular day and the red on the breast did not stand out so well as on the previous day. Michael Seago eventually saw the bird on the morning of the 4th and I had flight views later that afternoon having earlier walked all the way from Yarmouth along the Breydon north wall and out along the Fleet Dyke. On January 6th, Michael, Robin and I had further flight views of the goose, albeit at a distance over the vast expanses of these fresh marshes. Indeed the White-fronted gaggle was becoming more unsettled by the day and now wandered more freely from level to level. I personally last saw the Red-breasted Goose on the 13th when both Michael and Lowestoft birder Roger Coleman saw it in flight with a small gaggle of White-fronts near the 'Ruined Cottage' in the heart of these marshlands. It was last reported on the 28th, the observer possibly being Richard Richardson. Richard did definitely see it with other north Norfolk birders towards the end of its stay and was perhaps the last person to do so. By this time the White-fronts had increased in numbers to over 400, but quickly decreased during the last few days of January. Despite further visits, it was not seen or reported again. The weather had now become much milder and the gaggle of White-fronts had broken up into smaller groups, which was quite normal for that period. Very few birders actually saw the goose despite the fact the news did stretch across the county via the phone and postal service of the day. The only other local naturalist to see it to my knowledge was Robin Harrison, the Breydon authority of that period.

This was the first authenticated record of Red-breasted Goose for the county, the only other earlier claim being one supposedly killed at Halvergate in 1805. This was purchased by the Yarmouth naturalist Lilly Wigg in Yarmouth market which to his constant regret he accidentally plucked and cooked. It is stated that a friend dropped in, saw the feathers and identified the species. The late J. H. Gurney said of Wigg, "… we cannot be expected to credit a bird which was eaten and if a man calling himself a naturalist could not get the better of his gastronomic tastes, he must pay the penalty of not being believed". Many of the earlier records of Red-breasted Goose in this country involved White-fronted Goose as their main host species. Today the pattern has changed completely with Brent Goose seemingly the main host species in recent years. It was very nostalgic to find another Red-breasted Goose feeding with White-fronted Geese on the same Halvergate marshes some 40 years later in February 2001.'

An interesting comment is contained in 'Extracts from the Calendar of the Rev. William Whitear 1809-1826' published in the *Transactions of the Norfolk and Norwich Naturalists' Society* 1881-1882: 246 where in 1817, he mentions Lilly Wigg the Yarmouth naturalist mentioned in the above account, who ate the earlier Red-breasted Goose before realising the significance of the bird:

> 'According to Mr. Wigg the following birds of the Anas genus are very well flavoured. Red-breasted Goose, Brent Goose, Ferruginous Duck, Bimaculated Duck, Gadwall, Garganey. The Bean Goose is very badly flavoured.'

Jim Vincent, the head keeper of the Hickling Estate, writes in his personal interleaved copy of *The Hand-List of British Birds* (Witherby *et al* 1912), now owned by Moss Taylor, alongside Red-breasted Goose:

> '1914, nearly 18 years ago during a severe winter, my father shot a small goose which I feel certain after knowing more about birds was an immature of this species. I saw the species myself and told my father at the time it was a rare goose, though I was only 13 years of age, but it was foolishly eaten.'

Egyptian Goose
Alopochen aegyptiaca
The earliest dated reference we can find is in Henry Stevenson's *The Birds of Norfolk* Vol. lll. 1890: 41-43, where Thomas Southwell writes:

> 'It would be difficult to arrive at the exact date when either the Egyptian or Canada geese were first introduced into this country, though probably, as regards the former, at a remote period, but our local records of its occurrence in a supposed wild state extend no further back than the commencement of the present century, whilst the few notices of the latter are of a much more recent date.
> In Sir Willam Hooker's M.S. notes a pair of Egyptian Geese are said to have been killed near Harleston in December 1808, and one at Filby, near Yarmouth in 1815. Hunt, in 1815, figured this bird from a specimen killed some few years before at Kimberley, and states that another was shot in September, 1815, at Ormesby, near Yarmouth. Colonel Hawker mentions two killed in Norfolk, early in this century; and Mr. Joseph Clarke also informs me that one was shot at Yarmouth in 1833, and that the late Mr. Stephen Miller once followed a flock of several in Yarmouth roads. No mention, however, of either species is made by Messrs. Sheppard and Whitear (1825) or Messrs. Paget (1834).'

Ruddy Shelduck
Tadorna ferruginea
One was washed up dead on the beach at Snettisham on 13th September 1892.

J. H. Gurney writes in the *Transactions of the Norfolk and Norwich Naturalists' Society* 1893-1894: 649:

> 'A young male, which had been shot, was washed ashore at Snettisham, on September 13th, 1892. Eighteen others were obtained on various parts of the British coast, which in the opinion of Mr. F. M. Ogilvie, who wrote a very good paper about them, probably came from Southern Russia, where it breeds... A good many of these ducks are said to be bred in confinement in Holland, and our principal dealers generally have them in stock, but all sold by Castang and Cross

are bone-pinioned, as I am assured.'

Don Dorling writes in *The Birds of Norfolk* 1999: 160-161, of which he is co-author:

> 'The 1892 bird could well have been associated with a major influx of Ruddy Shelducks into western Europe that year, following an exceptionally dry summer in southern Europe when two or three birds reached as far east as eastern Greenland (Rogers 1982 in *British Birds* 75: 446-455), and thus may be the county's only wild bird.'

Common Shelduck
Tadorna tadorna
The earliest dated reference we can find is in Henry Stevenson's *The Birds of Norfolk* Vol. lll. 1890: 121-133, where Thomas Southwell writes:

> 'The most remarkable circumstance, however, connected with the past history of the sheld drake in this country is contained in the following note by Sir Thomas Browne, in his "Account of Birds found in Norfolk": -
> "Sheldrakes,*Sheledracus Jonstoni.* – Barganders, a noble coloured fowl *(vulpanser)*, which herd in coney-burrows about Norrold and other places;" and in a letter to Dr. Merritt, in 1688 (Wilkin's ed., vol. i., p. 402) he again refers to this species as "Burganders, not so rare as Turn[er] makes them, common in Norfolk, so abounding in vast and spacious warrens".'

In a footnote he adds:

> 'He uses the words *Bar*-gander and *Bur*-gander, presumably a contraction of burrow-gander, in reference to their nesting habits.'

Mandarin Duck
Aix galericulata
The Mandarin Duck is on the British List as an established feral species descended from escapes. Originally brought to a private collection at Richmond in Surrey prior to 1745, the first bird found living in the wild was shot on the Thames in Berkshire in 1866 (Palmer 2000). The species was first added to category C of the British and Irish List in 1971 and first appeared in the Norfolk Bird Report for the same year. The status of the Mandarin in Norfolk has always been beset by the problem of escapes from wildfowl collections. At Salhouse a pair believed to have escaped from a nearby collection bred annually between 1965 and 1971, while at Smallburgh a pair nested in a nest box 4m from the ground on an oak in 1977 (Taylor *et al* 1999).

Eurasian Wigeon
Anas penelope
The earliest dated reference we can find is by Sir Thomas Brown (1605-1682) in *Notes on the Natural History of Norfolk* 1902: 14:

> '…many sortes of wild ducks wch passe under names well knowne unto the fowlers though of no great signification as smee widgeon Arts ankers noblets.'

American Wigeon
Anas americana
The first fully authenticated and accepted record was a drake found at Cley by Bill Oddie on 15th November 1967.

Bill Oddie writes in *Gone Birding* 1983: 169-171:

'In 1967, again mid-November, I was back at [Cley] Coast Guards yet again, and the Grey Phalarope was *still* there. I apologised for failing to visit it the previous year, and drove off to scrutinise the wild-fowl on Billy's Marsh [opposite the then roadside hide]. I wasn't really much in the habit of looking at Ducks very thoroughly. I tended to assume that they were all Wigeon and Teal, with a few Pintail, Gadwall and Shoveler thrown in for luck. But that day some instinct must have suggested I look harder. I was with Andrew Lowe. He and I propped our telescopes on top of the car roof and began systematically scanning through the three hundred Wigeon grazing on the water meadow. I find there is only one way to check a large flock thoroughly and that is to mutter the identification of every single bird: 'Wigeon, Wigeon, Wigeon, Teal, Wigeon, Wigeon, Wigeon, another Wigeon, more Wigeon and... what the ****!' I don't recall which of us swore first, but it was certainly not in anger. There, amongst the familiar chestnut heads of the European Wigeon, was a green one – no, not a Mallard... pruce, full plumaged, male American Wigeon. Anxious to share our joy, we were rather pleased when another bird watcher drove past. We waved him to stop and pointed his binoculars in the right direction for him.

'American Wigeon out there. One hundred yards away, to the left of the gatepost.'

'I can't see it.'

'Go to the right hand end of the flock, and come back this way.'

'Where?'

'By the Pintail.'

'What Pintail?'

'The male in the middle. Next to that. American Wigeon.'

'Are you sure?'

'Of course I'm sure. Look, see that clump of reeds?'

'I can see ordinary Wigeon.'

'So can we. There's three hundred of them! And right in the middle there's an American Wigeon. By the clump of reeds.'

'Is it a male?'

'Yes. A male. A male American Wigeon.'

'Hmm. There's a Teal out there.'

'There's five hundred Teal; but there's only one American Wigeon. There, in the middle, with its head up; green head, cream stripe on the forehead. Can't you see it?'

'No.'

'Oh ****!'

He drove off. I'm honestly not sure if he *ever* saw it, or perhaps he wouldn't have known what it was if he had done. Fortunately, as *he* drove off, Richard Richardson skidded up to us on his motor bike. He had realised we'd 'got something' by the way we'd gone all red and excited:

'Richard – American Wigeon!'

'Wh-wh-where?'

'There.'

'Got it. Oh yes. Boo-boo-bootiful!'

A few minutes later the flock was disturbed (maybe Billy Bishop was chasing them off his marsh). The Ducks flew off and in the middle of them our bird – free-flying, no sign of wing clipping – surely a genuine wild vagrant. A first for Norfolk, a first for Richard and of course a first for me. It was a very significant first, too. The first proper genuine British rarity I'd actually found myself.'

However, a drake shot by Ralph Watling at Rush Hills, Hickling Broad on 15th September 1931 was thought at first to perhaps be the first county record. It was sent to Norwich Castle Museum on 17th September by Jim Vincent the then keeper of the Whitesela Estate at Hickling, but enquiries and searches for the specimen in 1990 were unsuccessful (Taylor *et al* 1999).

Most interesting is the fact that *Wild Bird Protection in Norfolk* 1931 records a drake Chiloe Wigeon being shot at Hickling Broad on September 14th or 15th, but fails to mention an American Wigeon. Could this bird be Vincent's "American" Wigeon? It does seem likely as a list by Vincent of the rarer wildfowl taken at Hickling fails to mention an American Wigeon but does include a Chiloe Wigeon shot at that time.

An enquiry to the Castle Museum, Norwich in early 2008 regarding a Chiloe Wigeon was more successful. They have a record of a Chiloe Wigeon *Anas sibilatrix* shot at Hickling on the 19th September 1931, a gift from Lord Desborough in 1931. Its museum number is NWHCM: 1931.148 and it was originally in the accession register as an American Wigeon *Anas americana*. Although the dates vary slightly it does appear conclusive.

Presumably overlooked, female American Wigeon are notoriously difficult to identify and only one has been identified in the field in Norfolk. A first-winter was found by Chris Mills at Holme on 27th January 2003 and identified after much deliberation. It remained at Holme until 13th March and was then seen at various north coast localities until 17th August. Interestingly, the *Norfolk Bird Report* 2003 gives the first date as 26th January.

There had been an earlier record, however, of one shot in error near Holkham on 2nd February 1988, the skin being held by N. V. McCanch (*Norfolk Bird Report* 1988: 285; *Norfolk Bird Club Bulletin* 51: 9-12).

Gadwall

Anas strepera

The earliest dated reference we can find is in Henry Stevenson's *The Birds of Norfolk* Vol. lll 1890: 157-163 where Thomas Southwell states:

'The Messrs. Paget, writing in 1834, remark that "two or three are generally shot every year on Breydon;" and still earlier records prove their partiality then, as at the present time, for the fresh waters of the more inland broads. The specimens from which Hunt's drawings ("Brit. Ornithology," vol. ii.), were made, were killed at Ormesby in April, 1818;'

Also known as the Heart-Duck and Summer Duck by Sheppard and Whitear in *A Catalogue of the Norfolk and Suffolk Birds, with Remarks* 1826: 56 where they write:

'In this part of the kingdom the Gadwall is not uncommon. We have seen a few which were killed in Norfolk.'

Eurasian Teal
Anas crecca
The earliest dated reference we can find is by James Fisher in the Foreword to Michael Seago's *Birds of Norfolk* (1967) where he writes:

'We know that around the year 1200 William de Warren of Wormgay rented a holding at Lynn for curlew, teal and other wildfowl.'

Sir Thomas Browne (1605-1682) writes in *Notes and Letters on the Natural History of Norfolk* 1902: 14:

'Teale Quequedula, wherein scarce any place more abounding. the condition of the country & the very many decoys especially between Norwich and the sea making this place very much to abound in wild fowle.'

Thomas Southwell adds in a footnote:

'It may seem strange that the abundance of Teal should in any way be attributed to the number of decoys, but such was really the case, the quiet and shelter afforded by these extensive preserves being very favourable to the increase of all the members of the Duck family, especially to those breeding in their immediate neighbourhood. In the returns of the old Decoys, Teal figure largely; in the present day they form a very much smaller proportion of the spoils.'

And in a letter to Merrett in the same volume page 83 Sir Thomas Browne writes:

'…we haue a kind of teale which some fowlers call crackling teale from the noyes it maketh it is almost of the bignesse of a duck coming late of the yeare & latest going away hath a russet head & neck with a dark yellow stroak about a quarter of an inch broad from the crowne to the bill winged like a teale a white streake through the middle of the wings and edges thereof the tale blackish. it may be called Querquedula maior serotina.'

Thomas Southwell adds in footnote:

'The above description certainly applies to the Common Teal, which was well-known to Browne (*vide supra*, p. 14), and that species is with us all the year; I cannot help thinking, however, that he had in his mind the Garganey, or Summer Teal, so called from the season of its visits to us. This species is known to the Norfolk gunners as the "Cricket Teal," and being slightly larger than the common species it might well be called by him "*Quequedula major serotina*".'

Green-winged Teal
Anas carolinensis
A drake located by N. J. Phillips and Richard Richardson that remained at Salthouse and Cley

on 7th-11th April 1964, was long considered the first for the county. In early 2008, an earlier occurrence of a drake shot at Breydon Water or the Bure Marshes near Great Yarmouth by Harry Smith *circa* 1959 came to light, and after consideration by the British Birds Rarities Committee it was accepted by them and became the first Norfolk record.

Peter Allard writes from his notes and recollections, not having realised the significance of the record at the time, due to the fact that it was then classified as the North American race of Eurasian Teal:

'In July 1963, I visited an old marshman who lived along the River Bure close to Great Yarmouth. His name was Harry Smith and he lived in Three Mile House alongside the river and was a well known wildfowler and self-taught taxidermist. It was well known that he had a very large collection of birds, all shot by his own gun from the marshes around the Bure and on Breydon Water. Riviere in *A History of the Birds of Norfolk* (1930) mentions him for his record of Red-crested Pochard shot on Breydon in December 1925. He also shot the 1934 Cattle Egret and various Glossy Ibises. All these birds were accepted records.

On July 15th 1963, I spoke to him at great length about various birds and he mentioned that "four or five years ago" he shot an "American Teal" (presumably meaning Green-winged Teal), but being a cagey old marshman, he was reluctant to show me this bird or any others that he had. However, as our conversation progressed, it became apparent that he knew my grandfather very well and apparently went to school with him. This certainly "broke the ice" and he said that he would like to meet him again sometime. I arranged a meeting shortly afterwards and both my grandfather and I walked the long distance along the river wall to see him and his wife. Unfortunately, I cannot find the exact date that this second meeting took place, it is in my notes somewhere, but it would have been towards the end of July or perhaps the early part of August 1963.

To cut a long story short, he showed me all his collection of birds, and having looked at the several Glossy Ibises he had shot over the years and other birds including the October 1934 Cattle Egret, he showed me the Green-winged Teal, perfectly set up in a case by itself, but unfortunately with no date. Harry Smith could not read or write, but was one of the cleverest men I knew. The Teal was indeed a drake Green-winged Teal with a very obvious narrow white vertical stripe displayed on both sides of the breast and no horizontal white line on the sides of the folded wing. The head pattern was similar to a Common Teal's, but with no yellow separating the green and red colourations. I had no doubt at the time that it was an adult drake Green-winged Teal and that Harry had shot it, *circa* 1959. The record of this Green-winged Teal is mentioned under 'Museum Collections' in my *The Birds of Great Yarmouth* (1990).

Unfortunately, when he died in the early 1970s, his collection was either destroyed or sold and its whereabouts is unknown. The Smith's lived a simple life and Harry's widow was a very timid and reserved person and any contact was difficult, although I did try to ascertain the collection's whereabouts on several occasions after his death.'

Mallard

Anas platyrhynchos

Formerly known as the Wild Duck, the earliest dated reference we can find is by Thomas South-well in Henry Stevenson's *The Birds of Norfolk* Vol. lll. 1890: 165-70 where he writes:

> 'It not unfrequently happens that ducks depart from their usual habit of nesting on the ground, and resort to trees for that purpose. Hunt ("British Ornithology," ii., p. 322) mentions that a huntsman to the then Mr. T. W. Coke, in the year 1782, killed a duck from her nest in a lofty Scotch fir in Holkham Park, much to his surprise, fully expecting to have killed a hawk.'

> He also, interestingly, mentions in a section of the book on Decoys in Norfolk that 'Sir Thomas Browne about the year 1663, refers to "the condition of the county (of Norfolk) and the very many decoys, especially between Norwich and the sea, making this place very much to abound in wild fowl." It may seem strange to speak of the decoy, perhaps the most deadly engine ever invented for the purpose of luring wild-fowl to their destruction, as being at the same time favourable to their abundance, but it is strictly in accordance with fact.'

Northern Pintail

Anas acuta

The earliest dated reference we can find is by Sir Thomas Browne (1605-1682) in a letter to Merrett in *Notes and Letters on the Natural History of Norfolk* 1902: 77:

> 'Have you a sea phaysant so commonly calld from resemblance of an hen phaisant in the head & eyes & spotted marks on the wings & back. & with a small bluish flat bill, tayle longer than other ducks, long winges crossing over the tayle like those of a long winged hawke.'

Garganey

Anas querquedula

The earliest dated reference we can find is in Sheppard and Whitear's *A Catalogue of the Norfolk and Suffolk Birds, with Remarks* 1826: 56-57:

> 'It seems probable that the Garganey sometimes breeds in Norfolk, as the Rev. Henry Tilney of Hockwold had a pair brought to him on the 6th May 1817, in the female of which was a perfect egg. And M. Youell has received a specimen of this Duck killed near Yarmouth on the 2nd of June 1820'

Thomas Southwell writes in Henry Stevenson's *The Birds of Norfolk* Vol. lll. 1890: 177-181:

> 'Hunt remarks (ii., p. 311), "we had a specimen of the male of this species (garganey) sent us to be preserved in the month of May, 1819. And a pair of these birds were shot on the 6th May, 1817, at Hockwold, in the county of Norfolk; the female had a perfect egg in her; from which circumstance they would doubt-less have bred in that neighbourhood."

He adds a footnote:

'Professor Newton informs me that among the eggs in the late Mr. Scales's collection, which were not burnt, and came into his possession, is one marked "Garganey, cut out of the bird." This is quite likely to be the egg mentioned above.

See the Eurasian Teal account above, regarding the second interesting footnote by Thomas Southwell.

Blue-winged Teal
Anas discors
A long-staying drake found by Chris Goate at Hardley Flood on 12th December 1971 remained until 12th March 1972.

Chris Goate writes:

'The first sighting was on 12th December 1971 when it was working on the edge of a reed bed, in open water, in the company of seven or eight Shoveler. Its behaviour was resting on the water and then swimming around, it was not observed feeding. It was seen on three more occasions before Christmas, always in the company of Shoveler. From 21st December until 19th February 1972 no sightings were made by the writer, although it is believed at least one sighting was made during this period. It has since been reported feeding on some "wettish" marshes together with Coot, this area, at Heckingham Marshes, is much favoured by Teal, Shelduck, Snipe, Redshank and Coot etc.

It was observed in good light through 10 x 50 binoculars and also a telescope. The most notable feature used to identify the duck were the large white cheek patches, which were very obvious both from side, and head-on views. The flanks were a mottled brown with the back a darker brown. A large white patch showed on each side under the tail. The size was estimated to be slightly larger than a Teal but smaller than a Pochard.

In flight the light blue wing patch was very evident, similar to a drake Shoveler's.'

(An account extracted from the unpublished files in the British Birds Rarities Committee archive)

John Eaton who saw the bird during its stay writes:

'During its 12 week stay I only saw the bird three times. Flight views only on Saturday January 8th 1972 when it was disturbed by shooting. Quite nice views as it moved around at the edge of the reeds with a group of Shoveler on Saturday February 19thand poor flight views during sleet showers on Saturday March 11th …'

Dave Holman writes from his notes and recollections of the time:

'This fine drake was found by C. R. Goate and seen by many observers during its three month stay. Despite many people seeing it the news did not get out widely. I lived in London at the time and despite several visits to Norfolk during the period of its residence I heard nothing of it. It was only a chance encounter with John Eaton in Epping Forest on the 4th March that I learned of its presence. Sunday 5th March found a car load of London birders arriving at Hardley Flood where we eventually located the object of our visit in a ditch in the marshy fields on the south side of the River Chet. It gave very good views in ditches and in flight between ditches but throughout our visit remained faithful to the south side of the river, never venturing on to the flood. Despite a three month stay we only scraped in with seven days to spare!'

Northern Shoveler

Anas clypeata
Thomas Southwell writes in Henry Stevenson's *The Birds of Norfolk* Vol. lll. 1890: 134-157:

'If the Broads and meres of Norfolk had not been such a *terra incognita* to the earlier writers on British ornithology, they would scarcely have doubted whether the Shoveler nested in England, and the fact of its being still a resident in, as well as a migratory visitant to, this county, may fairly lead to the conclusion that in the palmy days of the decoy system and long antecedent to their introduction, this species bred plentifully in our then un-reclaimed marshes.'

He adds an interesting footnote:

'If the term "popeler" was really applied, in olden times to the shoveler duck, as stated by Mr. Albert Way in the Camden Society's edition of the "Promptorium parvulorum" (Tom., ii., 1851), the earliest record of its occurrence in Norfolk is contained in the following brief entries in the "Household and Privy Purse Accounts" of the L'Estranges, of Hunstanton, for the year 1533: - "Itm iij popelers of store," "Itm v herns and a popeler of store"; articles of "store," as I have elsewhere stated, being supposed to represent the produce of the home farm or provisions previously purchased, whilst articles of "gyst" were undoubtedly given in lieu of rent. It is noticeable, however, that in no case is any price put to articles of "store" or "gyst," whether poultry and pigs from the farm, or cranes and plovers from the surrounding marshes; and thus in two separate entries we find the following strange mixture of edibles:- "Itm a Goos, a Pygge, a Crane, iiij Coynes, and a loyn of veile of Gyst." "Itm a Goos, iij Malards, ij Telys, and iij Coynes of store." I see no reason, therefore, to suppose that the popelers (whatever they may have been) were semi-domesticated birds, but as wild as the mallards, the bustard, the crane, and the hernsewe, all specially mentioned as "kylled wt ye crossbowe" and like them, no doubt brought in by the fowler on the estate who, with the falconer, is frequently mentioned in the "Accounts." As these two "itms," also, occur in the fifth and sixth weeks *after* the 29th day of March in that year (according o the accountant's method of reckoning), we may fix the date as early in May, the very month when the two "spowys" (whimbrel) received of "gyst," at the same time, would be passing northwards to breed, as the "May bird" of the Blakeney and Breydon gunners does to this day.

As to the identity between the word popeler and shoveler, Mr. Alfred Newton has kindly supplied me with the following note:- "It seems to me that popeler is only a corruption (by common metathesis) of "lopeler" – Lepelar Dutch, Lepler German, which are both equivalent to Loffler – from Loffel, a spoon or shovel. I find among German names for *Anas clypeata, Loffelente (i.e.,* spoon-duck), and Leppelschnute *(.e.,* shovel-snout), while, according to Bechstein, " *Anas glaucion*" is also called Spatelente, loffelente, and leppelscheute," (the last looking like a misprint for lepelschnute). "Lepeleend," *i.e.,* shovel-duck, is the Dutch name, or one of them, for *Anas clypeata.*" The same authority, however , points out that, on the other hand, the words shoveler and spoonbill have been so completely "mixed up" by early authors that it is next to impossible to determine whether the species referred to by any writer is the duck or the wader – *Anas clypeata* or *Platalea leucordia.* …'

If we disregard the above as not proven, as we surely must, the earliest dated reference we can find is by Sir Thomas Browne (1605-1682) in *Notes and Letters on the Natural History of Norfolk* 1902: 14, where in referring to the many sorts of wild duck he states:

'…the most remarkable are Anas platyrinchos a remarkably broad bild duck.'

Thomas Southwell adds in a footnote:

'*Anas platyrincus* here mentioned is the Shoveller.'

Red-crested Pochard
Netta rufina
A female 'taken' at Breydon in July 1818 was the first British occurrence of this rather attractive southern European and Asian species.

Thomas Southwell writes in Henry Stevenson's *The Birds of Norfolk* Vol. lll. 1890: 199-201:

'This beautiful duck has occurred in Norfolk some eight or nine times. The first recorded British specimen is thus referred to by Hunt in his *British Birds*:- "The specimen from which our drawing was made was killed on Breydon in the month of July, 1818, and is now in the possession of Mr. Youell, of Yarmouth." This bird was a female.'

It is not known what became of the John Youell collection at Yarmouth, and it is doubtful that any of the specimens still exist.

Canvasback
Aythya valisineria
A first-winter drake was discovered by Carl Donner at Wissington Beet Factory on 18th January 1997, the first British and only the second Western Palearctic record.

John Kemp who relocated the bird at nearby Welney (Plate 10) on the 21st writes:

'Early morning on Tuesday 21st January 1997 saw me carefully scanning through the Pochard flock in front of the main hide at Welney WWT. I had learnt from Carl Donner that he had found a drake Canvasback at Wissington B.F. pools on Saturday 18th January but had been unable to relocate it on subsequent visits. The almost complete icing up of the washes during severe weather in January had resulted in large numbers of Pochard moving onto unfrozen areas of water at Wissington and it was my hope that the Canvasback would appear at Welney with returning Pochard as conditions improved.

It was not long before my attention was drawn to the pale body and long angular head profile of the Canvasback swimming amongst a large number of Pochard (940 on 21st Jan). A long tapering black bill, slightly bulbous on base of upper mandible was possibly its most distinctive feature, but blackish feathering around the loral area and forecrown merging into a darker head than Pochard was also very apparent. A different nostril structure from Pochard resulted in one being able to see light through the nostril slit. It was clearly longer necked, more angular, almost ugly compared to the neater dumpier Pochards. A distinct double chin (or gular lump) was also present in one or two Pochard and therefore not wholly distinctive for identification purposes. The body colour was paler than Pochard, more obviously so in dull light, indeed it was difficult to pick out the Canvasback roosting on the bank, with its head tucked in, amongst hundreds of Pochards in bright sunny conditions. The upperparts were marginally darker than the flanks.

Initially the Canvasback was very shy, flying off at feeding times when grain was fed to the wild Pochard flock. By the end of its stay it became partly adjusted to the feeding regime and simply swam off to the further reaches of the lagoon, at no time attempting to join the hundreds of Pochard at the feed. In flight it was obviously larger than Pochard with longer angular neck and pale upperparts creating a pale 'saddle' contrasting with the darker wing coverts. Otherwise the wing pattern was similar to Pochard. It was fairly active in the mornings feeding by diving or dabbling in shallower water, but spent much of the middle of the day sleeping on the bank amongst hundreds of Pochard only moving when disturbed by the feeds. It was quite aggressive to other ducks and was seen to display to a female Pochard, throwing back its head and pointing its bill skyward then puffing out its neck, this display similar in all the Pochard types. On another occasion it vigorously pursued a feeding Dunlin along the shoreline.

The nightmare hybrid influence was initially foremost on my mind, this bird showing some differences from standard exaggerated models depicted in field guides. Some features needed clarification, it did at first appear not much larger than Pochard, it was certainly not as uniformly pale as field guide birds and it had a narrow dull diffuse grey subterminal band only visible at very close range and therefore not seen by most visiting birders as it came very close only on a couple of mornings before opening hours. (When it re-appeared during March, this band seemed to have almost disappeared, being only present on the right side of the bill). To allay fears of any hybrid influence I visited a small local wildfowl collection on two occasions (no they had not lost one!) where the male Canvasbacks showed slightly darker upperparts than flanks due to broader vermiculations on the upperparts. More importantly one bird, a female, showed an almost identical dull grey subterminal band only visible at close range and more obvious head on and from above. At any distance further across the pond the bill looked all black. The smaller than expected size of the Welney bird may be due to a lower swimming profile than Pochard as it miraculously transformed into a 'large angular lump' when flying.

It was aged as first-winter, amongst other things by its browner, darker upperwing coverts, marginally darker body colour than the extreme pale individuals of much literature and the mottled juvenile feathering of the centre of the lower breast.

The Canvasback was very erratic in its appearances being seen on January 21st, 23rd, 26th and 27th and February 1st, 6th and 22nd. (Also seen March 7th.) Initially it tended to be seen at Wissington B.F. when not at Welney though later it deserted Wissington B.F. for an unknown site.'

(An account published in the *Norfolk Bird Club Bulletin* No. 23: 4-6)

Common Pochard
Aythya ferina
Known to the wildfowlers of the time as Poker, Sandy Poker and Dunbird, the earliest dated reference we can find is in 'Extracts from the Calendar of the Rev. William Whitear 1809-1826' published in the *Transactions of the Norfolk and Norwich Naturalists' Society* 1881-1882: 260 where he writes:

'A female Pochard killed July 14th, 1818, was sent by Sir Jacob Astley to Corbett.'

Churchill Babington writes in *Catalogue of the Birds of Suffolk* 1884-1886: 185:

'Yarmouth, young birds (nestlings) mentioned as having occurred at this place not later than 1818 (Whitear's diary 261).'

Interestingly, the Rev. Richard Lubbock writes in *Observations on the Fauna of Norfolk* (1845), new edition by Southwell 1879: 151-153:

'With regard to the Pochard's breeding in Norfolk, the following is extracted from Girdlestone's memoranda: "Upon Hickling broad, August 16th, 1827, I found four Pochard, three of which I shot. They turned out to be all young fowl, no doubt bred somewhere in the vicinity. I am informed that this duck has bred upon Scoulton mere".'

Ring-necked Duck
Aythya collaris
A drake found by Colin Kirtland, visited Stanford Water and Tottington West Mere in the Stanford Training Area on 1st- 22nd April 1962.

Colin Kirtland writes from his notes and recollections of the time:

'During the late 1950s and early 60s my father worked for the War Office and was based in the Stanford Training Area. In those more carefree days, long before the insidious threat of terrorism, access was relatively unrestricted except when live firing was in progress. He took me there on a few occasions and I revelled in the freedom of exploring the wild expanses of uninhabited heathland where one could roam all day without seeing another person. In spring the cries of Curlew and Stone Curlew echoed all around and numerous Wheatears haunted the rabbit warrens. The meres held good numbers of duck, particularly Gadwall and in the scattered ruins of long-deserted farmhouses Barn Owls and Redstarts could sometimes be found nesting.

One day my father mentioned that he had visited a quiet, secluded mere at West Tofts which looked promising and suggested that it might be worth investigation. At the next opportunity he drove me to the camp where I borrowed his bike and cycled to the mere. It was surrounded by trees, with a dam at one end and reeds, willow and alder carr around the shallower margins. Spring sunlight shining through the trees dappled the calm water. It was a delightful spot but I thought it possibly too small to hold much of particular interest.

A first quick scan of the open water revealed an assortment of wildfowl so I stayed hidden in order to count them. There were small numbers of Little Grebe, Mallard, Gadwall and Teal near the reeds and just two Pochard and five Tufted Duck in the deeper water. However one of the latter attracted my attention as I first noticed an obvious purple gloss on its head. On closer inspection I could see that the head was distinctly peaked and lacking the drooping tuft, the flanks were grey, thinly bordered by white with a clear white crescent at the front, the tail was more prominent and the grey bill was strongly patterned, with a white band behind the black tip and another at the base. This was clearly no Tufted Duck!

In contrast to today's full bookshelves, bending beneath the weight of numerous heavy volumes, I had very few bird books at that time: an early edition of the Peterson field guide was my main reference with the Popular Handbook and the Handbook of Rarer British Birds, both birthday presents from generous friends, providing more detailed information. Luckily the Rarer Handbook included the Ring-necked Duck on the strength of just one record, the first for Britain at Slimbridge in March 1955 (The earlier occurrence of one at Leadenhall Market in 1801, said to have been taken in Lincolnshire, was not officially accepted). I recalled the illustration in the book. To my absolute delight I realised that this was the bird I was looking at! I could scarcely believe it. A chance visit to a small, rather insignificant mere, with no thought of finding anything out of the ordinary, and I had discovered not only a new bird for my list but a real rarity! It was by far the rarest bird I had ever found. Seeing any rare bird was a pleasure but the sheer thrill of actually finding one, completely unexpected, was immeasurably better. Resisting the temptation to jump up and down with excitement I hurriedly took down some notes and drew a sketch, realising the importance of obtaining a detailed description if the record was to be accepted, particularly if nobody else saw it.

I stayed for a further two hours, reluctant to leave, and in a circuit of the mere saw six Golden Pheasants, three Woodcock, sixteen Siskins and a Willow Tit. When I did decide to leave I must have been less careful, as all the diving duck took flight and only the Tufted Duck returned. However at my next stop, the even smaller Bagmore Pond just a mile away, there was the bird again, still with the two Pochard.

I cycled back to meet my father and tell him of my incredible luck. Arriving home I was eager to pass on the good news to my friends. But what was the date? April 1st. Would anyone believe me or would they think I was joking? I checked the identification in my book then ran to the phone box at the end of the road to call the only two friends who had telephones. The others would have to wait until I cycled round to tell them.

Fortunately the bird stayed for a further three weeks, spending most of the time on nearby Stanford Water and allowing several people the opportunity to see it. A few years later I also found the first for Cambridgeshire and although I have seen many since, including a winter flock of three thousand on a Florida lake, the thrill of discovering that first one on a spring day over forty-five years ago still burns brightly in the memory.'

Ferruginous Duck
Aythya nyroca
One was at Yarmouth in 1804 or 1805.

Phil Heath writes in *The Birds of Norfolk* 1999: 179:

> 'The first known Norfolk record would seem to be one illustrated in May 1805 by Sowerby, from a specimen sent from Yarmouth (Sowerby 1804-06).'

However, the first apparently authenticated and accepted records were two birds obtained near Yarmouth prior to 1824. Sheppard and Whitear write, presumably referring to these birds, in *A Catalogue of the Norfolk and Suffolk Birds, with Remarks* 1826: 58 under Castaneous Duck:

> 'Mr. Wigg has had two specimens of the Castaneous Duck, both killed at different times in the neighbourhood of Yarmouth. One of them was preserved by Mr. Youell; the flavour of the other was said to have been excellent. We have also been informed that the Rev. George Glover had a bird of this species, which was shot in Norfolk a few years since.'

Also known by 19th century naturalists as the White-eyed Pochard or White-eyed Duck, the earliest dated records, one of which may eventually be considered as the first authenticated county occurrence, are mentioned by Thomas Southwell in Henry Stevenson's *The Birds of Norfolk* Vol. lll. 1890: 208-210:

> 'Mr. E. S. Preston, of Yarmouth, had one of these birds in his collection, which was killed on Breydon, in December 1829; it was a male, not quite adult. This bird passed into the collection of the late Mr. Stevenson, and at his sale was purchased for the Norwich Museum… Two are mentioned in Mr. Lombe's notes, one a female killed at Rockland, on November 25th, 1826…'

The Breydon December 1829 specimen is cased and remains in storage at the Castle Museum, Norwich (Accession no. NWHCM: 1887.49.1).

Tufted Duck

Aythya fuligula

The earliest dated reference we can find is by Sir Thomas Browne (1605-1682) in *Notes and Letters on the Natural History of Norfolk* 1902: 14 where in referring to the many sorts of wild duck he writes:

> '… many sorts of wild ducks wch passe under names well known unto the fowlers though of no great signification as smee widgeon Arts' [Tufted Duck] 'ankers noblets.'

Thomas Southwell adds an interesting footnote here regarding local names of the various ducks, of which the Tufted is mentioned:

> 'The local names of the various Ducks are simply legion and differ both in time and place, not to mention the confusion occasioned by sex and season when these birds were not so well understood as at present. Many such names are quite lost, as "Ankers" and "Noblets," but the following are a few examples: Adult Smew, White Nun; female or immature Smew, Wesel Coot; the Wigeon was known as the Smee, Whewer, or Whim; the Tufted Duck, Arts or Arps; the Gadwall, Grey Duck or Rodge; the Pochard, Dunbird; the Shoveller, Beck or Kertlutock (Hunt); Pintail, Sea Pheasant or Cracker; Long-tailed Duck, Mealy Bird; Golden Eye. Morillon or Rattle-wing; Scaup, Grey-back, and on Breydon White-nosed Day Fowl; Scoter, Whilk; Velvet Scoter, Double Scoter (Hunt); Teal, Crick; Garganey, Summer Teal, Pied Wigeon, Cricket Teal; other names might be mentioned, and some will be found in the notes which will follow.'

Also in a letter to Merrett in the same volume page 82 Sir Thomas Browne writes:

> 'I send you the figure of the head of a cristated wild duck. it is black blackish in the greater part of the body some white on the brest & wings blewish legges & bill & seems to bee called *Anas macrolophos* as excelling in that kind.'

Thomas Southwell adds in a footnote:

> '*Fuliigula cristata* (Linnnaeus), the Tufted Duck.'

Greater Scaup

Aythya marila

The earliest dated reference we can find is by Thomas Southwell in Henry Stevenson's *The Birds of Norfolk* Vol. lll. 1890: 210-211:

> 'Except in very severe weather, the scaups spend the day far out at sea, coming in at evening to the shallows to feed on the crustaceans and molluscs which so abound on the "mussel scaups" (whence their name) on some parts of our coast; in hard weather they make their appearance in shore in considerable numbers, but even then adult birds are the exception. In Miss Gurney's notes (extracts from which will be found in the "Trans. Norfolk and Norwich Nat. Soc.," ii., p. 20) under date of February 4th 1830, occurs the following: - "Three starved

scaup ducks brought to us at Northrepps Cottage. Out of 80 ducks brought to Northrepps Hall about this date, 70 were scaups".'

Common Eider
Somateria mollissima
The earliest dated reference we can find is mentioned by Sheppard and Whitear in *A Catalogue of the Norfolk and Suffolk Birds, with Remarks* 1826: 57:

> 'An old male Eider Duck in full plumage was shot at Wells in the month of January 1820. There were two others in company with it at the time. In the stomach of this bird there was a considerable quantity of *Echini* and Crabs' claws.'

Thomas Southwell writes in Henry Stevenson's *The Birds of Norfolk* Vol. lll. 1890: 190-192, in a footnote to this species:

> 'The late Mr Whitear thus refers to this bird in his diary ("Trans. Norfolk and Norwich Nat. Soc., " iii., p. 252): - "1820, February 9th. I saw at Hunt's an old male eider duck in full plumage. Hunt informed me that this bird was killed last month (on the 27th) at wells…'

King Eider
Somateria spectabilis
An immature drake was shot off Hunstanton on 7th January 1888 (Plate 2). The specimen (Accession no. NWHCM: 1889.38) is on display in the bird gallery at the Castle Museum, Norwich.

Thomas Southwell writes in Henry Stevenson's *The Birds of Norfolk* Vol. lll. 1890: 384:

> 'In a foot-note at p. 192 of the present volume, I gave my reason for omitting this species from the "*Birds of Norfolk*," a step which I had already taken with Mr. Stevenson's full concurrence in 1879, in the second edition of Lubbock's "*Fauna of Norfolk.*" Mr Julian G. Tuck favoured me in the autumn of 1888 with some interesting notes on the birds observed by him at Hunstanton, and mentioned a young male "eider" seen by him cased at a fish-shop in that town, as apparently differing from other eiders that he had seen. As he had no books of reference with him he made a mental note of it as "a rather dark and small eider," and suggested that it might possibly be an example of the king-duck. I had an opportunity of examining this specimen in the last week of July, 1889 - unfortunately after my article on the eider had been printed off - and was delighted to find it a young male *Somateria spectablis*. The history of the bird is as follows:- It was seen alive off Hunstanton by several of the shore gunners, in January, 1888; among others, by Mr. Tuck's correspondent referred to in the "*Zoologist*," 1888, p. 148, and was eventually shot about the middle of that month. Mr. Osbourne, fishmonger, of Hunstanton, bought it, and for him it was preserved by Mr. Clark, of Snettisham. The specimen did not leave Mr. Osbourne's possession until I bought it of him, and transferred it to the Norfolk and Norwich Museum, where it now is.'

Interestingly, the Pagets record an earlier occurrence in *Sketch of the Natural History of Yarmouth and its Neighbourhood* 1834: 11 where they write:

'…a female shot on Breydon, July 25th, 1813 – Mr. Wigg.'

Thomas Southwell in the footnote mentioned above in Henry Stevenson's *The Birds of Norfolk* Vol. lll. 1890: 192 regarding this record writes:

'Messrs. Paget record a female *Somateria spectabilis*, on the authority of Mr. Lilly Wigg, as having been shot on Breydon, July 25th, 1813. With regard to this supposed occurrence, Mr. Stevenson, some years ago, favoured me with the following note:- "It is singular that the common eider is not named in Paget's list, and 'king eider' may have been written by mistake. In the days before Yarrell, I question if Wigg, or any one at Yarmouth, would have recognised the female of the king eider as distinct from the more common species." The Suffolk examples rest on an equally shadowy foundation, and are now universally rejected.'

Steller's Eider
Polysticta stelleri
A sub-adult drake was shot by George Barrow at Caister on 9th February 1830 (Plate 2). The specimen (Accession no. NWHCM: 1831.47) has been re-stuffed and remains on display in the bird gallery at the Castle Museum, Norwich.

Peter Allard writes in *The Birds of Norfolk* 1999: 184, of which he is co-author:

'A magnificent drake, though not quite fully adult, was obtained on Caister Marshes on 9th February 1830. It was shot during a period of harsh weather by George Barrow who first saw it sitting on a pool of water close to the River Bure. It constituted the first British record and is on display at the Castle Museum, Norwich.'

Thomas Southwell writes in Henry Stevenson's *The Birds of Norfolk* Vol. lll. 1890: 192-195:

'The Norfolk and Norwich Museum possesses what was for fifteen years the only known British-killed specimen of this beautiful arctic species - a male in almost perfect adult plumage, which was shot at Caister, near Yarmouth, in February, 1830. The "*Norfolk Chronicle*" of the 20th of the same month, contains a paragraph stating that "One of the greatest treats for those interested in Natural History is to be seen at that able and zealous ornithologist's, Mr. J. Harvey. This northern straggler is Anas stelleri of Pallas, western duck Pennant, described in his '*Arctic Zoology*.' It was shot near this place [Yarmouth] on the 9th inst., and is one of the handsomest of the genus except *A. spectablis*. Linn. It has not been noticed by any author to have visited this island." The occurrence was briefly announced by Mr. Yarrell to the Zoological Society on the 25th of January, 1831,("*Proc. Zool. Soc.* 1831,p. 35), and in the "*Magazine of Natural History*" for March of the same year (iv., p. 117) he recorded it, with the additional fact that the specimen was "in the possession of a gentleman at Acle;"

who there is every reason to believe, was the Rev. G. W. Steward, rector of Caister, the place where the bird was killed.'

He goes on to add:

'Harvey, into whose possession, as will have been seen, the bird immediately passed, was a well known dealer in wild-fowl, at Yarmouth, before mentioned in this work, and has long been dead; but Mr. Stevenson, with his usual care, enquired into the matter of his son, and left the result in writing. "The following" he says, "is young Harvey's account of Stellers's duck from Caister. Harvey was quite a lad when he saw a gunner, named George Barrow, returning from shooting with the bird in his hand. He followed him to the alley (the name of which he told me) with Bessey [another gunner], who got the pratincoles [cf. vol. ii., p. 65] and another man, and then went home and fetched his father. When he [the father] arrived with him, Barrow was going into Bessey's house with the duck, and Harvey, senior, bought it, but did not know what it was".'

A paragraph in A. H. Patterson's *Wild-fowlers and Poachers* 1929: 137 makes interesting reading:

'There's one handsome little duck' remarked Bellin, 'the Steller's duck, now in Norwich Museum, presented to the city by the Rev. Steward in July 1831. The bird had been shot in February the year before, and the Norfolk Chronicle made a lot of fuss about it, stating that "One of the greatest treats for those interested in Natural History is to be seen at... Mr. Harvey's... shot near that place" (Yarmouth). Stevenson gives a racy chapter to it in the Birds of Norfolk, stating therein that our Harvey – the second – saw one George Barrow carrying the bird, and followed him home with it; then ran home to the old man to go back with him to see it. The general opinion has been that the bird was shot on the shore at Caister – Stevenson merely says "at Caister". My father, who knew Barrow, got it from the man's own lips that he was on the Caister marshes, not a great way from the Bure, and the Black Boards, where he saw it sitting in a pool of water, and to use Barrow's own words, "I crept on my hands and knees, as close as I could get, but it was still too far off for a shot. My hands had become numbed with cold, and well nigh frozen; so I says to myself, 'If I don't get a shot now directly, I shall be too cold to get a shot at all.' However, the bird came within range, and I let go. One shot struck the duck just above the eye. I took out my handkerchief, and rolled it up, put it round the bird's neck, and strangled it" – an absurd way for any man to settle a miserable little fowl, you must admit. The Barrows of that period were noted for their eccentricities. I understand that Stevenson instituted a lot of enquiries about it, but omits my father's description.'

Long-tailed Duck
Clangula hyemalis
The earliest dated reference we can find is in Henry Stevenson's *The Birds of Norfolk* Vol. lll. 1890: 216-19 where Thomas Southwell writes:

'Messrs. Sheppard and Whitear speak of the long-tailed duck being unusually numerous in the winter of 1819-20... Hunt ("British Ornithology," ii., p. 303, foot note) also says, "we have been gratified with the examination of several specimens which were exposed for sale in the Norwich Market in the early part of November, 1819. It is the only instance we remember of this species being shot in Norfolk".'

For completeness, and interest, we include the Sheppard and Whitear comments mentioned above in full from *A Catalogue of the Norfolk and Suffolk Birds, with Remarks* 1826: 57-58:

'In severe weathers these ducks visit our shores and rivers; and they have been taken in the decoy at Herringfleet. In the winter of 1819-20 they were unusually numerous, particularly at Yarmouth, and many of them were killed. Some of these had the two middle feathers of the tail elongated, but in most of them these two feathers did not exceed the others in length.'

Black (Common) Scoter
Melanitta nigra
The earliest reference we can find is by Sheppard and Whitear in *A Catalogue of the Norfolk and Suffolk Birds, with Remarks* (1826) where they merely list '*A. nigra* (Scoter)' but make no comments on the species.

The Pagets in *Sketch of the Natural History of Yarmouth and its Neighbourhood* (1834) considered it '...common in some winters.'

The Rev. Richard Lubbock in *Observations of the Fauna of Norfolk* (1845), new edition by Southwell 1879: 163 writes:

'THE SCOTER (*A, nigra*) appears upon the coast every winter. I once observed one of these last as high upon our river as Thorpe. It very seldom quits the ocean.'

Surf Scoter
Melanitta perspicillata
Three drakes were seen by Emma Turner close inshore off Scolt Head on 2nd October 1925.

Emma Turner writes in *Bird Watching on Scolt Head* 1926: 75-76:

'On October 2nd, 1925 we started off early across Norton Creek, at low tide, and explored all the south side of the creek to Burnham Overy, returning across Overy Creek to the east end of Scolt Island. This takes about five hours, as it is not a walk that can be hurried because of the many likely places which have to be explored. Short-eared owls may be skulking in the rough stuff on the wall; kingfishers often frequent the creeks, waders paddle about in the mud on either side, and you never know what the gorse bank at Overy might hide. So it is a leisurely walk, and when you have carefully picked your way across the Overy estuary, you find a sheltered corner in the sand-hills and devour a frugal and well-earned lunch. After that there is the return journey along the shore while the incoming tide creeps up, and the westering sun gilds the sea and sands. I was tired that

October afternoon, and when my companion called my attention to a little party of birds inshore, I murmured – "Only scoters; tired of scoters." However duty compelled me to turn my glasses on them and I suddenly saw that these seven birds had white patches on the nape of the neck. They were surf-scoters. This was the first record of this species for East Anglia. That kind of thrill is wonderfully cheering and makes one forget all about fatigue.'

Interestingly, in her note in *British Birds* 19: 234, Miss Turner writes "the white nape patch was distinctly visible on three of them", so the identity of the other four scoters in the group remains unproven.

Three drake Surf Scoters off Scolt Head October 1925. (*Robert Gillmor*)

Velvet Scoter
Melanitta fusca

The earliest reference we can find is by Sheppard and Whitear in *A Catalogue of the Norfolk and Suffolk Birds, with Remarks* 1826: 57 where they comment:

'*A. fuscata* (Velvet Duck) This is a rare species, but it has been sometimes killed both in Norfolk and Suffolk.'

The Pagets write in *Sketch of the Natural History of Yarmouth and its Neighbourhood* 1834: 11:

'…occasionally shot in hard winters; several in the very severe one of 1829-30.'

Common Goldeneye
Bucephala clangula

The earliest dated reference we can find is by Sir Thomas Browne (1605-1682) in *Notes and Letters on the Natural History of Norfolk* 1902: 83-84 where he writes in a letter to Merrett prior to 8th May 1669:

> 'Haue you had the duck called Clangula in Ald. [drovandus] & Johnst. Wee haue one here wch answereth their descriptions exactly butt [*i.e.,* except] only in the colour of their leggs & feet.'

Thomas Southwell adds a footnote:

> 'Aldrovandus's figure of "Clangula" (head only, iii., p. 224) is too indefinite for determination. He says the feet are yellow, but Jonston, who refers to it under the name of *Anas platyrhincus* describes it fairly well (p. 145). *Clangula ab alarum clangore,* Aldrov., *i.e.* "Rattlewings," an old name by which the Golden-eye was known to the Norfolk gunners.'

He adds:

> 'Merrett says, in a letter (to Sir Thomas Browne) dated 8th May 1669, "The Clangula I know no more of than reading hath informed mee".'

Smew
Mergellus albellus

First referred to by Sir Thomas Browne (1605-1682) as, *Mustela variegate,* being the male and female, or either in immature plumage in *Notes and Letters on the Natural History of Norfolk* 1902: 13-14:

> 'Diuers other sorts of diuerfowle more remarkable the mustela fusca & mustela variegate the graye dunne & the variegated or partie coloured wesell so called from the resemblance it beareth vnto a wesell in the head.'

The female Smew was known to the gunners as the Weasel Duck and the drake the White Nun.

Red-breasted Merganser
Mergus serrator

Not distinguished from Goosander by Sir Thomas Browne between 1605 and 1682, Thomas Southwell writes in Henry Stevenson's *The Birds of Norfolk* Vol. lll. 1890: 226-229:

> 'All the birds of the genus *Mergus* are known to our gunners as "Sawyers, and, says Sir Thomas Browne, are "distinguished from other diuers by a notable sawe bill, to retaine its slipperie pray as liuing much upon eeles, whereof wee have seldome fayled to find some in their bellies".'

And the earliest dated reference to this species:

'In Sir Willam Hooker's MS. occurs a note initialled D[awson] T[urner], which states that many specimens of this bird were "shot near Yarmouth, December, 1829, and in January and February, 1830. Before that time very seldom seen".'

Interestingly, a reference by Robert Marsham (1708-1797) in Tim Sparks and John Lines' *Chapters in the Life of Robert Marsham Esq. F.R.S. of Stratton Strawless, Norfolk* 2008: 17 may be attributed to this species:

'Examined but not exact,....I could find none exactly like the bird showed me.'

Common Merganser (Goosander)

Mergus merganser
See the above species' account. The earliest dated reference we can find is by Robert Marsham (1708-1997) in Tim Sparks and John Lines' *Chapters in the Life of Robert Marsham Esq. F.R.S. of Stratton Strawless, Norfolk* 2008: 17:

'One like this Killed in Stratton 1758. Found it had some small carp in its stomach.'

Thomas Southwell writes in Henry Stevenson's *The Birds of Norfolk* Vol. lll. 1890: 229-232:

'The brothers Paget state that it is "occasionally here in severe winters," and Mr. Lubbock also mentions it as rare in perfect plumage. An entry in the Hooker MS. states that two specimens of the goosander were "taken alive by a fishing boat off the coast, December 29th 1830, very savage, attacking spontaneously the men that had them, and lacerating extremely their fingers by their bites".'

Sheppard and Whitear in *A Catalogue of the Norfolk and Suffolk Birds, with Remarks* 1826: 58-59 write:

'The young male of this species has been killed in Norfolk: it was in the plumage of the female; and Mr. Hunt found that the windpipe of this bird exactly resembled that of the Goosander.'

Ruddy Duck

Oxyura jamaicensis jamaicensis
One first located by G. H. (Josh) Scott at Welney on 10th January 1977, remained there until the 18th.

The Wildfowl Trust's annual report for 1977 (now the Wildfowl and Wetlands Trust) notes in the accounts for Welney simply "Other birds of interest...included...a Ruddy Duck" and does not refer to the record as a county first. This would possibly indicate that Josh was unaware of the significance of his find and that it was first noticed by the Norfolk Bird Report compilers the following year, where in the 1977 Report it again simply states "Ruddy Duck: Fens: Welney Jan. 10th-18th (GHS). The first county record." The NBR did not publish Reserves notes after the 1972 Report, which until then included Welney.

Unfortunately as both Josh, the then reserve manager, and the manager who succeeded him at Welney WWT are no longer alive, more information concerning this record is unlikely to be forthcoming.

First imported into Slimbridge in 1948, these began breeding, and between 1952 and 1973 about 70 unpinioned juveniles escaped, and feral breeding was first recorded in 1960. Until the early 1970s it remained a fairly scarce bird, with the population centred on the Midlands and Somerset. Since then their range had consolidated and expanded considerably. It was only admitted to Category 'C' of the British list as recently as 1971. However, with the recent controversial decision to eradicate the species from Britain because of its considered threat to the Spanish population of the White-headed Duck, it may once again become a scarce or even rare bird here.

Red-legged Partridge
Alectoris rufa
The earliest dated reference we can find is by Robert Marsham (1708-1797) in Tim Sparkes and John Lines' *Chapters in the Life of Robert Marsham Esq. F.R.S. of Stratton Strawless, Norfolk* 2008: 14:

> 'One shot in Norfolk January 1787 weight near 16 ounces, length 15.5 inches, broad 18 inches.'

Henry Stevenson's writes in *The Birds of Norfolk* Vol. l. 1866: 404-420:

> 'Its introduction into the Eastern Counties dates only from the close of the last century, when, about the year 1770, the Marquis of Hertford and Lord Rendlesham are recorded to have had large quantities of eggs imported from the continent, and the young birds, hatched under domestic fowls, were turned off at Sudbourn and Rendlesham, in Suffolk, on the repective estates of the above noblemen. From thence they soon spread to other portions of the county, and the adjoining parts of Norfolk…'

Grey Partridge
Perdix perdix
The earliest dated reference we can find is in a footnote in Henry Stevenson's *The Birds of Norfolk* Vol. l. 1866: 420-428:

> 'On the 7th of October 1797, the late Earl of Leicester, within an area of one mile of his manor at Warham, bagged forty brace in eight hours, at ninety-three shots, each bird killed singly; and on the same ground the day previously he killed twenty-two brace and a-half in three hours.'

Common Quail
Coturnix coturnix
Henry Stevenson writes in *The Birds of Norfolk* Vol. l. 1866: 429-435:

> 'Sir Thomas Browne alludes to there being "no small number of Quails" in Norfolk in his time,' (1605-1682) 'but although still reckoned amongst our

regular summer visitants, all local authors, since the commencement of the present century, agree as to the marked diminution in the numbers of this species of late years.'

Common Pheasant
Phasianus colchicus
The earliest dated reference we can find is in Henry Stevenson's *The Birds of Norfolk* Vol. l. 1866: 361-374, where he states:

'I know of no records relating to the Pheasant in England which afford any clue to the period when that noble species was first brought to this country, and though probably its acclimatization does not date further back than the Norman Conquest, yet it is still possible that our Roman invaders may have imported it at a much earlier period with other Imperial luxuries. Yarrell Brit. Bds., ii., 2nd ed., p. 420, note) quotes from Dugdale's "*Monasticon Anglicanum*" an extract, showing that in the first year of Henry 1., who began to reign in 1100, the Abbot of Amesbury obtained a 'license' to kill pheasants; and according to Echard's History of England, as quoted in Daniell's "*Rural Sports,*" the price of a pheasant Anno Dom. 1299 (being the 27th of Edward the First) was four-pence, a couple of woodcocks at the same period three halfpence, a mallard three halfpence, and a plover one penny. If we take then the above dates, only, into consideration, a residence in this country of over seven hundred years would surely entitle the pheasant to rank amongst our "British Birds," more particularly when the propensity of the hens to "lay away," and of the cocks to "foot it," on their own account, in search of food, shews a natural independence of character, opposed to the domesticated habits of our poultry, and impatient of the supervision and protection of man. The earliest notice of this bird in Norfolk occurs in the "Household Book" of the L'Estrange's, of Hunstanton, from which I have previously given extracts on the subject of falconry, and here the pheasant is specially mentioned both as a "quarry" for the hawks and an occasional article of luxury for the table. Thus in the 11th year of the reign of King Henry the Eighth (1519) appears amongst other "rewardes for bryngyng of p'sents." "Itm to Mr. Ashley svnt for bryngyng of a fesaunt cocke and iiij woodcocks ye xviijth daye of Octobre in reward iiijd;" also "Itm a fesand of gyste" (articles received in lieu of rent); and twice in the same year we find the following record; - Itm a fesant kylled wt ye goshawke".'

Golden Pheasant
Chrysolophuspictus
Although the earliest record of a Golden Pheasant in the wild was one seen in Norfolk in 1845 (Lever 1977; Long 1981; Browne *et al.* 1997), they were not turned down in Breckland until the late 1890s. This species was admitted to Category C of the British and Irish List in 1971 and in that year records first appeared in the *Norfolk Bird Report* (Taylor *et al* 1999).

Red-throated Loon (Diver)
Gavia stellata
Fossil remains indicate that this species is one of the first to have been recorded in the county.

Thomas Southwell writes in Henry Stevenson's *The Birds of Norfolk* Vol. lll. 1890: 272-274:

'To Mr. Clement Reid we are indebted for the discovery of the fossil remains of this species in the post-glacial deposit known as the "Mundesley River Bed" ("*Geological Magazine*," March, 1883, p. 97).'

The Mundesley River Bed is reckoned to be Ipswichian (an Interglacial that started about 135,000BP (Before Present) and lasted until about 73,000BP). It is thought that most species colonised Britain Post glacial (starting 12,000 yearsBP). Bird bones do turn up in earlier deposits, but they are often difficult to assign to a species with certainty. Dealing with fossil and subfossil material is fraught with problems of identification, especially when the available material is scattered and fragmentary (Dr A G Irwin *in litt*).

In more recent times the earliest reference we can find is by Sheppard and Whitear in *A Catalogue of the Norfolk and Suffolk Birds, with Remarks* 1826: 60 where they state:

'We have seen specimens of the Red-throated Diver in Norfolk, both in its full plumage and also in its speckled state: and Mr. Hunt says that it is not uncommoon at Yarmouth during the winter. – The position of the feet of Divers at the extremity of the body, and their horizontal motion, enable them to make rapid turns under water in pursuit of their slippery prey.'

Black-throated Loon (Diver)

Gavia arctica
Thomas Southwell writes in Henry Stevenson's *The Birds of Norfolk* Vol. lll. 1890: 269-272:

'Hunt, in his list, speaks of the black-throated diver as very rare in this county. Sheppard and Whitear (1826) merely catalogue the species without remark, and neither Gurney and Fisher, nor Lubbock give any definite information with regard to it. A note in Mr. Lubbock's copy of "Bewick" is as follows: - "In 1832 saw a very fine pair of these birds preserved by Smith; they were shot in Postwick Reach, about four miles from Norwich, in the winter of 1831-2. Stuffed for Mr. Penrice.'

Great Northern Loon (Diver)

Gavia immer
Thomas Southwell writes in Henry Stevenson's *The Birds of Norfolk* Vol. lll. 1890: 265-269:

'Mr. Stevenson, writing in 1863, expressed his belief that this species "is decidedly the most rare, in any plumage, of our three British divers," adding that he had known of only four or five examples during the previous twelve years. In the adult breeding plumage there can be no question as to its extreme rarity off the Eastern Counties, and, so far as I am aware, it has not been met with on the Norfolk coast in that stage; but in immature and winter plumage it cannot, I think, be considered so rare as the black-throated diver, though both species are far from frequent at any time. Sir Thomas Browne' (1605-1682) 'doubtless refers to this diver in the following passage:- "As also that large & strong-billd fowle, spotted like a starling, Clusius nameth *Mergus maior Farroensis*, as frequenting the Faro Islands, seated above Shetland; one whereof I sent unto my worthy friend

Dr. Scarburgh;" and in a letter to Merrett, he says that he has thrice met with this bird, which "were taken about the time of the herring fishing at Yarmouth. One was taken upon the shore not able to fly away".'

Yellow-billed Loon (White-billed Diver)
Gavia adamsii
An adult was found by C. J. and J. A. Hazell off Blakeney Point on 29th September 1985.

J. A. Hazell writes:

'The White-billed Diver was added to the county list on 29th September 1985 when an adult in non-breeding plumage was identified off-shore near Half-way House between Cley and Blakeney Point.

Having abandoned a fruitless early morning search for a reported Lanceolated Warbler beyond Cley Coastguard lookout C. J. Hazell and I continued birding as we walked towards the Point. Nearing Halfway house we noticed three observers (including P. Whiteman) studying a small party of divers some 70 yards off the tideline. I first looked at a summer plumaged Red-throated, then two non-breeding plumaged Black-throated. C. J. Hazell then drew my attention to another Black-throated in splendid summer dress. As I was admiring this last bird he excitedly exclaimed "Look at the large diver to its right – it has an all yellowish-white bill". All eyes quickly concentrated on this stranger. Agreement was soon reached as to identity: White-billed Diver! Within minutes over 150 observers had assembled to view the vagrant. As a result the group of divers rapidly drifted further out to sea. Suddenly all took flight, the White-billed and two of the Black-throated heading together towards us. When some 200 yards away all turned westward before finally swinging eastward and disappearing beyond the Coastguard lookout.

Description: A very large diver, dwarfing accompanying Black-throated and easily a third again their size. It seemed larger than any Great Northern in either summer or winter plumage which I have seen on more than a hundred occasions during the past sixteen years. This feature was noted on my only previous sighting of a White-billed (an adult in winter plumage in Buckie harbour 2nd April 1972) which I watched after observing 33 Great Northerns two days previously. Most obvious feature was the large bill which appeared longer than in a Great Northern. Initially it appeared pale yellowish-white. However, on closer inspection it was translucent white towards the tip, more creamy white behind this and yellow-white towards the base especially on the lower mandible. It was very deep at the base and the bottom profile line of the lower mandible paralleled the culmen for approximately a third of its length before becoming acutely angled to the bill tip. The upper mandible was very straight in its culmen line with just a slight downward curve – barely perceptive – towards the tip. The culmen was similarly coloured as the rest of the bill except for a small darkish area locally at its base in the region of the nasal grooves which blended into the blacker feathering of the forehead. The bill was carried pointing slightly upwards (like a Red-throated) accentuating the tip-tilted shape. There was no apparent dark gape line or cutting edges shown by pale-billed Great Northerns.

Upperparts: Fore-crown and crown dark brown; nape and hind neck a much paler brownish-grey and contrasting with the almost (except for a few pale tips to some scapulars and coverts) completely dark black-brown back and flight feathers. Strong blackish-brown patches came well round on the lower neck and upper breast. Sides of head dirty white, completely above the eye and also along the sides of the neck. Prominent ear-covert patch similarly coloured as nape and joining hind neck. Loral area whitish.

Underparts: Chin and front of neck very white and breast whitish. Softparts: Eye appeared dark and isolated in the side of the face by their dirty white area already described.

In flight the large size and slow wing-beats prompted such comments as goose-like. The bill was still carried uptilted.

A High Arctic bird, the White-billed Diver breeds above the tree-line from Murmansk and Nova Zemlaya eastward across Arctic shores of the USSR to Siberia and North America. Autumn dispersal following advancing ice begins in August/September, the western Russian birds wintering mainly off Norway. The majority of British records have been of adults. Interestingly, of the hundred recorded all but three have been since 1946. This first Norfolk occurrence is only the fifth record south of Yorkshire. J. T. R. Sharrock writes that White-billed Diver reports of late winter arrivals from January onwards in the fifteen-year period to 1972, suggest a small British population originating from a mid-winter movement across the North Sea from Norwegian gatherings. Since then increasing spring records in Shetland have led to the occasional bird summering there. This pattern suggests the late September Norfolk bird (at a time of year when observations are unusual) may well have originated in Shetland waters as opposed to an extremely early departure from the High Arctic.'

(An account published in the *Norfolk Bird Report* 1986: 419-420)

Yellow-billed Loon offshore near Halfway House September 1985. (*Norman Arlott*)

Pied-billed Grebe
Podilymbus podiceps
One found by Colin Kirtland at Welney on 9th November 1968, frequented the Washes until the 12th.

Colin Kirtland writes from his notes and recollections of the time:

'In my younger days I was so keen to go birdwatching that I would take any opportunity, even if I only had an hour or two to spare. One of my favourite winter destinations was the Ouse Washes, particularly when flooded as there were more birds and they were easier to see. Before the WWT reserve was established I would sometimes drive to Welney village and walk northward along the River Delph. The adjacent osier beds were far less extensive then, which allowed a clear view over the open water.

One November afternoon I left home knowing that I would only have a short time in the field before dark, but the flooded washes were a big draw. I arrived to find the water level fairly high although the road across to Welney was open. I parked and walked along the river, hoping that I might perhaps find an early Goosander or Goldeneye among the commoner wintering duck. The floods stretched into the distance, a broad silver ribbon with only a few protruding fence posts and nearly submerged gates breaking the calm surface. In the days before tripod-mounted telescopes were an essential item of equipment my telescope was an old-fashioned, four-draw, brass and glass monster. The normal method of use was to sit on a convenient bank, lean back and place the end on one's knee for some degree of stability. In winter this could be a cold, damp and muddy experience, so more often we relied solely on our binoculars and good eyesight.

I stopped regularly to scan through the multitude of wildfowl. Most numerous were the Wigeon, their constant whistling so typical of a winter flood. There were also hundreds of Mallard, Teal, Pintail and Shoveler; so many birds to look at and enjoy. This was the washes at their best. I searched through the swans and among a hundred or so Mutes was pleased to find seventeen Bewick's and a single Whooper – still a comparative rarity in those days. Two late Swallows were hawking for insects over the osiers and further away a large-looking diver headed up-river, a probable Great Northern. I was glad I had made the effort to come.

There were a few wildfowl ahead of me along the river: two Great Crested Grebes, a Little Grebe, twenty Tufted Duck and the hoped-for Goldeneye, three birds which nervously took flight. Suddenly a lone bird swimming only about twenty-five yards away caught my eye. With only a rear view its greyish-brown back and more rufous neck and crown vaguely suggested a female Smew, but as it turned sideways the bulky-looking head and large, pale bill (not pied in winter) were immediately obvious. I was looking at a Pied-billed Grebe! How lucky could I be? Content enough to enjoy the spectacle of thousands of birds in a wonderful setting, I had chanced upon a true rarity. Moreover with so many birds covering the water this was the nearest one!

It was after four o'clock, the light was fading and I needed as much detail as possible. Ignoring the damp grass I sat on the bank and pulled out my trusty 'scope. Examining the bird I could see that the chin, throat, belly and under-tail coverts were white, the front and sides of the neck and the flanks greyish-buff.

71

The darkest feathers were on the forehead and lores. It appeared quite uncon-
cerned and dived repeatedly, slipping beneath the water with barely a ripple.
Before leaving I approached even closer and it hid half-submerged in flooded
vegetation before swimming away.

Well satisfied I walked back to the car in the dusk, elated with my discovery.
A distinctive call caused me to look up: two Twite flew over heading south-west.
It had been a good afternoon! That evening I contacted a few friends and the
following morning a car-load of them managed to relocate the grebe, despite
searching in thick fog. It was seen just once again two days later, but may well
have stayed longer. On such a vast expanse of water a single bird could easily
escape detection.

This was only the third British record, following the first in Somerset (now
Avon) in 1963 and another on Yorkshire in 1965. Despite subsequently occurring
in Britain with frequent regularity it remained the only one for Norfolk, and
indeed for East Anglia until a second appeared in the spring of 1999.'

Little Grebe
Tachybaptus ruficollis
The earliest dated reference we can find is by Sir Thomas Brown (1605-1682) in *Notes and
Letters on the Natural History of Norfolk* 1902: 13:

'Mergus minor the smaller diuers or dabchicks in riuers & broade waters.'

Great Crested Grebe
Podiceps cristatus
The earliest reference we can find is by James Fisher in the Foreword to Michael Seago's *Birds of
Norfolk* (1967) where he writes:

'If the text of the *Blickling Homilies* be a Norfolk text, then the first Norfolk
birds mentioned in writing may be their *scealfor* (great crested grebe, probably),
culfre (woodpigeon) and *turtura* (turtle dove) of 970 or a few years before – a
millennium ago.'

Henry Stevenson writes in *The Birds of Norfolk* Vol. lll. 1890: 233-245, from notes taken
about 1861:

'With so many and such relentless enemies, the wonder is that a single loon
remains at the present time to grace our waters, than that their numbers for the
last twenty years should have steadily but surely decreased.'

Thomas Southwell adds in a footnote:

'Sir Thomas Browne' (1605-1682) 'thus refers to this bird, "*Mergus acutiro-
stris speciosus* or Loone, an handsome and specious fowle, cristated, and with
diuided finne feet, placed very backward, and after the manner of all such which
the Dutch call *Arsvoote*, they have a perculiar formation in the legge bone, which
hath a long and sharpe process extending above the thigh bone. They come
about April, and breed in the broad waters, so making their nest on the water,

that theire egges are seldom dry, while they are sett on".'

Red-necked Grebe

Podiceps grisegena

The earliest reference we can find is by Sheppard and Whitear in *A Catalogue of the Norfolk and Suffolk Birds, with Remarks* 1826: 50:

> 'We have seen a specimen of this bird in the collection of Mr. Hunt of Norwich, who informs us that he has had three others of the same kind killed in Norfolk. Mr. Wigg of Yarmouth has also had one shot in the neighbourhood of that place.'

However, the earliest dated reference we can find is by the Paget's in *Sketch of the Natural History of Yarmouth and its Neighbourhood* 1834: 12 where they write:

> '…very rare; three shot in January, 1828.'

Horned (Slavonian) Grebe

Podiceps auritus

Known as the Sclavonian Grebe, the earliest dated reference we can find is in Henry Stevenson's *The Birds of Norfolk* Vol. lll. 1890: 248-250, where Thomas Southwell writes:

> 'This bird is a regular and common early spring migrant to the Norfolk waters, but is rare in breeding plumage, thus differing from the next species, with which it is sometimes confounded… The occurrences later than the month of March have been comparatively few. Yarrell mentions a very fine specimen, which was killed near Yarmouth, in May, 1826; and the Rev. T. Berney, of Braconash, has one in his collection, shot by himself on Breydon, on May 14th, 1845 which is in perfect breeding condition;'

Black-necked Grebe

Podiceps nigricollis

Prior to 1813 any specific record of Black-necked or Slavonian Grebe was possibly suspect unless it was obtained or some point of description in the field, such as an up-turned bill, was described (J Gaskell *in litt*).

One was caught near Yarmouth in the autumn of 1817.

Moss Taylor writes in *The Birds of Norfolk* 1999: 104-105, of which he is co-author:

> 'The first British example of a Black-necked Grebe was one caught by a spaniel near Yarmouth in autumn 1817 (*Sheppard & Whitear* 1826).'

Sheppard and Whitear write in *A Catalogue of the Norfolk and Suffolk Birds, with Remarks* 1826: 50-51:

> 'We received a specimen of this bird from Yarmouth in the autumn of 1817. It was caught alive, and was remarkably tame, pluming itself with great composure

soon after it was taken.'

Thomas Southwell adds a footnote under this reference in Henry Stevenson's *The Birds of Norfolk* Vol. lll. 1890: 250-256:

> 'This curious tameness has been more than once exhibited by the Sclavonian, as also by the little grebe.'

Hunt, in *British Ornithology* Vol 3: 94, depicts a figure of the 1817 bird. For many years this was considered the first British example, until details of one shot in Cornwall on 15th March 1811 came to light.

Black-browed Albatross
Thalassarche melanophris
One was seen by Mick Fiszer flying east past Mundesley on 31st December 2002.

Mick Fiszer writes:

> 'As the year drew to a close I sat at home waiting for the evening weather forecast, before planning my birding for the last day of 2002. With the forecast predicting strong north-easterly winds and rain my options seemed somewhat limited to say the least.
> Thoughts went through my head; could I make a return visit to Norfolk's first Pallid Harrier at Stiffkey, should I check out the Crossbill flock at Bacton Wood or go on a wild goose chase in the Broads. In the end none appealed sufficiently and I opted for a morning's seawatching from the private hide at the Ship Hotel, Mundesley.
> So it was that I arrived at the car park just after dawn to open up the hide, the weather forecast proving correct with overcast skies, light rain and a stiff north-easterly wind restricting visibility to about 8 km.
> My hopes were not high, if I was lucky perhaps a late skua or even a shear-water. These expectations were hardly raised in the first half hour, with just the occasional Red-throated Diver and distant auk. Slowly things began to improve, however, with small flocks of Kittiwakes and a few Gannets moving east.
> At around 8.40 am I was scoping a line of seven Gannets estimated to be about 1.5 km offshore when, as they passed through my field of view, another bird sheared into sight and flew low to the water before rising up again. It was immediately obvious that this was not just another Gannet but a 'mollymawk', one of the smaller albatrosses, but which one...?
> As the bird approached I was fully aware of the enormity of the sighting. I hadn't experienced that 'gut feeling' and the bristling hairs on the back of my neck since the Soft-plumaged Petrel in June 1997 which I saw from the same hide. I assembled the following description in the few seconds available; slightly larger in body mass than the Gannets, but the striking and exceptionally long wings creating an image of a much larger bird. It was difficult to assess bill colour save to say it was not the bright orange of an adult. The underwing, however, was fairly easy to evaluate, the bird having both a broad dark leading and trailing edge to the wing with no thumbprint in the 'armpit'.

With this I was able to clinch the identification of Norfolk's first Black-browed Albatross, a species I had been watching at length in the southern Indian Ocean the previous month, further proof that the sea can yield surprises for the dedicated seawatcher at any time of the year.'

(An account published in the *Norfolk Bird Report* 2003: 278)

Albatross species
Thalassarche sp

Four earlier reports of albatrosses were never specifically identified and remain accepted only as albatross sp. The first was one seen flying west at Cley by Michael King and C. J. Oldershaw on 19th October 1977 (*British Birds* 71: 488). The second was seen moving east at Happisburgh by John Geeson on 9th November 1986 (*British Birds* 82: 508), the third, an adult, flew east at Cley on 11th October 1987 and the fourth, an immature, seen off Cromer, Sheringham and Salthouse on 18th October 1987. In 2008 both 1987 claims were still under consideration by the BBRC as potential Black-browed Albatross records. Should any of the four birds ever be specifically identified, it or they would become the first of that species for Norfolk.

Details of the first occurrence are as follows:

Michael King and C. J. Oldershaw independently noticed a very large sea-bird flying from the east approximately one quarter to one third of a mile offshore from Cley shingle ridge at 11.30am on 19th October 1977. It was watched in a light wind and, with the bright sunlight from behind them lighting the bird well, it made its way slowly past the observers parallel to the beach eventually passing out of sight to the west. Flight was characteristic of an albatross, three to four slow wing beats followed by a short glide, 10-25 feet above the surface of the calm sea. To the west it rose to about 100 feet and circled once in a glide before continuing.

Their first impressions were of the very large size of the bird. It could be compared with two Great Black-backed Gulls which were in the general area and was seen to be very much larger than the gulls. It looked like a huge Northern Fulmar with a large round head and massive bill. The chest was deep with the body tapering from there to the tail. The wings were very long and narrow and were held straight and stiff without the gull's prominent angles. The bird was pure white apart from the wings and back which were uniformly black. The underwings were white with black leading and trailing edges. Both observers had seen many Northern Gannets in various plumages and none showed the uniform black stripe from wing-tip to wing-tip across the back. M.K. had also seen the Black-browed Albatross at Hermaness, Shetland.

The bill was ravelled in what appeared to be a bunch of fishing net which was trailing below and behind the bird and appeared to be causing it some distress.

Both observers were completely satisfied that the bird was an albatross but neither was able to specifically identify it and it was accepted as an albatross sp by the BBRC.

(An account compiled from the unpublished files in the British Birds Rarities Committee archive)

Northern Fulmar
Fulmarus glacialis

Thomas Southwell writes in Henry Stevenson's *The Birds of Norfolk* Vol. lll. 1890: 359-361:

'The earlier Norfolk naturalists seem to have regarded this species as a rare bird. Sheppard and Whitear do not mention it. Hunt, in his "List," merely says that one killed at Yarmouth is in the possession of Mr. J. J. Gurney; in the Hooker MS. is mention of one taken at Yarmouth, on 18th November, 1829; the Pagets say that it is occasionally caught in the Yarmouth Roads; and Messrs. Gurney and Fisher speak of it as sometimes found off the coast in autumn;'

Fea's or Zino's Petrel

Pterodroma feae/madeira

One was discovered by Stefan McElwee flying east along the north Norfolk coast on 26th June 1997.

Peter Allard writes in *The Birds of Norfolk* 1999: 108, of which he is co-author:

'A Fea's or Zino's Petrel, the first accepted record for the county, flew east along the north Norfolk coast on 26th June 1997. It was seen passing the Blakeney Point seawatching hide at 13:40 hrs by Stefan McElwee and subsequently offshore at Cley, Sheringham and, finally Mundesley at 15:37 hrs (*McElwee* 1997, 1998). Owing to the difficulties in separating these species in the field, particularly in the case of a lone bird, this individual was accepted only as a Fea's/Zino's Petrel by the British Birds Rarities Committee, although it was considered almost certainly to have been a Fea's Petrel.'

Stephan McElwee writes:

'The 26th June 1997 greeted us with weather much like the rest of the month; cold, wet with strong north-east winds. I hadn't considered seawatching until the pager announced a Sabine's Gull and Cory's Shearwater past Cley. Midsummer birding blues banished as we headed for the Blakeney Point seawatching hide.
    I and fellow warden Saul Brown were enthusiastic as to the prospects of good birds, so much so that Janet Reed, the wife of Property Manager Joe, decided to come along, armed with the reserve's scope, for her first ever seawatch
    We arrived in the hide at 1.30 pm to be greeted by huge seas and light drizzle. It was obvious we were in for good seawatching as Manx Shearwaters flooded past along with a good number of Fulmars.
    At 1.40 pm whilst scanning the shoreline, I noticed a bird far closer than any seen previously and assumed a Manx Shearwater. I told Janet and Saul to get ready for great views when I saw its head. Avid seawatchers will think it crazy to claim identification of any seabird on head alone. But the instant I saw the bird head on, coming towards us I knew it had to be a Soft-plumaged Petrel. Indeed it was! I repeated 'Soft-plumaged Petrel' three times to my companions before shooting from the hide. I covered the distance to the lifeboat house in five minutes realising someone down the coast just had to see it. I quickly 'phoned' the news to Birdline and Birdline East Anglia.
    Richard Millington 'phoned' Steve Gantlett who was already watching the bird at Cley as the news came through. Richard, along with Ron and Sue Johns, managed to get to Salthouse in time. It was also seen independently at other watchpoints along the coast. It was an incredible series of events. Incidentally, the

petrel was only the second seabird of any species Janet Reed had ever seen!

It was similar to Manx Shearwater in overall size but not as powerful in build, the wings and body appearing thinner. It would almost be likened to a large swift with wings set well forward adding to a 'no necked' appearance. The rear end tapered off to give a pointed tail. The bird came in from the west at a height but then dropped to wave level. The impression was of a wobbly flight with a gentle twisting from side to side; no hard breaks like a Manx Shearwater. The bird often had both wings pointing towards the sea at the same time, producing a gibbon-like effect.'

(An account published in the *Norfolk Bird Report* 1997: 557)

Mick Fiszer who saw this bird at Mundesley, completely unaware at the time of it having been discovered earlier further west along the coast writes:

'The 26th June 1997, was a miserable sort of day with a light east-south-easterly wind turning to the north-north-east later in the morning accompanied by some rain.

Having spent the early part of the morning on the cliff tops at Mundesley to see if there was any movement i.e Swifts or Starlings, the usual mid-summer suspects. Without much joy I decided to take a break and visit my regular cafe in Bacton for a well earned mug of tea and a Kit-Kat.

Returning back into the field refreshed I made a brief stop at the Poacher's Pocket for a check on the sea.

A quick scan revealed a string of Gannets and a Manx Shearwater moving east, my mind was made up, time for a sea-watch. I returned to Mundesley and after opening up the hut and setting up my scope, it was obvious that the sea was quite lively with good numbers of Gannets interspersed at regular intervals by Fulmars and Manx Shearwaters moving east.

At approx 1537hrs I picked up a bird that I couldn't identify immediately, although still some way off, it was at least coming my way.

As it approached its flight pattern did not suggest Fulmar or Manx Shearwater being rather erratic, now only a few hundred yards away I began to appreciate its long wings and slighter form than a close by Fulmar.

Suddenly it banked over and gave a clear view of its upperparts, showing a distinct dark '*M*' across the flight feathers and upper wing coverts.

It was then I realised I was watching a '*Pterodroma* petrel' the fabled Fea's. I just felt a shiver go down my spine making the hairs on the back of my neck stand up. Unaware of what had been happening further round the coast that day I often wonder if I would have seen this bird had I known about it.'

Black-capped Petrel
Pterodroma hasitata
One, a female, was caught following severe gales on a heath at Southacre in March or April 1850 (Plate 4). It was acquired by Mr. E. C. Newcombe of Feltwell Hall. The specimen (Accession no. NWHCM: 1949.108) was presented to the Castle Museum, Norwich on 1st June 1949 by Lt. Col. T. S. N. Harding, also of Feltwell Hall, where it remains on display in the bird gallery.

Thomas Southwell writes in Henry Stevenson's *The Birds of Norfolk* Vol. lll. 1890: 361-364:

'The first occurrence in Britain of this rare wanderer, and (as will be seen in the sequel) perhaps extinct species, whose true and only home appears to have been the islands of Dominica and Guadeloupe, in the West Indies, was record in the "*Zoologist*" for 1852 (p. 3691), by Professor Newton. In March or April, 1850, a bird was observed by a boy on a heath, at Southacre in this county, flapping from one furze bush to another, until it got into one and was there caught by him. Exhausted as it was, it violently bit his hand, and he thereupon killed it. The late Mr. Newcome fortunately happened to be hawking in the neighbourhood, and his falconer, John Madden, seeing the boy with the dead bird, procured it, and brought it to his master, by whom it was skinned and stuffed.'

The specimen was apparently remounted some time between 1852 and 1865 (Dr A G Irwin *in litt*).

The only other British record is one found long-dead as a tideline corpse at Barnston, East Yorkshire on 16th December 1984.

Considered for many years to be extinct, the species was re-discovered breeding in Haiti and the Dominican Republic where there are now at least 1,000 pairs. The entire world population is centred in that area and is considered to be only about 5,000 birds (Birdife International fact sheet 2008).

Cory's Shearwater
Calonectris diomedea borealis
One was found dead at Salthouse by Brian Shergold, Sydney Reeves and Alan Mannering on 29th January 1966 and taken to Richard Richardson. It was of the North Atlantic race *borealis* and was the first to be specifically identified in Britain since both the Mediterranean and North Atlantic races were deleted from the British List at the time of the Hastings Rarities (*British Birds*, 60: 312 and *Norfolk Bird Report* 1966: 129). The specimen (Accession no. NWHCM: 1966.343) was prepared as a cabinet skin on 7th June 1966 and is now in the skin collection at the Castle Museum, Norwich.

Richard Richardson writes in his diary for that date:

'A dead Cory's Shearwater picked up on Salthouse beach and brought to me. Dead about a week but sent to Castle Museum.* First record for Norfolk.
Measurements:-
Wing 362 (tips much abraded)
Tail 139
Bill (length from feathering) 55
(depth at feathering) 20
(width at feathering 18
Tarsus 58
Middle toe with claw 72
Weight 17 and three quarter ozs
(see inside back cover).

Found by B. Shergold, S. K. Reeves and A. Mannering.
*fully skinned and preserved.'

The inside of the back cover of Richard's diary reveals a newspaper cutting from the *Eastern Daily Press*:

'*Rare seabird found dead in Norfolk*
A dead specimen of Cory's Shearwater (*Procellaria kuhlii borealis*) was found on Salthouse beach on Saturday. The bird was identified by Mr. R. A. Richardson, Mr. B. Shergold, Mr. S. K. Reeves and Mr. A. Mannering and is now at Norwich Castle Museum.
This is the first record for Norfolk for this species which is only rarely recorded on the British coast, although in recent years a number have been sighted off the south-west coast of Ireland. It breeds on islands in the eastern North Atlantic.'

Great Shearwater
Puffinus gravis
One was picked up dead on Caister beach on 22nd December 1892. Interestingly this brought the then Norfolk List of birds to 300 full species.

J. H. Gurney writes in the *Transactions of the Norfolk and Norwich Naturalists' Society* 1893-1894: 648:

'On December 22nd 1892, a Greater Shearwater was picked up at Caister, and brought to Mr. Smith; it is a very fine specimen, dark above and pure white beneath'.

Michael Seago writes in *The Birds of Norfolk* 1999: 109, of which he was co-author:

'Riviere included the first county record, one picked up on Caister beach on 22nd December 1892. It was on display for many years in the Connop Collection at Rollesby Hall and later at Wroxham, but its present whereabouts is unknown.'

Enquires in 2008 revealed that the specimen is in storage at the City of Birmingham Museum.

Sooty Shearwater
Puffinus griseus
One was caught by a boy on a fishing vessel at the mouth of the River Ouse on 25th July 1851.

Thomas Southwell writes in Henry Stevenson's *The Birds of Norfolk* Vol. lll. 1890: 364-365:

'The only Norfolk specimen of this bird of which I am aware is still pre-served in the Lynn Museum. At the time of its capture it was recorded by Mr. E. L. King as the "greater shearwater, *Puffinus cinerus*," "*Zoologist*," p. 3234, and a full description given, but a subsequent examination proved it to belong to this species, probably immature ("*Trans. Norfolk and Norwich Nat. Soc.*,iii., p. 474). I purchased the bird alive of a boy who had caught it at the mouth of the river Ouse as he was returning to Lynn in a fishing boat, it being apparently asleep on the water. This occurred on the afternoon of the 25th July, 1851. During the five days which it lived, it passed the day sleeping, but, as evening advanced, became more lively, and readily ate small fish, shrimps, or fresh beef. It probably died of some injury received at the time of its capture. After death it was set up by Foster, of Wisbech, who found it to be a male, and it was deposited in the Lynn Museum.'

The specimen remains at King's Lynn Museum (Accession no. KLLM: 1989.550).

Manx Shearwater
Puffinus puffinus
Thomas Southwell writes in Henry Stevenson's *The Birds of Norfolk* Vol. lll. 1890: 365-367:

'Sir Thomas Browne doubtless refers to this species in the following passage which occurs in the "Account of the Birds found in Norfolk:" –
"A seafowl called a sherewater, somewhat billed like a cormorant butt much lesser. A strong & fierce fowle houering about ships when they cleanse their fish. Two were kept six weeks, cramming them with fish which they would not feed on themselues. The seamen told mee they had kept them three weekes without meat. And I, giuing ouer to feed them found they liued sixteen days without taking anything." And, again, in the letter to Merrett, dated December 29 [1668], he says he sends "Also the draught of a seafowle called a sherewater, billed like a cormorant, fierce and snapping like it upon any touch. I kept 20 of them alive five weeks, cramming them with fish, refusing of themselues to feed on anything & wearied with cramming them, they liued 17 days without food. They aften fly about fishing ships when they cleane their fish and throw away the offell".'

He adds a footnote:

'Professor Newton tells me that the figures 20 certainly occur in the MS., but that they are probably a mistake.'

Balearic Shearwater
Puffinus mauretanicus
Known then as Levantine Shearwater, two were shot by George Long at Blakeney on 22nd September 1891.

H. F. Witherby writes:

'Mr. H. N. Pashley, of Cley, Norfolk, has kindly sent me word of two Levantine Shearwaters which were shot by George Long (a local wildfowler) on September 22nd, 1891, on the bar at Blakeney. One of these birds is in the collection of Mr. E. M. Connop, of Wroxham, who permits me to record it, and the other is in the collection of Mr. Percy Evershed, of Norwich, and both have been examined by Mr. T. Southwell. Mr. Pashley states that both birds were seen by Howard Saunders and Lt.-Col. H. W. Fielden, and were pronounced by the former to be true Levantines. It may have been due to a slip that they were not referred to in the second edition of the "Manual," but in any case their history and identification seem perfectly satisfactory.'

(Originally published in *British Birds* 2: 313)

H. N. Pashley refering to these birds as "Western Mediterranean Shearwaters" writes in *Notes on the Birds of Cley Norfolk*, 1925: 126:

'On September 22nd, 1891, 2 were shot on the Bar. The late Col. Fielden and Howard Saunders examined these birds and pointed out their distinctive features. One was in the Connop collection and the other in the collection of the late P. Evershed of Norwich. These specimens, now in the collections of Mr. W. R. Lysaght and Mr. J. B. Nichols, were recently examined by Mr. H. F. Witherby and pronounced to be of this form.'

The specimen that was in the former Connop collection is now in storage at the City of Birmingham Museum. The J. B. Nichols collection was dispersed when sold in June 1929, and most of the specimens cannot now be traced, including the Balearic Shearwater.

Long considered a race of Manx Shearwater, this species underwent several common name changes from Levantine, to Yelkouan, to Mediterranean (when split from Manx into the western Mediterranean race Balearic Shearwater, the other being the eastern nominate Yelkouan Shearwater). It was finally split from Yelkouan and given specific status as Balearic Shearwater by the BOURC in 1995.

Macaronesian (Little) Shearwater
Puffinus baroli
A male was found by a gamekeeper at Earsham on 10th April 1858. It was the first British record.

Thomas Southwell writes in Henry Stevenson's *The Birds of Norfolk* Vol. lll. 1890: 367-369, under the name of Dusky Shearwater:

'Mr. Stevenson contributed to the "*Trans. Of the Norfolk and Norwich Nat. Soc.*," vol. iii., pp.467-473, a full account of the occurrence of this interesting bird in the county of Norfolk, from which the following narrative of the event is extracted:-
"In the '*Zoologist*' for 1858 (p. 6096) I recorded the appearance, far inland in this county, of a petrel, which I felt little doubt at the time was an example of this rare species (rare, at least, on the shores of Great Britain), and which on examination recently, by the best authorities on these oceanic wanderers, has proved to be what I first described it.
"My original notes on this interesting bird may be thus summarised. About the 10th April of the above year it was found dead by a gamekeeper on the Earsham estate, situated close to the south-eastern boundary of Norfolk, and within a mile of the well-known town of Bungay in Suffolk. Captain Meade,

who at that time hired the hall and the shooting, brought the bird, in the flesh, to the late Mr. John Sayer, birdstuffer, of St. Giles', Norwich, who at once observed its marked difference in size from any Manx shearwaters he had ever seen. Being from home myself at the time, I did not examine the bird in a fresh state; but I saw it within a week of its being stuffed, and its resemblance to the figure of the dusky petrel in the third edition of Yarrell's 'British Birds,' and in the supplement to the second edition (1856), struck me forcibly at first sight; confirmed, to a great extent, by the comparison of its measurements (though a mounted specimen) with the description given of the species by that author.

"It proved, on dissection, to be a male in very poor condition, and probably had been driven so far inland by a gale, and met its death through coming in contact, at night, with a tree or some other object, having a wound on one side of the head, as if from a violent blow. It showed no appearance of having been shot at; and the feathers, except on the spot mentioned, were clean and unruffled; but the inner web of one foot was partially nibbled away, as though a mouse or some other vermin had been at it. Fortunately I noted these injuries at the time, which have enabled me to identify the specimen again, beyond any doubt, though lost sight of for the last thirteen years. Having been brought to the birdstuffer by Captain Meade, and returned to him when mounted and cased, I naturally inferred that the petrel belonged to him; and hearing some time after that he had left England, and all his effects at Earsham had been sold off, I presumed that this rarity was lost to us altogether. In the absence of the bird itself, I was unable to support my previous conviction as to the species; whilst subsequent accounts of extremely small Manx Shearwaters being occasionally met with, made me question my own judgement in the first instance; more especially as my acquaintance with that class of marine birds was somewhat limited at that time. I specially mention this, because it will explain why I did not bring then fact of the dusky petrel having occurred in Norfolk under the notice of either the late Mr. Gould, when publishing his '*Birds of Great Britain*," or of Mr. Dresser for his 'Birds of *Europe*,' neither of which authors has included this species in the above-named publications. The re-discovery of the Norfolk specimen was quite accidental. Early in the present year, Mr. J. H. Gurney, jun., and myself, being separately engaged in working out a complete list of the 'Birds of Norfolk,' and comparing notes on the subject, the right of this species to rank with other local rarities was questioned, and, 'drawing a bow at a venture,' Mr. Gurney put himself in communication with Mr. Hartcup, of Bungay, who proved to be a trustee for the family of the late Sir W. W. Dalling, Bart., and the Earsham estate. From him it was soon elicited that a good many birds killed on the estate were preserved at the Hall, and amongst these most fortunately, was found the dusky petrel of 1858. The thanks of this society, and of naturalists generally, are due to Mr. Hartcup for the opportunities he has afforded for a thorough inspection (with permission to photograph it) of this unique specimen; and having myself, first obtained the confirmatory opinions of Professor Newton and Mr. Osbert Salvin, it was exhibited by the latter at a meeting of the Zoological Society on the 16th of May, 1882".'

The specimen (Accession no.NWHCM: 38.994) is in storage at the Castle Museum, Norwich. The back of the case has a pencilled note in the hand of Thomas Gunn that reads

'Copied from an old label on glass. Dusky Shearwater. The only specimen of this species ever shot in England at Earsham April 15th 1856. Preserved by J. Sayer, of Norwich. Cleaned by T. E. Gunn, March/86.' We must assume that Gunn has made an error with the date.

An additional note in ink reads 'Published accounts give the date as April 10, 1858 & state that the bird was found dead (not shot). E. A. Ellis.'

European Storm Petrel
Hydrobates pelagicus
The earliest dated reference we can find is by the Paget's in *Sketch of the Natural History of Yarmouth and its Neighbourhood* 1834: 13 where they write:

> '…a few generally shot every winter. In November, 1824, between two and three hundred shot after severe gales.'

Sheppard and Whitear write in *A Catalogue of the Norfolk and Suffolk Birds, with Remarks* 1826: 54:

> 'This kind of Petrel sometimes makes its appearance on the coasts, and has been shot from the beach at Yarmouth.'

Churchill Babington writes in *Catalogue of the Birds of Suffolk* 1884-1886: 226:

> 'Numerous in the winter of 1827 and of 1828 off the Yarmouth coast (Hunt in Stacey's *History of Norfolk* lXlV).'

Leach's Storm Petrel
Oceanodroma leucorhoa
One found on Yarmouth beach on 5th December 1823 was in the collection of Mrs. J. Baker and is now in the Tolhouse Museum at Yarmouth. This individual somehow survived the German bombing on 18th April 1941 when most of the Tolhouse Museum's collection of birds and animals were destroyed. It had previously been mounted in case number 148 in this huge collection, amassed since the turn of the century. Unfortunately, the specimen is in poor condition and the head, which at some stage became separated from the body of the bird but was still in the case, is now missing altogether.

Thomas Southwell writes in Henry Stevenson's *The Birds of Norfolk* Vol. lll. 1890: 369-371, under the name of Fork-tailed Petrel:

> 'The following note on the occurrence of this species in Norfolk was contributed by Mr. Stevenson to Mr. Dresser's *Birds of Europe*:"-
> "The earliest record of this species in Norfolk is that recorded by Messrs. Paget as picked up dead on the beach at Yarmouth, on December 5th, 1823".'

He adds a footnote:

> 'Mr. Dawson Turner, also referring to the same bird, remarks that so stormy an autumn as that of 1823 "was never known".'

Interestingly, in 1928, A. H. Patterson writes in an unpublished manuscript, a copy of which is in Peter Allard's collection:

'In August 1896, among the effects of the late Tom Baker, one time Town Clerk of Yarmouth, sold by auction, was a small collection of birds that had belonged to Mr. Baker's mother, into whose hands they had come on the break-up of Stuart Girdlestone's collection. I went to the sale, and made the following list of the birds … The late Mr. T. Southwell [who died in 1909] had considered the whole collection had been lost sight of save one – the historic Jack Snipe.'

Amongst the list is – 'Lot 265 1 case Leach's Petrel, rare, Picked up on Yarmouth beach, 1823.' Patterson later mentions that Lot 265 was now in Yarmouth Tolhouse Museum.

Northern Gannet
Morus bassanus
Thomas Southwell writes in Henry Stevenson's *The Birds of Norfolk* Vol. lll. 1890: 292-295:

'Judging from the numbers of these birds which have been found far inland, or on the beach either in a dying condition or washed up dead upon the shore, it would seem that this species must be very susceptible to the influence of continuous stormy weather; it appears not unlikely that, owing to the fish retiring to the less disturbed waters at greater depths during stormy weather those birds which search for their prey on the wing are the first to succumb to the scarcity of food thus produced, and either perish or fly inland, when in their exhausted condition, they fall easy victims. Sir Thomas Browne' (1605-1682) 'records two such instances: "A white, large, and strong-billd fowle, called a Ganet, which seems to be a greater sort of *Larus*; whereof I met with one kild by a greyhound, neere Swaffham; another in marshland, while it fought, and would not bee forced to take wing; another entangled in an herring-net, which, taken aliue, was fed with herrings for a while".'

Great Cormorant
Phalacrocorax carbo carbo
Thomas Southwell writes in Henry Stevenson's *The Birds of Norfolk* Vol. lll. 1890: 287-289:

'Two hundred years ago the cormorant was a resident in Norfolk and the border of the adjoining county of Suffolk. It must now be regarded as an occasional and uncertain visitant to our coast, and less frequently still to some of the inland waters, almost invariably occurring in the spring and autumn months. Turner writing in 1544 of this bird under the name of "*mergus*," says that he had seen it nesting on the Northumbrian rocks at the mouth of the Tyne, as well as among herons in tall trees, in Norfolk. His evidence, quoted by Aldrovandi, in 1603, as that of "a certain Englishman," was repeated by Willughby in 1676; but Sir Thomas Browne, in his account of the birds found in Norfolk a few years earlier, gives more precise information; and speaks of "cormorants building at Reedham, upon trees from whence King Charles the first was wont to be supplied".'

Great Cormorant (Continental)
Phalacrocorax carbo sinensis

The earliest dated reference we can find is by Andrew Bloomfield in *The Birds of Norfolk* 1999: 115, where he writes:

> 'Two races [of Great Cormorant] breed in Europe, the nominate *P. c. carbo* which nest on sea cliffs around the coasts of Iceland, Norway, France and the British Isles, and *P. c. sinensis* which is largely a tree-nesting bird in the rest of Europe. Since 1981, growing numbers of tree-nesters have started to colonise inland locations in the Midlands and southern England and there are now 1,200 pairs of inland tree-nesting Cormorants which are considered to be *sinensis* (Millington 1998).
>
> Early recorders of Norfolk birdlife all mentioned the county as being home to breeding Cormorants. Writing in 1544, Turner commented that they regularly nested in tall riverside trees, usually amongst herons. Sir Thomas Browne (1835-36) recorded Cormorants nest building at Reedham in the 17th century, whilst Lubbock (1879) spoke of them breeding in the Fritton/Herringfleet area on the Suffolk border.'

It is therefore not unreasonable to consider that all tree-nesting Cormorants are, and probably always have been *P. c. sinensis*. See also the *P. c. carbo* account.

European Shag
Phalacrocorax aristotelis

The ealiest dated reference we can find is in Henry Stevenson's *The Birds of Norfolk* Vol. lll. 1890: 290-292, where Thomas Southwell writes:

> 'Unlike the preceding species,' [Great Cormorant] 'the shag, or crested cormorant, must be regarded as very rare on the Norfolk coast, where it has only been met with in winter, between the months of October and February. Hunt makes no mention of it, and the Messrs. Pagets merely remark it is "very rare." Messrs. Gurney and Fisher state that it is "occasionally met with, the specimens, which chiefly occur in autumn, being mostly immature." Mr. Lubbock also speaks of it as "very uncommon here."…
>
> In Mr. Lubbock's copy of "Bewick" occurs the following note on this species: - "1824, November 9th. A striking instance of the voracity of this bird occurred to me to-day. I shot one, which fell from a broken wing, the wing being fractured nearly close to the body, the impetus of its fall stunned it; on recovering it very gravely raised itself on its latter end and vomited *eleven* flunders, or butts, as they are provincially termed at Yarmouth; the one first swallowed, at least last ejected, was hardly acted upon perceptibly by the gastric juice, so rapid had been the work of destruction".'

He adds an interesting footnote:

> 'The annotator to Wilkin's edition of Sir T. Browne's works' (1605-1682) 'appears to be wrong in supposing the following passage in the "Birds found in Norfolk" is applicable to the crested cormorant or shag. The words are:

"besides [i.e., in addition to the common cormorant already mentioned] the rock cormorant, which breedeth in the rocks in northern countries, and cometh to us in winter, somewhat differing from the other in largeness and whiteness under the wings." Sir T. Browne's idea evidently was that the "rock cormorant was distinct from the bird which he knew to breed in trees in Norfolk, and was larger and whiter than that bird; but this description certainly will not suit the shag.'

Eurasian Bittern
Botaurus stellaris
The earliest dated reference we can find is of recorded breeding at Wormegay, Whinburgh and Cantley in 1300. See the account of the Spoonbill.

Henry Stevenson writes in *The Birds of Norfolk* Vol. ll. 1870: 159-174:

> 'Under the name of "bittour" this species is but once entered in the L'Estrange' [of Hunstanton 1519-1578] 'accounts, and is there specially mentioned as "klled wt ye crossbowe," but there is no reference to it as affording sport for the falconer in those days, although, according to Messrs.Brodrick and Salvin, it was a very favourite quarry for heronhawks when formerly abundant.'

Sir Thomas Browne (1605-1682) in *Notes and Letters on the Natural History of Norfolk* 1902 mentions:

> 'The Arsea stellaris botaurus, or bitour is also common & esteemed the better dish.' (compared to the heron) 'in the belly of one I found a frog in a hard frost at Christmas. Another I kept in a garden 2 yeares feeding it with fish mice & frogges. In defect whereof making a scrape for sparrows & small birds, The bitour made shift to maintaine herself upon them.'

Little Bittern
Ioxobrychus minutus
One was killed near Burlingham during the winter of 1819.

Henry Stevenson writes in *The Birds of Norfolk* Vol. ll. 1870: 154-159:

> 'Of its identification in this county, I find no record prior to the commencement of the present century, but in Messrs. Sheppard and Whitear's catalogue it is first mentioned, a specimen having been killed at Burlingham in the winter of 1819, as those authors were informed by Mr. Hunt of Norwich.'

The Sheppard and Whitear reference mentioned above is in *A Catalogue of the Norfolk and Suffolk Birds, with Remarks* 1826: 41.

Black-crowned Night Heron
Nycticorax nycticorax
One was obtained at Yarmouth *circa*1800.

Henry Stevenson writes in *The Birds of Norfolk* Vol. ll. 1870: 174-176:

'The earliest record I can find of the occurrence of this species in Norfolk is the statement in Sir W. Hooker's MS., on the authority of the late Mr. Lilly Wigg, that, "Mr. Stagg shot one of these birds in Yarmouth about the year 1800".'

He adds in a footnote:

'Like the subsequent specimen in 1824, this bird was shot from a tree in a nursery garden, as stated by Messrs. Sheppard and Whitear, although the date is not given by them.'

Interestingly, research reveals that there was an old specimen in the Great Yarmouth Tolhouse Museum collection, Case No. 54, obtained at Vauxhall Pleasure Gardens, Great Yarmouth. A Mr. Stagg was the owner of pleasure gardens somewhere in the town in 1800, so it is possible this may have been the original bird. Unfortunately the majority of the collection, including this specimen, was destroyed by German bombing on 18th April 1941.

Squacco Heron
Ardeola ralloides
One was caught in a bow-net hanging out to dry near Ormesby Broad in July 1820. It was only the second record for Britain following one in Wiltshire in 1775.

Henry Stevenson writes in *The Birds of Norfolk* Vol. ll. 1870: 151-154:

'This small but very beautiful species has occurred in the county in several well authenticated instances, the earliest of which I can find any record being the one noticed by the Messrs. Paget as caught in a bow-net that was hanging out to dry by Ormesby Broad in December, 1820." In Sir William Hooker's MS., however, although the same facts are stated, this bird is said to have been taken on the 11th July, but I have reason to believe that the former date is correct, as Mr. Dowell was informed by the present owner of this specimen, the Rev. F. Ensor, of Lustleigh rectory, Newton Abbot, Devonshire, that it was taken in the winter. It was captured alive, but as its proper food was not known, and it refused to eat, it was killed after a day or two, and its skin preserved.'

He adds a footnote regarding the Mr. E. W. Dowell of Jesus College, Cambridge mentioned above:

'See a minute [detailed] description of this bird by Mr. Dowell in the "*Zoologist*" for 1843, p. 78.'

Interestingly, the Rev. William Whitear writes in 'Extracts from the Calendar of the Rev. William Whitear 1809-1826' published in the *Transactions of the Norfolk and Norwich Naturalists' Society* 1881-1882: 253:

'1820 – July 28th, I am informed by Mr. Youell that a young male bird of the species *Ardea ralloides*, of Temminck, was killed this month at Ormesby, and is now in the possession of the Rev. G. Lucas of that place; it weighed 8.5 ounces.'

This rather conflicts with Stevenson's opinion regarding the accuracy of the month of its occurrence, and the general acceptance since then that it was December. It would appear that the actual month was indeed July.

Cattle Egret
Bubulcus ibis
A male was shot by Daniel Banham at Breydon Marshes on 23rd October 1917.

F. W. Smalley writes:

> 'On October 24th I received a letter from Mr. E. C. Saunders, of Great Yarmouth, asking me to go over to see a locally killed bird which had been brought to him for identification and preservation, and which he considered to be an example of the Buff-backed Heron (*Ardoela ibis ibis*). I, therefore, at once hastened over to Yarmouth, where I saw the bird in the flesh in Mr, Saunders' shop, and found his identification to be correct. The body was, by request, sent to Mr. J. H. Gurney, in order that the sternum might be preserved, and Mr. Gurney writes me that the stomach of the bird contained two good-sized water newts, the larva of a noctuid moth and an example of the fish known as Miller's Thumb (*Coyyus gobio*). The newts, which were sent to me, I submitted to my friend Dr. William Eagle Clarke, from whom I learn that they belonged to the species known as the Smooth Newt (*Molge vulgaris*).
>
> The bird in question was shot by one Dan Banham, on Breydon Marshes, on the Norfolk side of the river, on October 23rd, 1917. It was first observed by two boys, who reported a small white bird feeding amongst the cattle on the marsh. All three procured guns, and, surrounding the bird, it fell to the second barrel of Banham's gun.
>
> After being mounted, I took the bird over to Norwich, where Mr. Gurney and I compared it with skins in his collection, but were unable to say definitely whether the bird was an adult or a bird of the year in first winter plumage; the whole of the plumage being white with the exception of the head, which is tinged with buff on the crown. Whilst the primaries, secondaries and tail appear fresh moulted, the rest of the plumage on the wings and back shows considerable abrasion, from which I personally am inclined to consider the bird an adult. There were no signs of any active moult. The "powder-down puffs" were four in number, one on each flank and one on each side of the breast. It proved to be a male on dissection, and careful measurements taken by me at the time gave: *Length*, 520.5mm. (20.5 inches); *wing*, 248mm. (9.75 inches); *culmen*, 56mm. (2.2 inches); *tarsus*, 82mm. (3.25 inches). Mr. E. C. Saunders gives the colour of the soft parts as follows: *Beak*, chrome yellow, with a brownish tinge at the base and tip ot the upper mandible; *eyes*, golden yellow, skin round eyes a duller yellow inclined to grey, edge golden yellow; *legs and feet* brown-black, tibio-tarsal joints and soles greenish cast, toe-nails black.
>
> I believe this bird to be only the second authentic occurrence of the Buff-backed Heron in Great Britain: the first being the immature female from near Kingsbridge (Devon), shot towards the end of October, 1805 (Yarrell, IV., p. 187; Saunders, p. 375), as I do not look upon the evidence for the bird said to have been shot at Martock (Somerset), January 28th, 1909, reported by Mr. Stanley

Lewis (*Zool.*, p. 328; *cf. British Birds*, Vol. X., p. 70) as being satisfactory.'

(Originally published in *British Birds* 11: 146-147)

E. C. Saunders' diaries, now housed at the Colochester Museum, confirm the above details. The mounted specimen was photographed by A. W. Yallop of Great Yarmouth and it appeared in *British Birds* with the above article.

Interestingly, Peter Allard writes in *The Birds of Great Yarmouth* 1990: 31:

> 'Formerley known as the Buff-backed Heron, a male was shot by Dan Banham on Breydon marshes October 23rd 1917 and was then only the second British record. E.C. Saunders set it up, and it was purchased the following February by John Bruce Nichols of London, upon whose death it passed to the Booth Museum in Brighton.'

The specimen was donated to the Booth Museum, Brighton by A. Griffith and remains in storage there, B/01/Case 395A.

Also of interest, Arthur Foster Griffiths was born in Wales in 1856 and died in January 1934. Son of Dr. Griffith popular head of Brighton College, A. F. Griffiths was a member and at times Chairman of the Booth Museum Sub Committee. He edited later editions of the Booth Museum Catalogue, purchased and donated many birds for the Booth Museum collections including many items from the Nichols collection and was involved in the design of many of the cases built subsequent to Booth. There is a brass plaque in his honour in the entrance of the Booth Museum (Dr G Legg *in litt*).

Daniel Banham was the marshman for the Lockgate levels for many years, including the year the bird was obtained. The Lockgate levels are the marshes situated mainly between the north wall of Breydon Water and the railway line, from Breydon Junction where the line branches just west of Yarmouth to the Fleet Pump at the easten end of Berney Marshes RSPB reserve. We can reasonably assume that the Cattle Egret was shot close to Breydon north wall.

An earlier record was included by Stevenson in *The Birds of Norfolk* Vol. ll. 1870: 151, upon the evidence of a specimen in the Saffron Walden Museum, which was stated by Joseph Clarke to have been killed at Martham in 1827. Thomas Southwell, however, pointed out that this bird was not entered as British in the museum catalogue published in 1845, and for this reason discarded it from the Norfolk List (*Ibis* Vol. lll., Appendix D, p. 414) Riviere (1930).

Little Egret
Egretta garzetta
One was seen by Billy Bishop flying in at Cley from the east on the early morning of 7th May 1952. It remained feeding on the marsh for four days, an adult in full breeding plumage with its crest streaming out into the breeze. This bird was filmed by Mr. R. P. Bagnall-Oakeley (*Wild Bird Protection in Norfolk* 1952: 19).

Richard Richardson writes:

> 'On May 7th, 1952, Mr. W. F. Bishop, Warden of the Norfolk Naturalists'

Trust's sanctuary on Cley Marsh, Norfolk, reported a small white heron with yellow feet. The bird, which remained till May 11th was subsequently seen by many observers and proved to be an adult Little Egret (*Egretta garzetta*) in full breeding plumage.

The entire plumage was dazzling white with a pendant crest of long narrow feathers and, on the upper-parts, the delicate filigree of the nuptial "osprey" plumes. The bill and tarsi appeared blackish, the latter contrasting with the startlingly yellow toes – an unnecessarily garish feature likened by one observer to "yellow chamois-leather gloves." The bird appeared to feed on insects and small aquatic life on a flooded grazing-marsh, walking briskly about and often dashing to one side like a Greenshank (*Tringa nebularia*) to "snick" at something in the grass and water. It was at all times alert and distinctly wary; its obvious self-assurance and perfect condition served to rule out the possibility of its being an "escape" from captivity.

A unique coloured film was taken by Mr. R. P. Baganall-Oakeley and portrays perfectly the bird's appearance, habitat, feeding habits, flight and size compared to a Heron (*Ardea cinerea*).'

(Originally published in *British Birds* 46: 256)

Billy Bishop writes in *Cley Marsh and its Birds* 1983: 18:

'C. D. Borrer, who turned out to be the last of the Gentlemen Gunners, stopped at nothing to get his quarry. I well remember a little egret appearing on the Cley Reserve. He tried every trick he could think of to get this bird, despite the fact the shooting season had been over two months since. Every morning I met him at dawn with his loaded gun, and told him that he had no chance of getting that bird. These hardened collectors met fines with indifference. He told me once: "There'll come a dawn, maybe, when you'll oversleep!" I never did.

Borrer died in December 1961. Richard Richardson related a story to Peter Allard that he had to stand guard over the first Little Egret at Cley to stop it being shot.

Interestingly, Jim Vincent, the head keeper of the Hickling Estate, writing in his personal interleaved copy of *The Hand-List of British Birds* (Witherby *et al* 1912), now owned by Moss Taylor, appears to claim an adult Little Egret on Hickling Broad on 6th June 1912, however, in his personal diaries the record appears as a Squacco Heron.

Studies of adult Little Egret at Cley Marsh May 1952. (*Richard Richardson*)

Great (White) Egret
Ardea alba

One was found by Richard Butler at Hickling on 10th August 1979, it remained until the 18th having previously been seen in Lincolnshire on the 7th and 8th.

Dave Holman writes:

'This sighting was the first for Norfolk and only the 20th record for the British Isles, however, by the end of 2005 it was recorded as too frequent a visitor to be considered by the national rarities committee. This individual was thought to be the bird seen on Humberside a few days before being found at Hickling Broad by Richard Butler. Sadly the news was not circulated and it fell to Barry Jarvis and me to chance upon it on the glorious 12th. We saw it from the South Wall fly over Swim Coots and appear to be heading straight off, but it circled and landed out of view near Catfield Channel. We attempted to relocate it by checking from the old mill on the marsh but only managed to glimpse it briefly as it flew up and landed again at the entrance to Catfield Channel. We dashed to Hickling Village to put the news on to The Grapevine (no Birdlines, pagers or mobile phones) then hired a boat and set off to try to find it again. It seemed like a good idea, but even chugging through small reedy pools around the channel entrance failed to relocate it. As we left people were arriving and they walked in to good views from the South Wall. I returned in the evening and had further relatively poor flight views.

A very large all white heron only a little smaller than a Grey Heron in flight and much the same shape, but rather more rakish with a very pronounced neck bulge, slender body and very long trailing legs with large feet. A long pointed bill largely pale yellow with a smallish area of blackish at the tip. Legs and feet appeared all dark in flight, apparently black – certainly no yellow feet. Plumage all white – no plumes noticed on head or back.

Much better views were obtained the following day – nothing to add to plumage details – still all white and no apparent crest or back plumes even when perched. Very long dagger-like bill, largely quite bright yellow with black tip – about distal quarter. There was a pale fleshy (not fleshy colour) area from base of bill back to the eye. The iris was pale olive-grey, pupil black. Very long trailing legs appearing black in flight but when perched were noticeably yellowy-brown, particularly the upper part of legs.

When sitting on tree top it adopted a particularly hunched attitude with neck down into body markedly kinked rather than rounded. Its neck was very long and slender (snakey) with the small head merging straight into the bill. In flight again, much as a Grey Heron but rather more slender in all parts with longer more prominent legs.

It was seen flying with a Grey Heron when a direct comparison was possible showing it to be only slightly smaller than the heron.'

(An account compiled from Dave's notes and recollections of the occasion and from the unpublished files in the British Birds Rarities Committee archive)

It would appear that Dave Holman is wholly responsible for the acceptance of this record onto the Norfolk List. As far as we have been able to ascertain he is the only person to have submitted details of the occurrence to the BBRC.

Grey Heron
Ardea cinerea
The earliest dated reference we can find is breeding recorded at Wormegay, Whinburgh and Cantley in 1300. See the account of the Spoonbill.

Henry Stevenson writing in *The Birds of Norfolk* Vol. ll. 1870: 1-42 in the account of Great Bustard:

'Of our local records, the earliest point of date are contained in the (L'Estranges, Hunstanton) "Privy Purse Accounts," for the year 1527, we find the following entry:
The xljst weke.
Wednesday. Itm viij mallards, a bustard, and j hernsewe kylled wt ye crossbowe.'

In an interesting footnote in the account of the Grey Heron, after making reference to one of the county's oldest heronries at Wolferton Wood, he adds:

'In the L'Estrange "Household Accounts",' (1519-1578) 'occurs the following entry with reference to this very wood: - "Itm paid at Lynne when ye went on hawking to Wolferton wood for fyer and dryncke." It is possible, therefore, that even at that time the Wolferton heronry afforded the noblest sport of the day to the squire of Hunstanton.'

In a further footnote he adds:

'The following entries in the L'Estrange's "Accounts," also, mark the appreciation in which heron's flesh was then held: -
It. a hernsewe and xij rabbits of store.
It. ij hernesewes and xij rabbets of store.
Itm a pygge iij hernsewes and xvj rebbetts of store.
It. a fawne and ij hernsewes and xiiij rabbets of store.'

See also the account of the Great Bustard.

Purple Heron
Ardea purpurea
One was shot at Filby in 1810.

Henry Stevenson writes in *The Birds of Norfolk* Vol. II. 1870: 145-148:

'Mr. Hunt, under the name of *Ardea caspia*, or "African heron", records a specimen as shot "a few years since near Ormesby," which is no doubt the same bird which, in Sir William Hookers MS., is described as shot at Filby in 1810.'

The Pagets in *Sketch of the Natural History of Yarmouth and its Neighbourhood* 1834: 7 write under Crested Purple, or African Heron

'…has been killed either three or four times. One Col. Montagu had; another was sent to the British Museum by the Rev. George Lucas.'

Black Stork
Ciconia nigra
Three were recorded as being seen in Norfolk, possibly in the Yarmouth area, in 1823 but the first fully authenticated and accepted record was one shot at Westacre on 19th May 1867.

Henry Stevenson writes in *The Birds of Norfolk* Vol. ll. 1870: 182-183:

'If the American Bittern at present holds no place in our Norfolk list, I am able to include for the first time a not less interesting species in the Black Stork, an extremely rare and accidental visitant to this country. On 20th of May 1867, I received a letter from Mr Anthony Hamond, jun., informing me that a fine black stork had been shot by one of the gamekeepers in some meadows on the banks of the river Nar, at Westacre, about half-past four in the morning of the 19th. The bird, it seems, had been observed about the same locality on several occasions for more than a week, but had hitherto kept well out of shot, and only on the day previous to its death, Mr Hamond and myself had been watching a pair of gadwalls in the Nar, scarcely a quarter of a mile from the spot where the stork was killed. It proved on dissection to be an adult female, weighing over seven pounds, and measured, I am told, six feet two inches from tip to tip of wings. Its plumage showed no signs of having been in confinement, and owing to its extreme shyness, it was even at last obtained with much difficulty. This noble specimen now forms part of the fine collection of birds at Westacre High-house.
Although the first time this species has been known to be killed in this county,

it is probable that others may have visited our coast, and either escaped injury or passed wholly unnoticed. Thus, in Mr. Joseph Clarke's MS. *Notes on rare birds at Yarmouth and other parts of the county*, I find the following under the head of Ciconia nigra, "Three were followed in Norfolk for some days in the year 1823".'

White Stork
Ciconia ciconia
The earliest dated reference we can find is by Sir Thomas Browne in *Notes and Letters on the Natural History of Norfolk* 1902: 10 where he writes:

> 'The ciconia or stork I have seen in the fennes & some haue been shot in the marshes between this [Norwich] and yarmouth.'

In his third letter to Merret in 1668 he writes:

> 'I have seen two one in a watery marsh 8 miles of [Norwich], another shot whose case is yet to bee seen.

In a draft of a letter to his daughter Elizabeth, enclosing two pictures of a White Stork he writes:

> 'This is a picture of a stork I mentioned in my last. Butt it is different from the common stork by red lead coloured leggs and bill… The ends of the wings are black & when shee doth not spred them they make all the lower part of the back looke black, butt the fethers on the back vnder them are white as also the tayle. It fed upon snayles & froggs butt a toad being offered it would not touch it. The tongue is about half an inch long. The quills of the wing are as bigge or bigger than a swans quills. It was shott by the seaside [neere Hasburrowe] & the wing broak. Some there were who tooke it for an eull omen saying If storks come ouer into England, god send that a commonwealth doth not come after.'

Thomas Southwell comments in a footnote regarding Browne's description of the legs and bill, that Browne was evidently unfamiliar with the Stork. This was not surprising seeing that it was a very rare bird in Britain, and Southwell considered that Browne may have only seen immature birds previously as their bills and legs are duller coloured than the adult's.

Glossy Ibis
Plegadis falcinellus
One was obtained near King's Lynn on 18th October 1818.

Henry Stevenson in *The Birds of Norfolk* Vol. ll. 1870: 191-194, referring to this bird writes:

> 'In the various stages of plumage, however, to which the terms glossy, bay, and green have been applied by authors, this Ibis has been killed in Norfolk in many well-authenticated instances, the first of which I can find any exact record being the bird stated by Messrs. Sheppard and Whitear to have been seen by

them, and "shot in the winter of 1818, in the marshes on the western coast of Norfolk, near Lynn;" adding, moreover, "that it did not appear to have attained its full plumage, from the circumstance of its having four tranverse bars of white on its throat".'

Interestingly, J. E. Harting editor of the *Zoologist* writes in the *Zoologist* 1897: 464 of a much earlier record mentioned in the obituary of Andrew Mathews:

'We learn from his son (Dr. J. C. S. Mathews) that he leaves a collection of British Birds containing about 450 birds, chiefly obtained by himself and his father in Oxfordshire and the New Forest. This collection also comprises the first Ibis recorded in the country, shot in Norfolk 200 years ago and noted by Pennant.'

Eurasian Spoonbill
Platalea leucorodia
The earliest dated reference to the Spoonbill in Norfolk is contained in an ancient document, dated A.D. 1300, setting up a commission to enquire into the harrying of the eyries of the "Popeler or Shovelard" and other birds at Cantley and elsewhere in Norfolk.

Professor Alfred Newton writes in the *Transactions of the Norfolk and Norwich Naturalists' Society* 1895-1896: 158-160:

'A few weeks since, my friend Mr. John E. Foster, of Trinity College, kindly drew my attention to a passage in the lately published Patent Rolls of King Edward I (p. 546) as follows:-

"1300 March 22. Westminster.
MEMBRANE 24d
Commision of oyer and terminer to William de Sutton, touching the persons who entered the park of Hugh de Bardolph in Whynebergh and his free warren there and in Wyrmegeye, Westbrigg, Rungeton, Stowe Bardolph, Fynchham, Cauntele, Strumpshaugh, Castre by Jernemuth, and Scrauteby, hunted therein and carried away deer, hares and rabbits; carried away his eyries of sparrow-hawks, herons, spoonbills (poplorum) and bitterns in his several woods in Whynebergh, Cauntele and Wyrmegeye, his swans at Wyrmegeye, and his goods there and at Shuldham and Castre by Jernemuth, and assaulted his men at Shuldham, Whynebergh and Castre, co. Norfolk"

This additional evidence of the Spoonbill's breeding in Norfolk is perhaps the oldest on record and it is not surprising to find the bird mentioned by its ancient and often over-looked name "Popeler", Latinized of course to suit the language of the document.'

European Honey-buzzard
Pernis apivorus
The earliest dated reference we can find is in 'Extracts from the Calendar of the Rev. William Whitear 1809-1826' published in the *Transactions of the Norfolk and Norwich Naturalists' Society*

1881-1882: 251 where he recorded in late October 1819:

> 'Mr. Ayers, of Yarmouth has got a dark-coloured Honey-buzzard.'

Sheppard and Whitear write in *A Catalogue of the Norfolk and Suffolk Birds, with Remarks* 1826: 6 possibly referring to the same specimen:

> 'A dark-coloured specimen of this bird was killed near Yarmouth, and is now in the beautiful and extensive collection of British birds belonging to Joseph Sabine, esq.'

The Paget's in *Sketch of the Natural History of Yarmouth and its Neighbourhood* 1834: 2 refer to it as follows:

> 'Mr. Girdlestone knew this to have been shot near Yarmouth, once or twice.'

Black Kite
Milvus migrans migrans
One was observed by David Butt flying over West Runton on 14th May 1966.

Moss Taylor writes:

> 'David Butt, a school master at Cromer, had been a keen birdwatcher for many years and from January 1945 had kept the most comprehensive personal bird records that I have ever seen. He lived in West Runton and many of his journeys were made by bicycle, including trips to many parts of Europe and Asia. Sadly he died several years ago, but his widow, Valerie, kindly offered me his detailed note books, which cover a continuous period of over forty years, and it is from the one covering 1966 that the description of the Black Kite is taken.
> On the afternoon of 14th May 1966, David was in his West Runton garden with his three-year-old daughter, when he noticed she was inquisitively gazing up into the sky from her pushchair. On looking up he saw a large bird of prey, which he recognized instantly from his many trips abroad as a Black Kite. His note book records the details: "[Black Kite] seen at 1500 hours, last seen 1504 hours. First seen wheeling overhead, primaries outspread. Very large size, twice the size of two crows which pursued it, appeared brownish-black in strong sunlight, stiff primaries darker, brown-black undersurfaces of wings (glasses obtained). Long wings and tail with shallow yet noticeable indentation, not as deep as Red Kite's. Spread tail once clearly seen, still noted when folded. Moved west, few flaps, glide, soared to very great height, returning over garden from west. Suddenly lost to sight, crows seen descending. Primaries very stiffly held, spread tail square edged."
> One can only imagine the panic that must have ensued as David rushed indoors to get his binoculars, but fortunately the bird was still visible when he returned to the garden. At the time he was probably unaware of the fact that it was a new bird for the county and indeed was only the sixth British record, such was its extreme rarity in those days. How things have changed! His weather notes for the day: "Fine, bright, wind southerly" were ideal for just such a record. This bird was seen later that day over Salthouse and Cley, but not subsequently.'

Black-eared Kite
Milvus migrans lineatus
A first-year bird was first found at Snettisham on 24th November 2006 (finder apparently not known!), then seen again on 28th, 6th-16th and 24th December, visiting Ranworth on 17th before appearing in the Cley/Blakeney area from 26th December to 1st January 2007. Returning to the Snettisham area on 3rd-15th January 2007 it was also seen over Holkham and Warham Greens on the 15th and revisited Cley on the 16th before returning west from there on the 17th. It finally settled in the Snettisham area on the 19th where it was seen almost daily until 13th April. This interesting bird was in Lincolnshire on 2nd -21st November prior to moving into Norfolk, apparently returning to that county briefly on 12th April 2007. It was the first of this distinctive eastern race to have been identified in Britain and remained under consideration by the BBRC in early 2009.

Red Kite
Milvus milvus
The first dated reference appears in Stevenson's *The Birds of Norfolk* Vol. l. 1866: 26-27:

> '…being used in the days of hawking as a prey to the noble falcons, and Messrs. Brodrick and Salvin (*Falconry in the British Isles*,) speak of Thetford warren as a favourite locality for "Kite hawking," which was pursued by the Earl of Oxford and Colonel Thornton in 1773, and by Mr. Colquhoun, of Wretham, about 1775.'

White-tailed Eagle
Haliaeetus albicilla
The earliest reference we can find is by Henry Stevenson in *The Birds of Norfolk* Vol. l. 1866: 4 where he mentions:

> 'Sir Thomas Browne also, writing some two hundred years ago, speaks of the not unusual appearance of "the *Haliaeetus* or Fen Eagles," but adds "the great and noble kind of eagle, called *Aquila gesneri (chrysaetos)*, I have not seen in this country".'

He adds in a footnote:

> 'An account of the birds found in Norfolk," see Sir Thomas Browne's works, edited by Simon Wilkin, F.L.S., vol. iv., p. 313. [MS. Sloan, 1830, fol. 5, 22 and 31]. – Also, "Animals found in Norfolk", copy from Sir Thomas Browne's MS. in the British museum, published in the "Monthly Magazine" for 1805, pp. 106 and 410.
> These lists were undoubtedly written after 1636 in which year Sir Thomas took up his residence in Norwich…'

The first dated record we can find appears in the Pagets *Sketch of the Natural History of Yarmouth and its Neighbourhood* 1834: 3 where they refer to:

> '…one at Mautby in January 1811' with no further information.

Interestingly, Sheppard and Whitear write in *A Catalogue of the Norfolk and Suffolk Birds, with Remarks* 1826: 4, concerning an occurrence which would certainly appear to pre-date the above record by at least two years:

> 'Some years since a Sea Eagle was met with in the western part of Norfolk, and being only slightly wounded with a gun was with difficulty overpowered. It afterwards lived sixteen years in the possession of Henry Styleman, Esq. of Snettisham, at whose house we saw it in full vigour in the year 1818.'

Could the above gentleman have been the Henry Styleman Le Strange who was responsible for the building of Hunstanton, mentioned in the introduction to this book?

Egyptian Vulture
Neophron percnopterus
An adult, or near adult, was found at Scoulton by Chris Bishop on 28th April 2007. It was claimed in flight over Warham and East Barsham the following day.

Chris Bishop writes:

> 'Having finished a night shift in Stalham at 4.30am on Saturday 28th April 2007, and feeling wide awake, I decided to head out birding rather than go straight home. I had initially considered going to Sheringham for a walk along the cliffs but decided against this as I had left my pager at home and didn't want to risk missing out on something good. Instead I headed to Colney to look for the Iberian Chiffchaff, as this was barely a mile from home. The Chiffchaff was singing but not visible in the early morning gloom so I went for a brief stroll round UEA Broad instead. However, the bite in the wind proved too cold for me without a jacket so I headed home far sooner than planned. On checking my pager I noticed that there had been a Hoopoe at Watton the previous day, which was only 20 miles away so, cursing my tardiness, I went straight back out.
> As I drove along the B1108 I noticed a large pale bird in a field about 100 yards from the road, which was noticeably larger than the two Carrion Crows with it. I stopped for a quick look but the car was at an angle giving an awkward view through the windscreen, making it impossible to focus properly on the bird, although I could make out that the bird appeared almost white and had what looked like a longish orange bill. 'Cattle Egret' flashed through my mind and I excitedly got out of the car and raised my bins again. However, this time I let out a few expletives as I realised I was looking at a bird of prey with a bald yellow face and bill. 'Vulture' was the next word to come to mind (along with a few more expletives!) and I reversed into a lay-by, got my 'scope out and got on to the bird, which was facing me.
> My previous experience of vultures in the wild went back two and a half years, when I saw large numbers of Ruppell's, Lappet-faced, White-backed and Hooded Vultures in Kenya, and I had seen them more recently at Banham Zoo in Norfolk. I also had recent experience of Black and Turkey Vultures at other wildlife collections. The bird I was watching reminded me most of Hooded in size, structure and jizz, but the pale plumage put me in mind of Egyptian, a species I had only seen in books. However, with no experience of this species, and

no knowledge of whether any similar species existed, I was reluctant to name it as such. I checked the short pink legs for rings but couldn't see any so I tried to get in touch with Rare Bird Alert, but after unsuccessfully trying the office number, my only option left was to ring their hotline.

I described what I was looking at to the hotline: a large pale bird, but relatively small for a vulture, a yellow face and dark-tipped bill, plumage that was mostly dirty whitish, but grubby-looking and a bit patchy with greyish-brown tones (to my mind possibly indicating the bird was a sub-adult), pink legs and a 'punk' hair-do recalling a dandelion seedhead. The head was a slightly darker grey tone than the rest of the plumage.

I then sent texts to a couple of friends, saying I had a vulture species and needed help with the ID, before trying the RBA office number a few more times. Once again I checked the bird for rings and this time the vulture took a few steps and I was able to confirm that none were present, as well as being struck by just how short the legs actually were - I had initially thought the bird may be standing in a dip! I had spent about five minutes watching the bird on the ground and had worked myself into a state of utter panic but then the unthinkable happened – the vulture took flight!

It had slow, deep wingbeats and appeared much whiter in flight as the flight feathers were white as opposed to the pale greyish tone of the body feathers. The head appeared small but with a strikingly long bill profile for a bird of prey. I checked the wings and tail for obvious signs of damage or missing feathers, but could not see any. By this time the bird was its making slow progress over the road and I changed position to prolong my view. I again rang the RBA hotline while watching the bird, to add further details of it in flight, including a white wedge-shaped tail, about the same length as the breadth of the wings (which gave the bird a somewhat unbalanced look with its small head projection), and black flight feathers with a black bar across the secondaries on the upperwing.

I was struck by the huge, broad-based wings of the bird that made it look far larger than any of the 'usual' raptors we see here in Norfolk (including the Black Kite I had twitched earlier in the week). However, in steady flight it still took on something of an extremely large, broad-winged gull look, probably due to the relatively pointed wings. The underwings were strikingly black and white, with the black forming a broad band/trailing edge across the primaries and secondaries, while the underwing coverts were pure white. The black bar across the upperside of the secondaries was in addition to the black trailing edge to the wing.

The bird was being mobbed by several corvids, which it absolutely swamped in flight, appearing well over twice the size with its broad wings and comparative bulk. It eventually disappeared from view behind some trees and I could not relocate it, despite attempting to drive down a road that was headed in a vaguely similar direction to the bird. By this time my panic levels were at an all-time high as I realised that I was on the verge of a huge single-observer record with the possibility that the news would not get out for at least another hour. I decided that getting more people into the area as soon as possible was the best course of action so I drove to Watton hoping to find birders who might be looking for the Hoopoe.

As I arrived in the area the Hoopoe had been reported, I passed Dave Holman going the other way. After quickly turning round I was able to attract his attention and he stopped his car. Fortunately, he had the *Collins Bird Guide* with him, and, as my shaky fingers struggled to find the right page, the moment I saw the picture I was 100% certain that I had just had an Egyptian Vulture. We waved down David Norgate and convoyed back to the site, but sadly there was no sign of the bird.

I rang RBA again as soon as the first messages of the day started to filter through, and shortly afterwards the bird was 'mega alerted'. I spent the next seven hours driving the minor roads between Watton, Norwich and East Dereham trying to relocate the bird but to no avail.

My prayers for this not to be a single-observer record, were answered with the vulture's rediscovery the next day, although again the sighting was frustratingly brief, a real shame for a fantastic bird.

At the time of writing, the BBRC have accepted my description of the Egyptian Vulture and the record has been passed to the BOURC for ratification -I keep my fingers crossed for a positive outcome and a first for Norfolk.'

This record was accepted by the BBRC in February 2009 and passed on to the BOURC to determine its provenance before the species (currently in Category B) can be elevated back to Category A status.

The two previously accepted British records were both shot: at Kilvie in Somerset on October 1825 and at Peldon in Essex in September 1868, both were immatures. The 1868 bird was auctioned in 1910 for £38 17s (£38.85) and was used as a model for John Gould's portrait in *Birds of Great Britain 1862-73* (Evans 1994). An adult seen soaring over Bishop's Dyke, New Forest in Hampshire on 16th June 1968 was placed in Category D.

Western Marsh Harrier
Circus aeruginosus
Known to Alfred Newton as the Moor Buzzard and Sir Thomas Browne as the Bald Buzzard, the earliest reference we can find is in Henry Stevenson's *Bird of Norfolk* Vol. l. 1866: 35-37:

'… and there is no doubt that Sir Thos. Browne' (1605-1682) ' refers to this species when he says "Young otters are sometimes preyed upon by buzzards, having occasionally been found in the nests of these birds. **** There are the grey and bald buzzards in great numbers, owing to the broad waters and warrens which afford them more food than they can obtain in woodland countries".'

The Grey Buzzard being the male Hen and Montagu's Harriers and the Bald Buzzard the Marsh Harrier in Sir Thomas Browne's time.

Sheppard and Whitear write in *A Catalogue of the Norfolk and Suffolk Birds, with Remarks* 1826: 6, under Moor Buzzard:

'These birds breed in some of the marshes of Norfolk. They devour the eggs of wild ducks which frequent the same places, and have been caught in steel traps baited with a duck's egg.'

Northern (Hen) Harrier

Circus cyaneus cyaneus

The earliest reference we can find for this species is contained in the above account for the Marsh Harrier, but as the Hen and Montagu's Harrier were not separated until long after, it is unsafe to consider it an accurate reference for either species, although both were probably present at that time. So perhaps it is not unreasonable to consider it a good reference for both species.

Sheppard and Whitear write in *A Catalogue of the Norfolk and Suffolk Birds, with Remarks* 1826: 7:

> 'This bird breeds in the channel-fen at Barton in Norfolk, where we have more than once thought ourselves in danger of being attacked by it, when we had approached the place where undoubtedly its nest was concealed.'

Northern (Hen) Harrier (American)

Circus cyaneus hudsonius

A bird, firmly believed to be what was then known as the American Marsh Hawk, wintered in the Cley and Salthouse area from 26th October 1957 to 13th April 1958.

Ian (D.I.M.) Wallace writes:

> 'This is the long-delayed story of an immature ring-tailed Harrier *Circus* sp that wintered in the area of Cley and Salthouse, Norfolk, from October 1957 to April 1958. Plans for the co-authorship of an earlier paper foundered and with the passage of time the task was relegated to a low priority by several of the observers concerned. A chance meeting in May 1968 between two protagonists of a definite identification for this troublesome raptor revived interest and this paper is the outcome. It seeks to show that the harrier was an immature of the American race of the Hen Harrier *Circus cyaneus hudsonius*, called in America the Marsh Hawk.
>
> The Cley harrier was first seen at Cley by Richard Richardson on 28th October 1957. His initial impression was of "a big powerful ring-tail with beautiful cinnamon-chestnut underparts... obviously too large and powerful for a juvenile Montagu's [*C. pygargus*]". News of the bird and its unusual combination of characters quickly spread and observers flocked to Cley for the next five weeks. At this stage most observers formed the opinion that it was an immature Pallid Harrier *C. macrourus*, but some regarded its bulk as incompatible with that species. On 19th November A. E. Vine suggested to me in a conversation that it might be a young Marsh Hawk. This possibility was discussed at a meeting of the Cambridge Bird Club on the 15th: on the following day P. A. D. Hollom, I. J. Ferguson-Lees and other experienced observers assembled at Cley to test it. Although conditions for observation were not good, A.E.V's theory seemed more feasible than any other. By 4th December it had gained the tentative support of P. J. Hayman and had almost completely supplanted the earlier school in general parlance. There were questionable points, however, and the argument, as well as the bird itself, continued to receive attention throughout December. Thereafter general enthusiasm waned, though R.A.R. continued to watch the harrier throughout the winter. It was last seen on 13th April 1958.

During its stay the bird inhabited the entire coastal area between Cley and Salthouse, at first hunting over the reed-beds and marshes but later spending more time over the fields and heaths inland. In general it was a most spirited raptor, attracting mobbing by Carrion Crows *Corvus corone* (which it dealt with in no uncertain manner), a Merlin *Falco columbarius* and a Sparrowhawk *Accipiter nisus*. The only prey noted was a freshly killed full-grown Moorhen *Gallinula chlorops*.

Between October 1957 and February 1960 I collected from various sources, but particularly through the offices of I. J. Ferguson-Lees, several thousands of words describing, and several drawings illustrating, the harrier. These, together with my own notes and sketches, provided a very full record. The most detailed comments, with dates of field observations, came from H. P. Medhurst (29th October), M. J. Carter and P. R. Colston (2nd November), R.A.R. and myself (16th November and 15th December) and a careful summary of these descriptions follows…

Unfortunately the Cley Harrier occurred three months before rarity records became subject to assessment and reporting at national level with the setting up of the Rarities Committee, and it is therefore difficult to relate its arrival to those of other Nearctic species. It is worth noting, however, that it was shortly preceeded at Cley by the fourth British Short-billed Dowitcher *Limnodromus griseus* (*Brit. Birds*, 54:357) and by up to three Pectoral Sandpipers *Calidris melanotos* (*Norfolk Bird Report* 1957: 32). Elsewhere in Britain, September and October 1957 produced an above average crop of transatlantic vagrants, notably the first Summer Tanager *Piranga rubra* (*Brit. Birds* 56: 49-52).'

(Originally published in *British Birds* 64: 537-542, and included a detailed description, identification and details of range, habitat and plumage of adults, as well as sketches by Ian Wallace)

Peter Grant appeared to lay to rest the subject of American Marsh Hawk records in Britain, when he investigated the plumage of immature birds and found that there was a colour morph of Hen Harrier *C. c. cyaneus* that showed the unstreaked rufous underparts present in the Cley bird. See the very interesting and informative paper in *British Birds* 76: 373-376.

Pallid Harrier

Circus macrourus

A juvenile female was found by Stephen Votier and Richard Johnson at Cockthorpe/Stiffkey and Warham Greens on 24th December 2002.

Stephen Votier and Richard Johnson write:

'Pre-Xmas birding was a welcome relief to the festive frenzy. After several days of checking landfill sites and pig farms for gulls we were happy with our return of a first-winter Caspian Gull *Larus cachinans* at Blackborough End, but by Xmas Eve we were ready for a change of scene. So it was that we found ourselves birding the fields between Stiffkey and Cockthorpe Aerodrome – which turned out to be a very lucky twist of fate indeed.

We first noticed a ringtail Harrier quartering maize strips and heading straight towards us at about 1300 hrs. We had good, but brief, views and despite the late date we both looked at each other in utter disbelief and commented on how it looked just like a juvenile Pallid Harrier! However, no sooner was it in view than it was lost from sight, last seen heading west into the distance – yet another false alarm? After several hours of searching many fields in vain, we decided the best course of action was to head to the roost at Warham Greens. Almost immediately on arrival there it was, but this time alongside a young male Hen Harrier allowing direct comparison. We were now joined by Paul Lee, Rosemary Votier, Graham Hewson and Ken Parker and together we enjoyed some excellent prolonged views in the still bright evening light. By now excitement levels were rising and Pallid Harrier seemed to be the most obvious conclusion, but the identification process was not totally straightforward. It was an extraordinarily mild spell but surely Pallid Harriers should be wintering in Africa by now? Despite this we could not ignore what was staring us in the face, this bird looked really good, really, really good. After the light had faded we decided it would be advisable to consult the literature at home, after all this was an extremely rare bird, regardless of the date, and we did not want to contemplate the repercussions of many a wrecked Xmas simply on the basis of a stringy harrier? However, perusing the literature as well as video evidence just strengthened our resolve, the evidence was overwhelming. We had scored Norfolk's first Pallid Harrier – Merry Xmas.

Despite not being seen on Xmas day many observers were able to catch-up with the bird over the coming weeks into 2003. Typically it was encountered coming into the roost late evening, or departing early the next day, but on several occasions it was located feeding over or resting on inland fields during the day, where better views were enjoyed by many.

IDENTIFICATION

Notwithstanding the unusual date, with good views this bird was not too difficult to identify. Long tapering primaries with only four fingered feathers (five in Hen Harrier), rather elegant and buoyant flight, dark underside to secondaries contrasting with pale underside to primaries and unstreaked orange underparts all suggested either a Pallid *Circus macrourus* or Montagu's Harrier *C. pygargus*. The combination of distinctive pale collar, dark brown neck boa, neat black ear covert surround with pale crescent below the eye and pale grey tips to the inner-most primaries all confirmed this as a juvenile Pallid Harrier.

AGE AND SEX

The presence of unstreaked underparts and pale tips to the median and lesser coverts on the upperwing showed this bird to still be in full juvenile plumage, which is typical of Pallid Harrier at this time of the year (Forsman 1999). However, the sex was more problematic to diagnose. The size was very similar to young male Hen Harriers, but with slightly longer wings on average. There is much overlap in measurements between the sexes and iris colour is a more accurate method of assessing sex, becoming pale in males shortly after leaving the nest and all dark in females. While neither of us saw the bird well enough to judge the colour of the iris a number of observers have stated that the iris was indeed dark, indicating that this was a female.

This was the fourteenth record of Pallid Harrier in the UK and the third juvenile. After a gap of forty years there have 10 in the last ten years, correlating with the marked increase of records in continental Europe. However, this would appear to be the first winter record in Western Europe.'

(An account published in the *Norfolk Bird Report* 2002: 291-293)

Curiously, one had been claimed in the very same area in November/December 1995 but as a Montagu's Harrier was also present this was never submitted.

Montagu's Harrier
Circus pygargus

The introduction to the account for Hen Harrier would seem to be appropriate for this species also. First described in this country by George Montagu in 1802, the first dated Norfolk record we can find is a notation by William Fisher in his interleaved copy of the Paget's *Sketch of the Natural History of Yarmouth and its Neighbourhood* (1834), where he writes:

'Mr. Smith bought a specimen of this bird in Yarmouth market which was killed at Ormesby in October 1839. It was in immature plumage.'

Interestingly, the first county record of a melanistic bird was of a female shot near Yarmouth in September 1853 (Stevenson 1866). The specimen was formerly in the collection at the Castle Museum, Norwich.

Falconry in Norfolk

A most interesting section is to be found in Henry Stevenson's *The Birds of Norfolk* Vol. 1. 1866: 12-17, under the heading 'Falconry in Norfolk' containing the following information which should be mentioned at this point, as it certainly dates to a reasonable degree of accuracy the first mention of those species in the county:

'In the L'Estrange "Household Book" are many curious entries with reference to the purchase, keep, training, and other expenses of the various hawks used at that time (1519 to 1578), at Hunstanton Hall, including peregrines, goshawks, hobbies, and sparrowhawks, for whose care and training a falconer was kept, who probably occupied the same position on the estate as a head gamekeeper at the present time. In the eleventh and following years of the reign of King Henry the Vlllth we find –

Itm pd to John Maston for mewying and kepyng of ye goshawks from Chrosdtyde (the feast of the exaltation of the Holy Cross) unto ye xvth daye of Novenbre x shillings.
Itm pd at Lynne whan ye went on hawking to Woolferton wood for fyer and dryncke viij pence.
Itm pd yr ye sam tym for horsmete xiij pence
Itm delyvyd to hym the sam daye for a byll alowyd to Edward for hauks mett vij shillings and xj pence.
Itm in reward same day to Saunder the fawken for the tyme that he was wt me, or he entred into wage xvj pence.

For yor goshawk. Itm delyved to yow the xxij day of August by the hands of David to bye yor goshawk xl shillings.

Itm delyved you the xxij dsay of January, when yow went a hawking wt my uncle Roger Woodhous vij shillings and vi pence.

The following entries also indicate the kinds of game at which the different species of hawks were flown:-

Itm a fesant kyllyd wt ye goshawke.
Itm vj rabetts of store and ij ptriches lylled wt ye sperhawke.
Itm xiij larks kyllyd wt ye hobbye.
Itm xij larks kyllyd with the hobbye.
Itm ij ptrychys kyllyd wythe the hauks.
Itm ij fesands and ij ptrychys kyllyd wt the hauks.

Particular mention is made of the crossbow throughout the earlier portion of these records, and the birds killed with that weapon, as, cranes, mallards, wild geese, bitterns, herons, swans, and bustards, and in one instance "viij mallards, a bustard, and j hernsewe" are entered as killed at the same time. Soon, however, these entries become less frequent, although notes on the hawks and spaniels continue, till in 1533, in the 24th year of the reign of King Henry the Vlllth, the crossbow at last gives place to the gun, and thence-forward are chronicled only the victims of the new weapon, destined to work as great a change in our national sports as in the more terrible arena of the battle-field. Large birds, or those most easy of approach, would appear by the following extracts to have been specially sought by the yet unskilled gunner, whose unwieldy piece, with its slow and often uncertain discharge, must have made even "sitting" shots a difficulty, whilst as yet the higher art of "shooting flying" had scarcely dawned as a possibility on the minds of the sportsman.

Itm a watter hen kylled wt the gonne.
Itm a crane kylled wt the gonne.
Itm ij mallards kylled wt the gonne.
Itm a wydgyn kylled wt the gonne.
Itm pd the xxviij day of February to Southhous for yor saddle xiiij shillings and for gunpowder and other things that he bought for you at London, xxj shillings and x pence.
Itm delyved the same daye to Barms of London to bey gunpowder wthall, xx shillings.'

He adds a footnote:

"Extracts from the Household and Privy Purse Accounts of L'Estranges of Hunstanton, from A.D. 1519 to A.D. 1578;" Comunicated to the Royal Society of Antiquaries by Daniel Gurney, Esq., F.S.A.., in a letter to Sir Henry Ellis, K.H.., F.R.S., Secretary. March 14th, 1833.'

The question as to whether the 'hawks' mentioned in the above text were locally wild-caught and trained birds or captive bred and trained remains largely unanswered, some no doubt being the former. Certainly many wild-caught 'hawks' were brought to Norfolk from the Netherlands (Lubbock 1845, new edition 1879 by Southwell). But it does make very interesting reading.

Northern Goshawk
Accipiter gentilis
One was taken at Yarmouth in the summer of 1832.

Thomas Southwell in a footnote in the Rev. Richard Lubbock's *Observations on the Fauna of Norfolk* (1845), new edition by Southwell 1879: 29 writes:

> 'The Goshawk is one of the rarest of the Falcon tribe with us; in the adult plumage it is so rare that Mr. Stevenson believes the adult male killed at Colton in 1841, is the only example in mature plumage known with certainty to have been killed in Norfolk. In addition to those enumerated in the 'Birds of Norfolk,' Mr Lubbock in his notes mentions one shot at Yarmouth (near Acle in the MS. notes) in the summer of 1832.'

Interestingly, the Pagets write in *Sketch of the Natural History of Yarmouth and its Neighbourhood* 1834: 3:

> '…very rare; a fine specimen shot in 1833.'

It is conceivable that the Pagets and Lubbock are referring to the same bird.

Eurasian Sparrowhawk
Accipiter nisus
The earliest dated reference we can find is of breeding at Whinburgh, Cantley and Wormegay in 1300. See the Spoonbill account.

The Rev. Richard Lubbock writes in *Observations on the Fauna of Norfolk* (1845), new edition by Southwell 1879: 31:

> 'The female Sparrow Hawk was formerly prized for falconry. The L'Estrange Household-book (1519-1578) speaks on one occasion of six rabbits killed by the "sperhawke." This ancient record of expenses and manners, shows forcibly the great trouble and heavy cost of falconry. It appears to have been necessary, in the least rain, to dry the hawks on their return, gradually and carefully, by means of a large fire in a spacious apartment. On one occasion the Knight's breakfast at an Inn on a sporting morning costs five pence, and the fire which was used for the hawks eight pence. After a very wet day there is a charge of twenty pence for a fire for the hawks.'

Common Buzzard
Buteo buteo
Listed by Sheppard and Whitear in *A Catalogue of the Norfolk and Suffolk Birds, with Remarks* (1826), but not commented on, the earliest reference we can find is by the Paget's in *Sketch of the Natural History of Yarmouth and its Neighbourhood* 1834 who considered it '…not uncommon.'

While the Rev Richard Lubbock writes in *Observations on the Fauna of Norfolk* (1845), new edition by Southwell 1879: 25-26:

'The Common Buzzard is in these days anything but a common bird. Old books of Natural History speak of it as the most common of hawks.'

Roughleg (Rough-legged Buzzard)
Buteo lagopus
The earliest dated record we can find is in Henry Stevenson's *The Birds of Norfolk* Vol. l. 1866: 29-32:

'The following curious anecdote is extracted from a MS. volume, relating to the fauna of Yarmouth and its environs, now in the possession of Sir W. J. Hooker, K.H., who most kindly allowed me a perusal of it, and from which I am enabled to supply many interesting notes relating to this district:-(*Memoranda touching the Natural History of Yarmouth and its environs*, from 1807 to 1840, by Sir W. J. Hooker, K.H., Thos. Penrice, Esq., Mr. Lilly Wigg, Rev. John Burrell, Rev. R. B. Francis, and Dawson Turner, Esq.):- "On Friday, December 6th, 1816, the Holkham shooting party repaired to Warham, and were followed during the greater part of the day by a bird of prey, which constantly attended their motions, and was repeatedly fired at while hovering over their heads, without betraying the smallest symptoms of apprehension and alarm, even though the shot was heard to rattle on its feathers. In the afternoon it descended on a tree, where it allowed Mr. Coke, attended by a boy holding a dead pheasant dangling in his hand, to approach sufficiently near to get a shot at it, which brought it to the ground. It proved to be a most beautiful female specimen of that rare bird the *F. lagopus*, or rough-legged buzzard, measuring very nearly five feet across the wings, and two feet one inch in length. The male bird had attended the chase at Wighton, just in the same manner, two days before, and had boldly carried off from a heap of game two partridges. It was next day caught in a trap by the keeper, and both of them were presented by Mr. Coke to the Rev. G. Glover, as a most valuable accession to his collection of British Birds".'

Sheppard and Whitear write in *A Catalogue of the Norfolk and Suffolk Birds, with Remarks* 1826: 6, under Rough-legged Falcon:

'We are informed by Mr. Scales of Beechamwell, near Swaffham, that this bird annually visits the warrens at that place about the month of November, and continues there for some time in quest of rabbits... Not long since, a pair of Rough-legged Falcons were killed at Holkham...'

Golden Eagle
Aquila chrysaetos
One, probably an adult male, was found long dead on the saltmarshes at Stiffkey in November 1868. It remains the only Norfolk record.

Thomas Southwell writes in Henry Stevenson's *The Birds of Norfolk* Vol. lll. 1990: 375-376:

'The claim, and only claim, so far as the present writer knows, of this species to a place in the list of Norfolk birds, rests upon the finding of the remains of an undoubted specimen on the salt marshes at Sitffkey, as first recorded in the "*Field*," and subsequently by Mr. Stevenson in the "*Zoologist*" for October, 1869, p. 1863, as follows:-

"Golden Eagle in Norfolk.- A correspondent in the 'Field,' of December 19, 1868, announced that a golden eagle had been found dead in the Stiffkey Marshes, in this county, and that the sternum and feet were preserved. I have since had an opportunity of examining one of these feet, by which the species is clearly identified; and I am now enabled, for the first time, to record the occurrence of this eagle in Norfolk. The history of this specimen appears to be as follows:- It was first seen in November lying dead on the marshes, on the property of Mr. P. Bell, of Stiffkey, by a fisherman named Green, who mentioned the fact to Mr. T. J. Mann (the '*Field*' correspondent), who was at that time shooting in the neighbourhood: he immediately visited the spot and secured such parts as were most likely to identify the species, the carcase being then too far gone for preservation; but from his description of the tail-feathers, 'chestnut brown, shading off to a perfect black at the tips,' it was no doubt an adult bird. The foot sent to me in January last, by Mr. Mann, had the toes still supple, as if taken from a recently killed specimen; and from its small size, though having formidable talons, I have no doubt, on comparing it with the fine series of golden eagles in the Norwich Museum, that it belonged to a male bird. I could not ascertain at the time, either locally or from the Journal, that any eagle of this kind had escaped from confinement; and I suspect, therefore from the locality in which it was found, close to the sea, that it was the victim of some random shot off the coast, and died almost as soon as it reached the shore"'.

As mentioned by Mr. Stevenson, the sternum was preserved, and is with the feet still in the possession of Mr. T. J. Mann, of Hyde Hall, Sawbridgeworth. The determination of the species must therefore be considered satisfactory, but of course there remains the possibility of the bird having been an "escape".'

During the final stages of the work on this book, the authors became aware of an earlier claim for the county. According to William R. Fisher (co-author with J. H. Gurney of 'An Account of the Birds found in Norfolk' published in the Zoologist for 1846), the manuscripts of Charles Paget (co-author with his brother James of *Sketch of the Natural History of Yarmouth and its Neighbourhood* 1834) contained a note relating to a Golden Eagle killed at Yarmouth in 1783. The wording, reads; 'Golden Eagle, a bird of this species measuring some twelve feet in extent is recorded by Pennant to have been killed at Yarmouth in 1783.' Thomas Pennant (1726-1798), was a much respected naturalist and author of a number of publications. It is known that Pennant visited Yarmouth during this period and is presumed to have seen the bird. He had travelled widely in Scotland prior to 1783 and would surely have known Golden Eagles. Pennant's reference to this record is in *British Zoology* (1812 edition by Latham p.120).

The wording 'twelve feet in extent' caused some concern to the authors; however, the meaning of extent does include area or volume. We have included this claim as earlier authors of the county avifauna were apparently unaware of it.

Osprey
Pandion haliaetus
Sir Thomas Browne (1605-1682) writes in *Notes and Letters on the Natural History of Norfolk* 1902: 4:

> 'There is a lesser sort of Agle called an ospray wch houers about the fennes & broads & will dippe his claws & take up a fish oftimes for wch his foote is made of an extraordinarie roughnesse for the better fastening & holding of it & the like they will do unto cootes.'

Common Kestrel
Falco tinnunculus
The Kestrel is not mentioned by Sir Thomas Browne (1605-1682) in *Notes and Letters on the Natural History of Norfolk* (1902). The earliest reference we can find is by Sheppard and Whitear in *A Catalogue of the Norfolk and Suffolk Birds, with Remarks* (1826) where it is included but is not specifically assigned to either county, although presumably it was common in both. The Pagets in *Sketch of the Natural History of Yarmouth and its Neighbourhood* 1834: 3 describe it as '…common'.

Interestingly, known to them as the Kestril, Wind-hover and Hover Hawk, Sheppard and Whitear give a detailed account of the way in which Kestrels and other species have been caught, in *A Catalogue of the Norfolk and Suffolk Birds, with Remarks* 1826: 2-3:

> 'The Rev. Joseph Harrison has employed with success the following method of taking the Kestril. - A white napkin was spread in a meadow, and fastened at the corners with little hooked sticks. On the middle of the napkin a live sparrow was fixed by mean of a string three or four inches in length. Slender twigs were stuck up on both sides of the cloth, to prevent the Hawk from attacking the sparrow on either side. Two long slender twigs of weeping-willow, well covered with birdlime, were stuck in the ground, one at each end of the napkin, both forming an arch over the bird, but at such a distance that the sparrow could not touch them with its wings whilst fluttering; neither could any Hawk reach the sparrow without coming in contact with the limed twigs. The intention of the white cloth was to attract the attention of the Hawk at a greater distance to the sparrow fluttering upon it. The limed twigs were stuck so slightly in the ground, that if the Hawk, upon finding itself entangled, should struggle, they would have gone off with him and prevented his flight. Mr. H. observes, that twigs covered with birdlime, when long and slender, will stop the flight of the strongest bird, if fixed so as to pass off with him, when touched by his plumage; for they then become like a chain binding the wings to the body. By these twigs he has caught the Cuckoo, Pigeon &c., and has no doubt but that the Eagle, and every bird of prey, might be taken by them when their nests or haunts are discovered.
>
> The disposition of the Kestril is bold and familiar. Immediately upon the capture of one by the above method, Mr. Harrison placed him upon a table, and gave him the sparrow which he had killed when taken: he plucked and ate it in his presence, showing no more dread than if he had been brought up tame. After capturing three of these birds, Mr, H. made no further attempts upon them, as he considers them to be of great benefit to the farmer, and doing very little injury

to the sportsman.'

Red-footed Falcon
Falco vespertinus
Three were obtained at Horning, one at Yarmouth (Plate 6) and a female killed at Holkham, in May 1830.

Henry Stevenson writes in *The Birds of Norfolk* Vol. l. 1866: 19-20:

'I can find no earlier record of the occurrence of this rare species in Norfolk than the year 1830, when the following note, by the late Mr. Yarrell, appears in Loudon's "*Magazine of Natural History*" (vol. iv., p. 116):-"Three examples of this small falcon were observed together at Horning, Norfolk, in the month of May 1830, and fortunately all three were obtained. On examination they proved to be an adult male and female, and a young male in immature plumage. A fourth specimen has also been shot in Holkham park." Of the first three I am now able to give somewhat fuller particulars than have yet been published, the gentleman who shot them, Mr. Heath, of Ludham, having kindly answered all my enquiries. They had been noticed for some days before they were killed frequenting the arable lands adjoining the marshes, where they perched on the small bushes stuck up in the fields to prevent partridge netting, or settled on the ground apparently searching the soil for worms or insects. The old male and female were presented by Mr. Heath to Mr. Gurney, who still has them at Catton: and the young male to the late Mr. Edward Lombe, of Melton, whose fine collection is now at Wymondham, in the possession of his daughter, Mrs. E. P. Clarke.'

He adds in a footnote:

'I have a further corroboration of Mr. Heath's statement in the following note, made by Mr. Lombe, in his copy of "*Bewick's Birds*," most kindly extracted for me, with many others, by Mrs, Clarke:- "They were mostly seen in the middle of a fallow field, and the female was shot flying from the thorns. The male (immature) now in my collection was shot from an oak in the same field. The male (mature) shot on a heap of thorns. The stomach contained insects".'

Thomas Southwell writes in a footnote in Rev. Richard Lubbock's *The Fauna of Norfolk* new edition by Southwell 1879: 32:

'Of Mr. Heath's birds Mr. Lubbock says, in an unpublished lecture, that they "were observed during some very rough weather; four were in company, their actions and flight being perculiar, occasioned observation and pursuit, - they alighted upon the ground in a ploughed field, and when shot, the bills and legs were soiled as if they had been in pursuit of worms. This account comes from the gentleman who shot them".'

The Yarmouth specimen is stated by Stevenson (1866) as having beeen obtained in 1832, but Riviere 1930: 109-110, states:

'One killed at Yarmouth in May 1830, which came into the possession of D. B. Preston and was later purchased by Gurney, sen. This bird which is now in the Norwich Museum, is a young male moulting from juvenile to first summer plumage. It is recorded by the Messrs Paget, and by Stevenson, as having been killed in a marsh by Breydon in 1832, but Southwell states (Lubbock's *Fauna of Norfolk*, new edition, p. 32, footnote) that it was killed in 1830, and the case is inscribed in Gurney's handwriting "killed in a marsh immediately behind Vauxhall Gardens, Yarmouth; bought of D. B. Preston, May 1830".'

The Yarmouth specimen (Accession no. NWHCM: 1923.74.15) on display in the bird gallery at the Castle Museum, Norwich has the date 1st May 1830 on its label. J. H. Gurney Jnr. seems to confirm this when he offers the opinion that the Yarmouth bird was actually shot on 1st May, 1830, in *Rambles of a Naturalist* 1876: 283. This would appear to make that specimen the first county record, unless by sheer coincidence the other four May 1830 birds were also shot on that date. The Holkham specimen (Accession no.18.73) is in storage at the museum. It was mounted, but has been removed from its original case and now bears only museum labels (Dr A G Irwin *in litt*).

The cased male and female Horning birds (Accesssion no. NWHCM: 15.935) were on display at the Castle Musum, Norwich but are now in storage. The label on the case reads 'Two out of three red-legged hobbies killed by Thomas Heath Esq while feeding on earth worms after the plough & given by his son to Mr J. H. Gurney. The third bird is now at Wymondham. X at Horning *Erythropus vespertinus*' (D Waterhouse *in litt*).

1830 was obviously a year when a considerable invasion of Red-footed Falcons occurred. The Norfolk birds above were the first to be recorded in the British Isles apart from one shot near Doncaster, Yorkshire in April 1830. Interestingly, some reference sources indicate that the Holkham bird was obtained prior to 1830, but we can find no corroboratory evidence to support this.

Merlin
Falco columbarius
The earliest dated reference we can find is by Sir Thomas Browne in a letter to Merrett dated February 6th 1668-9 in *Notes and Letters on the Natural History of Norfolk* 1902: 78:

'The hobby and the merlin would not bee omitted among hawkes the first coming to us in the spring the other about the autumn.'

Eurasian Hobby
Falco subbuteo
See above under Merlin for the earliest reference we can find to this species, where the statement covers both species.

Eleonora's Falcon
Falco eleonorae
A first-summer bird was found by Pete Morris, Richard Thomas and Adrian Long at Hickling Broad on 6th July 1987.

Pete Morris writes:

'Following our exams, warm sunny weather enticed a number of us from the UEA Bird Club out for the day on 6th July. Having secured the use of the union minibus we headed for Waxham for an afternoon of R&R on the beach. Stopping to pick up supplies in Wroxham we decided to call in at Hickling Broad to look for Swallowtail butterflies. So at around 11.45 am we parked at the end of Weavers Way near Potter Heigham and began to walk along the raised bank. Almost immediately I noticed a dark falcon swoop low over the reeds and, upon seeing the dark moustachials, instinctively shouted out Hobby. However, as the bird turned and rose up, a distinctly rufous tone to the uppertail coverts and rump became apparent and on the basis of this feature Richard Thomas and Adrian Long both declared that the bird couldn't be a Hobby. At only about 100 metres range we had excellent views and as the bird climbed into the blue sky overhead, we were able to see it catching small insects in flight and on at least a couple of occasions eat them on the wing. After a few minutes the bird dived down low over the reeds again (possibly in pursuit of a dragonfly) and was lost to view, reappearing to circle above us for a further ten minutes or so before finally vanishing.

Although not seen alongside any other species, it gave the impression of being a medium to large falcon, though much longer and slimmer than a Peregrine showing noticeably long wings and a longish tail. Most noticeable, however, was the very slow and relaxed method of flight with distinctly slow, loose wingbeats. The upperparts were generally dark grey-brown, slightly darker on the crown though with a pale forehead, and a contrasting pale sandy-rufous tone to the uppertail, the latter finely barred darker. The throat and cheeks were off-white streaked contrasting with obvious dark moustachials. The rest of the underparts were off-white streaked with dark on the breast and upper belly. The undertail coverts were more or less unmarked thus appearing paler and the underside of the tail was finely barred. The underwing pattern was most striking with the underwing coverts being densely barred/spotted with blackish/brown and contrasting significantly with the paler, though still barred, primaries and secondaries.

Much debate then ensued as to the identity of the bird. Richard suggested Eleonora's Falcon but we were all convinced that the rufous tones on the rump and tail were wrong for that species. Aberrant Hobby and Red-footed Falcon were dismissed and we even began wondering about a Lanner or Saker though felt throughout that the shape and behaviour would surely eliminate these! We carried on to Waxham somewhat confused but itching to see some reference books,

Unfortunately time spent amidst literature just confirmed our suspicions at the time – the uppertail was completely wrong for Eleonora's. However, a look at a photo of a previous British record (a corpse at Patrington, Northumberland, in October 1981) confirmed that Eleonora's Falcons can have barred tails and we submitted it as such, convinced, though admittedly somewhat anxious about the tail! That was the last we heard for eleven years as the assessment of the record seemed to have been forgotten! Although I had only seen one Eleonora's Falcon prior to this observation I have seen many more since, almost on an annual basis during my tour leading exploits in Madagascar, Morocco, Turkey and Cyprus. I often thought back to the Hickling bird knowing that the distinctive shape and flight of that species is unmistakable, but had not managed to see another individual with the same tail pattern. In retrospect this can be explained by the fact that all but one of the 50 or so I have seen have been adults.

On 7th November 1998, feeling rather pleased having just found an American Wigeon at Leighton Moss, Lancs, I went into the shop to put out the news and started flicking through Dick Forsman's (at the time) new photographic book on raptors. My delight at finding the Wigeon almost immediately vanished when I got to page 481 – there it was, an Eleonora's Falcon with a rufous tail. Annoyed at the fact that our record had lay dormant for 11 years I now felt that I had the final evidence required for not only did Forsman's book show the feature but even hints it is a diagnostic feature of some first summer birds. That anomalous tail had now turned into the trump card and the bird has been accepted as the fourth record for the UK. In an era where the literature is so good for so many species, it is a mystery how the immature plumages of one of our most graceful raptors could have been so poorly portrayed for so long!

This is indeed the fourth British record following the first at Formby Point, Merseyside 8th/9th August 1977, the afore-mentioned Humberside individual and another on South Uist, Western Isles 14th June 1985. With the threat of global warming perhaps we should expect more in the future.'

(An account published in the *Norfolk Bird Report* 2000: 282-283)

Gyrfalcon (Greenland)

Falco rusticolus candicans
An adult male of the Greenland race was shot at Beeston on 24th January 1848 (Plate 6).

Henry Stevenson writes in *The Birds of Norfolk* Vol. l. 1866: 7-9:

'… this noble falcon has been fully installed amongst the Norfolk rarities, from the occurrence of an undoubtedly wild specimen at Beeston, near Cromer, in February, 1848. This beautiful example, a fine adult male, is in the possession of Mr. J. Gurney Hoare, of Hampstead.'

John Williamson reviewing the history and circumstances surrounding the Norfolk Gyr Falcon records in *Norfolk Bird Club Bulletin* 59: 11-17 writes:

'24th January 1848 – Beeston
A white-morph bird, described as being an example of *F. candicans,* (Greenland Falcon), was shot on this date on the Beeston estate of J. Gurney Hoare. This is the mounted specimen in the Norwich castle museum collection that has previously been published in the literature as an adult male (though the specimen (Accession no. NWHCM: 1876.10) had never been measured and sexed) shot on or about the 24th February 1848. Museum records state the specimen to have been presented to the collection as a gift by Charles R. G. Hoare (presumably a relative of the former original owner) in 1876. It is currently considered to be in fair condition, although somewhat faded, and is still

on display in the Museum Bird gallery. However, the documentation available with the specimen clearly indicates the date it was shot to be 24th January 1848. In addition, the specimen has now been measured and the biometrics and plumage confirm it to be an adult male.'

Gyrfalcon (Iceland)

Falco rusticolus islandus

One, possibly two, at north coast localities from Stiffkey to Cley, 20th December 1953 to 7th January 1954 at least.

Andy Stoddart and Steve Joyner write in *The Birds of Blakeney Point* 2005: 101-102, initially quoting D. J. B. White in *An Annotated Checklist of theBirds of Blakeney Point* (1981):

'White notes one seen on 20th December 1953, 'considered to belong to the Icelandic form *F. r. islandus*', though the species is now best regarded as monotypic but with variable morphs. This bird, seen by M.F.M. Meiklejohn, is described as being accompanied by a 'similar but much darker bird', with an implication that this too may have been a Gyr Falcon. Meiklejohn's notes from the time record that:-

"At 1100 hours on 20 December 1953 at Blakeney Point, Norfolk, I saw a large bird of prey (approximately buzzard size) fly down behind the sand-dunes.

The bird was a large falcon... above grey with brown admixture on wing coverts; underparts appeared white, but possibly had few dark streaks; head pale; thin streak downwards from gape... larger and stouter than Peregrine; tail rather long; head protruding more forward of shoulders than in Peregrine; slower wing flaps than Peregrine, but giving impression of great power and speed; wings set at right angle to body and in flight not sloping backwards so much as Peregrine; wings also broader. The bird's crop was distended and protruded, as if it had just been feeding.

When the bird was flying away, I caught sight of a second similar bird flying over the sea at some distance, and following it. This second bird was not seen well, but was generally much darker in plumage. It too had the crop distended. It was flying with faster flaps, as if to catch up to its companion..."

Further reports from our area followed. Notes in the county archive from an unknown observer (thought possibly to be Archie Daukes) record the following:-

"Dec. 26th – large lazy-flying slate-grey falcon, strikingly light below – observed at considerable distance flying over the W. end of Blakeney harbour. A better view of this bird was obtained on Jan 2nd when it flew past on Morston Marshes at about 100 yards."

and:-

"Dec 29th - a much paler and somewhat larger bird which gave the impression of being about one third larger than a Peregrine female was seen in flight near Stiffkey Channel... A very good view was obtained as the bird flew past in a heavy squall of wind at about 30 yards. Very light underparts and a partial moustachial stripe were plainly discernible."

The differences between these descriptions perhaps lend weight to Meiklejohn's observations of two birds.'

Originally considered to be of the race *F. islandicus*, John Williamson reviewing the history surrounding the Norfolk Gyr Falcon records in *Norfolk Bird Club Bulletin* 59: 11-17 considers:

'However, both the descriptions offered tend to suggest they were of the highly variable intermediate-morph, which at the time was considered to be indicative of 'Icelandic Falcon'. At the present time, there is apparently no firm evidence to suggest that Icelandic birds are anything other than resident and dispersive, and it is considered impossible to tell the difference between the greyer intermediate-morph birds found in Greenland and those from Iceland. Thus, an attempt to assign the accepted county records to a true provenance would now appear to be futile. Suffice to say, it is thought that most (possibly all) vagrant Gyrfalcons found south of the breeding range are from the more northerly (migratory) of the Arctic populations. Certainly at the present time, albeit partly due to a reluctance to accept records of darker birds due to the risk of escaped falconer's birds and purpose bred hybrids, virtually all of the British and Irish records relate to white-morph birds. This is a distinct contrast to many of the historical records that apparently relate to darker birds.'

Interestingly, J. H. Gurney jnr. and Thomas Southwell write in the *Transactions of the Norfolk and Norwich Naturalists' Society* 1884-1889: 264:

'There is an earlier [1848] Norfolk specimen in the Saffron Walden Museum, which was killed near Lynn.'

Enquiries were made early in 2008 to Saffron Walden Museum regarding this specimen, and their Natural Sciences Curator, Sarah Kenyon informs us that there is a reference to a Gyr Falcon from King's Lynn in Saffron Walden Museum's manuscript copy of *A Catalogue of British Birds and Mammals in the Saffron Walden Museum* compiled by Robert Miller Christy in 1883. The specimen number was SAFWM: 14a. The bird was an immature male Gyr Falcon and was from Lynn, Norfolk (presumably King's Lynn, Norfolk). It was presented to the museum by Joseph Clarke, honorary curator of the museum who died in 1895.

Unfortunately this specimen is no longer in the museum collection and is presumed to have been disposed of between 1900 and 1960. There does not appear to be any indication as to which race the bird was considered to be.

Peregrine Falcon
Falco peregrinus peregrinus
The earliest dated reference we can find is by Thomas Southwell in a footnote in the Rev Richard Lubbock's *Observations on the Fauna of Norfolk* (1845), new edition by Southwell 1879: 27-28 where he writes:

'The Peregrine occurs in this county most frequently during its spring and autumn migrations, but is occasionally killed in all the summer months; in some years it is more numerous than others. Hunt in his British Ornithology, ii. p. 9, states that "A nest of the Gentil Falcon has from time immemorial been found on Hunstanton cliffs;" this was written in 1815.'

Interestingly, Sheppard and Whitear in *A Catalogue of the Norfolk and Suffolk Birds, with Remarks* 1826: 2 make very interesting comments that indicate the problems faced by this species at the time:

'Mr. Hoy in Suffolk, trapped two of these birds, and has seen others at that place. He catches them by fastening baited steel traps, covered with moss, on top of a high tree, upon which he has observed them to be fond of perching… A pair of these birds bred many years successively in the cliffs at Hunstanton in Norfolk, though constantly deprived of their young, which were taken and trained to falconry by Mr. Downes of Gunton; but during the last three years they have ceased to build there.'

Peregrine Falcon (American)
Falco peregrinus anatum/tundrius
A Canadian-ringed female was found alive by a falconer near Norwich on 30th December 1986. Although never formally accepted by the BOURC, presumably for the reason that it was hand reared as part of a Canadian controlled release or introduction scheme, the account of this occurrence is interesting enough to warrant its inclusion here. The bird was presumed to have been released again by the falconer who found it.

Peter Robinson writes:

'Andrew Harrop's paper explaining the BOURC's rejection of two old records of Peregrine Falcon *Falco peregrinus* showing characteristics of one or other of the three North American forms (Harrop 2004) brings to mind a bird from New Brunswick, Canada, which was recovered alive in Norfolk. The individual concerned was ringed in Fundy National Park on 18th July 1986 and found near Norwich on 30th December the same year.

The circumstances of the recovery, as reported to me at the RSPB soon after by the falconer concerned, were somewhat unusual, and involved an encounter between the falconer's trained Peregrine and a free-flying Peregrine which the trained bird "brought down" alive. The bird was wearing a metal leg ring, number 98727721. I reported the details to the BTO, who subsequently traced the ringing source.

The records show that the bird, a female, was ringed as a pullus, and the ringing location, immediately west of the Gulf of St Lawrence, argues for it being *F. p. anatum*, which is less likely to occur naturally in Western Europe than the more migratory *tundrius* (Harrop 2004). The BTO's Species Recovery form assumes a possible ship assisted passage for this individual (though there is no evidence of this), and as such appears to play down any likelihood of the bird having crossed the North Atlantic "naturally". This inadvertently reopens the debate over whether North American birds reaching Europe via a known or possible ship-assisted passage qualify for acceptance. It is also possible that the bird was unlawfully removed from its Canadian nest after ringing, or even trapped post-fledging, and then transported to Europe, before escaping, though at the time of its recovery the bird was not wearing falconry equipment. Moreover, given the level of legislative abuse at the time, involving both Peregrines and other birds of prey, on both sides of the Atlantic, it is of course possible to imagine even more complex scenarios to explain this bird's appearance in Norfolk. We must, however, question the likelihood of any reasonably intelligent thief or illegal dealer leaving in place an easily removable ring which might prove their own guilt or that of any subsequent recipient.

Given the known circumstances, this record seems unlikely to gain acceptance by the BOURC. Nonetheless, in view of the BOURC's recent rejection of the only two earlier British contenders, the above details should perhaps at least now be subject to a formal rejection procedure.'

(Originally published in *British Birds* 97: 478-479)

Water Rail
Rallus aquaticus
The earliest dated reference we can find is by Sir Thomas Browne (1605-1682) in *Notes and Letters on the Natural History of Norfolk* 1902: 15 where he comments:

'Gallinula aquatica more hens. And a kind of Ralla aquatica or water Rayle.'

Spotted Crake
Porzana porzana
The earliest reference we can find is by Sheppard and Whitear in *A Catalogue of the Norfolk and Suffolk Birds, with Remarks* 1826: 48, where they write:

'There can be no doubt that the Spotted Gallinule breeds in the marshes of Norfolk. We have seen a considerable number of its eggs at Yarmouth, which as well as its young, were found in the neighbourhood of that place. And we are also in possession of an egg taken from a female of this species which was killed in the marshes below Norwich.'

The Pagets in *Sketch of the Natural History of Yarmouth and its Neighbourhood* 1834: 10 considered it '…not uncommon at Belton &c.'

Little Crake
Porzana parva
The first record for the county, and only the second for Britain, was one found in a poulterer's shop in London in May 1812 amongst some birds sent 'from Norfolk'.

Henry Stevenson writes in *The Birds of Norfolk* Vol. ll. 1870: 396-401:

'The first example of the Little or Olivaceous crake known to have been procured in this county (only one other having been previously noticed as killed in England), is stated in the Appendix to the supplementary volume of Montagu's "*Ornithological Dictionary*," to have been discovered by Mr. Foljambe "in a poulterer's shop early in the month of May 1812, together with some other valuable birds, which had recently been received from the fens of Norfolk".'

In a footnote regarding the locality of the shop he adds:

'In London according to Yarrell, but the locality is omitted by Montagu.'

A bird found, presumably by chance, in a poulterer's shop in London together with some other valuable birds recently received from the Fens of Norfolk seems a little sketchy to be seriously considered as the first authentic Norfolk record.

With this in mind perhaps the first authenticated county record should be considered as the one shot at Buckenham Ferry in August 1827.

Henry Stevenson writes in *The Birds of Norfolk* Vol. ll. 1870: 396-401:

'In the late Mr. Lombe's MS. notes, supplied me by his daughter, Mrs. E. P. Clarke, of Wymondham, I find the record of "a little gallinule" shot at Buckenham Ferry, in August 1827…'

He adds further on in the Little Crake account that he sees no reason to doubt the authenticity of this record.

Baillon's Crake
Porzana pusilla
An immature was shot at Barton Fen in the autumn of 1830.

Henry Stevenson writes in *The Birds of Norfolk* Vol. ll. 1870: 401-403:

'Mr Lubbock in his "Fauna," (*Observations of the Fauna of Norfolk,* 1845) states that, to his knowledge, "it has been shot three times on Barton Fen, and appears far more rare than it really is, as it creeps and skulks about, and scarcely any dog, however sagacious, can compel it to fly." The same author also remarks in a communication to Yarrell, "On the 2nd of April, 1833, a fen-man of my acquaintance killed an adult male of this species, upon a marsh at Dilham, in this county; it is now in my possession. Three years previously he had killed another at Barton, an adjoining parish; it was late in autumn, and the bird was in immature plumage".'

Interestingly, according to Ticehurst (1932), Sheppard and Whitear saw a specimen in the collection of a Mr. Crickmore of Beccles on 13th December 1819, which had been obtained on the Waveney near that town. He references the 'Extracts from the Calendar of the Rev. William Whitear 1809-1826', which was published in the *Transactions of the Norfolk and Norwich Naturalists' Society* Vol. 3: 231-262.

As the river Waveney divides Norfolk and Suffolk it may well have been obtained in Norfolk.

Corn Crake
Crex crex

The earliest dated reference we can find is by Sir Thomas Browne (1605-1682) in *Notes and Letters on the Natural History of Norfolk* 1902: 28 where he comments:

'…the Ralla or Rayle wee haue counted a dayntie dish.'

Thomas Southwell adds in a footnote:

'The Land Rail (*crex pratensis*) or Daker hen, is doubtless here referred to, as the Water Rail has already been mentioned (p. 15 *ante*) as "a kind of *Ralla aquatica*".'

Common Moorhen
Gallinula chloropus

The earliest dated record we can find is in Henry Stevenson's *The Birds of Norfolk* Vol. ll. 1870: 411-425:

'In the L'Estrange "Household Book" this species is once, and only once, alluded to, under date of 1583 – "Itm a watter hen kylled wt the gun."- A first victim evidently to the then new weapon of destruction, and affording to the unskilled gunner of those days, the easy shot still sought for by the school boy or or other tyro in the use of firearms.'

Allen's Gallinule
Porphyrio alleni

The first of just two British records (and only accepted by the BOURC in 1974) is of a juvenile captured alive as it landed in an exhausted state on board a fishing vessel off Hopton on 1st January 1902. Taken into Yarmouth, it was kept alive by a local taxidermist Walter Lowne for two days on a diet of mealworms. It was then preserved, sold and passed into the collection of John Bruce Nicholls, where it remained for over 25 years. It was sold at a London auction on 29th June 1929 and has not been traced since.

Claud B. Ticehurst writes in *A History of the Birds of Suffolk* 1932: 463-464:

'The Gallinules are just those species which one hesitates to include in the list of British birds because they are not infrequently kept in captivity, and owing to their unexpected slimness of body are prone to escape more easily through some aperture than would be credited. Three African and one American species have been recorded in Great Britain, and all are surmised to have escaped from captivity, and in most cases I think this is probably correct. Nevertheless, if any of them has a claim to be considered as having occurred in our island of its own free will, I think that this species has the strongest. The sole occurrence is of an immature bird which alighted on a fishing-boat off the village of Hopton near Lowestoft on 1st January 1902. It was taken alive to Lowne of Yarmouth and was in the late Mr. J. B. Nicholl's collection. There had been a strong south-west wind the previous day. This specimen was evidently migrating, but whether from our shores from captivity, or to our shores from elsewhere, one can not determine, but since the bird alighted on a boat close to land in an exhausted condition, the latter explanation seems the more feasible. Of course it is just possible it may have escaped from captivity somewhere on the Continent, but I do not think this species is so frequently kept in captivity as the other Gallinules are, and this fact is in favour of our Suffolk bird being a genuine migrant, as well as the fact that it was an immature bird and not an adult.

Allen's Gallinule ranges from Senegal and Abyssinia to the Cape, and has occurred several times in South Europe, nearly always in winter, which again is in favour of our bird being a true wild specimen. Moreover, showing the wandering propensities of this species, it has twice been taken 190 miles out at sea off the Liberian coast.

Mr. J. H. Gurney, who has already weighed the "pros and cons" concerning this specimen, ascertained that at that time none had been lost from Woburn Abbey, where many species of foreign birds were kept in semi-captivity.'

Robert Hudson writing in an article on Allen's Gallinule in Britain and the Palearctic in *British Birds* 67: 405-413, states:

'The Suffolk Record
This Suffolk occurrence was first published by Gurney (1902), who identified the bird from skins and books lent by Professor Alfred Newton. On the morning of 1st January 1902, a juvenile Allen's Gallinule was captured alive when it alighted in an exhausted state on a fishing boat off the village of Hopton; there had been high winds from the south-west the previous day, though by the 1st the wind had moderated a little and veered WSW. The distance from the coast at which the bird was captured was not stated; but since it was recorded off the little village of Hopton, rather than off the towns of Lowestoft or Great Yarmouth, it must have been quite close inshore. The bird was taken to a Great Yarmouth taxidermist, who kept it alive for two days. It was then preserved, and passed into the collection of J. B. Nichols, where it remained for over 25 years; but its present whereabouts are unknown to me.

Gurney ascertained that no Allen's Gallinules had been lost from the Woburn ornamental collection in Bedfordshire. However, it is known that in the early years of the century small numbers were imported from time to time, and kept by the London Zoo and several wealthy landowner-aviculturists (M. D. England *in litt.*), though possibly dealers might have been less interested in importing the dowdy juvenile than the brightly coloured adult. Gurney noted that the plumage of the Suffolk specimen showed no traces of captivity. It is not unreasonable to suppose that large birds imported by commercial dealers would have shown physical signs of close confinement, since at that period tropical birds inevitably experienced a lengthy sea voyage in transit. As a juvenile, the Suffolk bird could not have moulted in captivity. Publication of the record in *The Zoologist*, abstracted in the *Avicultural Magazine* for March 1902, failed to produce any reports of losses. Thus I do not believe that there is any particular reason to suppose that this bird was an escape; indeed, for a juvenile to be found exhausted on a boat after a southerly gale constitutes a set of circumstances more indicative of genuine vagrancy. Ticehurst (1932) eschewed square-brackets for this record; Witherby *et al.* (1941) referred to it in neutral terms, pointing out other occurrences the same year in Tunisia and Morrocco; while Bannerman (1963) recommended complete acceptance…

In his account of the Suffolk record, Gurney (1902) felt that the month of occurrence might weigh against it; though he knew of December records from the Mediterranean; contemporary ornithologists could not understand why a tropical species should travel north into the European winter, and I have no doubt that this was a factor which helped to keep Allen's Gallinule off the British and Irish list then. Nowadays we have a better understanding of the involuntary processes which lead to vagrancy. This can be caused through reversed migration, that is, moving in the opposite direction to the appropriate one for the season; or through disorientation, perhaps due to overcast conditions blotting out visual clues and resulting in downwind drift; or through simply being blown off-course by winds of opposing direction and greater speed than the bird's airspeed…

From 15th December 1901 there was a large anticyclone well to the north over the mid-Atlantic, moving to a more normal position near the Azores by the 19th. This gave northerly-type weather over Britain and Ireland and the north-west Atlantic, but westerly weather spread across by the 23rd. In particular, a vigorous depression moved north-eastwards to north-west Scotland during 29th-31st December, with winds widely strong to gale force. During the same three days the Azores anticyclone split into two: one cell moved west into the Atlantic, while the other moved east to Algeria and then southern Europe. Such a splitting is not a common event (it had not occurred during the previous six weeks), and it allowed the development of south-easterly winds across Morrocco, turning through south to south-west as they approached France and Britain within the warm sector of the depression off Scotland. The associated cold front was slow moving, with waves over central Britain during 30th-31st, but it had cleared south-east England by 1st January; hence the reported decrease and veering of the wind between 31st December and 1st January, referred to by Gurney in his original account of the Suffolk record. Thus there was an anticyclone temporarily over Algeria, and strong south-westerly winds between it and Britain, conditions eminently suitable for downwind drift from the western Mediterranean Basin to southern England.'

Prior to the County Boundary changes in 1974 Hopton was in Suffolk.

J. B. Nichols was an avid and rich collector who paid serious money for mounted specimens to add to his collection, housed in a substantial Victorian house at 2, Cedars Road, Clapham Common, London SW4. He even paid £315 for a Great Auk's egg in 1902. However, Nichols is generally regarded as lacking in thoroughness and failing to properly check the authenticity of the reputedly British-taken specimens acquired for his collection.

Although there were many buyers at the sale of the Nichols' collection, several dealers were present who sold their purchases on, more or less immediately, to other collectors. A number of specimens passed to the Leicester Museum, whilst others found their way to the Harrison Museum in Sevenoaks, Kent. However, the bulk of the collection passed into the hands of Ashley Kilshaw Marples at Spalding, Lincolnshire. This collection was later housed at the Ayscoughfee Hall Museum under the care of the Spalding Gentlemen's Society.

This vast collection was recently donated to the Leicester Museum and Art Galleries, joining the other previously obtained specimens from the Nichols' collection. Efforts to trace the Allen's

Gallinule at all of these locations in 2008 failed, and it would appear that the specimen probably no longer exists.

Common Coot
Fulica atra
The earliest dated reference we can find is by Sir Thomas Browne (1605-1682) in *Notes and Letters on the Natural History of Norfolk* 1902: 15:

> '…fulica cottae cootes in very great flocks upon the broad waters. upon the appearance of a Kite or buzzard I have seen them vnite from all parts of the shoare in strange numbers when if the Kite stoopes neare them they will fling up [and] spred such a flash of water up with there wings that will endanger the Kite. & so keepe him of agayne & agayne in open opposition. & an handsome prouision they make about their nest against the same bird of praye by bending & twining the rushes & reeds so about them that they cannot stoope at their yong ones or the damme while she setteth.'

Common Crane
Grus grus
The first dated record we can find is in Henry Stevenson's *The Birds of Norfolk* Vol. ll. 1870: 125-130:

> 'To return, however, from mere speculation to the few scattered facts that remain to us respecting the history of this species in Norfolk, we find five entries in the "Household Book" of the L'Estranges', of Hunstanton, of cranes supplied to their larder between the years 1519 and 1533, the last being one of the few birds recorded in this list as "killed with the gun."

> 1519. "The vth weke" (after the 25th of September; about October 30th.) "Itm pd for a crane and vi plovs xx pence., and ij coyness iiij pence. – ij shillings - …

> "The ixth weke" (about November 27th.) "Itm a goose, a pygge, a crane, iiij conyes, and a loyn of veile of gyste (articles received in lieu of rent.')

> 1526. "The xxxixth weke" (after the 25th March, about December 23rd). "Itm iiij mallards and a crane kylled wt the crosbowe."

> 1533. "The xxvjth weke" (after the xxixth day of March, about September 26th). "Thursdaye, Itm a crane, vj pence."

> 1533. "The xxxviij weke" (after 29th of March, about December 19th.) "Tewysdaye, Itm a crane kylled wt the gun".'

Interestingly, John Buxton and Michael Seago write in *The Birds of Norfolk* 1999: 229-31, of which Michael Seago was co-author:

> 'Historically it is not absolutely certain whether the Crane bred in Norfolk

before the 20th century, but the bird featured on the menu in banquets until about 1600 and Southwell (1901) was convinced that an ancient record from the Norwich Corporation of a payment for a 'young Pyper Crane' proved breeding in the county – 'there is no room for doubt that in the year 1543 the Crane bred at Hickling'.'

Little Bustard
Tetrax tetrax
One was shot at Mundesley in November 1820.

Miss Anna Gurney writes in the Extract from her Note-book in the *Transactions of the Norfolk and Norwich Naturalists' Society* 1874-1875: 19:

'1820 Nov. A Little Bustard shot at Mundesley.'

J. H. Gurney writing in the same volume on page 22 states:

'I possess a coloured drawing, made by Miss Gurney, of this specimen, which is, as was to be expected, in winter, or perhaps female plumage; this is an earlier occurrence than any of those recorded from Norfolk, in Stevenson's "Birds of Norfolk," vol. ii, p. 43.'

Thomas Southwell writes in the *Zoologist* 1890: 462-463:

'The following letter, from the late Mr. J. H. Gurney, refers to the earliest known instance of the occurrence of the Little Bustard in the county of Norfolk. It was not known to Mr. Strevenson when he wrote the article on this species in the second volume of his 'Birds of Norfolk', but will be found mentioned in some "Extracts from the Note-book of the late Miss Anna Gurney, of Northrepps," published in the "Transactions of the Norfolk and Norwich Naturalists' Society" (vol. ii. p.19).
The coloured drawing referred to represents an example "in winter, or perhaps female plumage." The letter is dated "Northrepps Hall, 10th April, 1890," and possesses a melancholy interest from the fact of its having been written only the day before Mr. Gurney was seized by the attack which ended fatally on the 20th of the same month: - "Dear Mr. Southwell, - I have just been referring to Miss Gurney's drawing of the Pomatorhine Skua, and on looking through the portfolio I observe one (also by her) of a Little Bustard, shot at Mundesley in November, 1820. I do not think that Mr. Stevenson has mentioned this specimen and possibly you may like to do so in your Appendix – Yours very truly, J. H. Gurney".'

There are two distinct populations of Little Bustard *T. t. tetrax* breeding in southern Europe and *T. t. orientalis* which breeds from central Europe eastwards. The latter population is partially migratory and of the six Norfolk specimens examined, all six proved to be of this race. It is therefore reasonable to assume that the 1820 Mundesley bird was of this race.

Great Bustard
Otis tarda
We can find no dated records earlier than the following.

Henry Stevenson writes in *The Birds of Norfolk* Vol. ll. 1870: 1-42:

> 'Of our local records the earliest point of date are contained in the published
> extracts from the Household Books of the L'Estrange's, of Hunstanton, where, in
> the "Privy Purse Accounts," for the year 1527, we find the following entry:
> The xljst weke.
> Wedynsday. Itmviijmallards,a bustard,andjhernsewe kylled wt ye crosbowe.
>
> And, again in the year 1530, amongst the list of gratuities –
> "Itm in reward the xxvth day of July to Baxter's svnt of Stannewgh (Stanhoe)
> for bryngyng of ij yong busterds, ij pence".'

He adds a footnote regarding the date:

> 'There is apparently but one earlier notice of the great bustard in Britain,
> viz., in the works of the celebrated Scotch historian, Hector Boethius, published
> in the year 1526, whose remarks on this species are referred to by Willoughby.
> The entries in the Northumberland Household Book, which was commenced in
> 1512, and in which bustards are mentioned, are also nearly contemporary with
> the Hunstanton records.'

Interestingly, Thomas Southwell writes in Henry Stevenson's *The Birds of Norfolk* Vol. lll.
1890: 397:

> 'The entry in the le Strange Household Book of 1527 has been cited (p.
> 2) as the earliest record of the bustard in Norfolk; but Mrs. Herbert Jones in
> Her "Sandringham Past and Present" (London, 1883), quotes (p. 23) from the
> Chamberlain's accounts of the Borough of King's Lynn, preserved among the
> Corporation documents of that time, to the following effect:- "In 1371 the 44th
> of Edward III., 39s. 8d. was paid for wine, *bustards*, herons, and oats, presented
> to John Nevile, Admiral".'

Displaying male Great Bustard in the Brecks. (*Norman Arlott*)

Eurasian Oystercatcher
Haematopus ostralegus
The earliest dated reference we can find is in Henry Stevenson's *The Birds of Norfolk* Vol. ll. 1870: 122-125:

> '… but abundant as they must have been in former times on Hunstanton beach, this species occurs but once in the "L'Estrange Accounts," viz., "The xxx-viijth weke," 1525, "It. pd to Nicholas Grey for a sepye, a redshancke, and a stynte, ij pence".'

Black-winged Stilt
Himantopus himantopus
One was seen at Hickling Broad on 9th June 1822; it was shot on the 10th.

Henry Stevenson in *The Birds of Norfolk* Vol. ll. 1870: 244-248, writes:

> 'I find mention of one killed in Northwold Fen, in June, 1822 on the western side of the county; and a pair are stated by Messrs. Paget to have been shot on Hickling Broad during the same year. Of one of these, which was shot by himself, Mr. Lubbock communicated the following interesting particulars to Yarrell's "*British Birds*":-"On the 9th of June, 1822, I was returning in the evening from fishing upon Hickling Broad, when a bird of this species flew past the boat within thirty yards. The legs were extended behind, even more in proportion than those of a heron; the wings were much arched; the flight vigorous and regular; the colour and the length of limb made me guess what it must be. I asked the fenman who was with me, what *he* guessed it to be? He considered it a Ruff which had been caught, as is sometimes the case in our marshes, by a horse-hair snare, and had broken away with it. When I told him that I believed it to be a very rare and

valuable bird, he wished to go in immediate pursuit, but I overruled that, as there was not more than half-an-hour's light remaining, and the bird, if shot at ineffectually, might leave the country in the night. We searched for it early the next morning, and found it in precisely the same place as the evening before. When shot it was standing in a pool of shallow water, mid-leg deep, apparently snapping at insects in the air as they buzzed around it.'

Interestingly, Arthur Patterson writing in the *Yarmouth Mercury* on 6th January 1934, related that this bird was in the collection of T. Baker of Yarmouth (at one time the Yarmouth town clerk). At the sale of his bird collection in August 1896, following his death, the Black-winged Stilt was acquired by Ben Dye of Yarmouth in whose collection it took prime position. When Ben died in November 1933, the bird was donated, along with the rest of his collection, to the Tolhouse Museum, Yarmouth. Unfortunately the majority of the museum's collection was destroyed by German bombing on 18th April 1941.

Pied Avocet
Recurvirostra avosetta
The earliest dated reference we can find is in Henry Stevenson's *The Birds of Norfolk* Vol. ll. 1870: 237-44:

'Sir Thomas Browne,' (1605-1682) 'unfortunately, gives scarcely any information as to the localities frequented by it in his time, merely speaking of the "shoeing-horn" as "a summer marsh-bird and not infrequent in Marshland,"'

He adds in a footnote:

'In a letter to Dr. Merrett in 1668 (Wilkin's edition, vol. i., p. 400), Sir Thomas describes this bird as "a shoeing-horn or barker, from the figure of the bill and barking note; a long made bird, of white and blackish colour; fin footed; a marsh bird; and not rare some times of the year in Marshland".'

Eurasian Stone-curlew
Burhinus oedicnemus
The earliest dated reference we can find is in Henry Stevenson's *The Birds of Norfolk* Vol. ll. 1870: 51-64:

'The Great plover, Stone-Curlew or "Culloo" as the name is locally pronounced, has also a special claim to its title of "Norfolk" plover (independently of its former abundance in this county), inasmuch as this bird appears to have been first made known, in a graphic form, to British ornithologists by Sir Thomas Browne, who about the year 1674 forwarded a drawing of it to the celebrated John Ray, taken from a specimen killed near Thetford…'

Sir Thomas Browne (1605-1682) writes in *Notes and Letters on the Natural History of Norfolk* 1902: 23-24:

'There is also an handsome tall bird Remarkably eyed and with a bill not aboue 2 inches long commonly calld a stone curlew butt the note thereof more

126

resembleth that of the green plouer & breeds about Thetford about the stones & shingle of the Riuers.'

And in his third letter to Merrett dated September 16th 1668 he writes:

'Stone curlews I haue kept in large cages they have a prettie shrill note, not hard to bee got in some parts of Norfolk.'

Cream-coloured Courser
Cursorius cursor
One was at Morston in the autumn of 1847.

Henry Stevenson in *The Birds of Norfolk* Vol. ll. 1870: 48-51, writes:

'This very rare straggler, from more southern climes, has not hitherto been included amongst our accidental visitants, but having been killed once in the adjoining county and observed on two separate occasions in Norfolk by very reliable witnesses, I think it may be now fairly included in the present list. The first intimation of the probability of this bird having appeared on our coast was given me by the Rev. E. W. Dowell, who writes, "in the autumn of 1847, Mr Wood, of Morston, near Blakeney, told me that there was a strange bird frequenting his fields, something like a plover, which ran very fast. He had seen it for several days, and it appeared very tame, but, although I went after it at once, of course it was gone. From Mr. Wood's description, I had no difficulty in recognising this bird as the Cream-coloured Courser." To this statement I may add that Mr. Wood is well acquainted with all the ordinary forms of plover, *Tringoe*, and other shore-birds frequenting that portion of the coast, and but for some marked peculiarity in this instance would not have informed Mr. Dowell of the supposed rarity.'

The second county occurrence was also a sight record at Westacre in the autumn of 1855 or 1856 in the company of Lapwings. It was shot but managed to escape and was never seen again. The third record was the first to be obtained, and may eventually be regarded as the first fully authenticated county occurrence. This specimen is a first-autumn bird shot at Thornham Beach on 3rd October 1934, and is on display in the bird gallery at the Castle Museum, Norwich (Accession no. NWHCM: 1935.16).

Coincidentally the only one in recent years, in 1969, was also first seen at Morston.

Collared Pratincole
Glareola pratincola
The first authenticated record was of a pair shot on Breydon wall on 21st May 1827 by John Bessey.

Henry Stevenson writes in *The Birds of Norfolk* Vol. ll. 1870: 64-66:

'In the month of May, 1827, as stated by the Messrs. Paget, a pair of prat-incoles were shot on Breydon wall, and the same birds, in Sir William Hooker's MS., are stated to have been male and female, and their stomachs filled with beetles. These specimens, as I am also informed by Mr. Joseph Clarke, of Saffron Walden (from whom Yarrell obtained his information respecting them), were shot on the 21st of May, by a fisherman named John Bessey, who sold them to the late Isaac Harvey, a game dealer, at Yarmouth, for twenty shillings [£1]. They were extremely dirty and smeared with blood, and Harvey's wife washed them "as she would stockings," and hung them out on a pole to dry; but, in spite of this rough usage, they were subsequently re-sold by Harvey for £7. Captain Longe, when residing at Yarmouth, took some pains to trace out this pair, but was unable to do so, nor have I been more fortunate through enquiries made in other quarters.'

He adds in a footnote:

'Bessey's son remembers their being killed, and thinks they may have been purchased by either the late Mr. Sparshall, of Norwich, or Sir R. Adair's father.'

Interestingly, details, as well as the specimens, came to light early in 2003 of a pair of Collared Pratincoles that apparently pre-dated the first Norfolk records. These birds and the provenance for them, is at present held by Chelmsford Museum. The pair was originally in the Sir William Boulton collection at Beverly in Yorkshire and Sir William Boulton's original diary entry for that period clearly reads in good legible handwriting '*Glareola Pratincole*, or Collared Pratincole male and a female shot off the Breakwater near Yarmouth November 1810 by Mr Hunt, Schoolmaster, Yarmouth' (Allard 2004).

The details and photographs of these specimens were sent to the British Ornithologists' Union Records Committee, as, if accepted, they would pre-date the earliest county records and become the second and third British records. But after consideration the record was rejected. Although the identification was not in doubt, the committee was unwilling to accept the record primarily because it involved a pair, apparently in breeding plumage, in November (a very unlikely combination of factors), and the provenance was considered to be too sketchy. A decision with which the authors of this book concur.

These birds are in fact mentioned by Southwell in Stevenson's *The Birds of Norfolk* Vol. lll. 1890: 407-409:

'Professor Newton has very kindly forwarded me a series of letters with reference to a pair of these birds said to have been killed in Norfolk, in 1810, now in the collection of Mr. Thomas Boynton, of Ulrome Grange, Lowthorpe, Hull. It appears that Mr. Boynton purchased these birds of Dr. W. W. Boulton, of Beverley, who stated that he was informed they were "shot off the breakwater, near Yarmouth, November, 1810, by Mr. Hunt, schoolmaster, Yarmouth," but Dr. Boulton has "quite forgotten the name of the old man from whom he purchased them."

Whether these are the pair of pratincoles referred to by Mr. Stevenson (vol ii., p. 64) as killed in May, 1827, on Breydon wall, and which he, with the assistance of Captain Longe, was unsuccessful in tracing, it is now impossible to say. Hunt, in his list of Norfolk Birds, so often before referred to, says these birds were killed in the "autumn" of 1827, but the entry in the Hooker MS. is very precise, and settles the date beyond question. It states in an entry dated "May 21st, 1827," that they were "shot on the marsh near Breydon, Yarmouth, to-day, are now in possession of Mr. Harvey;" the Pagets say they were killed on "Breydon wall," which may well be the "breakwater near Yarmouth," and we have only to supply the forgotten name of Harvey to Dr. Boulton's account of the purchase, and to suppose the date "1810" (in support of which there is no contemporary evidence) to have been a slip of the memory, to identify these birds with the pair killed on Breydon in 1827.

Mr. J. H. Gurney, jun., has seen these birds, and is of opinion that their appearance is indicative of their having been set up from skins. Supposing, however, that they are the pair referred to in the "*Birds of Norfolk*," the rough treatment they were admitted to have received (l. c., p. 65) would amply account for this appearance.'

Oriental Pratincole
Glareola maldivarum

An extremely confiding first-summer bird was first discovered by June Self at Roseacre Riding Stables, Gimingham on 14th May 1993. However, the events of its discovery and subsequent identification are far less simple than that statement suggests.

Dave Holman writes:

'Tuesday 18th May 1993 was a pleasant day around the county, Short-toed Lark, Black Kite, Hoopoe and Temminck's Stint all being seen. I was manning Birdline East Anglia during the evening and little expected the last call of the evening to throw me into a dilemma. Dave Nicholson rang to say that his friend Chris Payne had been at Roseacre Riding Stables collecting manure and had seen what he felt was a pratincole. Dave and Chris returned to the site that evening but drew a blank. After some deliberation and discussion it was decided to not raise hopes by putting out news of a possible pratincole but Dave and I would check it out early next morning. Around 5am on 19th May I arrived at the most unlikely looking site and found Dave already there but the area covered in dense, damp mist. Feeling pretty unenthusiastic we stood chatting and slowly the mist cleared but no sign of any pratincole-like birds. We decided to wander to the riding stables with a view to requesting permission to wander over the paddocks but we never got that far! As we walked along the road the view over the paddocks changed and suddenly Dave was shouting that he had found the pratincole only about thirty yards away in the grassy paddock. Instead of punching the sky in jubilation he chose to thump my shoulder several times (a useful tip here is do not stand close to Dave Nicholson when he finds a rare bird, it can be a painful experience).

So here we were at 6.00am with a pratincole in front of us and heavy rain starting to fall. We decided to give it one push to check the underwing colour. As whichever species it was, it would be a new one for Dave, I opted to do the gentle push while he kept his bins trained on it. The short flight across the road to the potato field revealed a red underwing but no white was noticed, however, we were both concentrating on the underwing colour. We had eliminated Black-winged but we couldn't believe that it had no white trailing edge to the secondaries so we decided to phone it in as a probable Collared but with the possibility of Oriental not ruled out.

Dave had to leave at this juncture and left me watching it close to the road-side in the potato field. Next on the scene came Keith Bailey and together we watched it from the sanctuary of my car as it preened frequently between really heavy showers allowing us to become pretty certain that it was in fact an Oriental Pratincole for it still showed no trace of white tips to the secondaries, the overall base colour of the upperparts seemed rather dark (but poor weather conditions were making everything dull), the red underwing coverts were frequently seen as was an orangy buff wash on the flanks continuing under the belly and the tail was surprisingly short and relatively shallowly forked. At about this stage Richard Millington, Steve Gantlett and Mark Golley arrived and the bird obligingly flew back across the road allowing all the salient features of Oriental Pratincole (the first for Norfolk and only the third record for Britain) to be seen and the message on Birdlines to be rapidly changed. In view of the narrow roads in the area Richard and I went to see the proprietor of the riding stables and explained the situation and likely turn out for such a rare bird. June Self (of Roseacre Stables) very kindly checked with her neighbouring farmer (Alan Cargill) and access to the adjacent field for parking and viewing was allowed throughout the duration of the bird's stay. An old horse feed bucket was quickly cleaned and placed by the entrance to the field (a rather more professional collecting pot was soon prepared) and I am pleased to report that over £1,200 was collected for charities of June's choice (£500 to a cancer appeal, £500 for a machine to detect early eye disease and £200 to a local sports' association charity). June did phone BIS to praise the behaviour of some 2,000 visitors in the first five days. She also confessed to being quite entertained by the large gatherings of birders and was amazed at how far many of them had travelled to see the bird, she thought she would miss the excitement once the bird and birders had departed but I am sure she is happy to have her quiet life back again.

To clarify the dates of this bird's visit:- June Self first noticed this strange bird in her paddock on Friday 14th May but thought little of it, on 18th May it was spotted by Chris Payne who reported it to Dave Nicholson, the rest is as reported above. It remained in the area until about midday on 3rd June but was rather elusive towards the end of its stay. At about 1 pm on 3rd June there was a report of a pratincole flying west at Weybourne and on 4th June it was seen briefly but well amongst the Sea-pink by Halfway House along Blakeney point before flying off west at 10.15. That still was not the end of the story for on 5th June it was relocated at Burnham Norton where it stayed unfortunately giving only occasional distant flight views up to about 21st June. It would be nice to think that it might yet resurface elsewhere.'

(An account published in the *Norfolk Bird Club Bulletin* No 5: 5-7)

Black-winged Pratincole
Glareola nordmanni
An adult found by Billy Bishop at Cley on 3rd July 1966 remained until the 5th. Over 60 birders admired this splendid bird during its short visit.

Billy Bishop writes in *Cley Marsh and its Birds* 1983: 50:

'In 1966, while I was close to East Bank a strange bird flew past me which proved to be a black-winged pratincole. Other exotic visitors which have flown, as it were, into my binoculars, include a long-billed dowitcher, another American wader'.

Richard Richardson writes in his diary:

'3rd July: WFB spotted a strange bird from the roadside hide which turned out to be a beautiful Black-winged Pratincole. Everyone here watched it for the whole day from 1030hrs GMT. It spent much of its time on the 'Bath Marsh' (about 400 yards from the Coast Road), either just sitting and preening or running swiftly about to snap at flies on the grass. Sometimes it flew round above the marsh like a large wader swerving from side to side and doubling back with a graceful agile flight. Often it climbed steeply into the air like a Black Tern to take a high-flying insect and it was frequently chased by Lapwings, Black-headed Gulls and once a Common Tern. The black wing-linings were clearly visible as it banked close by in brilliant sunshine and the absence of white on the tips of the secondaries confirmed the identification. The upper parts were rich brown and the breast was paler than I'd expected. The forked tail and white rump were very noticeable. After each quick run along the ground it wagged its hind-parts up and down. A new bird for Norfolk and for everyone who saw it.

4th July: The pratincole spent all the morning on saltmarsh but left to the SW over Cley village at 11.30 GMT it was not to be seen in the afternoon. It returned at about 17.30 GMT. Last evening I went back alone at dusk, expecting the bird to be of similar feeding habits, and I was not disappointed. I stood for some time in fading light watching it make repeated flycatching sallies from the ground at the rate of between six and eight sorties per minute. I did the same thing this evening and the bird behaved similarly.

5th July: The pratincole watched flying eastwards over Bank early this morning and not seen again.'

Moss Taylor adds in *Guardian Spirit of the East Bank* 2005: 137:

'The story of the discovery of this bird and its eventual identification is possibly apocryphal but is nevertheless worth repeating. When initially spotted by Billy Bishop it was flying in front of the roadside hide, from where the reserve permits were sold. He identified it as a swift from its outline and the fact that it was hawking for insects; it then landed on the dry marsh and he thought it was a tern; finally it started to run around whereupon he immediately realised it was actually a pratincole!'

There is a kind of moral to that story in that initial identification is often tricky and sometimes wrong. We have all been there. The important thing is that attention was drawn to the bird and it was eventually correctly identified. First impressions do count but are not always right! See the Black Lark account.

Little Ringed Plover
Charadrius dubius

Two found by Michael Seago at Breydon Water on 14th June 1943 were thought to be the first county records (Allard 1990, Taylor *et al* 1999), but two earlier records have recently come to light.

One was seen at Martham Holmes, Hickling by Lord Edward Hay, Colonel Lister Cooper and Jim Vincent on 28th May 1920.

Jim Vincent writes:

> 'I was interested to read of the Little Ringed Plovers (*Charadrius d. curonicus*) breeding at Tring (*antea*, p. 90) and as previous records of its visits to our shores are so few I wish to record a bird of this species at Hickling on May 28th, 1920, which was seen by Lord Edward Hay, Colonel Lister Cooper and myself in a small shallow fresh-water pool.
>
> The bird was remarkably tame, and allowed us to watch it for some time, and a sketch was made of the bird to compare notes on arrival back at Whileslea Lodge, and both Lord Edward Hay and Colonel Lister Cooper were satisfied as to its identity.
>
> In 1918, during the War, I found two pairs of this species breeding between Calais and Gravelines, and so was able to recognise the species on this occasion at Hickling.
>
> The size of the bird, its narrow chest-band and the frontal markings from the base of the bill to the crown showing white, black, white, brown, together with the yellow circle around the dark pupil gave the bird a striking facial appearance and its yellowish legs were outstanding.
>
> We all possessed powerful field glasses and were able to see every detail of this fully adult bird, which at this stage could not be confused with the ordinary Ringed Plover.'

(Originally published in *British Birds* 32: 155-156)

Another was seen by Constance Gay and Ted Piggin, at Hickling Broad on 2nd May 1940.

Jim Vincent writes:

> 'A little ringed plover was seen on the wader grounds by Miss Gay and Mr. Piggin who also heard its call. They returned to the Lodge to fetch me to see it also and I feel sure the identification was correct.'

(Originally published in *Wild Bird Protection in Norfolk* 1940: 18)

Common Ringed Plover
Charadrius hiaticula

The first dated reference we can find is in a footnote in Henry Stevenson's *The Birds of Norfolk* Vol. ll. 1870: 84-96:

'Mr. Alfred Newton informs me that "Ringel" is at the present day a Norsk name for this bird. The term sea-dotterel, also, frequently but erroneously applied to this plover, is of somewhat ancient date, as we find it thus used in two instances in the' (L'Estranges) 'Hunstanton "accounts" – It. pd to ye fowler (xxiiij weke 1525) at Corbetts for iij duss and di stynts, v spowes, iij white plovs, and ij redshanks, and ij 'sedotterells' xvj pence'.

Sir Thomas Browne (1605-1682) in *Notes and Letters on the Natural History of Norfolk* 1902: 23 writes:

'Ringlestones a small white & black bird like a wagtail & seems to bee some kind of motacilla marina common about Yarmouth sands. they lay their egges in the sand & and shingle about june and as the eryngo diggers tell mee not sett them flat butt upright likes egges in salt.'

Thomas Southwell adds a footnote:

'The Ringed Plover is evidently the bird here referred to, but I have never known the name of Ringlestones applied to this species in Norfolk, nor have I met with it elsewhere. The Eringo is no longer an article of commerce, and its diggers are extinct, but their tradition as to the position in which the eggs of this bird are said to be placed - a "vulgar error" which does not accord with the writer's experience. When the full complement of four eggs is laid, they are arranged with their pointed ends towards the centre of the nest, which is slightly hollow in the soil. The concavity of the nest therefore, as well as the disproportionate size of the larger end, gives the eggs somewhat the appearance of being placed in the position referred to, but the small end of the egg is always visible. Sir Thomas Browne does not seem to have been aware of the remarkable fact of this essentially marine bird habitually nesting on the sandy warrens about Thetford in the south-west of Norfolk, far from the sea, which it still does, though in reduced numbers, and is there known as the Stone-hatch, from its habit of paving its nest with small stones.'

Killdeer

Charadrius vociferus
One was discovered by Ian Smith in a field close to Breydon south wall on 28th March 2005 (Plate 10).

Ian Smith writes:

'Looking forward to a bank holiday weekend with some good weather and some birding (especially when working during the week when the weather had been good) is always special and bank holiday Monday 28th March was no exception. Sadly the weekend had been disappointing with low cloud and mist rolling in off the sea making birding virtually impossible on both Saturday and Sunday.
The local weather forecast for Monday gave a glimmer of hope. With the mist due to clear and the morning somewhat brighter with much better visibility and

only occasional mist patches, I was off to Breydon, arriving on the south wall sometime after 9.00 am. The tide was coming up and the majority of waders were being pushed towards the eastern end of the estuary with good numbers but nothing unusual. I started the 2-3 mile walk along the south wall with little to look at for the first mile, gradually convincing myself there was not much about; a male Hen Harrier and Short-eared Owl over the marshes were the first indication of things improving.

About half way along the wall near a small wind pump I noticed a small group of Golden Plover in a field and 'scoped' them just in case any early Dotterel might be amongst the 12 birds present. On scanning the plovers I noticed a larger flock of 40-50 Golden Plovers in the adjacent field. I had just walked past without noticing them and while scanning through the flock I noticed a wader on its own to the right of the plovers. It was smaller with white under-parts and two distinctive breast bands, surely it had to be a Killdeer! The bird showed very well in the field and I could not believe I had just fulfilled one of my ambitions to find a first for Norfolk. It was 11.45 am and I watched it for 10 minutes before deciding I had to contact someone and let the news out, although this was a bit awkward as I didn't have a mobile phone with me.

I started walking back hastily and after only a few minutes a family on bikes came along the bank towards me. I quickly looked to see if the bird was still there, the time now was 12.05 pm. Fortunately the person had a mobile phone with him and was quite happy to lend it me so I could contact local birder Keith Dye who lived not far from Breydon. "He's in the shower" came the reply from his other half. I almost shouted "tell him I've found a rare bird at Breydon" and within a minute I was talking to Keith and telling him I'd found a Killdeer along the south wall. He said he would be there as quickly as possible and I promised to stay with the bird. After a few minutes on the phone and thanking the family, I started making the short walk back feeling happy that other birders would soon be enjoying the bird. Just as I was getting close to the field at 12.20 pm I saw the plover flock fly off west; I hoped the bird would still be present but sadly it had gone with them. I walked further along the wall to check the surrounding marshes but to no avail, only an early singing Sedge Warbler by way of compensation. Feeling rather disappointed I waited until Keith arrived and told him the bad news; despite much searching by birders arriving from far and wide the bird was not relocated during the rest of the day.

Amazingly next day the Killdeer was re-found early in the morning in the exact same field and was seen by hundreds of grateful birders until dusk, although not seen subsequently. I was happy many people got to see it rather than one single over-the-moon observer!'

(An account published in the *Norfolk Bird Report* 2005: 294-295)

Kentish Plover

Charadrius alexandrinus
Two birds were obtained at Yarmouth in 1827.

Henry Stevenson in *The Birds of Norfolk* Vol. ll. 1870: 97-100, writes:

'The earliest record I can find of this species having been recognised on the Norfolk coast, is contained in a paper by the late Mr. Yarrell, in the "*Zoological Journal*" for 1827 (vol. iii., p. 86), "on the occurrence of some rare British Birds," in which he notices the recent occurrence of two immature specimens at Yarmouth, and describes the difference in their plumage as compared with examples, at the same age, of *Charadrius hiaticula*. Of our local authors, Hunt includes it for the first time in his list of "*Norfolk Birds*," published in Stacy's history of the county in 1829; and under the name of the "Alexandrine plover," states that "a beautiful one in the Norwich museum was killed at Yarmouth." When once it had been pointed out as a rarity, however, and its distinctive features made known, the Breydon gunners seem to have had no difficulty in supplying specimens to collectors.'

Greater Sand Plover
Charadrius leschenaultii
One, believed to be an immature, was identified at Breydon by Peter Allard on 17th April 1981.

Peter Allard writes from his notes taken at the time:

'Saturday, April 17th 1981 was one of those days when cool easterly winds had been prevailing for several days and there was precious little in the way of spring migration to cheer one up. I had visited Breydon Water the previous day, one of my local patches, and seen little apart from an interesting Redshank which had very pale yellowish legs, one Spotted Redshank and 15 Ringed Plovers. Anyhow, already having teamed up with John O'Sullivan, the RSPB regional officer at Norwich and local birder Terry Boulton, the three of us ambled along the north estuary wall until we reached the second observation hide. We scanned the flats for any interesting waders on the incoming tide, noting only six Bar-tailed Godwits, two Black-tailed Godwits, six Turnstones and the first two Greenshank of the spring. A splendid drake Red-breasted Merganser added a little spice as it swam on one of the creeks close by. Little else was seen of note until suddenly I became aware of a distant smallish wader on a strip of mud several hundred yards away. It was by itself, but it looked interesting and on focusing my telescope on the individual, it had to be a Kentish Plover, the first here this spring. Both John and Terry were soon focusing their telescopes on the bird, John remarking almost immediately that it was a female. The bird remained distant and unfortunately, there was a slight haze and the light was against us, so views from the hide were difficult, but there was nothing else it could be. However, there was something odd about this bird. My notes recall that the head looked large, it had a brownish crown and there appeared to be a slight trace of a breast band. Both John and Terry seemed convinced that it was a Kentish Plover, so knowing they were happy as to identification, I began to scan for other waders on the tideline. John happened to see it fly off and land even further away, almost to the edge of the mudflats alongside the main channel where it remained until all the other waders were disturbed by what was possibly a bird of prey. The morning passed without it reappearing at the eastern end of the estuary.

Terry Boulton saw Bill Fairless later during the morning and mentioned the

Kentish Plover to him. Bill, having never seen one before, decided to try his luck along the south wall of Breydon in the afternoon. The tide, having receded by now, was ideal for waders and Bill had no trouble relocating it on the south wall flats. It was again by itself, but was later joined by a small group of Dunlin and Ringed Plover. Bill noticed amongst other things that it was slightly larger than both of these species. As he had never previously seen a Kentish Plover, he decided to return home to look it up in his bird identification books. At the same time, I was at home close by during the afternoon and decided to have another look for what we all presumed was a female Kentish Plover. A quick walk through the passages of Cobholm and I was soon on the estuary wall where I, luckily, met Bill who directed me instantly to where he had last seen the bird. The mere mention of the bird being larger than Ringed Plovers sent alarm bells ringing, as fresh in my mind were recent occurrences of three Greater Sand Plovers in Avon, Orkney and West Sussex. I had recently read the account of two of these birds in 'British Birds' and had rather luckily checked the identification features of Greater Sand Plover myself.

The bird was still present on the south wall flats and on focusing my telescope on the wader, which was fortunately relatively close; there was no problem identifying it as a Sand Plover. A Turnstone was initially alongside, and it was judged to be of similar size. When a Ringed Plover landed alongside, it was noted that it was approximately 30% larger in body size. It was certainly a Greater Sand Plover on this alone rather than Lesser Sand Plover. Luckily, Bill managed to take one reasonable photograph of it feeding with both Ringed Plovers and Dunlin alongside the edge of the main channel. Its movements were likened to that of a Grey Plover, slower and totally unlike those of the accompanying Ringed Plovers. The shape of the head was very unusual indeed, having a very high domed crown, whilst the neck was noted as looking like it had sunk into the shoulders giving the bird a very characteristic appearance. The blackish bill was conspicuously large both thicker and longer than those of the Ringed Plovers. The bill was especially thick at the base and blunt ended. The length was estimated to be two thirds the length of its head. The long legs, about one inch longer than Ringed Plovers were described as of olive colouration, but in certain light conditions, a reddish hint could be detected. The mantle was a very sandy colouration with whitish underparts and an indistinct narrow breast band, only detectable however at close range. At certain angles, there was a hint of chestnut on the sides of the breast.

After 30 minutes of excellent viewing, there became this great urgency to inform other birders of its presence. Racing home, which luckily, was not too distant, hurried phone calls were made to Michael Seago, Giles Dunmore and Terry Boulton. There was no need to phone Adrian Boote, he had just called round for a chat which saved a few vital seconds for the tide was beginning to flood and the south wall flats would soon be covered. Within a short space of time, Adrian, Terry and I were all watching this bird at ranges down to some 20 yards. It fed on several quite sizeable worms, washing them first in a pool of water before swallowing them. Bill Fairless soon rejoined us, but by then the bird was further out on the mud and had flown a short distance. In flight, a distinct paler wing-bar was noticeable to all. The tide was by now rapidly flowing in, and suddenly, the Sand Plover, together with 15 Ringed Plover took flight and head-ed low north-east across to where the 'lower drain' runs parallel to the north wall. Within seconds of the bird flying off, Giles Dunmore appeared, all out of breath and complete with his brand new Optolyth telescope. Deciding on what to do next, it soon became obvious that we needed to be on the north wall close to where it was originally seen from. With Adrian declining to pursue the bird further, three cars were soon hurrying through Great Yarmouth and along the Acle New Road towards the second hide area. In what seemed an eternity to Giles, we soon climbed the north estuary wall and quickly located our star bird, Giles gleefully remarking that it was literally the first bird he had seen through his new telescope. Giles's experience was very useful indeed and he also agreed that it was very likely a Greater rather than a Lesser Sand Plover. With the light now fading fast and the tide still rushing in, Giles, Terry, Bill and the writer had to depart at dusk hoping this great rarity would still be present the following morning.

With clear skies overnight, we had been rather too optimistic and despite a thorough search by many observers along both estuary walls during the following day, it was not seen again. The Greater Sand Plover had presumably departed overnight. Details of this individual, along with a photograph, were later submitted to British Birds Rarity Records Committee and the record was eventually accepted as a Greater Sand Plover, the first for Norfolk. It was indeed only the fourth record for Great Britain, the first having been seen in West Sussex only as recently as December 1978. For the unfortunate birders who braved Breydon Water on Sunday April 18th looking for the Greater Sand Plover, their wait for another would not be too long. A slightly more colourful individual, a first-summer or adult female was identified at Cley in north Norfolk on July 30th 1985 and it remained there until August 21st attracting large crowds of admirers before making a final appearance at Blakeney Point on September 2nd.'

Caspian Plover
Charadrius asiaticus
The first British record was first seen by Samuel Smith in a large market garden bordering the North Denes at Yarmouth on 22nd May 1890 (Plate 3). It was shot by Arthur Bensley later that day. The specimen (Accession no. NWHCM: 1890.39) remains on display in the bird gallery at the Castle Museum, Norwich.

Thomas Southwell writes in Henry Stevenson's *The Birds of Norfolk* Vol. lll. 1890: 382-384:

'It was with no little pleasure, therefore,' [referring to an article by a Mr. Harting contributed to the '*Ibis*' in 1870 regarding distribution and migration routes, that concluded that it was quite possible the Caspian Plover might occur in England] 'that on the evening of the 23rd of May 1890, I received from Mr. Lowne, of Yarmouth, the fresh skin of a handsome full plumaged male of this species which he sent for determination, as the bird was unknown to him.

I subsequently learnt the following particulars with regard to this interesting occurrence. During the morning of the 22nd of May, a date very nearly coinciding with the second appearance of the Caspian Plover in Heligoland, two strange birds were seen in a large market garden, known as Sacret's piece, bordering on the North Denes, at Yarmouth, which attracted the attention of a man named Samuel Smith, who works the garden for a Mr Bracey, but he had no opportunity of a shot. About 5.30 pm., when they were on the golf ground, which forms a portion of the denes, Smith's step-son, Arthur Bensley, saw them, and having a gun with him, tried to get both birds in line for a double shot, but being unsuccessful, selected the brighter of the two, its companion being at the time about six yards distant from it; when he fired, the paler bird, presumably the female, flew off in a westerly direction, and was no more seen. Very shortly after, the bird was purchased of Smith by Mr. H. C. Knights, by whom it was shown in the flesh to Mr. G. F. D. Preston, and taken the next morning to Mr Lowne for preservation; he, as before stated, forwarded the skin to me the same evening. The weather was very warm at the time, Mr. Lowne would not risk sending the bird in the flesh, hence it was that I saw only the skin, but I may mention that it had all the appearance of having been very recently removed, and that there were still many living parasites remaining on the feathers. Mr. Gurney also saw the skin while it was in my possession. The sternum Mr. Lowne sent to Professor Newton. The total length of the bird when in the flesh, Mr. Lowne tells me, was eight inches, and its weight two and a quarter ounces. Mr. Knights was good enough to give me the first offer of the bird, and through the liberality of some friends of the Norwich Museum I was enabled to purchase it for that institution, and to send this first British example of the Caspian plover for exhibition at the meeting of the Zoological Society, on the 17th of June.'

The *Yarmouth Independent* carried an article about the Caspian Plover on 28th June 1890, which included further interesting information, the details apparently provided by E. A. Butler of Herringfleet House, writing to the *Field* the previous week. The man who shot it sold it to H. C. Knights, a corn merchant of St. Georges Road, Great Yarmouth for three shillings [£00.15]. Knights sold it to Southwell for £10 whereupon the money was raised by several friends to donate the specimen to the Castle Museum. It is also mentioned that the bird was still on view at Lowne's Shop on Fuller's Hill. Knights' brother was apprentice to Walter Lowne.

Auther Patterson writes in *Nature in Eastern Norfolk* 1905: 214-215:

'A new species of parasite found on it was submitted to Dr. E. Piaget, who proposed to name it *Nirmus assimilis*. The bird itself, after death, was left at a house next door to where I then lived, and placed on the top of the clock to be out of the way of the cat!'

Eurasian Dotterel
Charadrius morinellus
The first dated reference we can find is in Henry Stevenson's *The Birds of Norfolk* Vol. ll. 1870: 76-84:

'That in earlier times this species was not only sought for by the fowler in this county, but afforded sport even for Royalty in the old hawking days, is shown by some entries in a curious MS. diary of Hans Jacob Wurmser v. Vendenheym, who accompanied Lewis Frederick Duke of Wurtemburg, in his diplomatic mission to England in 1610. The Duke, proceeding by Ware, Royston, Cambridge, and Newmarket, appears to have arrived at Thetford on the 7th of May, where King James the First was then staying for the enjoyment of hare hunting and hawking, his favourite diversions; and on the following day, "après que son E(xcellence) eut disn'e aveq sa Ma;te le duc de Lenox qui l'estoit venu visiter deuant disne le menu a la shasse ou l'on courrut le lievre, 'fit voller ung espervier et prient des Doterelles, oiseau wui se laisse prendre par une estrange maniere ainsy que nous avons veu. Et qui se peult mieulx dire qu'escripre." To my friend Mr. J. E. Harting, of Kingsbury, I am greatly indebted for a verbatim copy of such portions of the original MS. as relate to these pastimes, it being important to ascertain the name actually used by this writer, in order to identify satisfactorily the species referred to. He suggests also, and apparently with much reason, that "the writer must have enquired the name of the bird on the spot, and, instead of translating it, simply put down the English word as it was given to him".'

American Golden Plover
Pluvialis dominica

An adult in full breeding plumage accompanied a group of Grey Plover at Breydon on 8th-17th June 1976. It fed and roosted on the tidal flats and occasionally resorted to the adjacent fresh marshes at periods of very high water. Found and photographed by Peter Allard it finally departed with nine Grey Plovers at midday on 17th June, heading high north-east out to sea.

Peter Allard writes from his notes taken at the time:

'Being an early riser, and with Spoonbills having been seen regularly on Breydon Water during the previous few days, 8th June 1976 saw me out on the south wall of Breydon before 06.00 hrs prior to starting a day's work. Two immature Spoonbills were soon located on the tideline, sweeping their long bills in characteristic style in the shallow waters by the Ship Drain. The weather was warm with a light sea breeze and amongst the waders noted was a party of eight freshly arrived red-coloured Knot. Accompanying them were a few Dunlin, but to my surprise a splendid male Kentish Plover was noted close by the entrance to the Ship Drain, the third here this spring. The tide was by now rising and a newly arrived small trip of Grey Plovers joined the other waders on the tideline, seven in total and another wader which I initially considered to be a Golden Plover in full breeding attire. This bird looked a little unusual however, being very bright in colouration and the undersides were entirely black. The white sides to the breast terminated about half way down, similar to those of the Grey Plovers. I was a little puzzled, but continued enjoying views of the male Kentish Plover before heading to work an hour or so later.

Throughout the day, the strange Golden Plover seen at Breydon concerned me, but an evening visit to Winterton dunes where both Redwing and Fieldfare were seen pushed the Golden Plover to the back of my mind. However, the unusual Golden Plover was seen distantly the following morning at first light far out on the tideline and concerns were growing as to its true identity. The evening was spent browsing through various identification books and in Roger Tory Petersen's *A Field Guide to the Birds* on plate 24 was the Breydon bird, a Lesser Golden Plover in full breeding plumage. Total disbelief took over, but the Breydon bird was identical to the one in Petersen's plate without a shadow of a doubt. Would it still be present in the morning I asked myself, almost willing the bird to be there.

Luck was with me the next day, it was still present, and the previously strange looking Golden Plover was now a superb Lesser Golden Plover in full breeding attire. A few phone calls were made and at least two local birders managed to see it during the day. It was a very tidal bird and was still in company with the small trip of Grey Plovers that had arrived on the 8th. At periods of high water, the group were simply nowhere to be found and presumably spent their time on adjacent marshlands waiting for the tide to recede.

The 11th June saw a number of local birders arriving as early as 04.30 hrs to catch the early morning tide and hopefully see the bird as well. It was still present, much to my relief again. Giles Dunmore from Norwich turned up a little later along with others and obtained excellent views from the estuary wall as it fed on the tideline. Giles considered the Lesser Golden Plover to be one of the best birds he had seen for some time. The weather throughout this period had been fine with light southerly winds and as each day progressed, we all thought the bird would disappear in such fine conditions. Several long range photographs were taken on the 12th, both in colour and in black and white as it accompanied the Grey Plover flock. It really was a superb bird with dark golden upperparts, a prominent white forehead which extended above the eyes and down the sides of the breast where it widened before terminating above all black undersides. The greyish axilliaries were prominent in flight, an identification feature confirming it to be a Lesser Golden Plover, with a long primary projection and wing-tips extending well beyond the tail.

Some considerations were made as to which race this bird belonged, the American or the Asiatic. Most observers were leaning towards the American race once the bird had been heard to call, a musical quite loud piping double or treble note followed shortly afterwards by a single note. Michael Seago managed to view the bird on the morning of the 15th after returning from holiday and was fortunate to hear it call, describing it as a three note piping flight note.

There was some confusion at the time as a lone Northern race Golden Plover was additionally present during this period, feeding mainly on the saltings at the eastern end of the estuary. Some observers were claiming this bird as the Lesser Golden Plover, however, this poor bird was sick and only had one eye. The Lesser Golden Plover stayed until the morning of the 17th when the Grey Plover party, which had increased to nine, suddenly became very flighty due possibly to a change in wind direction. It was last seen on the mudflats at 10.30 hrs and at midday, the Grey Plover party headed seawards, presumably taking the New World visitor with them. An afternoon visit at 14.00 hrs failed to find the Lesser Golden Plover or any of the Grey Plovers on the tideway despite an extensive search.

This record was initially accepted as the second Norfolk record of Lesser Golden Plover, the first being at Wisbech Sewage Farm on 10th August 1974. However, in 1986, the two races of this species were split by the BOURC, the Asiatic race became Pacific Golden Plover and the American race became American Golden Plover. The Wisbech 1974 record could not be specifically assigned to a species, but the 1976 Breydon Water record was accepted as an American Golden Plover, thus becoming the first Norfolk record.'

Pacific Golden Plover
Pluvialis fulva

A summer plumaged adult found by Gary Hibberd and identified by Andy Stoddart was present on pools at Holme and in Thornham Harbour with other waders on 20th-22nd and 26th July 1989.

Andy Stoddart writes:

'A summer-plumaged American Golden Plover was reported from Holme late on 20th July 1989. It was still there the following morning until disturbed by a Marsh Harrier so that on my arrival in the early afternoon it was nowhere to be seen. It was eventually relocated at great range in Thornham harbour among Curlew, Whimbrel, Redshank and Grey Plover. Strategic wading produced further views, but these were mainly distant or in flight and not sufficient to disillusion me of the bird's supposed identity. Eventually it settled into a large creek near Thornham village and the closer, though brief, views afforded here came as something of a surprise for it showed no elongated primary extension, strikingly spangled wing-coverts and a white flank line. This was all completely wrong for American Golden Plover – surely it had to be a Pacific Golden Plover? Views reverted to being poor for the remainder of the day, but I saw it closer the following morning on Holme wader scrapes. Any remaining uncertainties were quickly eliminated.

I was able to add further details to my notes: It was a very small, bright 'Lesser' Golden Plover, looking tiny and fragile even when standing next to a Green Sandpiper. The body was small (with no elongated rear-end of strongly projecting primaries), slim and flat-bellied when alert, but more rounded and dumpy when relaxed. The head, bill and eye were proportionally all quite large-looking. The legs were very long, the exact length of exposed tibia varying according to posture, but looking grotesquely long whenever the bird was alert or running. Close views showed that the tip of the large tertial fell level with the tail tip, with a short primary projection beyond, only three primary tips being visible. The bird looked tiny in flight, with narrow wings and a slim torpedo-shaped body.

It was an adult, presumably a male, in virtually full summer plumage with black underparts. The only trace of moult was some buff flecking on the lores and in the malar region. The forehead was extensively white, practically reaching the base of the culmen. This continued into a broad white supercilium and ear-coverts surround and led into a moderate-sized breast-side patch and a white flank line of uniform width separating the black underparts from the folded wing. This flank line was identical on each side and inlaid with a few scattered black chevrons. The undertail-coverts were patched black-and-white. The lateral and longest undertail-coverts were white with black running down the central feathers for two-thirds of their length. Sparse white flecking was present around the vent and there was a single gold feather on each flank. The upperparts were very heavily spangled with very large bright notches and tips to each feather, mainly bright golden on the mantle and scapulars, but contrastingly white on the wing-coverts. There was less spangling on the crown, nape and hindneck, making these areas slightly darker. The tertials, some of which were quite faded and worn, were blackish-brown barred whitish-buff and the primaries were dark brown. Legs were a dull greenish-grey. In flight the dusky underwing and axilliaries were most striking. The upperparts in flight were uniform golden with a thin white-wing-bar.

The bird remained very flighty and mobile in the Holme/Thornham harbour area for the remainder of the 22nd, but most observers who arrived that day managed to see it. It then went missing, presumed to have gone, but was finally reported briefly at Holme on 26th July. Pacific and American Golden Plovers were until recently treated as conspecific under the name of Lesser Golden Plover. Pacific Golden Plover breeds in northern Siberia and extends across the Bering Straits into western Alaska wintering around the shores of the Indian Ocean, in south-east Asia, Australia and the Central and western Pacific Islands and a few even reach California. Such a bird would seem a prime candidate for vagrancy, but they are surprisingly rare in Britain with only six accepted previous occurrences: in Lincolnshire, Humberside (2), Lothian (2) and Shetland. The expected east coast bias to the (British) records so far hopefully means that Norfolk is well-placed to receive another of these supremely attractive Asian plovers. On the evidence so far, July would seem to be as likely a month as any for the next one...'

(An account published in the *Norfolk Bird Report* 1989: 429)

American/Pacific Golden Plover
Pluvialis dominica/fulva
The first county occurrence of Lesser Golden Plover, as it was known until the two races were split into separate species in 1986, was an adult found by John Moyes at Wisbech Sewage Farm on 9th August 1974. When the British Ornithologists' Union Records Committee split the species this record could not be assigned to either, so it remains American or Pacific Golden Plover (*The Birds of Norfolk* 1999: 249). Should it be assigned to either species in the future it would then become the first county record of that species, as it pre-dates both the first fully authenticated American and Pacific Golden Plovers for the county.

John Moyes writes from his notes and recollections of the time:

'Noted briefly on the 9th August on my usual evening visit to Wisbech Sewage Farm. The following day Saturday 10th August 1974 I had much better views down to a few yards range, when the bird was in company with a few Eurasian Golden Plovers plus 13 other species of wader including 40 Curlew Sandpipers and a Red-necked Phalarope.

Golden Plovers of both southern and northern races (not now considered races but mere geographical variants) *Pluvialis apricaria apricaria* and *P. a. altifrons* were regular visitors to the Farm in varying numbers, coming in from the surrounding arable fields to drink and bathe usually late afternoon and evening. Upon studying the small group of *apricaria* a slimmer distinctly grey bird with comparatively longer legs and without the rather pot-bellied appearance of Golden Plovers was apparent. A full description was then taken down, supplemented by field sketches, noting the broad white supercilium, long wings and lack of 'spangling' of yellow on the mantle. The bird flew occasionally in company with Golden Plovers when the grey not white, axilla and underwing, diagnostic features were noted. The bird was an adult as it retained some black patches on its belly and towards the tail. On the descriptions available to me at the time I considered the bird to be *Pluvialis dominica* and it was accepted as this by B.B. Rarities Committee. At this period in ornithological history both *dominica* and *fulva* the Pacific Golden Plover, were recorded as one species the Lesser Golden Plover. It was not until ornithologists found the two geographical "races" nesting in the same locality in Western Alaska, without interbreeding, that taxonomists decided to split the two races into separate species under American Golden Plover and Pacific Golden Plover respectively despite a certain percentage of birds being impossible to assign to either species even when in the hand.

However, most individuals now, with much better known and well documented feld characteristics, can readily be separated without too much difficulty.

A second *Pluvialis dominica* was present on the Farm in 1985, from September 30th to October 4th when all the field characteristics were noted, taking care to eliminate grey-phase *apricaria*. Other good birds seen on the Farm in this the final year of its existence were Pectoral Sandpiper, White-rumped Sandpiper and Buff-breasted Sandpiper, with up to 200 Curlew Sandpipers.

An interesting trait in the American Golden Plover was its aggressive attitude towards other wader species, including Curlew Sandpipers. It is known that some birds of both *dominica* and *fulva* will defend feeding territory when on migration, often quite vigorously, a behaviour not associated with the rather quiet benign habits of Golden Plovers generally.'

European Golden Plover
Pluvialis apricaria
The earliest dated reference we can find is in Henry Stevenson's *The Birds of Norfolk* Vol. ll. 1870: 66-76:

'As a delicacy for the table, this species deservedly stands in high estimation, and in earlier times, from such records as remain to us, appears to have been as highly valued. In the L'Estrange "Household Book" for 1520, we find the Vicar of Thornham's servant receiving various gratuities for the bringing of plover, as presents, and when purchased the prices may be gathered from the following items: - "pd. For a crane and vj plovs, xx pence; "vj plovs, xiiij pence;" "vj plovs, xij pence;" and "iij plovs, vj pence;".'

Interestingly he adds:

'At a Royal feast , also, at Kirtlinge, Cambridgeshire, in September, 1577, we have xxviij plover purchased at xxx shillings; yet, strange as it may seem to the modern epicure, at the very same festivities, in honour of our "good Queen Bess," xviij gulls were provided at a cost of iiiijli. shillings; and this with lambs at five shillings and pigs at a shilling a piece.'

Grey Plover
Pluvialis squatarola
Known by some of the earlier writers as the Swiss Sandpiper and Helvetic Sandpiper the earliest dated reference we can find is in Henry Stevenson's *The Birds of Norfolk* Vol. ll. 1870: 101-103:

> 'There is little doubt, I think, as suggested by Mr. H. Gurney, that the "white plovs," which occur once in the "Household Accounts" (for 1525) of the L'Estrange's, of Hunstanton, with other shore birds such as redshanks, "stynts," and "sedotterel," were of this species in their winter plumage.'

Sociable Lapwing
Vanellus gregarius
A very obliging bird was found by R. Neale, the assistant Wildfowl Trust (now the Wildfowl and Wetlands Trust) warden, at Welney on 3rd September 1977. It remained in the area until the 25th.

Tony Hopkins, Education Officer with the Wildfowl Trust at the time, recorded that it first arrived in the morning, and thereafter spent its mornings on the washes and flighted out to the surrounding agricultural land in the afternoons, usually with Lapwings though they were generally hostile towards it. From his observations the bird appeared to be an adult.

Steve Gantlett who observed the bird on the 4th writes:

> 'A rumour of a Sociable Plover on the Norfolk Ouse Washes at Welney was enough to send me and a number of other observers over there. Apparently only distant flight views without binoculars had been obtained at this stage.
> After an hour's wait the bird finally flew up out of the distant long grass with a few Lapwings. Fortunately it flew towards us and landed on an area of short grass and was then watched feeding in full view. Good views were thus obtained in flight and on the ground, with a telescope.
> Its shape was basically as a narrower more pointed-winged Lapwing, although slightly smaller. In flight it showed a tricoloured pattern of brownish with black primaries, white secondaries and white tail with a fairly broad subterminal black band. On the ground it appeared uniform sandy-brown above and off white below, and it showed bold off-white supercilia meeting at a 'V' on the nape. Its breast was slightly streaked and marked brownish and it had a short, typical plover bill and quite long blackish legs. Jizz on the ground was much as a Lapwing. It was not heard to call.'

(An account extracted from the unpublished files in the British Birds Rarities Committee archive)

Northern Lapwing
Vanellus vanellus
The earliest dated reference we can find is by Sir Thomas Browne (1605-1682) in *Notes and Letters on the Natural History of Norfolk* 1902: 20 where he comments:

> 'The lapwing or vannellus common ouer all the heaths.'

Red Knot
Calidris canutus
The earliest dated reference we can find is in Henry Stevenson's *The Birds of Norfolk* Vol. ll. 1870: 354-361 where he writes:

> 'In the L'Estrange (of Hunstanton 1519-1578) "Household Book" knots are twice mentioned with other waders – "Itm pd to hym for a curlewe, a dosyn knots, a dosyn redschanks and stynts, ij teals -.""Itm pd to the fowler for ijj dosyn and di [half] of knots, - iiij shillings. - j pence - ".'

An interesting note by Sir Thomas Browne (1605-1682) in *Notes and Letters on the Natural History of Norfolk* (1902) is well worth mentioning here:

> 'Gnats or Knots a small bird which taken with netts grow excessively fat. If being mewed & fed with corne a candle lighted in the roome they feed day & night, & when they are at their hight of fatness they beginne to grow lame & are then killed or as at their prime & apt to decline.'

Sanderling
Calidris alba
The earliest dated reference we can find is by Sir Thomas Browne (1605-1682) in *Notes and Letters on the Natural History of Norfolk* 1902: 19-20:

> 'A may chitt a small dark gray bird little bigger then a stint of fatness beyond any. it comes in may into marshlands & other parts & abides not aboue a moneth or 6 weekes.'

Thomas Southwell adds a footnote:

> 'Mr. Stevenson, "Birds of Norfolk," ii., p. 233, gives his reasons for coming to the conclusion that the Sanderling (*Calidris arenaria*) is here referred to, which the absence of a hind toe (see third letter to Merret) tends to confirm.'

In the third letter to Merrett (1668), Sir Thomas Browne writes:

> 'The Avicula Maialis or may chitt is a little dark gray bird somewhat bigger then a stint which cometh in may or the later end of April & stayeth about a moneth. A marsh bird the legges & feet black without an heel the bill black about 3 quarters of an inch long they grow very fatt & are accounted a dayntie dish.'

Semipalmated Sandpiper
Calidris pusilla
The first British record was an adult commencing to moult from summer into winter plumage on Arnold's Marsh, Cley on 19th July 1953. It was found by Peter Clarke who pointed it out to Paul Kirby and Richard Richardson. It was later filmed by Dick Bagnall-Oakeley down to two metres and remained until the 24th.

A. H. Daukes writes:

'On 19th July 1953, an unusual wader was observed on Arnold's Marsh, Cley, Norfolk, by P. R. Clarke, who pointed it out to P. D. Kirby and R. A. Richardson. It was subsequently watched for some hours at a few yards range by these three observers, myself, Mrs R. F. Meiklejohn and W. F. Bishop, the official watcher of Cley Marsh. We came to the conclusion that it was a Semipalmated Sandpiper (*Calidris pusilla*).

Attention was first drawn to the bird by its predominately grey colouring and its peculiar leisurely method of feeding, rather after the manner of a Knot (*Calidris canutus*). In size the bird was slightly, but definitely, larger than a Little Stint (*C. minuta*), one of which was present for comparison, and in colour rather paler and more grey; the light backward pointing V mark on the back, which is a conspicuous feature of the Little Stint, was entirely lacking: the breast was streaked with grey and the under-parts were pure white. There was a noticeable black line from the top of the upper mandible to a point just behind the eye, where the line broadened into an irregular grey black band extending along the top of the ear-coverts, and there was a light superciliary stripe. The wing-coverts were much abraded, pointing to its being an adult bird in the last of its summer plumage. The bill was black, shorter and noticeably stouter than that of a Little Stint, and seemed to broaden at the end. The legs, when wet, appeared to be black, but when dry, were seen to be very dark olive green. The usual note was a husky, throaty "churup" and an occasional very faint "chit", the latter only audible at a few feet. On the wing the bird looked very uniform grey, with an almost imperceptible wing bar: tail pattern much as Little Stint.

Every endeavour was made to catch the bird, which was quite tame, and to identify its footprints, but the mud was too liquid for this to be done. A small hide was erected by R. P. Bagnall-Oakeley and 100 feet of colour cine-film were obtained at very short range, together with several 'stills' down to a distance of six feet, two of which are reproduced here (Photos 4 & 5). Copies of these were sent to Roger Tory Peterson, the well known American ornithologist, who wrote to say that the bird was quite definitely a Semipalmated Sandpiper. The colour film has since been seen by many people including other New World ornithologists and who all agree on the identification.'

(Originally published in *British Birds* 47: 131-132)

Red-necked Stint
Calidris ruficollis
An adult in summer plumage was found at Cley by Mark Golley in the evening of 29th July 1992.

Mark Golley writes from his notes and recollections of the occasion:

'July 29th had been a pleasant but not exactly earth-shattering, early autumn day. Indeed, it had been a relatively good day by most localities' standards: Curlew Sandpipers, a pair of Garganey and an impressive Yellow-legged Gull, were all present. But to me, this was just another standard Cley late July day. The weather had been fine until mid-afternoon when it began to cloud over. By early evening it was dull, damp and cool, even a little murky.

With the scrapes on the south side of the reserve being well-watched of an evening, I decided to head from my Assistant Warden's hut on the beach towards North Scrape and on towards Arnold's Marsh and Sea Pool, seeing if there had been any new shorebird arrivals since the afternoon circuit. After checking North Scrape, I began walking from North Hide towards the East Bank (at around 6.20pm) and, passing the brackish pools midway between the two spots, I casually glanced at a furtive group of (newly arrived?) waders on the pools ahead of me: it seemed to be a group of some 20 Dunlin and the first 'Little Stint' of the autumn.

As this was the first stint of the new season passage, I decided to take a slightly closer look. Using a fence post as a tripod I 'scoped the bird, which was decidedly uncooperative. Three or four glimpses revealed an interesting salmon-pink wash on the throat, but soon the flock moved off heading towards North Hide. Somewhere in my subconscious (and presumably having noted more features than I realised) I knew I had to head back to North Hide and pay this interesting bird a little more attention. It certainly felt as though it deserved another look. An initial scan revealed nothing. Neither did the second, nor the third. After a brief chat on the two-way radio with Richard Millington, mentioning my initial thoughts as to what I may be confronted with, I scanned again and there, three islands back, was the clearly squat, stocky stint shuffling through vegetation.

My pulse quickened following my first good 'scoped views. So many 'pro' features, but why no robin-like throat?!? I was excited, exasperated and frustrated all at once. I began taking in every detail with my battered, trusty Kowa. All seemed to fit Red-necked Stint… but surely not? And still – in my naivety – why didn't it have a brick-red neck like the Blacktoft bird?!?

By now I was willing someone to arrive. One, two, three checks out of the hide – no one looming on either the western or eastern horizons. After the fourth peep out of the hide, there was the distinctive frame of Eddie Myers. Relief! I motioned him urgently into the hide and, after explaining my rationale, and Eddie watching the bird for several minutes as we discussed the features on show – he agreed – it had to be a Red-necked Stint.

The low slung posture, flat back and round body all fitted nicely with our experience of the first British record at Blacktoft Sands some six years previously. Given the distance and failing light, the plumage was difficult to note fully, but the dark capped appearance, dark mantle with staw-coloured 'tramlines', dark scapulars contrasting with grey-looking coverts, unmarked salmon bib and black chevrons on the breast sides all demanded Red-necked Stint. After 20 minutes or so, the flock flew to Simmonds Scrape.

Eddie and I hurried to firm ground, pushing our bikes as fast as we could and then hurtled, as fast as we could, down the Beach Road towards the south side of the reserve. As we began running towards Daukes' Hide, we met RM who, alerted to the fact that the bird had jumped from one side of the reserve to the other, was just coming off the reserve. He agreed that, in principal, the stint looked interesting. However, the July gloom was descending fast, the light failing quicker than any of us wanted and it was clear that there was to be an anxious wait until the new dawn…

To my absolute frustration, there was no sign of the bird the following day. I discussed the bird with various local birders, Eddie and I met Martin Elliot and he was left in little doubt that a Red-necked Stint was at large. But try as we might, there was nothing around the reserve that day, or the three days that followed…

The story may well have died a death there and then – no digiscoping in the early 1990s, notebooks and scrappy sketches were often all that could be relied on – unless the bird in question lingered long enough for long lenses to be unleashed upon the quarry.

Thankfully, this particular tale resolved itself in the very best manner possible. A busy first weekend of August meant that there was more time spent checking permits than spending time searching for Britain's second Red-necked Stint. On a sunny Sunday, 2nd August, my radio crackled in the Cley Visitor Centre – it was Richard Millington. He was in North Hide and he was sure that he was watching the Red-necked Stint!

And that was the start of a splendidly busy day – soon, the Beach car-park was full to bursting, and the Beach Road itself became a secondary car parking avenue. With a Greater Sand Plover appearing later in the week, at least £1,500 (a significant figure in the early 1990s) was raised for the then, Norfolk Naturalists' Trust. At the time, as assistant warden on the reserve, I was in charge for the two days that the Red-necked Stint was present on the marsh. As a British second and Norfolk's first, the bird was bound to draw observers from far and wide and the two hides that overlooked the North Scrape at the time could only accommodate so many bodies at once, so a rota system was organised. Birders arriving on site were immediately made aware of this and, with the help of Eddie Myers and Martin Elliot in particular, the proceedings passed without a hitch. Everyone seemed to appreciate the situation and remained patient and good-natured whilst waiting for their five minute 'stint' in the hide.

The overall 'jizz' of the bird was subtly different from a Little Stint, not looking at all small headed or round bodied, but square headed and short-billed. The low-slung posture was very apparent as was the already mentioned shuffling feeding action. Although larger looking the Red-necked Stint showed a minimal primary projection, similar to Little Stint, together with a distinct tricoloured appearance: dark upperparts, grey wings and white underparts. Other features included straw-coloured mantle braces, pale supercilia and the infamous warm flush to the breast. The bird performed well all day, but after a distinct change in the weather and one too many Sparrowhawk flushes it departed high and westwards on the morning of 3rd August.

Description

Upperparts:
The mantle was dark brown, streaked blackish, bordered by creamy 'braces', the scapulars were equally dark, with extensive blackish centres, rich chestnut fringes and pale tips. The whole of the closed wing was contrastingly grey; all the coverts, and tertials, were plain, dull steely grey with paler, silvery edgings. The cap was brown, streaked blackish, and isolated from the mantle by the pale creamy, lightly streaked nape and from the suffused dark loral stripe and rear

ear-coverts by quite broad off-white supercilia which met across the forehead.

Underparts:

The chin appeared off-white, but the whole of the 'face', throat and upper breast were washed with a clear, pale tangerine, richest and most luminous on the centre of the upper breast where it formed head-on, an orangey halter effect. Since no dark streaking pervaded the colour, the bib appeared delicately translucent. A gorget of fine dark chevrons bordered the lower rim of the orange breast, and these fanned out into a series of small black arrowheads on the white of the upper fore-flanks. The lower breast to vent was pure white.

Bare parts:

The bill, as well as being shorter than that of Little Stint, was distinctly deeper at the tip and appeared very slightly decurved, and the legs were black.

The intensity of the rufous on the upper breast and throat of adult Red-necked Stints is quite variable and the Blacktoft bird was considerably brighter than the Cley individual. Interestingly, both British birds occurred just a few days after records in Sweden.

The Red-necked Stint is the East Asian counterpart of Little Stint. It breeds in north-east Siberia and winters from south-east Asia to Australia. This is the first record for Norfolk and only the second for Britain, the previous sighting coming from Blacktoft Sands RSPB Reserve, East Yorkshire (then Humberside) in 1986.'

Little Stint
Calidris minuta
Previously known as the Little Sandpiper, the earliest reference we can find is by Sheppard and Whitear in *A Catalogue of the Norfolk and Suffolk Birds, with Remarks* 1826: 43 where they just state:

'We have received this bird from Yarmouth…'

The Pagets in *Sketch of the Natural History of Yarmouth and its Neighbourhood* 1834: 9 refer to it as:

'…not uncommon about Breydon…'

Temminck's Stint
Calidris temminckii
Two obtained at an undisclosed locality in May 1830 were the earliest dated record for the species in the county, but the account is rather too vague to be considered as the first Norfolk records.

Henry Stevenson writes in *The Birds of Norfolk* Vol. ll. 1870: 363-366:

'This species was not included by Messrs. Sheppard and Whitear in their Catalogue in 1825, nor by Mr. Hunt in his "*List*" published in 1829; but in Selby's "*British Ornithology*" "a male and female, killed in Norfolk in May, 1830," are stated to be in his possession;'

Stevenson continues:

> '...and in the "Magazine of Natural History" for 1837 (new series, vol. i., p. 117), Mr. J. Hoy has recorded two specimens, birds of the year, as killed near Yarmouth, in September 1835, and an adult bird, on Breydon, in the following May.'

Perhaps the 1835 account is more suitable as the first authentic record.

Interestingly, William R. Fisher, co-author with J. H. Gurney of "An Account of the Birds found in Norfolk" (1846), wrote in his own interleaved copy of the Paget's *Sketch of the Natural History of Yarmouth and its Neighbourhood* (1834), now owned by Peter Allard:

> 'Four birds of this species have been killed here since the beginning of last month (Sept. 1843) and it has no doubt been frequently overlooked. One killed by D. Preston is in his collection. Four or five were killed in May 1844.'

The Pagets (1834) considered that it probably occurred.

White-rumped Sandpiper
Calidris fuscicollis
Known at the time as the Bonaparte's Sandpiper, one was found at Cley by D. D. Harber and identified by A. R. Mead-Briggs and L. Salmon on 1st October 1948, remaining until the 2nd.

D. D. Harber, A. R. Meade-Briggs and L. Salmon wrote:

> 'Early in the morning of October 1st, 1948, one of us, D.D.H., saw from the East Bank, Cley, Norfolk, a small wader which seemed to him rather different from the Dunlins (*Calidris alpina*) feeding near by. It kept apart from other waders, moved somewhat rapidly, seemed rather small for a Dunlin and had a short bill and white belly. Inspection through a telescope, however, showed that it could not be a Little Stint (*Calidris minuta*), as had been at first suspected, since it was only slightly smaller than a Dunlin and had a streaked and speckled breast. Its upper-parts had much the same coloration as those of a Dunlin in winter plumage and D.D.H. finally decided that it also was of this species.
> A few minutes later A.R.M-B. and L.S., who were proceeding along the base of the sea wall, came within a few yards of this same bird and, being likewise puzzled by its appearance, put it up. It flew a short distance, uttering a short, sharp call which was quite unfamiliar to both observers and which they noted at the time as sounding like "jeek." It also showed a white rump above a dark tail as it flew. They were then able to get within 20 feet of the bird and noted it was much like a rather small Dunlin in winter plumage, with a short, almost straight black bill and black legs. The coloration of the upper-parts was greyish brown and the breast was streaked and spotted with the same colours. The belly was white and there was a whitish eye-stripe. In flight A.R.M-B. noted a paler shade on the wing, but L.S. did not notice this. Both observers noted the absence of a

wing-bar.

It was realized that the bird could only be a Bonaparte's Sandpiper (*Calidris fuscicollis*) and L.S. went to fetch D.D.H. Meanwhile the bird had been chased by a Dunlin and had flown some distance away, joining other waders. On arrival D.D.H. made his way over the mud towards the flock of feeding waders. On his approach the bird flew up alone, with a low, rather twisting flight, showing its white rump and giving its call, which D.D.H. also found quite unfamiliar and which sounded to him like a short, sharp, "zeet." It then disappeared amongst other flying waders and could not be found again, either then or later in the day.

Early in the morning of the next day, October 2nd, D.D.H. went with Mr. D. H. Brown to look for the bird in the same locality. Few waders were at first present and the bird was not found. However, a little later, on coming back to the area, it was seen that a number of waders had arrived and, on approach, the Bonaparte's Sandpiper flew up from among these, being the only bird to do so. It uttered the same short, sharp call as before, which was new to Mr. Brown also, and its white rump was seen by both observers. The flight was the same as before, low and rather twisting. The bird disappeared over the East Bank, but was found again a few minutes later feeding in a small pool with Ringed Plovers (*Charadrius hiaticula*). It now allowed a near approach and it was possible to get within 30 feet of it. Inspection through binoculars (10 X 50 and 12 X 40) showed all the features previously described as being seen when the bird was on the ground. In addition the chin and throat were seen to be white and it was noticed that the markings on the breast terminated in a rather definite line, somewhat reminiscent of the American Pectoral Sandpiper. The short black bill seemed very slender, as also did the black legs. On this occasion the bird's movements were more deliberate than had been the case on the previous day and were very similar to those of a Dunlin. A short flight (during which the characteristic call was again given) showed once more the white rump and the dark tail. There was a vague palish shade on the wing but no wing-bar. When put up again the bird made off into the neighbouring marshes and was seen no more.

Since all of us had to leave the district later that same morning no further attempt to find the bird was possible.

This appears to be the first record of Bonaparte's Sandpiper for Norfolk.'

(Originally published in *British Birds* 42: 331-332)

Baird's Sandpiper
Calidris bairdii
One was found by John Clark, Graham Easy and Colin Kirtland at Wisbech Sewage Farm on 22nd July 1963. It remained until 6th August.

John Clark and Graham Easy write:

'The occurrence af a small drab sandpiper at Wisbech Sewage Farm at the same time as a Stilt Sandpiper in July and August of 1963 was mentioned in that Report (CBR 1963 page 2). Despite some very full descriptions that were obtained and the large number of observers involved, there was at the time some dispute over the identification. At first thought to be a poorly marked, "misshapen" Broad-billed Sandpiper it was soon realised that the bird rather resembled Baird's in shape, call and other general features. Unfortunately the news of Broad-billed spread, thus several visiting watchers fell into the belief that the bird under observation was that species. In fact the resemblance was superficial, nevertheless the finer points of method of feeding, the shortness of the finely pointed bill etc. seem to have gone unheeded by some. Now, after 2 years of data gathering we feel we are able to publish the record as a Baird's Sandpiper (also accepted by BB).

First noted at Wisbech S.F. on July 22nd-28th, 1963 (CAEK, ORM, JAWM) and confirmed on July 29th by JSC and GMSE. Last seen on Aug 6th (JFW Bruhn). (Descriptions and comments have also been received from JFWB, DDH, CN, AEV). By alighting on the opposite side of the R. Nene on July 29th it became a new Cambridgeshire species.'

(Originally published in the *Cambridgeshire Bird Club Report* 1964: 20-21)

An earlier record of one shot at Hunstanton on 16th September 1903 was for 83 years considered to be the first county record, and for a period of time, the first British record. This alleged occurrence was unrecorded until 1909 when attention was drawn to it by Gurney in the *Zoologist* 1909: 124 and by Witherby in *British Birds* 3: 29. The specimen was allegedly shot at Hunstanton on 16th September 1903 and was received by George Bristow, the taxidermist at St Leonards, Sussex on 19th September, where it was examined by M. J. Nicholl and afterwards passed into the collection of Sir Vauncey Crewe. Because of the connection between Bristow and the 'Hastings Rarities' infamy (*British Birds* 55: 299-345 and 86: 22), this record was eventually officially deleted from the Norfolk List in 1992 (see an interesting letter from Michael Seago regarding this in *British Birds* 86:22), elevating the Wisbech Sewage Farm bird to the first county record.

Pectoral Sandpiper
Calidris melanotos
One was shot at Breydon on 17th October 1830 (Plate 3).

Henry Stevenson writes in *The Birds of Norfolk* Vol. ll. 1870: 367-370:

'The first British killed specimen of this rare *Tringa*, as was the case also with the broad-billed Sandpiper, was procured on Breydon, and its occurrence is thus recorded by the late Mr. J. D. Hoy in the "*Magazine of Natural History*" for 1837 (New series, vol. i.. p. 116):- "It was killed on October 17th, 1830, on the borders of Breydon Broad, an extensive sheet of water, near Yarmouth, rather celebrated for the numerous rare birds which have, at different times, been observed and shot on its banks and waters. The person who killed it remarked that it was solitary, and its note was new to him, which induced him to shoot it. It proved to be a female on dissection. It was preserved by the late Mr. J. Harvey, of Yarmouth, as a curious variety of *T. variablis*, with some doubts as to whether it might not be a new species. I detected the bird in Harvey's collection, and felt convinced it was an undescribed species of *Tringa.*" *In* corroboration of the above, it is stated by Yarrell that Mr. Hoy having obtained the bird, sent it up to him, in London, for inspection, where Audubon, then staying in England, had the opportunity of examining it, and "he immediately confirmed the previous notion that the bird was an example of the *Tringa pectoralis* of America".'

This bird was in John D. Hoy's collection at Stoke-by-Nayland, Suffolk until his death in 1839. It then passed to his sister Mrs. Lescher of Boyles Court, Brentwood where it was photographed in about 1880. Efforts to trace the Pectoral Sandpiper in 2008 were unsuccessful and it may no longer exist.

See in the Broad-billed Sandpiper account for further details regarding this noted collection.

Arthur Patterson makes some interesting observations about Isaac Harvey, the taxidermist who mounted the Pectoral Sandpiper, in *Nature in Eastern Norfolk* 1905: 79:

> 'This same Harvey was held in no high repute by local sportsmen and collectors, who were not always sure of receiving back the same birds they sent to him for preservation; indeed, at times, no bird came back at all; some accident would befall a valuable and rare example; it was "nibbled by a rat," or "the cat found and ate it." Suspicion was not seldom aroused, and it was hinted that the true facts of the disappearance of the specimen were not altogether to the disadvantage of the taxidermist. Harvey's wife usually undertook the buying, or the taking in, of birds; and most probably knew where they went. A son [Alfred Isaac] followed in the father's footsteps who was both an excellent taxidermist and keen at detecting a rare bird. Nor did he always return specimens. It was no rare thing for him to anathematise his household mice in no measured terms when customers called for their birds.'

Christopher Frost, on the same subject, writes in *A History of British Taxidermy* 1987: 70:

> 'One evening in the 1880s, Alfred Harvey was with a group of contemporaries when the conversation turned to taxidermists. One of their number, 'Admiral' Gooch, a gentleman gunner who had fallen on hard times, said to Harvey: "You bird-stuffers are a lot of swindlers. Your cat ate more birds than mice. I know a purple sandpiper and a blacktailed godwit, not to mention a little bittern, which the same cat ate. I'm very much mistaken if I haven't seen the skins of all three in R…'s collection of local birds. No doubt pussy did eat the birds after you'd skinned them. She ate a glaucous gull once, didn't she? So I hold that bird-stuffers are all cast in one mould; they'd cheat their own grandmothers".'

Sharp-tailed Sandpiper
Calidris acuminata
A bird was shot at Yarmouth in the last week of September 1848 (Plate 3).

Peter Allard writes in *The Birds of Norfolk* 1999: 262, of which he is co-author:

> 'The first at Yarmouth in the last week of September 1848, was originally considered to be a Pectoral Sandpiper (then called American Pectoral Sandpiper) but was recognised as an example of the Sharp-tailed Sandpiper by Thomas Southwell in 1892.'

He adds that the bird (Accession no. NWHCM: 1850.25) is at the Castle Museum, Norwich where, it still remains on display in the bird gallery, and concludes that it was examined by Dave Britton in 1979 and aged as an adult.

B.B. Riviere writes in *A History of the Birds of Norfolk* 1930: 206-207:

> 'The authenticity of the first specimen, which is in the Norwich Museum, was at one time in doubt. It was brought in the flesh to Knights, the Norwich bird-stuffer, in September 1848, by a man named Wilmot, who stated that he had shot it at Yarmouth, and it was later purchased by J. H. Gurney, sen., and recorded by him as an American Pectoral Sandpiper (*Zoologist*, 1849, p. 2392). Upon subsequently being offered by Wilmot two freshly killed specimens of another American species, the Red-winged Starling, Gurney became suspicious that he had been put upon with regard to the Sandpiper, and expressed his doubts as to its authenticity in a further note (Op. cit., 1849, p. 2568). In 1892, however, it was re-examined by Southwell, who discovered that it was an example, not of the American, but of the Siberian species (Op. cit., 1892, p. 406), and for this reason, together with the fact that Roberts, the Norwich taxidermist – by whom it was later restuffed – stated that it had undoubtedly originally been set up from the flesh and had been badly wounded in the neck and leg, he decided that its authenticity as a Norfolk specimen should be accepted, an opinion which appears to have been justified by the subsequent occurrences of the species in the county.'

Interestingly, this was the first British record, in fact the first four county occurrences, at Yarmouth in 1848, Caister in 1865, Terrington Marsh in 1868 and Breydon in 1892, were the only British records until one in Scotland in October 1956. The 1865 and 1892 specimens are also at the Castle Museum, Norwich and the 1868 bird is at King's Lynn Museum. There have been no more county records, which is perhaps surprising in view of the fact that there had been a further 23 British occurrences by the end of 2007.

Curlew Sandpiper
Calidris ferruginea
Formerly known as the Pygmy Curlew, the earliest reference we can find is by Sheppard and Whitear in *A Catalogue of the Norfolk and Suffolk Birds, with Remarks* 1826: 43:

> 'Several of these birds have been killed at Yarmouth in the autumn. One of them, which was shot at that place in the month of August, had a red breast, and was in plumage similar to the one in a summer dress preserved in the British Museum… It is more solitary than the Dunlin, not more than a pair being seen together; and is a stupid bird, suffering a boat to approach close to it. The legs of this bird when fresh killed are of a pale-green, but when dried they appear black.'

Hunt in Stacey's *History of Norfolk* 1829: 66 writes:

> 'One killed at Yarmouth, in the Norwich Museum'

Stilt Sandpiper
Calidris himantopus

An adult, still largely in summer plumage, remained at Wisbech Sewage Farm from 19th July to 7th August 1963. It was trapped, ringed and photographed by Dr Clive Minton on the first date. It was only the third British record.

Clive Minton writes:

'At 11 p.m. on 19th July 1963 a wader which could not readily be identified was caught in a mist-net at Wisbech sewage-farm, on the border of Lincolnshire and Norfolk. It had not previously been observed in the field. It was examined in the hand by Mr. and Mrs. J. A. Hardman, G. Gould, D. Stanyard, my wife and myself and the following description taken:

Upper-parts: crown dark brown with some white flecks; pronounced white stripe just over eye; buffish orange-brown ear-patch about 7.5 mm across; dark brown patch connecting eye and base of bill; nape lighter than crown and mantle; mantle and scapulars dark brown with pale buffish-white edges to feathers, extensively abraded; rump white with some slight barring, particularly in centre; upper tail-coverts widely barred brown and white; tail dark fawn-brown (but lighter than mantle) with centres of individual feathers almost pure white; wings uniform brown except for small white top to secondaries and secondary-coverts, most marked on innermost feathers; wing-coverts heavily abraded. *Under-parts:* from base of bill to under tail-coverts strongly barred brown; barring extremely heavy on upper breast. *Soft parts:* bill slender, black, slightly downcurved at tip; legs long, olive-green, wrinkled and scaly as in adult rather than juvenile bird. *Measurements:* wings 135-136 mm, with 5th, 6th and 7th primaries emarginated (and 4th slightly); bill 41.5 mm to feathers, 49 mm to base of skull, with down-curve beginning 12 mm from tip; tarsus 43 mm, tibia 30 mm to feathers, feet projecting about 30 mm beyond tail.

The bird was not weighed but appeared to be fat and in excellent condition. It was photographed in colour and then released at 7 a.m. on 20th July 1963. The flight somewhat resembled that of a Snipe *Gallinago gallinago* and the contrast of white rump and dark wings was somewhat between a Green Sandpiper *Tringa ochropus* and a Wood Sandpiper *T. glareola*.

The bird was subsequently observed feeding on the bank of the River Nene, just in Cambridgeshire, at a range of forty yards in good sunlight. The rapid feeding rate recalled that of a dowitcher *Limnodromus sp.* The general "jizz" did not closely resemble that of any common British wader. The ear-patch was clearly visible in the field and the eye-stripe was most pronounced between the dark crown and the dark patch in front of the eye.

The description fits that of a Stilt Sandpiper *Micropalama himantopus* still largely in summer plumage. The abraded mantle and wings were typical of an adult wader in autumn. The good condition of the bird and the absence of strong westerly winds in the period immediately preceding the occurrence suggested that it had not recently crossed the Atlantic. It remained at Wisbech sewage-farm for nearly three weeks, during which time it was seen by a number of other observers, and it was last reported by R. Harrison and R. A. Richardson on 7th August.'

(Originally published in *British Birds* 57: 125-126)

Ringed adult Stilt Sandpiper with Dunlins at Wisbech Sewage Farm July 1963. (*Gary Wright*)

Purple Sandpiper
Calidris maritima
One was shot at Yarmouth on 24th October 1819. In the following decades this species was known to the Yarmouth gunners as the Scandinavian Sandpiper.

The Rev. William Whitear writes in in late October 1819 in 'Extracts from the Calendar of the Rev. William Whitear 1809-1826' published in the *Transactions of the Norfolk and Norwich Naturalists' Society* 1881-1882: 251:

> 'Mr. Sabine's servant shot a Purple Sandpiper at Yarmouth last week (October 24th).'

Whether the Sabine referred to is the eminent ornithologist and explorer Edward Sabine or his elder brother Joseph is unclear, if indeed either. But in May 1819 Edward Sabine set sail for Baffin Bay and the Canadian North Western Territories and didn't return until 1820. Presumably his servant would have accompanied him.

Dunlin
Calidris alpina
The earliest dated reference we can find is in Henry Stevenson's *The Birds of Norfolk* Vol. ll. 1870: 371-384 where he writes in a footnote:

> 'In the L'Estrange (of Hunstanton 1519-1578) "Household Book" this species, under the name of "stynt," is frequently included amongst the shore-birds purchased of the "fowler" and others; occasionally as many as three dozen and a half at one time. On one occasion we find the following birds thus curiously priced:- "It. a curlewe v pence, iij teles [teal] and iij stynts iij pence, and iij

plovs vj pence"; and at another time the fowler received one penny for a dozen. "Itm pd to hym for a dosyn stynts - - ij ob." [two halfpence]'

Broad-billed Sandpiper
Limicola falcinellus
The first British record was one shot at Breydon on 25th May 1836.

John D. Hoy of Stoke Nayland writes in Charlesworth's *Magazine of Natural History* Vol. l. 1837: 116:

> 'During the last summer, another bird of the Tringa family, new to this country, has been obtained from the same locality; the Flat-billed Sandpiper Tringa platyrhyncha of Temminck's "Manual", it was shot on the 25th May, 1836 on the muddy flats of Breydon Broad. It was in company with some Dunlins and Ringed Plovers. From the season of year, it had probably acquired its summer plumage; and it very closely agrees with the description of the nuptial garb of the species as given by M. Temminck. This bird is rather inferior in size to the Dunlin, but may be always readily distinguished from that species by the perculiar form of the bill, as well as considerable difference in plumage. This specimen was preserved by a friend of mine, who did not notice the sex. It is probable that this sandpiper may occasionally be found on our eastern coasts during the time of its periodical flights, but from its similarity to one or two closely allied species, has hitherto escaped detection.'

This bird was in Hoy's collection at Stoke Priory, Stoke-by-Nayland, Suffolk, until his death in 1839, at the age of 42. This large and noted collection was then dispersed amongst family members. Some specimens remained at Stoke-by-Nayland with his brother, but the majority passed to his sister, Mrs. Lescher of Boyles Court, Brentwood, Essex. When Claude Ticehurst looked at it in 1912, the collection was in excellent condition. Upon Mrs. Lescher's death the collection was donated to the Prittlewell Priory Museum in Southend. Efforts to trace the Broad-billed Sandpiper in 2008 were unsuccessful and it is likely that it no longer exists.

Interestingly, the next Norfolk record was also obtained at Breydon, 20 years later on the same date.

Buff-breasted Sandpiper
Tryngites subruficollis
One was obtained at Sheringham on 29th July 1832. The specimen (Accession no. NWHCM: 1832.55) is in storage in the skin collection at the Castle Museum, Norwich.

Henry Stevenson in *The Birds of Norfolk* Vol. ll. 1870: 358-359, having mentioned the first British record in Cambridgeshire in 1826, writes, initially quoting Yarrell in his sixteenth volume of the *Linnean Transactions*:

> "A few years afterwards Mr. John Sims, who had then removed to Norwich, obtained a second example of this species, which was killed at Sherringham, on the coast of Norfolk, and which he preserved for the Norwich Museum."
> 'Amongst the British birds in that institution (No. 240) this local rarity,

although in rather a dilapidated condition, is still preserved, and according to an entry in the donations book of that date, it was killed at Sherringham, July 29th 1832 and was presented by Mr. Arthur Upcher.'

Ruff
Philomachus pugnax
The earliest dated reference we can find is by Sir Thomas Browne (1605-1682) in *Notes and Letters on the Natural History of Norfolk* 1902: 20-21:

> 'Ruffes a marsh bird of the greatest varietie of colours euery one therein somewhat varying from other. The female is called a Reeve without any ruffe about the neck, lesser then the other & hardly to bee got. There are almost all cocks & putt together fight & destroy each other. & prepare themselues to fight like cocks though they seeme to haue no other offensive part butt the bill. they loose theire Ruffes about the Autumne or beginning of winter as wee haue obserued keeping them in a garden from may till the next spring. They most abound in Marshland butt are also in good numbers in the marshes between norwich & yarmouth.'

Jack Snipe
Lymnocryptes minimus
The earliest dated reference we can find is by the Pagets in *Sketch of the Natural History of Yarmouth and its Neighbourhood* 1834: 9 where they write:

> 'Mr. C. Girdlestone offered a sovereign to anyone who would bring him a specimen of this bird, shot in summer. In 1822, he had one brought him in June; and in the same month, in 1824, he himself saw a pair on Bradwell common: about two years after another specimen was shot. As, perhaps, no one in the kingdom was ever more practically acquainted with these birds, his authority may be considered indubitable. Mr.Miller says he has had jack snipe's eggs brought to him; they were smaller, and more elliptical shape than those of the common snipe, which they otherwise exactly resembled.'

The Rev. Richard Lubbock in *Observations on the Natural History of Norfolk* (1845), new edition by Southwell 1879: 118-121 writes:

> 'The abundance of these sluggish little birds has no reference to the number of the Common Snipe. I find, by notes made at the time, that in October, 1824, in two day's shooting, thirty seven Snipes were killed by a friend, only five of which were "whole" Snipes; and that later in the same month, nineteen Jack Snipes were shot in one morning, and only one opportunity afforded of firing at a "whole" bird.'

Common Snipe
Gallinago gallinago
The earliest dated reference we can find is in Henry Stevenson's *The Birds of Norfolk* Vol.ll. 1870: 305-334, where he writes in a footnote:

> 'It is somewhat singular that in the L'Estrange (of Hunstanton 1519-1578)

"Household Book" snipes are but once entered, "Itm v snypys," but no price given, and they were probably too common for Sir Thomas Browne to notice them in his "List".'

Great Snipe
Gallinago media
Known to the old naturalists and gunners as the Solitary or Double Snipe, Henry Stevenson writes in *The Birds of Norfolk* Vol. ll. 1870: 299-305:

'In Mr. Hunt's "List" five examples are said to have been killed in the same week, in various parts of the county in the autumn of 1826.'

While Sheppard and Whitear write in *A Catalogue of the Norfolk and Suffolk Birds, with Remarks* 1826: 47:

'We have examined several specimens of this bird killed in Norfolk. Its legs are of a light flesh-colour, blended with a slight tinge of green. The length of its bill is subject to great variation.'

Long-billed Dowitcher
Limnodromus scolopaceus
Formally known as the Brown Snipe and Red-breasted Snipe, the first specifically identified Long-billed Dowitcher for Norfolk, a first-winter male, was shot at Horsey on 9th October 1845 by the Rev. Richard Rising of Horsey Hall.

Henry Stevenson in *The Birds of Norfolk* Vol. ll. 1870: 348-350, referring to the last of three well authenticated records of Red-breasted Snipe he knew of, writes:

'The last that I am aware of as killed in this county, which is now in Mr. Rising's collection at Horsey, was shot by himself, in his own marshes, on the 9th of October, 1845, a male bird, changing from summer to winter plumage, and which was in company with another which he did not shoot as it was raining hard at the time, and from a hurried glance at the one he had killed, he took it for nothing more than a young redshank.'

Upon Rising's death, his collection was sold on 17th September 1885, and this specimen was purchased by John Gurney for 13 guineas (£13.65), the second highest price out of the 142 lots. It was given by him, as a gift, to the Castle Museum, Norwich the same year (Accession no. NWHCM: 1885.25) and remains on display in the bird gallery.

Short-billed/Long-billed Dowitcher
Limnodromus griseus/scolopaceus
Two earlier 'well authenticated' records of Red-breasted Snipe are referred to in Henry Stevenson *The Birds of Norfolk* Vol. ll. 1870: 348-350, as follows:

'The first, killed at Yarmouth in the autumn of 1836, is described by Yarrell as in the collection of the Rev. Leonard Rudd, of Yorkshire, who forwarded the bird to London for his inspection.'

He adds in a footnote:

'This specimen is also recorded in the "*Annals of Natural History*" for 1839 (vol. iii., p. 140), by Mr. Thomas Paine, jun., of Yarmouth, who states that it "was shot on Yarmouth beach, in October, 1836, and had not completely obtained its winter plumage when procured." He had been favoured with a sight of this bird by Mr. Leonard Rudd.

He then continues:

'A second example is thus recorded by the late Mr. Hoy in the "*Annals of Natural History* for 1841 (vol. vi., p.236). "We learn from Mr. J. H. Gurney that a specimen of the red-breasted snipe was killed near Yarmouth early in October. Our informant adds that it was a male, and had nearly completed its change from summer to winter plumage." This bird, which was formerly in Mr. S. Miller's collection at Yarmouth is now in Mr. J. H. Gurney's possession…'

Interestingly, a notation in William Fisher's interleaved copy of the Pagets *Sketch of the Natural History of Yarmouth and its Neighbourhood* (1834) gives the date of the first bird as 12th October 1836.

Neither of the two specimens mentioned above could be assigned to specific species' status when Red-breasted Snipe was split into Short-billed and Long-billed Dowitcher in 1950, so must be regarded as dowitcher sp. But should one or both specimens ever gain specific recognition one or the other could become Norfolk's first Short-billed Dowitcher or Long-billed Dowitcher as both pre-date the first accepted record of a Long-billed. However, as the present whereabouts of both specimens is unknown, and it is doubtful whether they even still exist, that eventuality is unlikely.

Eurasian Woodcock
Scolopax rusticola
The earliest dated reference we can find is in Henry Stevenson's *The Birds of Norfolk* Vol. ll. 1870: 272-298:

'In the L'Estrange "Accounts," also, we find an entry in the year 1520, of three woodcocks purchased in Snettisham market for sixpence; and in 1522 of six purchased from John Long, of Ingoldisthorpe, for tenpence.'

Black-tailed Godwit
Limosa limosa
The earliest dated reference we can find is in Henry Stevenson's *The Birds of Norfolk* Vol. ll. 1870: 248-253:

'Both by Ray and Pennant, and amongst later authors by Bewick and Montagu, the name of yarwhelp or yarwhip is associated with this species, and it is no doubt the same which Sir Thomas Browne refers in a letter to Dr. Merrett (December 29th 1668), in which he asks, "have you a yarwhelp, barker, or latrator, a marsh bird about the bigness of a godwit?" and in his general list of species he remarks – "Godwyts, taken chiefly in Marsh-land; though other parts are not without them; accounted the daintiest dish in England; and, I think, for the bigness of the biggest price." In support of this statement, it may be mentioned that Pennant describes them as "taken in the fens, in the same season, with ruffs and reeves, and when fattened are esteemed a great delicacy, and sell for half-a-crown or five shillings a piece".'

He adds in a footnote:

' "Whelp Moor," near Lakenheath, probably derived its name from this species.'

Bar-tailed Godwit
Limosa lapponica
The earliest reference we can find is by Sheppard and Whitear in *A Catalogue of the Norfolk and Suffolk Birds, with Remarks* 1826: 46 where they comment:

'We have examined specimens of this bird killed in Norfolk in various states of plumage. Those met with in autumn have been in the dress of the Common Godwit of English authors: but when the individual was killed early in the spring, it was in a state of change between that bird and the Red-breasted Snipe of Montagu.'

Little Curlew (Little Whimbrel)
Numenius minutus
The first for England and only the second for Britain, almost certainly an adult, was located by Pete Antrobus, Richard J. Walker, John Gregory and Jane Whittaker in rough grazing fields between Blakeney and Cley on 24th August 1985 (Plate 11).

Richard Walker and John Gregory write:

'The coastal path which extends between Blakeney and Cley, Norfolk, runs along an elevated sea-wall which divides the mud-flats of Blakeney harbour from a series of rough grazing fields on the landward side. These fields prove particularly attractive to the less estuarine species of wader which occur on the north Norfolk coast, in particular Lapwing *Vanellus vanellus*, Golden Plover *Pluvialis apricaria*, Curlew *Numenius arquata*, and Whimbrel *N.phaeopus*.
On the afternoon of Saturday 24th August 1985, P. Antrobus, JG, RJW and E. J. Whittaker were walking along this sea-wall. At 13.45 GMT, at a point approximately equidistant between Blakeney and Cley, PA and RJW independently noticed a small brown wader flying low above the surface of one of the rough grazing fields, at a distance of about 50 m. Unsure of its identity, they alerted JG and EJW to its presence, and all four observers watched the bird through binoculars as it continued its flight across the field and alighted alongside a loose feeding-flock of Lapwings, Golden Plovers and Starlings *Sturnus vulgaris* at the far end of the field. The bird started to feed actively, occasionally flying short distances around the field, and eventually joining up with a small flock of Curlews and Whimbrels also in the field.

When first picked up in flight, it was obviously a small *Numenius*, with its streaked brown plumage and relatively long, down-curved bill. The most noticeable feature, however, was that its upperparts were wholly brown, and lacking the white rump of its more familiar congeners. It also seemed to have a paler supercilia, similar to Whimbrel, and first thoughts were that it could be a Whimbrel of the North American subspecies *N. p. hudsonicus*, which does not show a white rump – yet this individual seemed too small, and its bill too short for that possibility. When it landed, a truer impression of its size was obtained: body size it was approximately the same as, or a little smaller than the accompanying Golden Plovers, but with relatively longer bill and legs. Under closer scrutiny with telescopes, it was confirmed that the bird did have paler supercilia, and also a paler crown stripe, further emphasised by a dark line through the eye and a darker lateral crown stripe.

By now, it was apparent that it was either a Little Whimbrel *N. minutus* or – extremely unlikely as it may be – an Eskimo Curlew *N. borealis*. Good views in flight in bright sunshine revealed that its underwing was a warm buff in colour, thus eliminating Eskimo Curlew, which shows a cinnamon underwing. Convinced that it was a Little Whimbrel, a species PA, JG and RJW were all familiar with, one of the party was despatched to 'Nancy's Café' in Cley to spread the word to the many other birders in the area. The bird stayed around until dusk, feeding almost continually and occasionally flying short distances, but invariably associating with Curlews and Whimbrels, and allowing good views for the assembled crowds.

The following day, it was again seen in the same area, but later in the day it flew to Cley, where it fed for a short time in the Eye field before moving farther down the coast to Salthouse. Thereafter, it seemed to divide its time between Blakeney and Salthouse until its last reported sighting on 3rd September 1985. During its 11-day stay, it was seen by several hundred observers.

The following description is compiled from notes taken by JG and RJW:

Jizz An obvious *Numenius*, resembling small slim, short-billed Whimbrel. It appeared elegant and delicate whilst feeding, and reminiscent of Upland Sandpiper *Bartramia longicauda* due to erect carriage and 'pump-sction' mode of feeding. Marginally smaller than Golden Plover in size; bill noticeably less down-curved than Whimbrel's and proportionately shorter – estimated to be 1-1.25 times length of head.

Head Narrow buffish crown-stripe extending from base of bill onto rear of crown, bordered by dark lateral crown-stripe. Prominent creamy buff supercilium, and dark smudgy eye-stripe, barely noticeable in front of eye, but broadening slightly beyond eye and terminating on ear-coverts. Eye-stripe broken immediately before and after eye, giving appearance of thin eye-ring. Head otherwise creamy buff and unstreaked. Appeared generally pale-faced, with large, dark eye.

Upperparts Neck finely but densely streaked with brown, generally washed greyish buff. Density of streaking often caused appearance of darker, ill-defined triangle on side of neck when head held in certain position. Mantle and rump noticeably darker brown than neck, with bolder, more substantial dark streaking and mottled with buff.

Tail mid-brown, with darker, narrow, evenly spaced barring.

Wings Appeared long-winged, with black-looking primaries and long, dark tertials, broadly edged buff with prominent notchings. Scapulars dark brown edged with creamy and rufous-buff spots. Upperwing-coverts dark brown with broad buff edgings giving 'spangled' appearance. In flight, upperwing-coverts appeared as paler wing panel, this effect being emphasised by black primaries and very dark leading edge to wing. Secondaries dark brown.

Underparts Upper breast washed greyish buff, with fine, darker streakings which terminated on breast, there forming indistinct pectoral band. Remainder of underparts paler, with very faint buffish wash. Indistinct darker streaking in form of short, thin, evenly spaced bars on flanks and below carpal joint of closed wing. Undertail-coverts washed buffy grey with darker spots. Underwing-coverts warm buff, with very fine, close brown barring.

Bare Parts Bill dark brown, with pinkish basal half to lower mandible. Legs and feet pale bluish grey. Eye large and dark.

After reference to Prater *et al* (1977, *Guide to the Identification and Ageing of Holarctic Waders*), the bird was adjudged to be a juvenile, as the tertials lacked the 'tiger bars' characteristic of adults of this species, the broad buff edgings and notches being a feature of immatures. Similarly, the scapulars of an adult should show large, better-defined creamy-white spots. The bird was considered to be in fresh plumage, again indicative of a juvenile.

When the Little Whimbrel was first sighted, the weather was warm and bright, with fresh, variable (though mostly westerly) winds: conditions which had been prevalent for several days. A study or the weather maps for the middle two weeks of August 1985 suggests no obvious weather pattern which could have carried a bird whose breeding grounds are situated in Eastern Siberia and whose wintering grounds are in Eastern Indonesia to Australia, to the shores of Great Britain. When the bird was first seen to alight, its immediate and voracious feeding was suggestive of its having newly arrived following a long flight. We conjecture that the bird had just arrived from Scandinavia, having rested there for several days following a 'reverse migration' which carried it over the North Pole. Indeed, the only other reported sightings of this species in the Western Palearctic tend to suggest that the species undergoes an early migration. The first record was from Norway on 14th July 1969, whilst the only previous record for Britain and Ireland…uvenile at Sker, Mid Glamorgan, from 30th August to 6th September 1982 (*Brit. Birds* 76: 438-445) – constituted almost a carbon- copy occurrence of the Norfolk record, since both conveniently turned up over the August Bank Holiday weekend.'

'We have consulted John Marchant, whose opinion was that this individual was 'almost certainly adult'. Eds'

(Originally published in *British Birds* 80: 494-497)

On a more personal note we include John Gregory's recollections of the event, sent to us in 2007.

'Saturday 24th August 1985. As was often the case, the 'Manchester Mega Listers' were in Norfolk for the weekend. A bit of a daft name but pretty descriptive as all we did was race around the country upping our British Lists. In those days we were still getting over twenty new birds each year.

Whilst we were all avid local patchers, by August the lack of rarities in the North West was getting beyond a joke so we decided to head for Norfolk for the bank holiday weekend. The team was myself John Gregory, my girlfriend Jane, Pete Antrobus (better known as Tripod for obvious reasons) and Richard (Tufty) Walker. We left Manchester on the Friday night, managed to reach the White Horse in Blakeney for a last pint and then off to Beach Hotel (for the uninitiated – the open shelter in Cley beach car park) for a great night's sleep – not!

After some early morning birding around Cley reserve we headed for Nancy's Café and joined the queue of birders waiting for it to open and get their early morning fix of information and bread pudding. These were the pre-pager and Birdline days when you had to be either on the grapevine or phone Nancy's if you needed info. We ordered our usual 'pot of tea' for one with 5 cups, extra hot water plus 5 helpings of bread pudding. This was birder fuel! One piece of this swilled down with a cup of tea could keep you going for a week! Nancy's assistant Ethel was as friendly as usual, updating us with Cley village gossip and her plans for her forthcoming two weeks holiday to Cromer! Brilliant times.

Whilst eating we listened to the news coming in. There seemed to be a lot of wader movement around the country but nothing that would drag us away from the North Norfolk coast. We decided to head out towards Blakeney marsh with the intention of getting away from the crowds.

At around 9am we left Nancy's, drove to Marsh Lane and walked out across Blakeney fresh marsh to Blakeney bank. As we walked, we noticed big numbers of Whimbrel and Curlew on the move and we reached the bank just as another flock of mixed waders flew by. We were strung out and separated by around 100m at the time. I spotted an obvious small Whimbrel with the flock and at the same time heard Tripod shout out "What the ****'s that?" followed by "I don't know what it is but I found it!" Tufty came running over and shouted "It's got to be a Little Whimbrel or an Eskimo Curlew."

We all knew that the former was much more likely; the most optimistic assessment of the status of Eskimo Curlew was precarious. We then spent a frustrating and anxious ten minutes grilling the bird and noting its dark rump and trying to remember, if we ever knew, the difference between the two species. We knew of at least three boffins who would be able to come up with the answer on the spot but who were probably musing on tertial moult patterns over a pot of tea in Nancy's. Remember this was in the days before mobile phones so it was decided that one of us had to run to Nancy's to raise the alarm. Almost immediately Tripod's dodgy knee conveniently started to spasm and Tufty lit up three rollies simultaneously so it was left to me to run the couple of miles back.

About 20 minutes later I ran gasping into Nancy's and shouted "We've found a Little Whimbrel … but er, I suppose it could be Eskimo Curlew." Looking back, I was expecting a flurry of activity, interest and even a few pats on the back.

Instead I was confronted by one of the afore-mentioned boffins who said, simply "Well which one is it – haven't you looked for the cinnamon underwing?" I rather began to wish that the earth would open up and swallow me! Had we made a huge mistake? I was saved by the whisper getting out into Nancy's garden and a rush of birders who were only too eager and excited to see the bird. I was swept along in a wave of questions – "Where is it?", "Is there someone still with it?", "What's it doing?" and bundled into a car and driven around to Blakeney.

Thankfully, the bird had only moved a short distance. News was spreading quickly and before long most of the Norfolk residents had seen the bird and the first wave of national listers were arriving. The bird stayed put for most of that afternoon and was seen by a few hundred birders. Jane decided to phone home to give her parents the news only to overhear the chap in the phone box regaling the person at the other end of the phone with the story of how he personally had found the Little Whimbrel!

Long before dusk we were in the King's Head in Letheringsett celebrating a 'once in a lifetime' find. What had started as a quiet weekend's birding had become one of the most memorable for all of us. We drank and celebrated long into the night and laughed heartily when a young resident of the 'hotel' was ill all over Tufty's brand new (and very expensive) sleeping bag which he had recently purchased for our upcoming birding trip to Nepal. We woke to find lots of cars in the car park and Tufty angrily discussing laundry logistics with the rather pasty looking birder who was still running off to the loo every few minutes!

The first birding news that filtered through on the Sunday was that the Little Whimbrel had not been relocated. Had it dropped in for a 'dine and dash' we asked ourselves? Pretty soon, however, it showed up at Salthouse to the mass relief of the assembled twitchers. It gave itself up for most of the day and remained in the Cley area until 3rd September – since when there has not been another British record. Another blocker from the 80's and for me a kind of justice, I was in Norway at the time the first Little Whimbrel turned up at Kenfig Pool in S Wales and arrived *just* as it flew north into the Welsh Mountains, never to be seen again.'

Whimbrel

Numenius phaeopus

The earliest dated reference we can find is in Henry Stevenson's *The Birds of Norfolk* Vol. ll. 1870: 199-203, where he writes:

'The fact also that *spowes* in the L'Estrange (of Hunstanton 1519-1578) "Accounts" are nearly always mentioned in connection with other shore-birds, such as knots, ring-dotterel, redshanks, &c., all easily procurable then, as now, from Hunstanton beach, seems to confirm the impression that some grallatorial species was thus designated; and that this was no other than the whimbrel is, I think, sufficiently evident from the fact that in Iceland, Norway, Sweden and Denmark, the names "spoi," "spou," "spof," and "spove," are respectively applied either to this bird or the curlew, whilst the curlew is specially and repeatedly named in the L'Estrange accounts.'

Eurasian Curlew
Numenius arquata
The earliest dated reference we can find is by James Fisher in the Foreword to Michael Seago's *Birds of Norfolk* (1967) where he writes:

> 'We know that around the year 1200 William de Warren of Wormegay rented a holding at Lynn for curlew, teal and other wildfowl.'

Henry Stevenson writes in the *The Birds of Norfolk* Vol. ll. 1870: 194-199:

> 'In the L'Estrange (of Hunstanton 1519-1578) "Household Book" we find no less than seven entries relating to this species; in one instance a pair are received as a present; in another, two received of "gyste" (in lieu of rent.) Single Curlew are purchased at from four pence to five pence each, and on one occasion three fetched, in Snettisham Market, two shillings (the then price of a fat sheep), whilst at the same time three woodcocks were procured for sixpence. The most startling fact, however, for modern housekeepers appears as follows, in the year 1519; - "Itm pd for a goose v pence., a Pygge iij pence., ij Curlews xij pence".'

Terek Sandpiper
Xenus cinereus
One was found by Peter Allard at Breydon on 1st June 1975. Its arrival coincided with a period of very strong northerly winds and it was seen from midday until dusk feeding in a tidal creek close to the estuary wall.

Peter Allard writes from his notes taken at the time:

> 'The morning of 1st June 1975 was bitterly cold and certainly very unseasonal. There was a strong northerly airflow, a little snow had fallen and real birding was being questioned. However an early morning visit to the Winterton and Horsey area from before 06.00hrs proved extremely productive with both male Red-backed Shrike and Golden Oriole seen and a ring-tail Montagu's Harrier in the dunes area. Also of great interest was a late Hooded Crow together with a very strong northerly passage of Turtle Doves. From 06.00hrs and for the next three hours, an amazing total of 569 were logged moving along the sandhills. An excellent start to the day, however, little did I realize that much better was still to come.
> I left the Winterton area around midday and then visited the eastern end of Breydon Water having previously realized the tide was reaching its peak around early afternoon. Walking along from Vauxhall Station to where the lower drain curves around by the north wall, I began to scan around at the distant waders on the tideline. Noting 27 Grey Plovers, 2 Greenshank, a single Bar-tailed Godwit, 6 Knot and a scattering of Oystercatchers in the lumps area, the smaller waders had already begun creeping in towards me at the base of the flood wall approximately half-a-mile away from the town. Most, as expected, were Dunlins and at least 120 Ringed Plovers were present, a very good total considering it was now June. Then I had the shock of my life, at approximately 13.30hrs a slightly larger wader suddenly appeared from nowhere along the edge of the drain and it was immedi-

ately apparent that it was something unusual. Once I had trained my telescope on it, it was quickly identified as a Terek Sandpiper, a wader not previously recorded in Norfolk. The most striking feature was the long, thin and upturned bill, especially curved more towards the tip. However, at this vital moment, a passing train put the bird to flight and the Terek moved further west along the drain to join a flock of Dunlin. With great excitement, I began creeping along the flood wall. With luck and perhaps a bit of skill, I managed to obtain views of this exciting wader down to approximately 30 yards and hastily noted all the rest of its features including the yellow legs which had a slight hint of orange in the sunlight. Its size was obviously larger than the Dunlin close by and it was considered to be slightly larger than a Curlew Sandpiper. It had a very similar wing pattern in flight to a Redshank, but the impression that I had of it on the ground was of a very miniature Greenshank. The underparts were whitish with slight streaking noted on the breast and it had a very slight trace of an eyestripe on a very streaky head. The upperparts were noted as mottled brownish-grey with a very distinctive black line at the bend of the wing. There was also another less distinctive blackish streak on the mantle noted at various angles as it fed actively amongst the salting creeks. In flight, the very pale rump and tail were obvious and it was heard to call on several occasions, the flight notes being described in my note book at the time as a quiet trill.

It was now very obvious to me that news of this great rarity needed to be quickly spread and a hasty run back along the flood wall to Great Yarmouth was required. Several 'fluttered' phone calls were made, from the red phone box at Vauxhall Station, to various local birders. By the time I had returned to the area in question, the tide had risen considerably and all the waders had now retired to the lumps high tide roost to await the turn of the tide. Within what semed a very short space of time, both Terry Boulton and Michael Seago had arrived on the scene and we all began to scan for the Terek through the viewable waders. Within minutes and with a great bit of luck, it reappeared out of nowhere feeding by itself on the eastern side of the nearest saltings. For the next hour or so it showed well despite being very active, feeding with vigour and had possibly only recently arrived. The light conditions were excellent now and it gave perfect views to a small, but ever increasing number of out of puff birders for the rest of the afternoon and early evening. These included Don Dorling, Dave Holman, Rod Martins, Giles Dunmore and John Eaton amongst others. During the late afternoon and evening and with the tide ebbing, it moved back along the north wall to where it was first located, but was still giving excellent views to the chasing pack. It was looked for the following morning and briefly claimed, however the observers in question later withdrew this claim and it appeared to have left overnight.

This was the first record of Terek Sandpiper for Norfolk and was at the time believed to be only the 11th for Great Britain. The second for Norfolk was to follow very shortly with one turning up at Cley on July 2nd, which remained there for three days. Some will suggest that it was the same individual, but we shall never know. I was very fortunate however to find a third individual at Breydon on 5th July 1978, but as with the first bird, its stay was all too brief and it disappeared overnight. Breydon Water at the moment remains the place for Terek Sandpipers to be seen in the county with four of the present 11 county records being noted there.'

Common Sandpiper
Actitis hypoleucos
Not mentioned by Sir Thomas Browne (1605-1682) in *Notes and Letters on the Natural History of Norfolk* (1902) and although included by Sheppard and Whitear, under Summer Snipe, in *A Catalogue of the Norfolk and Suffolk Birds, with Remarks* (1826), they give no Norfolk reference. The earliest reference we can find is by the Pagets in *Sketch of the Natural History of Yarmouth and its Neighbourhood* 1834: 8 where they considered it '…common'.

Spotted Sandpiper
Actitis macularius
An adult in summer plumage was found by Billy Bishop at Cley on 7th June 1957, and it was also present on the 8th.

Billy Bishop writes in *Cley Marsh and its Birds* 1983: 49-50.

'…in 1957, again on my daily walk around the Reserve, I flushed a small wader that appeared to be, and had the call of, a common sandpiper. A little later I again saw this bird as it settled on the edge of a marshy pool. I was immediately struck by the fact that it had large, round, blackish spots on the breast and flanks, also that it showed a conspicuous white eye stripe. The legs were a dull straw colour and the proximal part of the bill was a dull orange, while the distal portion was a very dark brown. In flight the wing pattern did not appear to differ appreciably from that of a common sandpiper. I got a tremendous thrill when I realised I was looking at a spotted sandpiper in summer plumage, an American visitor and the first recorded for Norfolk.'

On page 82 of the book the date is given as the 5th, presumably a misprint, which was not corrected in the 1996 edition.

Interestingly, Gurney and Fisher mention an earlier record in 'An Account of the Birds found in Norfolk' published in the *Zoologist* 1846: 1324:

'An example was killed at Runton near Cromer, September 26th 1839, the only instance we know of the occurrence of this species in Norfolk.'

Green Sandpiper
Tringa ochropus
The earliest reference we can find is by Sheppard and Whitear in *A Catalogue of the Norfolk and Suffolk Birds, with Remarks* 1826: 45 where they comment:

'It is seen in these counties throughout the winter.'

The Pagets in *Sketch of the Natural History of Yarmouth and its Neighbourhood* 1834: 8 considered it '…not uncommon.'

Solitary Sandpiper
Tringa solitaria

The first of just two county occurrences was seen by Jim Vincent at Rush Hills, Hickling Broad on 1st-2nd August 1942.

Jim Vincent writes:

> 'On August 1st, 1942, at Rush Hills, which is being fed down by cattle, a sandpiper rose and flew a short distance and alighted on an old heap of rushes in the water. Here it stood bobbing its tail up and down. There was no white on the rump, and in flight the bird was not so dark as a Green Sandpiper, but darker than a Wood Sandpiper.
>
> It also looked smaller than a Green Sandpiper. I found the bird again near the same spot on the following day and with glasses was able to make a close observation as it was remarkably tame, and flew only short distances. Its size, appearance and habits answered the description of the Solitary Sandpiper as given in the *Handbook*.'

(Originally published in *British Birds* 36: 96-97)

It does seem rather surprising that such a major rarity as the Solitary Sandpiper should gain acceptance as the first Norfolk record on the somewhat brief account above, but at the present time that is the case.

Perhaps the second occurrence has a case for elevation to the status of first fully authenticated county record.

It was first seen by Billy Bishop at Cley on 3rd September 1947 and remained in the Cley/Salthouse area until the 29th.

T. Hedley Bell, C. K. James, G. W. Rayner and C. C. Rose (the "undersigned observers" referred to in the account below) sent in particulars to *British Birds* from which the following account was compiled:

> 'For almost the whole of September, 1947, a Solitary Sandpiper (*Tringa solaria*) frequented the Cley and Salthouse marshes, but especially the latter, and was seen by the undersigned observers, from whose notes the following particulars have been drawn up by the Editor.
>
> The bird was first seen by the watcher, Mr. W. F. Bishop, on September 3rd. The most complete particulars were obtained by Mr. and Mrs. C. C. Rose and Miss C. K. James on September 6th, when it was watched for about 20 minutes in an excellent light at a range of about 10-15 yards, and the same observers had a briefer view on September 7th. A good view in sunlight with x12 binoculars at about 80 yards range was also obtained by T. H. Bell on September 29th, while G. W. Rayner had a somewhat brief but valuable view on September 12th, when the bird pitched quite close to him, displaying the under-wing and axillaries, as described below.
>
> The bird was noticeably slender and elegant and the size was noted as about that of a Wood Sandpiper (*Tringa glareola*) (G.W.R., T.H.B.) or rather smaller

than a Green Sandpiper (*T. achropus*) (C.C.R., C.J.K.). The crown, nape and back were noted by C. C. R. and C. K. J. as dark olive-green patterned with white, the rump being dark like the back instead of white as in a Green Sandpiper. At longer range these parts appeared dark mottled-brown to T. H. B. The throat and breast were buffish (with darker streaks: C.C.R., C.K.J.) and the rest of the under-parts white. The darker centre of the tail was seen by all the observers and the white lateral tail-feathers with dark bars were clearly seen by C. C. R. and C. K. J. The bill was black with whitish feathering at the base and the legs were noted as pale yellowish (T.H.B.) and by G. W. R. as "light", though C. C. R. noted them as appearing dark green.

The flight was fast and irregular and the bird landed abruptly (C.C.R., C.K.J.). On September 12th it was put up by G. W. R., when he was walking along East Bank, and suddenly pitched again only some 10-15 yards away. On alighting it stretched its wings above its head, displaying their black underside and the axillaries strikingly barred with black and white. It stood momentarily thus before tripping out of sight and was not seen again.

When watched by T. H. B. it was on partially flooded ground with numerous islets of green vegetation and it spent its time feeding along the borders of these islets. When observed by C. C. R. and C. K. J. it was feeding at the edge of, and occasionally just within, reeds at the side of a pool.

The bird was also seen by Mrs. R. F. Meiklejohn and Miss D. Steinthal on September 8th, by the same observers and Col. Meiklejohn on the 11th, and independently on September 8th by E. C. Arnold and R. H. Higgins. Particulars supplied to *British Birds* show that less adequate views were obtained than those described above, but the distinctive features of the dark rump and centre of tail and light outer-tail feathers were observed and Mr. Arnold noted the call as one which was new to him and sounded like "peet-weet". None of the undersigned heard any call-note.'

(Originally published in *British Birds* 41: 354-355)

Spotted Redshank
Tringa erythropus
One was shot near Yarmouth on 29th October 1818.

Henry Stevenson writes in *The Birds of Norfolk* Vol. ll. 1870: 203-207:

'Under the name of the Cambridge godwit, in Sir W. Hooker's MS., I find the first notice of the occurrence of this species in Norfolk, a specimen shot near Yarmouth, on the 29th October, 1818.'

Interestingly, Sheppard and Whitear (1826) knew this species as the Spotted Snipe.

Greater Yellowlegs
Tringa melanoleuca
A first-winter was found by Peter Allard at Breydon on 8th September 1975.

Peter Allard writes from his notes taken at the time:

'September is usually one of the best months for wader watching at Breydon Water especially as this is typically the best time for juveniles to make their first appearances. Following a period of north-easterlies, the morning of 8th September 1975 saw the first westerly winds for several days. The early morning weather was fine and mild and the light conditions were excellent, the forecast for the rest of the day remained reasonable. I visited Breydon Water before planning a trip to Winterton Dunes to see the three Dotterel that I had seen there the previous day. With a rising tide forcing waders towards the eastern end of the estuary, I made my usual way towards one of the hides about a mile from the railway station. When alongside what locals call the Lower Drain, an unidentified largish wader took flight with a Greenshank at around 09.30hrs and headed south low over the mudflats. The wader was unknown to me, but the lack of any wing bar, a white square-cut rump which did not extend up the back and the noticeable yellow-orange legs trailing out as it flew gave it a distinctly yellowlegs feel. The large size, noted as fractionally larger than Greenshank gave further consideration to it being a Greater Yellowlegs. Unfortunately, the bird had flown out of sight right across the entire length of the north flats and put down somewhere near the entrance to the Five Stake Drain close to the main navigation channel.

Rushing back to a vantage point that overlooked this area, the bird was luckily relocated feeding alongside the main channel, head down and rushing through the shallow water at speed for about five or six strides before stopping. With the aid of my telescope, the very long distinctive yellowy-orange legs were most obvious even at this range. The mantle colouration was quite dark with slight streaking on the flanks. The head and crown were additionally dark with a slight pale eye stripe and the breast was noted as greyish becoming paler on the under-parts. The dark coloured bill appeared straight and was adjudged to be slightly longer than that of a Greenshank, one of which was not too far away. The bird itself was again considered slightly larger than a Greenshank, but with a slightly smaller head and having a thinner neck, its appearance was unlike that of its feeding neighbour. It flew a short distance on one occasion revealing again the square-cut white rump, dark back and the lack of any wing bar confirming in my mind that this was indeed a Greater Yellowlegs. At least 20 minutes were spent scribbling down a detailed description of this bird whilst at the same time trying to convince myself that another great rarity had been found at Breydon Water.

Rushing the now shorter distance back to Vauxhall railway station, phone calls were made to several local birders asking if possible they could come straight away. First on the scene was Terry Boulton, but by the time he had arrived, the tide had risen considerably and most of the mudflats had been covered, with the waders mostly asleep on the saltings. However, it was soon rediscovered quite by chance asleep with a party of Redshanks where it remained for over an hour. Giles Dunmore was the second person to arrive in the early afternoon, and after some initial views of it asleep, it began to feed along the edge of the main channel giving reasonable views for the three of us using our telescopes. There was no doubt by now as to its identification, it was a Greater Yellowlegs, a first for Norfolk for this very scarce American wader. It had unfortunately disappeared by the time Adrian Boote arrived, but thinking that it may still be somewhere in the Five Stake Drain area, we decided to view from the south bank of the estu-ary. This worked well as we soon had reasonable views as it fed once more along the far edge of the main channel, but had not expected that it would fly straight towards us and land within a few feet of where we had positioned ourselves. Its stay was brief, however, and it soon relocated back to its favoured feeding area.

The Greater Yellowlegs was still present the following day and it was now being realized that it favoured the Lower Drain area at low tide close to the north bank of Breydon Water. News of its arrival had obviously spread quickly overnight and some 40 or so birders had already gathered on the bank to view this Yankee vagrant. It proved very obliging in this particular drain area before it flew away in a north-westerly direction at high tide calling. This was the first time that I had heard it call, a very mellow call similar to that of a Greenshank, though perhaps not quite so loud. It returned as the tide receded, much to the delight of the expectant crowd that had increased considerably awaiting its return. This was to be the pattern during its six- day stay, feeding at low tide in the Lower Drain area and roosting somewhere to the north-west along the lower Bure marshes at high tide. It proved very popular during the duration of its visit, it was only the 12th British record and was last seen by Don Dorling, I believe, at the entrance to the Lower Drain late in the evening of September 13th. There was no sign of it on the morning of Saturday the 14th, but the weather had changed considerably by now and we were once again in a north-easterly wind pattern which provided the freshly arrived disappointed week-end birders with a chance of sea-watching and some Scandinavian migrants in the coastal bushes.'

Common Greenshank

Tringa nebularia

The earliest references we can find are by Sheppard and Whitear in *A Catalogue of the Norfolk and Suffolk Birds, with Remarks* (1826) where they just record its presence with no comments, and by the Pagets in *Sketch of the Natural History of Yarmouth and its Neighbourhood* 1834: 8 where they considered it:

'…not uncommon with the common godwit.'

Lesser Yellowlegs

Tringa flavipes

One was located at Wisbech Sewage Farm by M. Densley, Arthur Jenkins and W. J. Lloyd on 17th September 1966.

M. Densley writes:

'When first seen by M. Densley it was in the company of several Dunlin. The most striking feature of the bird was the rich pale ochre legs (much the same colour as Lesser Black-backed Gull). Strongly resembling Redshank in size and proportions, it appeared slimmer, which gave the bird a more "leggy" look, although the legs were probably proportionately the same as that species. The dark bill was also similar to Redshank, but had a suggestion of uptilting. Mantle and upperparts were medium-brown with a strong flecking similar to Wood Sandpiper. A faint pale eye-stripe was noted.

In flight the upper wing surfaces showed as a uniform darkish brown, this colour extended across back leaving only the rump and tail as a very pale grey.

Some slight barring was noticed on the tail.

Later M. T. Barnes was able to watch the bird for the best part of an hour. His description differs from the above inasmuch as he considered the bird smaller bodied than Redshank with longer yellow legs. The underparts were white apart from some streaks on the throat, breast and along flanks. Fed off surface rather than probing. In flight the shape resembled Spotted Redshank.'

(Originally published in the Cambridgeshire Bird Club Report 1966: 31)

Marsh Sandpiper
Tringa stagnatilis
One was found at Blakeney on 20th September 1964.

T. Hedley Bell writes:

'On 20th September 1964 between 6.00 p.m. and 6.30 p.m. in brilliant sunshine I took a stroll down the east side of the Blakeney Channel towards the estuary for the purpose of watching waders being driven up the estuary by a fast flowing incoming tide. At the point where the Cley Channel opens into the estuary a man who was a stranger to me asked me to help him identify a wader on the far side of the Channel about 50 yards away.

The bird was slightly smaller than a Redshank, of which one or two were in the vicinity for comparison, but it was very much more graceful and less robust and was walking to and fro with a rapid gait in a horizontal position picking insects or seeds off the surface of the water at the edge of a large area of spartina marsh. The most striking features were the general paleness of the whole of the body, the small head and slim neck. The forehead, sides of the face, the front of the neck and the whole of the underparts were pure white, except for a short darkish line through the eye. The crown, back of the neck, and upperparts were a pale brownish grey giving a speckled effect. The bill was very slim, straight and dark, probably black, and appeared to be slightly longer than the length of the head from front to back. The legs were long for the size of the bird and were greenish. As the tide came in the bird presently flew low down a few yards further into the marsh in a direct line from where I was, thus giving an excellent view of the flight pattern. In flight the primaries showed up to be rather darker and there was no wing bar. The back, rump and upper tail coverts were all white except for some faint markings towards the end of the tail. As the bird was flying directly away from me it was not possible to see the extent to which the legs and feet extended beyond the tail.

The bird did not call when it rose.

I have no doubt in my own mind that the bird was a Marsh Sandpiper, and this appears to be the first record for the area as the species is not listed in "The Check-list of the Birds of Cley and neighbouring parishes" (Richardson: 1962).'

(An account extracted from the unpublished files in the British Birds Rarities Committee archive)

This record was accepted by British Birds Rarities Committee and appeared in *British*

Birds 58: 361. However, the record was considered unacceptable by the Norfolk Bird Report Editorial Committee and was not published in the 1964 Report. Both Richard Richardson (who apparently saw the bird) and Michael Seago (editor of the Report) considered it to be a Wood Sandpiper. It was later re-considered by the County Records Committee and the earlier decision upheld. For reasons unknown to the authors of this book the BBRC was only recently informed of this local decision. However, to have the record re-considered by them would require new information, and as Richard and Michael are no longer alive and their diaries fail to mention the occurrence, it is very unlikely that the BBRC decision will be overturned. Interestingly, the BBRC originally rejected the record on the grounds that Wilson's Phalarope had not been ruled out, but re-considered and accepted it after further communication with T. Hedley Bell.

Although the record remains a national one, it is not included in Norfolk's records at the present time. However, following recent developments, this record is being re-considered by the Norfolk Rarities Committee, who probably acted outside their remit in rejecting a nationally accepted record. It remains to be seen if it is finally accepted as the first county occurrence when the Norfolk Rarities Committee meet later this year. The authors of this book feel that the record should be unequivocally considered the first for the county.

T. Hedley Bell died recently. He was a widely experienced birder and one time Chairman of Manchester Ornithological Society, joint editor of the Cheshire Bird Report and the author of *The Birds of Cheshire* (1962). He was also instrumental in the Solitary Sandpiper at Cley in 1947 gaining acceptance.

Because of Norfolk's refusal to accept the above occurrence, a bird found by Dave Farrow at Cley on 14th August 1979, where it remained until the 19th, has for almost 30 years been considered the first Norfolk record and we include the account here.

Dave Farrow writes from his recollections and notes taken at the time:

'This story really begins on 13th August 1979. School summer holidays, a rich and luxurious time of daily birding, exploration, and most importantly, no school! On the morning of the 13th I made a very early morning twitch to Hickling Broad, driven by my good friend and 'primary lift-provider' Richard Drew, to see our first ever Great White Egret. At 5am the bird kindly gave us a great view in a fly past, and then we zoomed back home to Watford for the start of the working day. On arriving home, a large and exciting-looking parcel was waiting for me. My new Bins! A beautiful pair of Zeiss Jena Jenoptem 10x50s, complete with 'new binocular smell', far superior to the 8x30s I had been using. A stroll round the local patch followed almost immediately, but I decided I had to give them a proper field test, so where better to do that than North Norfolk.

The following morning I hitch-hiked the 140 miles to Cley, arriving around lunchtime, and walked into Daukes hide. I settled in, scanning the migrant waders. The birds sparkled with clarity through the new optics; Greenshanks, Spotted Redshanks, Whimbrels flying over, Little Stint, Ruff, a rather pale looking Ruff... a very skinny pale-looking Ruff, a very skinny pale-looking Ruff with a very thin bill... Er, that's not a Ruff! Nor is it a Greenshank, though with similar whites and olive-greens. It looks rather like a miniature Black-winged Stilt! Heart racing, sweat dripping onto the eyepieces of the new bins... That must be a Marsh Sandpiper! I watched it further, as it elegantly waded about, set about sketching and scribbling notes, and it drifted out of sight behind one of the islands. At this point I decided to inform the rest of the hide.

"Excuse me, there's a Marsh Sandpiper over there!"

There was a slight movement in my direction, people peering out.

"Where is it then?"

"Oh, it's just gone behind that island"

"Well I can't see one, you are probably looking at a Ruff, young man"

"Oh no I'm not, it's definitely a Marsh Sand! It's all pale and skinny with a really thin bill"

"Or perhaps a Spotted Redshank, they are quite pale"

"No, this has greenish-ochre coloured legs"

"Well perhaps it's a…"

"There it is, coming out now"

Silence, as the bird revealed itself, and realisation dawned.

"Well you appear to be correct! Well spotted!".'

Interestingly, Jim Vincent, the head keeper of the Hickling Estate, writes in his personal interleaved copy of *The Hand-List of British Birds* (Witherby *et al* 1912), now owned by Moss Taylor, alongside Marsh Sandpiper:

'I saw a bird of this species with two other persons on the mud hovers known as Warbush. The bird was very tame. I flushed it and it flew away soon returning to the same place. It was like a small Greenshank.'

No date is given but the handwriting is very similar to the Little Ringed Plover sighting, which would put this record circa 1920.

Wood Sandpiper
Tringa glareola
Two or three were obtained at Yarmouth in 1829.

Churchill Babington in *Catalogue of the Birds of Suffolk* 1884-1886: 132-133 states:

'…two or three killed near Yarmouth 1829, one in the possession of Mr. Girdlestone (Hunt, *Stacey's History of Norfolk* p. 68).'

The Pagets also refer to this species as the Long-legged Sandpiper in *Sketch of the Natural History of Yarmouth and its Neighbourhood* 1834: 8 where they state:

'…a pair shot in the spring of 1833.'

Originally not distinguished from Green Sandpiper *Tringa ochropous* and not referenced in Tunstall's List, Wood Sandpiper was first described in Pennant's *Arctic Zoology* (1784f.) and included in Latham's Synopsis shortly afterwards, though it was not considered British at the time. Montagu's *Dictionary* (1802) distinguishes the two passage migrants, arguing that one of them is either Pennant's *glareola* or a new species. One supposes that only those who read Montagu's *Dictionary* closely would have been on the look out – this may explain why it took another generation before a Norfolk specimen was identified.

Separation of the two species probably occurred in Scandinavia since Pennant seems to have followed Linnaeas. Pennant, therefore, appears to be the first British writer to refer to Wood Sandpiper and may very well be responsible for the English name (J Gaskell *in litt*).

Common Redshank
Tringa totanus
The earliest dated reference we can find is in Henry Stevenson's *The Birds of Norfolk* Vol. ll. 1870: 207-215:

> 'As an article for the table, the redshank is of but little repute at the present day, being sold by the gunners for about two shillings a dozen; and even Sir Thomas Browne alludes to it as "of common food, but non dainty dish." The numerous entries, however, of this species, in the L'Estrange accounts [1519 - 1578], together with plovers, spowes, and other shore-birds, show that they were generally eaten at that time…'

Ruddy Turnstone
Arenaria interpres
Previously known as the Sea Dotterel the earliest dated reference we can find is by Sir Thomas Browne in a letter to Merrett dated February 6th [1668-9] in *Notes and Letters on the Natural History of Norfolk* 1902: 76 where he writes referring to a drawing:

> 'A draught of the morinellus marinus or sea doterell I now send you. the bill should not have been so black & the leggs more red, a greater eye of dark red in the feathers of wing and back: it is lesse & differently colourd from the common dotterel, wch cometh to us about March & September. these sea-dotterells are often shot near the sea.'

Thomas Southwell adds in a footnote:

> 'The Sea Dotterel which Wilkin supposes to be the Ring Plover, is undoubtedly the Turnstone. Willughby says, "Our honoured Friend, Sir Thomas Browne, of Norwich, sent us the picture of this bird by the title of the Sea Dotterel." This is also mentioned in the fifth letter to Merrett.'

Wilson's Phalarope
Phalaropus tricolor
One was discovered at Wisbech Sewage Farm by John Moyes and S. Greenwood on 28th September 1967.

John Moyes writes:

> 'First noted on Sept. 28th feeding on hardened mud and picking vigorously from side to side "shank" like. In sunlight at any distance looked very pale grey with black primaries and pale orange legs. The following day another individual was present on the farm which was both smaller and darker than the first bird. The two were seen together from Oct. 2nd-18th, the smaller individual remaining

until Nov. 4th. On size and plumage differences these were considered to be male and female.

Whilst together the two birds established a feeding routine of walking in file in sticky mud at the margins of shallow pools picking from the surface with rapid bill actions. As well as spinning in typical phalarope fashion on water they often performed a similar action on dry land. Often noted feeding with head completely submerged whilst swimming and were frequently observed bill-sweeping like Avocets in shallow muddy water. On occasions were seen to snatch insects out of the air.

Flew with fairly leisurely wing-beats showing no obvious wing-bars, although secondary coverts were edged white. Looked very pale in flight, with grey wings and tail and dull white rump. Tips of feet projected beyond tail.

The larger bird, well over 9 inches, was presumably a male. The crown, nape and hind-neck were grey, the back a grey-brown with white edges to scapulars and secondary coverts. Primaries were very dark grey-brown. The chin, forehead, breast, flanks and belly were silvery-white, although the flanks of the male were suffused grey. Dark line through the eye with grey band extending down from this on sides of neck and on to the scapulars. The black bill was 1.5 times the length of the head and was very fine and straight. Legs were orange yellow in female and yellow ochre in male and were noticeably thick for size of body.'

(Originally published in Cambridge Bird Club Report 1967: 33)

Interestingly, although this species was only added to the British List as recently as 1954, the two Wisbech Sewage Farm birds were part of an influx of at least nine Wilson's Phalaropes identified in Britain and Ireland in 1967. Both were photographed by Dick Bagnall-Oakeley and appeared opposite page 198 in the *Norfolk Bird Report* 1967.

Red-necked Phalarope

Phalaropus lobatus
The first Norfolk record appears to be one killed in winter plumage at Breydon in 1824.

Henry Stevenson writes in *The Birds of Norfolk* Vol. ll. 1870: 439-443:

'About Yarmouth, even as far back as 1834, they were described by Messrs. Paget as "very rare," although Mr Miller possessed a pair – one in winter and one in summer plumage – the former possibly the same mentioned in Sir William Hooker's MS. notes as killed on Breydon in the winter if 1824, but this species is not mentioned by Messrs. Sheppard and Whitear.'

The Mr. Miller mentioned above was Stephen Miller, an enthusiastic collector of rare birds who resided in Southtown, Great Yarmouth. His celebrated collection was sold by auction in 74 lots at Yarmouth in September, 1853, but the bad state of preservation of many of the specimens rendered them of little value.

The stepmother of celebrated Yarmouth naturalist Arthur H. Patterson cleaned Miller's collection for him when she worked as a domestic in Miller's service, interesting the young Patterson greatly by her "quaint descriptions of the birds whose cases she used to dust"

(Patterson 1905).

Perhaps a bird shot at Scoulton Mere in August 1829 should be considered the first definite record of this species in Norfolk. It was in Henry Stevenson's possession and sold as Lot 164 in the sale of his collection on 12th September 1887. The reason for the sale, as given in the catalogue, was 'a change of residence'. Stevenson died less than one year later in August 1888.

Red (Grey) Phalarope
Phalaropus fulicarius
The earliest dated reference we can find is eight or nine near Yarmouth in the winter of 1828.

The Pagets in *Sketch of the Natural History of Yarmouth and its Neighbourhood* 1834: 9 state:

'…rather rare; eight or nine [killed] in the winter of 1828.'

Pomarine Jaeger (Skua)
Stercorarius pomarinus
An immature was taken at Northrepps in October 1822.

Thomas Southwell writes in Henry Stevenson's *The Birds of Norfolk* Vol. lll. 1890: 348-353:

'The first in point of date would be the original of a large coloured drawing by Miss Anna Gurney, now at Northrepps, of an immature specimen, which was taken at that place in October, 1822; the bird itself was not preserved.'

Parasitic Jaeger (Arctic Skua)
Stercorarius parasiticus
The earliest dated reference we can find is in Sheppard and Whitear's *A Catalogue of the Norfolk and Suffolk Birds, with Remarks* 1826: 54:

'We are informed by Joseph Sabine, Esq. that he procured a young Arctic Gull, killed on a rabbit-warren near Brandon the beginning of October 1819. In the same month another bird of this species was shot at Yarmouth.'

Thomas Southwell writes in Henry Stevenson's *The Birds of Norfolk* Vol. lll. 1890: 353-357:

' In Whitear's "*Calendar*," as printed in the "*Trans. Of the Norfolk and Norwich Nat. Society*" (iii., p. 250), under date of 26th September 1819, occurs the following entry: - "I am informed by Mr. Sabine that he procured a young arctic gull on a warren, near Brandon (Suffolk), the beginning of this month. About the same time an old bird of the same species was killed at Yarmouth, and is now in the possession of Hunt. N.B. The weather was mild at the time. "Mr. Youell informs me that about a week since a young arctic gull, answering to the black-toed gull of Latham, was killed at Yarmouth." These specimens are also mentioned in the "*Catalogue of Norfolk and Suffolk Birds*." In his "*List*" Hunt says, "this species is extremely rare (probably meaning in the adult state): - Girdle-stone, Esq., some few years ago sent the writer of this a specimen alive, which is now in his collection." This may possibly have been the adult bird which Mr.

Whitear says was "killed" at Yarmouth and was given to Hunt.'

Long-tailed Jaeger (Skua)
Stercorarius longicaudus
The earliest reference we can find is by Gurney and Fisher in 'An Account of the Birds Found in Norfolk' published in the *Zoologist* 1846: 1384 where they write:

> 'The young bird not infrequently occurs in autumn.'

However, the first reliable and dated record was of an immature found dead at Hockham, in the Brecks, in September 1847.

Thomas Southwell writes in Henry Stevenson's *The Birds of Norfolk* Vol. lll. 1890: 357-359, under Buffon's Skua:

> 'Perhaps the first reliable record of the occurrence of this species in Norfolk is to be found in a communication from Professor Newton to the "*Zoologist*," p. 2149, where he states that in September, 1847, an immature specimen was found dead at Hockham.'

Great Skua
Stercorarius skua
The earliest dated reference we can find is by Sir Thomas Browne (1605-1682) in *Notes and Letters on the Natural History of Norfolk* 1902: 8:

> 'In hard winters I have also met with that large & strong billd fowle wch clusius describeth by the name of Skua Hoyeri sent him from the faro Island by Hoierus a physitian. one whereof was shot at Hickling while 2 thereof were feeding upon a dead horse.'

Thomas Southwell adds a footnote:

> 'Willughby ("Ornithology," English Ed., p. 348) gives a good description of the Great Skua (*Stercorarius catarrhactes*) under the name of *Catarracta*, a skin of which he says was sent him by Dr. Walter Needham, and rightly identified it with the Skua which Hoier sent to Clusius, but his figure is evidently drawn from a skin of the Great Black-backed Gull. Hoier, whose name so often occurs about this time in connection with birds from the north, was a physician, living at Bergen in Norway. The Great Skua still breeds in sadly reduced numbers on the Shetland and Faroe Islands, but is rarely met with in Norfolk.'

Ivory Gull
Pagophila eburnea
A first-winter bird was found at Brancaster on 5th January 1978 by Kevin and Jean Gaffney, who, unsure of what species of gull they had found, called at Peter and Margaret Clarke's house in Holme village to ask their assistance in identifying it. Peter and Margaret returned to Brancaster with them and identified the bird as an Ivory Gull. It remained in the Brancaster/ Burnham Overy and Holkham area until 9th January. It frequently fed on an almost totally

buried dead seal on the beach, as well as on other tideline corpses and allowed a close approach by those observers fortunate enough to see it.

Margaret Clarke writes:

'A flush of pink sunlight tinted an otherwise lifeless grey sky as we rounded Brancaster beach-gap and followed the shore eastwards in the direction of Scolt Head. At first glance life seemed minimal, but when we scanned the distant tide-line, what was at first thought to be a white polythene sack suddenly raised its head and entered, so to speak, the land of the living. Was it perhaps some sort of snowy-white carrier pigeon? We soon saw that the reason for the bird's intent stillness was the appeasement of hunger, for underneath its tearing beak gleamed the iridescent head of a drake mallard, and though we were now within 40 yards of our quarry, mere human presence would not, as yet, induce this strange bird to leave its succulent breakfast.

On the ground it did indeed resemble a carrier pigeon, and boasting a thick horn-coloured beak was quite unlike any other sea bird of our acquaintance. Its legs were black and comically short, while the feet were webbed and splayed out flatly, suggesting a stout strength. The snow whiteness of the plumage was relieved only by measly black dots on the back and tail, and a crow-dark bill which merged into a smudge of dark feathering around the eye and under the chin; in short it looked like a very white bird which had recently had its head tipped, a quarter way only, into a bottle of ink!

We advanced a few steps nearer, and were soon able to identify it as an immature Ivory Gull, a bird of the most northerly Arctic ice-packs and a species never before recorded in Norfolk. Eventually, it became aware of our unacceptably close presence and flew about 100 yards to the west, where it instantly began to feast on the half-eaten corpse of a small wader, which was a poor sort of exchange for a mallard. The gull thought so too for on the homeward walk when we necessarily disturbed it a second time, it quickly sailed back again to its more substantial meal of wild duck.

In flight the startling whiteness of the feathers was even more apparent than on the tideline, though the outspread tail and wing-quills were delicately tipped with a row of black dots like the edge of a butterfly's wing. Two or three times it soared almost vertically into the grey wintry sky, keeled over for a brief second, and then gently swooped down again to the carrion on the tideline. Buoyant and tern-like, it flew as if borne on invisible air currents. Only on the shore, supported by those inadequate legs, did it appear dumpy and somewhat clumsy.

Unfortunately this stranger's stay in Norfolk was short-lived. It was last observed on January 9th on the beach by Gun Hill before heading eastwards. Within 48 hours gale-force winds suddenly sprang up producing a wild night with heavy rain.'

(An account published in the *Norfolk Bird Report* 1978: 6-7)

Although he didn't initially find and identify the Ivory Gull, credit for the acceptance of this record should go to Ray Kimber, who was the Brancaster Golf Club professional at the time, as he was apparently the only observer to submit details of this record to BBRC.

Ray Kimber writes:

'The Ivory Gull was first seen at lunchtime on 5th January 1978 feeding on a dead drake Mallard, and again on the 6th in the same place feeding on the Mallard, a Knot and a Black-headed Gull. It was feeding in the same place on the 7th but on the 8th an early morning high tide had washed the dead birds off the beach and Mick Ramsay found it searching along the tide line in thick fog. On the 9th it was feeding on a dead seal near the golf clubhouse and by 11.00 it had gone from our beach.

Description:- Bill grey, fairly short and dagger-shaped with a yellowish tip. Gape dull pink. Head basically white with a few grey smudges on the crown. The area between the bill and eyes and under the chin was dark grey, looking black in flight. Back white with a few black flecks. Breast and underparts were pure white. Wings white with small black tips to the primaries and with pale grey marks on the leading edge near angle of wing. Tail was rather short and white with small black tips to each feather. Legs were short and black.

It looked like a large white pigeon at a distance due to its stocky body, short legs and rolling walk. Flight was light and easy, on quite broad-looking wings. The wings reached beyond the tail at rest giving a pointed look to its rear end. It did not consort with the other gulls and the only bird to go near it was a Common Gull, which drove it away from the Knot it was feeding on. It was a little longer but much heavier than the Common Gull, which by comparison looked very long legged and skinny.

When disturbed it flew and settled on the sea but came back as soon as the danger had passed. It was extremely tame.'

(An account extracted from the unpublished files in the British Birds Rarities Committee archive)

First-winter Ivory Gull feeding on partially-buried dead seal at Brancaster January 1978. (*Robert Gillmor*)

Sabine's Gull
Larus sabini

An immature was obtained at Breydon on 17th October 1881. The specimen was in the Connop collection at the City of Birmingham Museum, but enquiries at the Museum in 1988 failed to locate it.

Henry Stevenson writes in the *Transactions of the Norfolk and Norwich Naturalists' Society* 1881-1882: 373:

> 'The gunners and bird dealers in Yarmouth were much exercised last October (1881) by the appearance on Breydon, and its vicinity, of two small gulls with slightly forked tails which, when shot answered to no species with which they were aquainted. One of these specimens, killed October 22nd, 1881, which I was fortunate enough to secure for my collection, was sent to me in the flesh, and being in immature plumage – as was also the other bird obtained on the 17th - I should have had some difficulty in identifying it but for the forked tail. In its adult state, Sabine's Gull was, of course well known to me, and on turning to the coloured representations of the young in Gould's '*Birds of Great Britain*' and in Dresser's '*Birds of Europe*', I found my specimen most accurately delineated, the peculiar markings on the back and wing-coverts being quite unmistakable. It proved on dissection, to be a female, and the other, which was purchased by Mr. Connop of Caister, was ascertained by Mr. Lowne a birdstuffer at Yarmouth, to be a male.'

Thomas Southwell writes in Henry Stevenson's *The Birds of Norfolk* Vol. lll. 1890: 319-320:

> 'October 1881, will long be remembered in Norfolk for the severity of a storm which occurred on the 14th of that month. It was purely cyclonic, beginning in the south, and passing successively to south-west, west, and north-west, and was accompanied by a deluge of rain such as has been rarely experienced in this county; the seven following days were calmer but very cold, the mean, 43 degrees 3', being about 6 degrees below the average temperature. One result of this exceptional weather was the arrival on our coast of several rare birds; among others, Buffon's and Richardson's skuas and little gulls, but the 17th and 22nd were rendered notable by the appearance on Breydon of two immature examples of Sabine's gull, the first known to have occurred in this county. One of these northern strangers was sent to Mr. Stevenson in the flesh, and proved upon dissection to be a female; the other, a male was purchased by Mr. Connop, of Caister, in whose collection it now is; Mr. Stevenson's bird subsequently found a home in the Norwich Museum.'

Interestingly, B. B. Riviere notes in *A History of the Birds of Norfolk* 1930: 239-240:

> '…but Geo. Smith, the Yarmouth dealer, into whose hands they first came, states in his MS. diary that they were shot on the 18th and 20th October.'

Taxidermist Walter Lowne's diary for 1881 records October 18th for the first, shot at Breydon by William 'Strike' Sharman and October 20th for the second, shot on the beach by

Jimmy Hurr.

The second bird mentioned in the above account was bought for nine guineas (£9.45) by Thomas Southwell in the sale of Stevenson's collection, after his death, in 1887. On Southwell's death in 1909 the bird was presented to the Castle Museum, Norwich by J. J. Colman, where it remains on display in the bird gallery (Accession no. NWHCM: 1887.47).

Black-legged Kittiwake
Rissa tridactyla
Listed by Sheppard and Whitear in *A Catalogue of the Norfolk and Suffolk Birds, with Remarks* (1826) but not commented on, the earliest reference we can find is by the Pagets in *Sketch of the Natural History of Yarmouth and its Neighbourhood* 1834: 13 where they considered it '… rather rare.'

Slender-billed Gull
Chroicocephalus genei
A pair of adults, in full breeding plumage, was discovered by Martin Gilbert at Cley Marsh on the afternoon of 12th May 1987 (Plate 11).

Paul Varney writes:

'May the 12th 1987 began as a normal working day until a late afternoon visit to Snettisham to see a Hoopoe. Having enjoyed excellent views of this bird as it flopped along on rounded black and white wings looking like a large moth, I was on the return journey when given the news of two Slender-billed Gulls at Cley, a new bird for the county. On arrival there I joined the throng at the North Hide as light began to fade, but was able to enjoy views of these easily identifiable gulls through the Questar telescope of Bryan Bland.

The birds were found by Martin Gilbert, from Runcorn who was visiting Cley to see a Wilson's Phalarope, and scanning the pools from Teal Hide. He was able watch the southern wanderers as they fed 'ankle' deep in water, pecking food directly from the surface, before they took wing and flew to the North Pool. In flight they revealed long pale wings and a noticeable contrast between sharp red bill and clean white head.

They were both adults, one about the size of a Black-headed Gull with the other appreceiably (about 15%) larger. The most striking feature was the amazingly clean white head, neck and breast, the head being long and pointed. The bill was long and fairly weighty and in poor evening light looked black, contrasting markedly with the white plumage. The mantle was very pale grey, paler than a Black-headed, with a similar wing pattern on the perched birds. The eyes appeared small. They remained in the same area until dark.

The following dawn the birds were eventually located in a slightly different area of the marsh, giving excellent views in the improved light and showing additional features not visible the previous evening. The larger bird was much smarter with a very noticeable rose-pink flush on the breast and belly, whilst the other bird showed less bright pink. Bills were bright red as were the eye rings and legs. The birds were displaying to each other, confirming that they were a pair – the larger bird being the male. When displaying the male stretched its neck which was very long: a characteristic of this species.

The birds stayed in the area three days and thanks to the considerable efforts and understanding of Bernard Bishop and David Abdullah, the warden and his assistant at Cley, were seen by a large number of birdwatchers. Throughout the stay the male remained very protective towards the female, frequently positioning himself between her and other gulls and often chasing them away. They were also seen to copulate on numerous occasions, leading to hopes that they would settle down to breed. On the last evening of their stay they were watched until dark from the Richard Richardson Hide, having earlier flown in from Blakeney Harbour. They were not seen again, to the great chagrin of the weekend birders.

There are only three previous accepted British records: first-summer birds in Sussex in June and July 1960 and again in April 1963 and a 'pink' adult which appeared in Kent on several dates between July and September in 1971 with presumably the same bird at Minsmere on 15th August that year.

The species has an irregular disjointed distribution from southern Spain and France, eastwards to the Black Sea. Presumably the pair of Slender-billed Gulls were part of the same displacement of Mediterranean birds which brought the Black-winged Stilts to Holme.'

(An account published in the *Norfolk Bird Report* 1987: 101-102)

Bonaparte's Gull
Chroicocephalus philadelphia
One, thought to be a second-winter, was seen by Ian (D.I.M.) Wallace, moving north-west close inshore at Bacton Gap on 2nd September 1967.

Ian Wallace writes from his notes taken at the time:

'In the afternoon, we arrived at Bacton to find a "west wind breaking up the clouds". Of the long wooden shack into which I decanted the in-laws, wife, first daughter and dog, I noted that "at least the sea is outside the door". First brew downed, "I indulged in lengthy sea watching with staggering results". My second stare out lasted from 1700 to 1900 hrs and altogether 329 birds of 25 species showed offshore, mostly passing "left" or NW along the coast and into the wind. Black-headed Gulls were the second commonest seabird and just before 1845 "some stopped to feed just to the north of by beach top watch points, all within 100 yards".

At 1845, I spotted a smaller gull among them. It also stopped to feed "briefly". Through 9 x 30 binoculars (and probably a God awful Nickel Supra at x 25), its size was "obviously smaller than Black-headed", with "only three quarters of their bulk and wingspan". Its flight action was "lighter... with fast wingbeats and more tern-like flutter when turning". Other comparisons indicated on the sketch included "smaller (black) bill", (more) "indistinct spot" on rear cheeks and a distinct difference in the pattern of the outer half of the wing, with "broader white area... on both sides (= surfaces)". Thus the whole of the underhand was "paler" (translucent), lacking any dusky lining.

There were two puzzles, the shape of the wing tip, noted as "rather broad and recalling Little Gull when turning in flight" and with three separated primary tips visible, and a narrow dark tail band. Hence my ageing of the bird a "sub-adult (not 1st year)"- I cannot explain how others have promoted it to "adult"- and I was completely happy with its identification when at 1850 it went on.

(In 1983 or later, I must have checked the bird out again in comparison with the BWP texts. They and Witherby's plumages showed that a winter head was possible in August, primary replacement continued into September and 2nd year birds could have dark tipped tail feathers.)

With the wind continuing westerly and then northerly, reaching gale force on the 5th, I was not surprised to see another Nearctic gull on the 7th, a first autumn Sabine's. Altogether after another wind switch to the east, my 36 hours of seawatching on 11 days (to the 14th) produced 74 species passing or coming in. I have only matched such diversity of passage and arrival from Flamborough Head in the late 1970s, the last years of birds galore.

Taken now to be a bird mostly of winter and spring in Ireland and the west, the reach of Bonapartes's Gull to the east coast does seem to have weakened (1 in 5 from 1958 to 1985 but only 1 in 32 from 1986 to 1996). Conversely, English midland records have mounted (1 in 8 from 1986 to 1996), the birds appearing in flocks of Black-headeds – just like the Bacton bird!'

No age was given for this bird in the *Norfolk Bird Report* (1967), *British Birds* 61: 344 or Seago(1977) but in 1987 *British Birds* 80: 541 stated that the 1967 bird '…was apparently adult retaining some first-summer features.' No source was given. Later references to the bird aged it as adult, apart from Evans (1996) who considered the record unacceptable and included it in square brackets, having previously referred to it as an adult in Evans (1990).

Common Black-headed Gull

Chroicocephalus ridibundus
The earliest dated reference we can find is by Sir Thomas Browne (1605-1682) in *Notes and Letters on the Natural History of Norfolk* 1902: 10 where he writes:

'Larus alba or puets in such plenty about Horsey that they sometimes bring them in carts to norwich & sell them at small rates. & the country people make use of their egges in puddings & otherwise. great plenty thereof haue bred about scoulton mere, & from thence sent to London.'

Little Gull

Hydrocoloeus minutus
Thomas Southwell writes in Henry Stevenson's *The Birds of Norfolk* Vol. lll. 1890: 320-322:

'Probably the earliest Norfolk specimens were a pair in Mr. E. S. Preston's collection, said to have been killed on Breydon, in December 1829, the same severe winter which produced the Steller's Duck.'

The Pagets in *Sketch of the Natural History of Yarmouth and its Neighbourhood* 1834: 13 considered it '…rarely met with'.

The species was first described in 1813 when an immature was shot on the Thames at Chelsea. The specimen was at the Castle Museum, Norwich but it could not be located when enquiries were made in 2008.

Ross's Gull
Rhodostethia rosea
An adult in immaculate pink breeding plumage was found by Eddie Myers at Cley Marsh on 9th May 1984.

Eddie Myers writes:

'After a morning's birding at Cley on May 9th 1984 I decided to complete my visit by looking at Arnold's Marsh. I arrived there at 11am finding three Little Gulls asleep on a sand bar in the centre. Each was in first-winter plumage. I then noticed a small pink gull in the far corner of the Marsh swimming with a group of Black-headed Gulls. Viewing with my telescope and to my great surprise I realised the stranger was a Ross's Gull: an adult in full summer plumage. After commandeering two passing non-birders to keep an eye on the bird, I raced to Walsey Hills to telephone the exciting news. Within an hour forty observers had arrived and by the end of the day 150 people from as far away as London had seen their first Ross's Gull. This is the first accepted record of this Arctic stray in Norfolk and one of the few mainland observations of an adult in breeding dress.

This rarity was similar in size to a Little Gull. Very buoyant on the water, it floated with tail and wing-tips pointing upwards. On the wing it appeared very graceful displaying long pointed wings and a diagnostic wedge-shaped tail. A broad area of white was revealed on the trailing edge of the wings which were dark grey below. The upperparts were palest grey, the underparts beautiful rose-pink extending to the black necklace which was thickest at the nape. The head was paler with red eye ring. The delicate bill was black and the legs bright red. The bird walked in the manner of a dove with short steps and nodding domed head.

This fabulous gull spent the next day at Blakeney Point, returning to Cley (and to a large appreciative audience) May 11th and 12th. Here, almost surrounded by Black-headed Gulls and Avocets, it was quite unmistakable. From time to time it fed while swimming against the current, rapidly picking at the surface in the manner of a phalarope. The flight was light and buoyant, periodically dipping to the lagoon to seize food, accompanied by foot paddling. Its final performance was at Titchwell on 13th/14th (Plate 12) where it provided close-up views to many watchers from far and wide.

Day after day of strong north-easterly winds almost certainly drove this vagrant so far south. Formerly, to most birdwatchers, an almost mythical phantom, Ross's Gull now seems bent on becoming an annual winter wanderer – usually to Shetland and to north-east England. Latest information reveals 40 occurrences in Great Britain. Even so it remains exceptionally rare in north-west Europe.

The late James Fisher described Ross's Gull as "one of the most mysterious birds of the world". At the turn of the century evidence pointed to a high Arctic breeder perhaps nesting on some seldom visited island. One can imagine the surprise and interest aroused when the secret of the breeding place was revealed in the summer of 1905 by a Russian explorer. He established that the secretive bird nested not on the frozen Arctic, but in well-wooded marshy river valleys in extreme eastern Siberia, sometimes nearly a hundred miles south of the tree line. No other large breeding sites have ever been discovered.

The precise winter range is still somewhat unknown, but it has been established from observations made in the Polar basin outside the breeding season that Ross's Gull does not migrate southwards, but makes a contrasting shift northwards into the Arctic Ocean to one of the most desolate and forbidding areas of the world. Recent observations by a Swedish expedition discovered hundreds of Ross' Gulls among the pack ice and drift-ice bordering the Barents and Greenland Seas north of Franz Josef Land and Spitzbergen. Here, this elusive bird was one of the most numerous species on the ice-floes, congregating about any dead whale or other windfall food source.'

(An account published in the *Norfolk Bird Report* 1984: 96-97)

Laughing Gull
Larus atricilla
A first-winter bird was identified by Mick Fiszer at Walcott seafront on the morning of 25th December 1991.

Mick Fiszer writes from his notes taken at the time:

'On 25th December 1991, having opened all our Christmas presents my next task was to visit the family graves at Mundesley to lay wreathes. I usually do this on my own as it also gives me an excuse to stay out birding, as the kitchen can be a dangerous place. However, on this occasion my youngest daughter Karen wanted to come with me.

Having laid the wreathes I was thinking of what to do. It was a beautiful day so I decided to drive along to Walcott, have a walk along the beach with Karen and at the same time check out the Purple Sandpipers at their roost on the slipway on the seafront.

We arrived at the Poacher's Pocket just before 9 o'clock with the high-tide predicted at half-past. While we were walking up to where the Purple Sandpipers would be, we were mucking about with me pushing Karen off the sea-wall onto the beach. Suddenly Karen stopped and looking up she shouted "Look dad, that poor gull is covered in oil", words that will forever stick in my mind.

Looking up I was totally gobsmacked for right above my head was a first-winter Laughing Gull (a species I was familiar with from a visit to Texas in 1986). Forgetting all about the sandpipers I tried to give chase to see where it had gone to after it disappeared behind some houses. (In Karen's words "Dad's legs were going up and down but he was not going anywhere. I just stood and laughed").

Having failed to re-locate the gull I phoned Robin Chittenden at Birdline East Anglia telling him to alert other birders to the possibilitry of finding a Laughing Gull further up the coast.

Having returned home without any joy and eaten a very large Christmas dinner I was about to crash on the sofa when Paul Lee and Julian Bhalerao rang to say they were coming over to look for the gull. All three of us spent the rest of the afternoon searching but to no avail. I decided that evening that I would return the next morning at the same time to see if the bird was present.

So it was that around 9 o'clock next morning I stepped onto Walcott seafront, almost immediately the Laughing Gull flew over my head and landed in amongst the houses on St Helena Rd. This time I knew exactly where it was and quickly followed, finding the bird feeding on a turkey carcase. Having enjoyed the bird for a few minutes I phoned the news out and within the hour was joined by several Norfolk stalwarts.

The bird remained into the New Year giving hundreds of people a good start to their year list. It also made the local fish and chip shop happy as the owners took advantage of the crowds, opening up the shop in what was supposedly 'out of season'.'

Franklin's Gull

Larus pipixcan
An adult, in full breeding plumage was found by Keith Dye at the eastern end of Breydon Water on 30th June 1991.

Keith Dye writes:

'On Sunday 30th June 1991 I headed for Breydon Water to watch the waders and gulls on the incoming tide, reaching the east hide near the Breydon Bridge, overlooking the area known as the 'Lumps' at 0935. The tide still had a considerable way to go before the top at around 1215, the light to moderate south-westerly wind and the predicted height would make it a reasonably high one, bringing the birds into the north east corner of the estuary. At approximately 1000 I was joined in the hide by Terry Moon, a birder from Bedford who was on holiday in the area. Up to this time the highlights had been Greenshank and Little Gull.

At 1050 I noticed a smallish, dark winged, black-hooded gull standing by itself on a spit some 300 yards to the north west of the hide. I drew Terry's attention to it and we watched it for a while before it flew westwards and landed on the more distant flats about half a mile away with Black-headed Gulls. It stood out very well among them with its much darker wings. It was smaller than the Black-headed Gulls and in shape similar although larger, more bull-necked and deeper chested than a Little Gull and sporting a full black hood with thick white eye crescents. Its wings and mantle were a plain dark grey, the colour of a British Lesser Black-backed Gull, with a white band separating the grey from the black and white primarie. In flight a clear white trailing edge to the wing was wrapped around the primary tips giving the rounded wings a shorter appearance. With a white body, white tail with grey central feathers, and red bill and legs, it was obviously a full adult and was a species neither of us had seen before.

I racked my mind to come up with its identification. No European gull fitted this bird so it must be an American. The only two I could think of, that fitted the size, were Bonaparte's and Franklin's, I'd seen neither. I recalled reading that American birders sift through their Bonaparte's Gulls for vagrant Black-headed and as this individual certainly did not resemble a Black-headed Gull, Franklin's seemed a good candidate. I asked Terry to keep his eye on the bird until I returned and rushed off home, a fifteen minute walk away, and confirmed its identity as an adult summer Franklin's Gull. Further checking showed it to be the first for Norfolk. My elation is best summed up by a comment made at the time by my six-year old son Robert. "Dad's home mum, he has found a rare bird and is all excited and jumping up and down, just like me when I am going to a party". He had captured my mood precisely.

I passed the word of its presence to Great Yarmouth Bird Club members and Birdline East Anglia before heading back to Breydon. On my arrival I found that the Franklin's Gull had flown back to within 250 yards of the hide, ahead of the advancing tide and was asleep. By this time birders were arriving and over the next two and three-quarter hours we were treated to excellent views of it preening, wing stretching, walking about and making short flights. At 1445 it flew strongly low across Breydon in a southerly direction. Gaining height over the main navigation channel it flew high over the Breydon wall and bridge, the last I saw of this splendid individual.

It returned to Breydon but was lost from sight flying up the estuary. At around 1800 it was relocated at Burgh Castle, at the western end of the estuary, by Alan Tate who left his wife watching the bird while he rushed back to Yarmouth to let everyone know its whereabouts. It was seen well on the flats at Burgh Castle until 2115 when it appeared to go to roost on Breydon with the other gulls. Alan noted that when seen against the sun on the flats it was easily picked out among the Black-headed Gulls by the way it waddled rather than walked. It was looked for extensively from first light the following day but was not seen, so had apparently departed overnight. An estimated several hundred birders were lucky enough to see this bird on the one day of its stay.

Franklin's Gull breeds in Canada and the northwest and central United States of America. It winters in the Pacific from Guatemala to Chile. This individual brings the British records for the species to nineteen.'

(An account published in the *Great Yarmouth Bird Club Newsletter* No. 2 in September 1992. An edited account was published in the *Norfolk Bird Report* 1991: 258-260, as part of an article detailing the occurrences of the three North American gulls new to the county that year.)

Franklin's Gull is a North American inland nester on the praries of Canada and USA described as 'accidental' on the Atlantic coast in New World Field Guides. Thus its appearance here was quite unexpected. This Breydon individual, photographed at a distance by Robin Chittenden and Jack Levene, brings the British and Irish records of the species to nineteen. Interestingly, what was almost certainly the same individual, had lingered earlier in the month at Teeside and returned there at the end of August before being seen on and off in North Yorkshire, South Yorkshire and Humberside until early December. *(Norfolk Bird Report* 1991: 260)

An earlier previously accepted record of one at West Runton on 29th October 1976 was withdrawn by the observers in 1983.

Mediterranean Gull
Larus melanocephalus
An adult male was shot at Breydon by Charles Harwood on 26th December 1886 (Plate 5). It was the second British example, but the first to be correctly identified on being found.

George Smith writes in the *Transactions of the Norfolk and Norwich Naturalists' Society* 1886-1887: 391:

> 'On 26th December, 1886, a fine adult specimen of this species was shot on Breydon, Great Yarmouth: a fine male by dissection. I was fortunate enough to purchase this great rarity about one hour after its capture. At first I did not recognize what species I had; but consulted the 4th edition of Yarrell, and found an excellent description given by Mr. Howard Saunders. I at once found out what a prize I had obtained. This rare bird was shot purely by accident, with a cartridge the shooter (wildfowler Charles Harwood) could not extract. He was simply wanting any bird that might come, for a discharge of this cartridge, and luckily it was *Larus melanocephalus* which came in the way, as I believe this is the first authentic specimen which has been obtained in Great Britain. I am also glad to be able to write that it was shot in my own county, Norfolk; adding to my rich old county's avifauna one of the greatest rarities in Great Britain. On the morning of its capture, as I was walking on Yarmouth beach, I saw, as I thought, a *Larus minutus*; it came close to me and showed its white wings, but I thought it was rather large for a Little Gull; in about two hours after this I had in my hands the *Larus melanocephalus*. I had the pleasure of inspecting it before the life-tints were altered. It was seen in the flesh by Mr. J. H. Gurney, Junr., Mr. T. Southwell, and Col. Fielden. The breast-bone, etc., I am cleaning for preservation.'

Smith reportedly bought the bird from Harwood for five shillings (25p), having realised it was a rarity even before it was identified. Once the identification was confirmed he offered it to collector E. M. Connop for £200 and when this was refused he increased the price and offered it to Lord Lillford for £300. Again it was refused and he again increased the price. He eventually offered it to a rich titled Jewish banker at a still more advanced figure, but that gentleman also refused. It eventually passed out of Smith's hands, much to his regret, and was sold to Robert Chase of Birmingham for two figures and added to his great collection (Patterson 1929).

The specimen is now in storage at the City of Birmingham Museum. Although originally preserved as a study-skin, it was mounted in a case by Birmingham taxidermist John Betteridge in January 1917.

Patterson humorously comments in the 'List of Breydon Birds' in *Wildfowlers and Poachers* 1929: 70 'Mediterranean Black-headed Gull – Accidental; *George Smith's Magnum Avis*'.

Interestingly, the first British example was recorded by Stevenson (1890) as one obtained by Mr. Whitely of Woolwich who, without recognising it, sold it to the British Museum. This example was a bird of the previous year and was said to have been shot in January 1866, near Barking Creek (*Ibis*, 1872, p. 79).

Mew (Common) Gull

Larus canus

The earliest dated reference we can find is in 'Extracts from the Calendar of the Rev. William Whitear 1809-1826' published in the *Transactions of the Norfolk and Norwich Naturalists' Society* 1881-1882: 251 where he recorded on the 13th December 1819:

> 'I went to Yarmouth, and the following day went shooting on Breydon…I killed on this and the following day some Common and Black-headed Gulls

in different states of plumage. I found that the bills of the young and old birds of both species differed from each other in colour, and agreed with Temminck's description of them; the same applies to the legs.'

Churchill Babington in *Catalogue of the Birds of Suffolk* (1884-1886) writes:

'Common along the whole length of the coast; found not uncommonly in the interior. Whitear found that the bills, as well as the legs of the young and old birds differed in colour; he shot them on Breydon on 13th December 1819 (*Diary*, 251).'

Babington would appear to have misread the diary entry.

Interestingly, Sheppard and Whitear referred to this species, without comments, in *A Catalogue of the Norfolk and Suffolk Birds, with Remarks* (1826) as Sea Cob. So it is reasonable to assume that Sir Thomas Brown (1605-1682) in *Notes and Letters on the Natural History of Norfolk* (1902), when mentioning the presence of "seamewes & cobs", is referring to this species.

Ring-billed Gull
Larus delawarensis
A first-winter was found by Neil Bostock, standing on the ice covering an almost frozen Pentney Gravel Pits on 5th February 1991.

Neil Bostock writes from recollections and notes taken at the time:

'During the early part of February 1991 an area of high pressure created a period of clear skies and strong frosty conditions which produced ice on many areas of open water in the county. At the time I was working outdoors conducting agricultural field trials in and around West Norfolk and often took some time when travelling between trial sites to have a break and enjoy some birding. On 5th February 1991 I was working close to Pentney Gravel Pits and decided to pop in and see if anything had been brought in due to the hard weather. On arrival I was dismayed to find almost all of the water surface frozen removing any chance of seeing any Smew or perhaps a scarcer grebe; the only birds present were a number of gulls which were perched forlornly on the ice. At around 12am I set up my scope and began to look through the gulls; the majority were Common Gulls with birds in adult winter and 1st-winter plumages. As I scanned through the flock I found a 1st-winter bird which appeared markedly paler mantled and larger and heavier-bodied than the surrounding Common Gulls which immediately started to grab my interest. Suspecting a Ring-billed Gull I hurredly began to assess the other characters of the bird. The bill was indeed thicker, heavier and more parallel-edged and looked yellowish-pink with a broad black band on the tip reminiscent of a Glaucous Gull. At higher telescope power a narrow yellowish tip to the bill could be discerned. The bill looked blunt-tipped compared to the narrow more pointed bills of the adjacent Common Gulls. The head appeared squarer and flatter crowned than Common Gull with a distinct peak behind the eye. The eye appeared more forward in the head compared to Common Gull; it was dark and had a dark area immediately either side of the eye giving the bird a meaner squint-eyed impression. The head had faint buffish streaking particularly on the nape. The breast had feint buffish mottling. I next checked the tertials to further eliminate Common Gull and also 2nd-winter Herring Gull and was pleased to see the tertials to be uniform brown with narrow pale fringes lacking the extensive white on the tips and edges or the barring of a 2nd-winter Herring Gull. With increasing elation I looked at the wings observing the pale buffish abraded median coverts and the pale grey greater coverts, concolorous with the mantle compared to the darker brown median and greater coverts of the 1st-winter Common Gulls. Finally I observed the longish looking pink legs; the last of a suite of characters which confirmed I was observing a Ring-billed Gull. After watching the bird for some time the loafing gulls began to fly away and at 12:15pm the gull moved off with the bulk of the group. It was seen briefly in flight appearing long winged and exhibiting a pale central wing panel concolorous with the mantle which extended onto the inner primaries contrasting strongly with the secondary and outer primaries. The tail had a broad dark brownish-black band which was not clear cut across its width but was more diffuse with variegated brownish bars extending up the outer feathers. It was observed to continue to fly westwards perhaps heading towards other foraging areas such as Blackborough End Refuse Tip, King's Lynn Docks or the Wash.'

Interestingly, another, a second-winter and presumed female by its small size, was discovered by Mark Eldridge at The University of East Anglia Broad, Norwich on 15th October of the same year.

Lesser Black-backed Gull
Larus fuscus graellsii
Listed by Sheppard and Whitear in *Catalogue of the Norfolk and Suffolk Birds, with Remarks* (1826) but not commented on, the earliest dated reference we can find is by the Pagets in *A Sketch of the Natural History of Yarmouth and its Neighbourhood* 1834: 13 where they comment:

> '…rare; two shot, April 1821.'

Thomas Southwell writes in Henry Stevenson's *The Birds of Norfolk* Vol. lll. 1890:333-339:

> 'Owing, probably, to want of acquaintance with the various stages of plumage which the larger gulls assume ere they reach maturity, the early authorities appear to have regarded this species as much less frequent than it really is. Messrs. Sheppard and Whitear simply catalogue the *Lardae*, giving no information except with regard to the black-headed gull and the skuas; Hunt, in his "List" appears to regard the lesser black-backed gull as a great rarity, so much so that he remarks, "a specimen of this rare gull was shot near Yarmouth;" the Pagets also evidently regarded it in the same light, for they designate it as "rare," and add that there were "two shot April 1821;" doubtless both these observations refer to the adult bird only. Mr. Lubbock, I think, errs in the other extreme when he states that this species and the herring gull "are perhaps the most common of the larger species here," but Messrs Gurney and Fisher form a much more accurate estimate, observing that it "occurs on the coast throughout the year, except during the

Richardson.
1957.

Plate 1 *Previous page* Eurasian Collared Dove, adult and young, Overstrand 1956. (*R.A.Richardson*)

Plate 2 *Top* Steller's Eider, sub-adult drake shot on Caister Marshes 1830. Castle Museum, Norwich. (*Chris Taylor*)
Bottom King Eider, immature drake shot off Hunstanton 1888. Castle Museum, Norwich. (*Peter Allard*)

Plate 3 *Top left* Caspian Plover, adult male shot near Yarmouth North Denes 1890. Castle Museum, Norwich. (*Chris Taylor*)
Top right Sharp-tailed Sandpiper shot at Yarmouth 1848. Castle Museum, Norwich. (*Chris Taylor*)
Bottom Pectoral Sandpiper shot at Breydon 1830. (*Peter Allard*)

Plate 4 *Top* Black-capped Petrel, female found alive at Southacre 1850. Castle Museum, Norwich. (*Chris Taylor*)
Bottom Whiskered Tern, adult female shot at Hickling Broad 1847. Castle Museum, Norwich. (*Chris Taylor*)

Plate 5 *Top* Mediterranean Gull, adult male shot at Breydon 1886. City of Birmingham Museum. (*Jon Clatworthy*)
Bottom Gull-billed Tern, adult male shot at Breydon 1849. Castle Museum, Norwich. (*Chris Taylor*)

Plate 6 *Top left* Red-footed Falcon, first-summer male shot at Yarmouth 1830. Castle Museum, Norwich. (*Chris Taylor*)
Top right Gyr Falcon, adult male shot at Beeston 1848. Castle Museum, Norwich. (*Chris Taylor*)
Bottom Eurasian Scop's Owl, found alive at Cromer 1861. Castle Museum, Norwich. (*Chris Taylor*)

Plate 7 *Top* White-spotted Bluethroat, male found at Sheringham 1906. Castle Museum, Norwich. (*Chris Taylor*)
Bottom White's Thrush, male shot at Hickling 1871. Castle Museum, Norwich. (*Chris Taylor*)

Plate 8 *Top* Spotted Nutcracker, shot at Rollesby 1844. Castle Museum, Norwich. (*Chris Taylor*)
Bottom Arctic Warbler, shot at Blakeney Point 1922. Castle Museum, Norwich. (*Chris Taylor*)

Plate 9 *Top* Oriental Turtle Dove, first-winter female shot at Castle Rising 1946. Castle Museum, Norwich. (*Peter Allard*)
Bottom Richard's Pipit, taken at Yarmouth North Denes 1841. Castle Museum, Norwich. (*Peter Allard*)

Plate 10 *Top* Canvasback, first-winter drake Welney 1997. (*Iain Leach*)
   Bottom Killdeer, Breydon 2005. (*Neil Bowman*)

Plate 11 *Top* Little Curlew, probable adult Salthouse 1985. (*David Cottridge*)
Bottom Slender-billed Gull, pair of adults with adult Black-headed Gull Cley 1987. (*Pete Wheeler*)

Plate 12 *Top* Ross's Gull, adult Titchwell 1984. (*Steve Young*)
Bottom Pacific Swift, Cley 1993. (*Julian Bhalerao*)

Plate 13 *Top* Black Lark, adult male Winterton 2008. *(Mike Lawrence)*
Bottom Red-flanked Bluetail, female or first-winter male Yarmouth 1994. (*Barry Jarvis*)

Plate 14 *Top* Grey-cheeked Thrush, juvenile Croxton 2004. (*Dawn A. Balmer*)
Bottom Asian Desert Warbler, male Blakeney Point 1993. (*Julian Bhalerao*)

Plate 15 *Top* Trumpeter Finch, first-summer male Blakeney Point 2008. (*Steve Gantlett*)
Bottom Black-and-white Warbler, How Hill 1985. (*Pete Morris*)

Plate 16 *Top* White-crowned Sparrow, adult male Cley 2008. (*Steve Gantlett*)
Bottom Dark-eyed Junco, probable first-summer Langham 2007. (*Dave Curtis*)

nesting season; but not in large numbers." In the immature plumage it is certainly not rare, especially in autumn, but adults are decidedly uncommon. It is difficult, perhaps impossible, to distinguish between the young of this and the next species [Herring Gull] when on the wing; my observations must therefore, be taken to apply to the united forces of the two species. Which predominates it is difficult to say, judging from the frequency of the adults, *Larus argentatus* should be the more numerous.'

Lesser Black-backed Gull

Larus fuscus intermedius
The first dated reference we can find of this Scandinavian race is by B. B. Riviere in *A History of the Birds of Norfolk* 1930: 248 where he writes:

> 'This dark-mantled form of Lesser Black-backed Gull has proved to be at least an occasional visitor to the Norfolk coast in spring and autumn, and as it is very likely to be overlooked, it is possible that it occurs more regularly. One which was killed in Norfolk on 30th May 1887 was identified by C. B. Ticehurst in the collection of Mr. E. C. Saunders of Yarmouth (*Brit. Birds*, vol. vii., p. 59). Two were seen by me on Breydon on 1st May 1913 (*Ib.*, p. 24), and one which is now in my collection was shot at Cley on 4th September 1922 (*Op. cit.*, vol. xvii., p. 259). A Yarmouth-killed specimen in the Norwich Museum, presented by Stevenson in 1859, although not quite fully adult, also appears to be of this form.'

Herring Gull

Larus argentatus argenteus
Listed by Sheppard and Whitear in *A Catalogue of the Norfolk and Suffolk Birds, with Remarks* (1826) but not commented on, the earliest reference we can find is by the Pagets in *Sketch of the Natural History of Yarmouth and its Neighbourhood* 1834: 13 where they considered it '…rather rare', but see Thomas Southwell's comments on the Lesser Black-backed Gull above.

Herring Gull

Larus argentatus omissus
One originally thought to be the first Yellow-legged Gull but subsequently re-identified as the Baltic form of '*argentatus*', was shot by John 'Pintail' Thomas at Breydon on 4th November 1886. Originally in the Connop collection at Rollesby Hall and later moving to Wroxham Hall, following Connop's death in 1911 the collection was purchased by W. P. Lysaght of Chepstow, Monmouth. The entire collection was donated to the City of Birmingham Museum in 1954. Recent enquiries reveal that the specimen is again at the City of Birmingham Museum after being in storage at Birmingham University.

Thomas Southwell writes in the *Transactions of the Norfolk and Norwich Naturalists' Society* 1897-1898: 417:

> 'Whilst engaged in making a catalogue of the fine collection of British Birds in the possession of Mr. E. M. Connop of Rollesby Hall, near Great Yarmouth, Mr. Cole, the Norwich bird preserver, pointed out to me a Herring Gull, which he said the late Mr. Stevenson had examined in the flesh, and believed to be

Larus cachinnans. At his request Mr. Cole had noted the colour of the soft parts on the back of the case, and a careful examination led me to endorse the opinion expressed by Mr. Stevenson. Mr. Howard Saunders had also been good enough to examine the bird, and expresses himself quite satisfied with the correctness of the determination. The bird was shot by the veteran gunner John Thomas, on Breydon Water, near Great Yarmouth, and sent by him in the flesh to Mr. Cole, on the 4th of November, 1886; it proved to be a male on dissection, and differed from the Common Herring Gull in the darkness of the mantle; the legs were a beautiful lemon yellow, and the bare ring round the eye deep orange-red. The mantle and orbital ring still retain their normal colour, but the legs have unfortunately been painted pale yellow, which Mr. Cole assures me he imitated from nature. The late season at which this southern species was killed seems remarkable; but still later in the same year (on December 26th), and in the same locality, a beautiful example of the Mediterranean Black-headed Gull was killed. I am not aware of any previous occurrence of *L. cachinnans* in Britain having been recorded.'

H. F. Witherby first cast doubts concerning its identification in *A Practical Handbook of British Birds* Vol. ll. 1924: 753 in a footnote, where he writes:

'The only British specimen has been examined by Dr. J. J. Dwight and myself (by the courtesy of its owner Mr. W. R. Lysaght) and found not to belong to the Azores-Canaries form *atlantis* which Dr. Dwight has recently described as distinct. Hartert considers the Mediterranean bird [*michahellis*] distinguishable from more eastern birds [*cachinnans*] on account of the paler and usually white or whitish patches on the inner webs of the outer primaries of the latter. This is, however, a somewhat variable character, and while the webs of the outer primaries in the British specimen (which is an adult) are not whitish they are pale ash-grey and, moreover, are not fully grown, the bird being in moult. The name *cachinnans* is, therefore, retained for the single British example which might have reached Norfolk from north Russia or Sweden with perhaps more probability than from the Mediterranean.'

However, Witherby writing in the reprinted edition of the *Handbook of British Birds* Vol. V. 1952: 95, under Scandinavian Herring Gull *L. a. omissus*, states in a footnote:

'The determination of the race of the Norfolk specimen in the *Practical Handbook* was doubtful (see footnote, p. 573). I have now re-examined the bird by the kindness of Mr. W. R. Lysaght, and find that the grey on the mantle and wing coverts exactly matches that in Norwegian specimens of *L. a. omissus*. The ash-grey of the inner webs of the primaries is also as in *L. a. omissus* and is much extended towards the tips of the feathers.'

Philip Palmer recorded this bird as *Larus michahellis* in *First for Britain and Ireland 1600-1999* (2000). He was not aware of its determination as '*omissus*' until after the book had gone to print.

Yellow-legged Gull
Larus michahellis

Because it was classified as a subspecies of Herring Gull until 1998 and the method by which records of the yellow-legged race(s) were treated in the *Norfolk Bird Report* up to and including 1996, it is very difficult, if not impossible, to assess which one should be considered the first county record. The first mentioned occurrence of the race *michahellis* is in the *Norfolk Bird Report* 1997 when one was at Lynn Point on 3rd July, with birds at Hickling, Yarmouth/Breydon, Blakeney Point, Horsey, Martham Broad, Tunstead, and Cley the same year. Obviously there were earlier records but all were just referred to in the reports as Herring Gulls with yellow legs or yellow-legged races.

The first records of yellow-legged birds appear in the 1961 *Norfolk Bird Report* where it simply states in the Systematic List:

> 'Single adults with yellow legs at Scolt, Aug. 23rd (RC) and at Blakeney, Nov. 4th (HH).'

There is little or no evidence to support a claim for either to be seriously considered as the first Yellow-legged Gull for the county. Perhaps both should remain on record as adult Herring Gulls with yellow legs, of undetermined species or race.

The next was one seen at Great Yarmouth South Denes by Peter Allard on 15th August 1964, which would certainly appear to carry a reasonable provenance to be claimed as the first Norfolk record of this species.

Peter Allard writes from his notes and recollections of the time:

> 'I can offer no excuse why this record was not in my 1964 "Recorded Bird Notes", but appears in my field notes only. Perhaps it was an oversight, or just possibly it did not mean much at the time. I am fortunate that I can still find my field notebooks for 1964, others during that decade have not survived the passage of time. It is also unusual that this record first appears in the 1973 *Norfolk Bird Report*, but was not in the 1964 report. I believe I may have uncovered the sighting whilst researching a gull article that I penned for the 1973 *Norfolk Bird Report*; I have vague recollections of unearthing it many years ago. Anyhow, as for its omission from *The Birds of Great Yarmouth* (1990), the brain cells had obviously started to turn grey even then.
>
> Now to the field notes for August 15th 1964, "...visited Cantley for most of the morning, saw various birds (all listed) and 27 Ruff along the Acle New Road" and so on. All the Cantley birds appear in my full notes, but afterwards, according to my field notes, I had a quick look at the Great Yarmouth harbour's mouth (saw nothing it seems) and then stopped to look on the grass by the South Denes Power Station on the way back. My notes (written in pencil) state:
>
> > '...plenty of gulls as usual, nothing of interest except an adult Herring Gull with bright yellow legs, the nearest bird to me, bird darker than other Herring Gulls with white head and bright yellow and red beak. Bike fell over in the wind flushing most of the gulls and this bird then flew off towards the fish wharf.

Looked for and not seen again, but one Turnstone along fish wharf quayside. Going to be late home again.'

Whether this qualifies for the first Norfolk record of a Yellow-legged Gull *Larus michahellis* is obviously debatable. Certainly, August was, or perhaps still is, one of the better months to see Yellow-legged Gull in Norfolk. The white head means very little, but adult Yellow-legged Gulls are always clean looking birds and the bright yellow legs noted is useful for identification of this species, but the darker bird scribbling could be interpreted in perhaps several ways. I would like to think that in mentioning it was a darker bird I meant that the wings and mantle were darker, I'm reasonably sure it does on reflection, despite the observation being nearly 45 years ago. Additionally, the bright yellow and red beak noted is interesting, adult Yellow-legged Gulls usually have very noticeable red bill spots, perhaps a little brighter than adult Herring Gulls.'

Caspian Gull
Larus cachinnans
A second-winter was identified at Cley by Richard Millington and Mark Golley on 18th November 1997.

Richard Millington writes:
    'Identifying a county first is rarely a prolonged issue, yet the identification of Norfolk's first Caspian Gull was a process of gradual discovery that spanned, in fits and starts, a period of several years. The summer of 1994 had been good for what were then colloquially known as 'large white-headed gulls' at Cley, but the following summer was even better, and coincided with the beginnings of a general taxonomic shift which was to eventually culminate in the elevation of Yellow-legged Gull to full species status. Mark Golley had already been documenting the annual occurrences of *michahellis* at Cley, but I had to learn fast to get up to speed with the identification and ageing of this 'new' bird. I knew gulling could be infectious, as I had spent untold hours gazing at gull gatherings in my youth, but here was a new challenge that soon had us both thoroughly hooked.
    Hours, days and weeks were spent gazing at gulls, and before long we both felt that we had a pretty good idea of what we were looking at. Yet at the same time there were occasional birds which foxed us completely. They were similar to, but different from, the standard Yellow-legged Gulls that Mark and I had become used to – more elegant and with a poise all of their own – and we began to pick them out on 'jizz; alone. At around the same time, one or two European birders had begun to flag up the unlikely occurrence of the 'eastern' subspecies of Yellow-legged (then still a Herring) Gull: the form *cachinnans*. Mark and I believed we were seeing the same thing at Cley, but solid identification info was hard to come by and we struggled to progress much further. I took to visiting municipal dumps on the outskirts of London to accompany Lars Jonsson during his studies of Lesser Black-backed Gulls, and Lars kindly passed on some invaluable identification insights, and even pointed out the odd Caspian Gull! All experiences and any titbits of information were eagerly devoured and, by the autumn of 1996, Mark and I felt sure we had seen several gulls at Cley which fitted the *cachinnans*

bill, and we became confident enough to point the odd one out to visiting birders (including Jon King). However, it was only after the 'definitive' article appeared in *British Birds* in 1997 that we were truly able to measure up our observations against an authoritative reference. This two-part paper [Garner, M., Quinn, D. & Glover, B. 1997. Identification of Yellow-legged Gulls in Britain. *British Birds* 90: 25-62 & 369-383] detailed the structural and plumage characters needed to secure an identification and, needless to say, the next Caspian Gull at Cley was diligently documented; a second-winter seen on 18th November 1997 duly became the first Norfolk record. Subsequent sightings have established that Caspian Gull is a regular visitor to the county, just as Mark and I had suspected for some years. . .and ten years on, it too has been granted species status.'

American Herring Gull
Larus smithsonianus
A third-calendar-year bird was found by Peter Wilson at Blackborough End Tip on 28th February 2004, which was present next day and again on 29th May and 5th June.

Peter Wilson writes:

'Bitter north-easterlies brought increasingly frequent sleety showers on the morning of 28th February 2004 but with 1,900+ gulls present at Blackborough End Tip I felt it worth persevering. After about two hours I was scanning through a number of large gulls which had begun settling on the steep bank below the tipping area when a dark Herring-type with a contrasting pale head immediately grabbed my attention. The bird was facing away and at 200-250 metres distance so at this stage I was not overly excited. Being a keen gull enthusiast I am aware, to some extent, of the variability within European Herring Gulls and the pitfalls (particularly of dark 1st-year *argentatus*) but even so *smithsonianus* (however unlikely) needed to be eliminated. I watched the bird for 10-15 minutes until 10.28am when all the gulls took flight and I was not able to relocate the bird despite spending considerable time trying. The distant and fairly brief views were frustrating to say the least. That night I was left with a few awful and rather hopeless photos and a gut feeling that the bird may indeed have been an American Herring Gull despite this being Norfolk and not Cornwall!

Next morning I was determined to have another go along with my wife Dawn Balmer (who had been away at a conference on the 28th). Sundays are usually a waste of time at the tip as the gulls soon tire of the inactivity but we felt it worth a quick look at least. Amazingly Dawn's luck was in as the bird was soon picked up in flight amongst the few birds present. In a panic I set the scope up on the bird after it had settled and Dawn grabbed a look while I got hold of the camera. After a few quick shots with the camera (which was unfortunately on the wrong setting) all the gulls were spooked and that was that. Again we waited some time but with no gull in sight on a sunny Sunday morning we knew there was little chance of seeing the bird again that day. At least Dawn had seen the bird and now we had a better, if over-exposed picture but we were still some way from a watertight description. Although we alerted a few friends who made visits to the tip over the next few days the bird was not seen again. I looked at the photos a good deal over the ensuing weeks and felt convinced the bird was an American

Herring Gull. Several features, not least the smooth brown underparts and hind neck were, I believed, beyond the normal variation in European Herring Gull.

During another visit to the tip on 29th May, whilst searching for Caspian Gulls, I was shocked to see the bird "magically" appear in my view. This time I was ready for it and with the bird loafing in full view I confidently put the news out of a bird "showing characteristics" of American Herring Gull at Blackborough End Tip, Norfolk. Chas Holt made it in time but the gulls were disturbed before other birders began to turn up, I waited as long as possible until I had to leave by which time it had not reappeared though with the gulls feeding well on the refuse and the day still young I was sure it would return. The last time I saw it was a week later on 5th June when three Caspian Gulls were also present (something of an infrequent "meeting" of forms!). Following circulation of pictures, some observers suggested the bird may be a 3cy and not 2cy as I had reported. I immediately accepted this; clearly the bird was indeed a 3cy. Although annoyed at ageing the bird wrongly, it was a fairly retarded individual (as American Herring Gulls not infrequently are at this age) and initial views were less than good. Looking back I should have realised it was a 3cy when it reappeared in May but probably I was set in my thoughts. Ultimately this still remains one of my most satisfying finds, all the more so given how few have been identified away from the south-west and west coasts of Britain.

American Herring Gulls are undoubtedly rare birds in Britain, especially in the east (even a recent upsurge of interest in *larids* has not resulted in a marked increase in sightings). That said, my view is that a few might still be slipping through the net and although I will not be holding my breath, another Norfolk record is not out of the question, perhaps most likely a 2cy bird in May…'

Although not yet officially accepted by the BBRC it is hoped that it will be. The record was submitted soon after its occurrence, but was apparently mislaid or lost. It was re-submitted in 2008 and remains under consideration by the BBRC.

An earlier record of a juvenile showing the characters of this form (then a subspecies) at Cley on 31st December 1997, was not submitted to the British Birds Rarities Committee; given the rigorous criteria now required for identifying American Herring Gull, the finders feel the identification should remain unproven.

Iceland Gull

Larus glaucoides
One was obtained at Caister in November 1874.

Thomas Southwell writes in Henry Stevenson's *The Birds of Norfolk* Vol. lll. 1890: 336:

'An exceedingly rare bird on the Norfolk coast; it seems probable that most of the specimens said to have been met with were small and pale-coloured examples of the glaucous gull, a much more common species.

Mr. J. H. Gurney, jun., in his list of Norfolk birds contributed to Mason's history of the county, says, "Mr. Stevenson and I, after numerous enquiries, can only certify one undoubted specimen, viz., a young female in the possession of Mr. G. Smith, of Yarmouth, which was shot at Caister, near Yarmouth, in

November 1874." This specimen was examined by Mr. Howard Saunders, who confirmed its identity. All the other recorded specimens have proved on examination to belong to the glaucous gull in one or other stage of plumage.'

B. B. Riviere writes in *A History of the Birds of Norfolk* 1930: 252-253:

'The only authentic example of this rare winter visitor known to Southwell was an immature female, mentioned by Gurney in his "List of Norfolk Birds" in Mason's *History of Norfolk*, which was killed at Caister in November 1874. G. Smith, of Yarmouth, who received this bird, states in his MS. Diary that it was shot on 14th November and was purchased by Dr. Crowfoot, of Beccles.'

Churchill Babington in *Catalogue of the Birds of Suffolk* 1884-1886: 254 states:

'A specimen shot at Yarmouth some years ago, identified by Mr. Howard Saunders; formerly in the possession of Mr. W. M. Crowfoot; he gave it to Mr. George Smith, of Yarmouth, who now has it (W. M. Crowfoot *in litt*).'

This would indicate that Smith received the specimen again, having originally sold it, and is confirmed by the Castle Museum, Norwich who, after Smith's death in December 1916, purchased it for nine shillings (45p) at the auction of his collection in 1917. Unfortunately, the specimen (Accession no. NWHCM: 1911.80), having become moth-eaten, was destroyed in August 1956 (D Waterhouse *in litt*).

The Accession number for the specimen should have been 1917.80, but was misread when being transcribed onto the records, and as the specimen no longer exists cannot now be given another.

Interestingly, Babington (1884-1886) gives the first Norfolk record as:

'…one killed at Yarmouth in 1851 (J. O. Harper in *Nat*. for 1852, page 132; an immature bird from Yarmouth, stuffed by Knight (Newcombe collection), the wings in this specimen extend about an inch beyond tail (Newcombe MS).'

Thomas Knight was a taxidermist who worked in Norwich during the period 1830-1870. We must assume that this bird was one of the records examined and considered to be a Glaucous Gull.

Also of interest is one mentioned by C. B. Ticehurst in *A History of the Birds of Suffolk* 1932: 405 where he writes:

'No doubt many of the records of this bird related really to the Glaucous Gull, but I think the following are genuine:- a male (Hele coll.) obtained at Thorpe 16th January 1874; one at Yarmouth 1848 (Dennis coll.) I consider also to be an Iceland Gull, though Babington thought it a Glaucous; it is a second year bird. A male from Breydon 22nd September 1880 (Connop coll.) was no doubt correct, as Southwell must have seen it…'

However, the 1848 specimen which is now at the Castle Museum, Norwich, was critically examined by Dr. Tony Irwin in late 2008 and confirmed as a Glaucous Gull.

Glaucous Gull
Larus hyperboreus
The earliest dated reference we can find is by Thomas Southwell in Henry Stevenson's *The Birds of Norfolk* Vol. lll. 1890:343-346:

> 'This species is not mentioned by either Sheppard and Whitear (1826) or the Pagets (1834), but Hunt (1829) in his list records "…a fine specimen killed at Yarmouth," and adds, "Mr. Norman, of Docking, has another, killed in his neighbourhood." Mr. Lubbock, in his copy of Bewick's birds, has a note written in July, 1831, of one shot off Yarmouth by a fisherman, but the date of the occurrence is not given.'

Interestingly, William R. Fisher, co-author of 'An Account of the Birds found in Norfolk' published in the *Zoologist* for 1846, in his interleaved copy of the Paget's *Sketch of the Natural History of Yarmouth and its Neighbourhood* (1834) notes that three *Larus icelandicus* were shot by Mr. D. Preston on the South beach at Yarmouth on 4th January 1830 – all young birds.

Although both Glaucous Gull and Iceland Gull (which was first described in 1821) were referred to as *Larus icelandicus* by several early 19th century authors, it was not until William Yarrell's first edition of the *History of British Birds* appeared in 1837 that the differences between the two species became widely known.

The authors of this book consider that these three birds were much more likely to have been Glaucous Gulls than Iceland Gulls.

Great Black-backed Gull
Larus marinus
Listed by Sheppard and Whitear in *A Catalogue of the Norfolk and Suffolk Birds, with Remarks* (1826) but not commented on, and considered 'common' by the Pagets in *Sketch of the Natural History of Yarmouth and its Neighbourhood* (1834), the earliest dated reference we can find is in Henry Stevenson's *The Birds of Norfolk* Vol. lll. 1890: 341-343, where Thomas Southwell writes:

> 'Miss Anna Gurney, of Northrepps, in a paper contributed to the "Mag. Nat. Hist." for 1830 (iii., p. 155), on the "Natural History of the Neighbourhood of Cromer," writing of gulls, says, "one which we had young in the autumn of 1823, and which proved to be the large black-backed gull, did not acquire his final plumage till the summer of 1827; his bill turned from black to yellow, but the scarlet spot was not perfect till July, 1828. The next spring he died".'

Sooty Tern
Onychoprion fuscata
The first Norfolk record was one seen by John Sladen Wing in Blakeney Harbour on 11th September 1935.

John Sladen Wing writes:

> 'On September 11th, 1935, as my wife and I were returning from Blakeney

Point to Blakeney, by motor-boat, a tern, unknown to us, flew in front of the boat, only a few yards off, and then flew by the side of the boat.

What struck us, and the boatman, was the size of the bird. It was about as big as a Sandwich Tern.

We noticed the white forehead and black band through lores and eyes. The under-parts were white; the upper-parts, bill and wings were black.

We have since identified it, without doubt, at the British Museum, as an adult Sooty Tern (*Sterna fuscata*).'

(Originally published in *British Birds* 29: 187)

Interestingly, B. B. Riviere mentions an earlier occurrence in *A History of the Birds of Norfolk* 1930: 239 in square brackets:

'Early in April 1900 a Sooty Tern, which is now in the Norwich Museum, was picked up dead on some heathland in the parish of Santon Downham, about half-a-mile on the Suffolk side of the Little Ouse and a quarter of a mile from Thetford Warren. It came into the possession of Mr. Nunn of Little Lodge Farm, for whom it was stuffed by F. Rix of Thetford, and was identified at Mr. Nunn's house in the following September by W. G. Clarke (W. G. Clarke, *Zoologist* 1903, p. 393).

Gurney and Southwell included this specimen in the birds of Norfolk on the grounds, it would appear, that Thetford Warren is in the administrative county of Norfolk ("Fauna and Flora of Norfolk"; additions to Part XI.: "Birds (4th list)" *Norfolk and Norwich Nat. Soc. Trans.*, vol. vii., p. 733). In view, however, of the fact that Clarke states that the bird was picked up a quarter of a mile from Thetford Warren and half-a-mile on the Suffolk side of the Little Ouse, which is here the county boundary, its claim to be included in the Norfolks list appears to me to fail.'

C. B. Ticehurst adds some interesting extra detail to this record in *A History of the Birds of Suffolk* 1932: 424:

'Rarities are sometimes found by chance. In 1903 the late W. G. Clarke noticed a stuffed bird in a house near Thetford which he and Southwell subsequently identified as a Sooty Tern. It appears that early in April 1900 a Mr. J. Nunn, while rabbiting on the Suffolk side of the boundary near Thetford Warren, found the bird dead in the bracken and had it preserved. It was in very poor condition and had been dead about five days.'

He gives a reference *Transactions of the Norfolk and Norwich Naturalists' Society* vii. p. 752.

The 1900 specimen (Accession no. NWHCM: 1904.3) was purchased four years later by the Castle Museum, Norwich for £5.00, where it remains on display in the bird gallery.

Adult Sooty Tern with Sandwich Terns at Blakeney Harbour September 1935. (*Gary Wright*)

Little Tern
Sternula albifrons
The earliest dated reference we can find is by Robert Marsham (1708-1797) in Tim Sparks and John Lines' *Chapters in the Life of Robert Marsham of Stratton Strawless, Norfolk* 2008: 17:

> 'I had a bird in 1789 that answered nearly to this, but not exactly, from tip of wings (24) inches the body less than a blackbird.'

Marsham knew it as the Lesser Sea Swallow or Genser.

Known as Lesser Tern in their day and by the earlier naturalists and gunners, Henry Stevenson and Thomas Southwell give an interesting list of 'local' names for the species in *The Birds of Norfolk* Vol. lll. 1890: 309-312:

> '...little mows', 'sea swallow', 'small perl', 'chit perl', 'dip-ears' and 'shrimp catchers'

Gull-billed Tern
Gelochelidon nilotica
An adult male was shot at Breydon on 14th of April 1849 (Plate 5).

Thomas Southwell writes, in Henry Stevenson's *The Birds of Norfolk* Vol. lll. 1890: 307-308:

> 'On the 14th April, 1849 an adult male in full breeding plumage, now in the Dennis Collection at Bury, was killed on Breydon, and, according to the statement attached to the specimen, was 16 inches in length and weighed 8.25 ounces.'

Interestingly, Peter Allard writes in *The Birds of Great Yarmouth* 1990: 81:

> 'The first six Norfolk occurrences were all obtained in the Yarmouth and Breydon Water area. The first was shot on Breydon on April 14th 1849, obviously a record year as another was obtained there on July 31st and two more were shot

on the estuary on September 1st. Another was taken at Yarmouth in early July 1851 and two were obtained near Yarmouth – presumably Breydon Water – on May 8th 1878. Yet another was collected on September 5th 1896 on Breydon again, [Arthur] Patterson commenting: "…a proceeding always regrettable in the case of rare birds putting in an appearance here".'

The April 1849 specimen, along with others from the Dennis Collection, was transferred to the Castle Museum, Norwich (Accession no. NWHCM: 2009.91) from Bury St. Edmunds Museum in July 2008.

The Rev. J. B. P. Dennis was a master at the Bury St. Edmunds Grammar School. His large collection of birds, all carefully dated with the place of capture attached, many of which came from the neighbourhood of Yarmouth, was donated to the Bury St. Edmunds Museum at Moyes Hall after his death in October 1861. This collection was noted by Ticehurst to be in a fair state of preservation in 1912, but when he visited it again in 1927 it was sadly in the last stages of decay. Following a change of policy at the museum in 2008, many of the remaining cases were disposed of and a number of the best Norfolk specimens went to the Castle Museum, Norwich for safekeeping.

Caspian Tern
Hydroprogne caspia
An immature was shot at Yarmouth on 4th October 1825.

Peter Allard writes in *The Birds of Great Yarmouth* 1990: 81-82:

'The first British example of this spectacular tern was obtained at Yarmouth and almost certainly on Breydon Water on October 4th 1825. It proved to be an immature… It is interesting to note that thirteen of the first fourteen Norfolk records were all in the Yarmouth area.'

This is certainly the latest recorded date for the species in the county and the only one identified as an immature. At the time of the publication of Churchill Babington's *Catalogue of the Birds of Suffolk* (1884-1886) the bird was in the possession of Mr. G. Thurtell of Eaton near Norwich, but its present whereabouts is unknown.

Interestingly, the Pagets in *Sketch of the Natural History of Yarmouth and its Neighbourhood* 1834: 13, while referring to the above record seem to suggest the possibility of an earlier occurrence when they write:

'…one in Norwich museum which was shot here; another October, 1825.'

Yarrell (1845) clears up any ambiguity in the Paget's comments, when referring to the first mentioned, he says:

'The Rev. G. Steward, Rector of Caistor presented this specimen in 1831 to the Castle Museum, Norwich, after it was shot near that place in 1830.'

Whiskered Tern

Chlidonias hybrida

An adult female, flying high over Hickling Broad was shot by a Mr. Sayer on 17th June 1847 (Plate 4). This specimen (Accession no. NWHCM: 1901.32) is on display in the bird gallery at the Castle Museum, Norwich.

Thomas Southwell writes in Henry Stevenson's *The Birds of Norfolk* Vol. lll. 1890: 306-307:

> 'Mr. J. Gurney possesses the only Norfolk specimen of this rare tern, which was shot on Hickling Broad, on the 17th of June 1847, by the late Mr. J. Sayer, of Norwich. Mr. Gurney, in recording its occurrence in the "*Zoologist*" for 1847, p. 1820, remarks, "It proved to be an adult female, and contained ova in an advanced stage, the largest being apparently almost ready to receive the shell. In the stomach were found the remains of about 20 lavae of the broad-bodied dragonfly".'

John Sayer was a well-known taxidermist of St Giles Street, Norwich, being in business from 1826 until his death, aged 51, in 1866. The business was continued by T. E. Gunn who had been apprenticed to Sayer.

Black Tern

Chlidonias niger

Once known as the Mire Crow and Blue Darr, the earliest dated reference we can find is in Henry Stevenson's *The Birds of Norfolk* Vol. lll. 1890: 312-316, where Thomas Southwell writes:

> 'It can hardly be any other species than this which is mentioned in a letter by Sir Thomas Browne to Merrett, dated 29th December, 1668, as the "sterne," and said by him to be "common about broad waters and plashes not farre from the sea," since Turner to whom in the preceding paragraph Browne had referred, almost unquestionably meant this bird, as usual latinising the English word, which he writes "*sterna;*" but particularising its small size and blackish colour. Turner [p.64] spoke of its excessive clamour during the breeding season, which was enough to deafen those who lived near the lakes and marshes it frequented, and as he was personally acquainted with the fen district of the Eastern Counties, his experience may not impossibly have been derived from that portion of it bordering upon or comprised in Norfolk. Pennant, in his regrettably short description of the East Fen, which he visited in 1769, writes in almost similar terms:- "The pewit gulls and black terns abound; the last in vast flocks almost deafen one with their clamors." What the East Fen of Lincolnshire then was, the south-western corner of Norfolk continued for some years longer…'

White-winged Tern

Chlidonias leucopterus

One of two adults was shot at Horsey Mere by Mr. Rising's keeper, from a small flock of Black Terns on 17th May 1853. These were the first to be recognised in Britain, a fact not mentioned in Taylor *et al* (1999).

Thomas Southwell writes in Henry Stevenson's *The Birds of Norfolk* Vol. lll. 1890: 316-318:

'The first recorded Norfolk specimen of this beautiful tern was killed from among a flock of fifteen or twenty black terns, on Horsey Mere, on the 17th May, 1853, and, as stated by Mr. Yarrell ("*Zoologist*," p. 3911), was shown to him in the flesh. It passed into the possession of the late Mr. Rising, of Horsey, by whose keeper it was killed. At the dispersal of that gentleman's collection it was purchased by the late Mr. William Jary. From the information given to Mr. Rising, it appears probable that two of these birds were associating with ordinary black terns, but his keeper supposing it to be merely a variety, and having killed five of the commoner species, did not shoot the other although he had every opportunity of doing so. The 17th of May is the date usually assigned for this occurrence, but in Mr. Rising's own note, in his copy of Yarrell, from which I gather the above particulars, the 18th is the day mentioned.'

At the sale of the Rising collection upon his death in 1885 the specimen was bought for 12 guineas (£12.60). Its present whereabouts is not known.

Sandwich Tern
Sterna sandvicensis
The first reference we can find is by Sheppard and Whitear in *A Catalogue of the Norfolk and Suffolk Birds, with Remarks* 1826: 51 where they write:

'The Sandwich Tern has been killed at Yarmouth.'

Perhaps surprisingly, Henry Stevenson writes in *The Birds of Norfolk* Vol. lll. 1890: 298-300:

'The first recorded example of which I am aware is mentioned in the Hooker MS. as "taken on Yarmouth beach, in September, 1827".'

The Pagets in *Sketch of the Natural History of Yarmouth and its Neighbourhood* 1834: 12 considered it '…not uncommon.'

Lesser Crested Tern
Sterna bengalensis
An adult was found by Steve Gantlett associating with Sandwich Terns on Blakeney Point on 9th August 1983. It was the second British record.

Steve Gantlett writes:

'On the afternoon of 9th August 1983 I was birdwatching on Blakeney Point looking for a Long-tailed Skua which had been reported in the area a few days previously. I scanned casually through a group of Sandwich Terns resting on the upper beach, and was astonished to see a larger tern with a bright orange bill standing amongst them.
By sheer coincidence just 24-hours previously I had been reading the latest *British Birds* magazine (August 1983 issue) which contained a detailed article

describing how an orange-billed tern in South Wales had been mis-identified as a Lesser Crested Tern when it was, in fact, a Royal Tern. The article pointed out, amongst other things, that Royal Terns could appear much smaller (and therefore much more like Lesser Crested Tern) than previously realized and depicted in the popular field guides. I was determined not to make the same mistake so I, wrongly as it turned out, announced the Blakeney bird as a Royal Tern.

I watched it for just a few minutes, obtaining reasonable views, and then hurried off to alert others. Joe Reed, the National Trust warden, kindly allowed me to use his telephone and by evening some 40 or so birders had hastened to the site at the very tip of Blakeney Point. Fortunately the hundreds of Sandwich Tern chicks in the area had just about all fledged, so there was no problem of observers disturbing this sensitive and important breeding colony. Next morning several hundred bird-watchers arrived. Fortunately the bird didn't disappoint them, and finally it was seen in the area almost daily until 17th September.

As the bird stayed for so long it gave many observers the opportunity to study it in detail. Any doubts that I had that it might be a Royal Tern were debated with others and, as discussions developed, we came to realize that many of the identification features in the current literature were wrong! The bird was in fact a Lesser Crested Tern, a newcomer to the British List!

I obtained the following description of the bird:

A tern very slightly larger than a Sandwich Tern with a striking orange bill. At rest very similar in shape to the accompanying Sandwich Terns, and over-all just slightly larger and heavier. In flight it was distinctly longer-winged. Bill orange with slightly paler tip, of much the same length as Sandwich but significantly thicker especially at base, dagger-like and straight. Legs blackish, much as Sandwich in length and proportion. Extensive white forehead containing only slight blackish flecking. Tiny blackish mark immediately in front of eye. Short but shaggy black crest normally held quite erect – distinctly more so than Sandwich, and when relaxed extending a short way only down nape. Mantle and upperwings pale grey, slightly darker than Sandwich. Tail very slightly paler grey than rest of upperparts with extreme outer edges white. Quite deep fork to tail with slightly longer streamers than Sandwich. Rump pale grey very slightly paler again than tail. In flight upperwing showed darker grey wedge of central primaries, the outer two primaries and the inner ones being relatively pale silvery-grey. Underwing largely whitish with dusky tips to outer four primaries only. Upperparts white. Normal attitude on the ground was a proud 'shoulders forward' stance displaying to Sandwich Terns, particularly to those standing about carrying sand-eels.

The final correct identification was certainly delayed because Lesser Crested Tern, especially the race likely to be involved in European records, is such a poorly known species and is treated misleadingly in the literature. Lesser Crested Terns occur from East Africa east to Australia with some geographical variation in appearance across their range. There is also a little-known population in coastal Libya, which apparently winters in the south west at least as far as The Gambia in West Africa: it is these birds which are likely to be responsible for the British and European records. Interestingly, the East African Lesser Crested is now known to be rather smaller and darker than those from Libya. Since the descriptions in

European field guides are based on East African birds, it is scarcely surprising that the Blakeney individual appeared rather larger and paler than expected.'

(An account published in the *Norfolk Bird Report* 1986: 412-413)

Common Tern
Sterna hirundo
The earliest dated reference we can find is by Thomas Southwell in Henry Stevenson's *The Birds of Norfolk* Vil. lll. 1890: 301-305:

> '…all the older writers speak of the tern as exceedingly common. Sir Thomas Browne (1605-1682) refers to the "Hirundo marina or sea swallowe, a neat white and forked tayle bird butt much longer than a swallowe;" which may be safely taken to be the common tern.'

Roseate Tern
Sterna dougallii
The first fully authenticated record for Norfolk was an adult male shot at Hunstanton by George Hunt on 12th July 1880. The specimen (Accession no. NWHCM: 1888.32) is on display in the bird gallery at the Castle Museum, Norwich.

However, Thomas Southwell writes in Henry Stevenson's *The Birds of Norfolk* Vol. lll. 1890: 300-301:

> 'The roseate tern is included in Hunt's "List" (1829), where it is stated to be "very rare." The Messrs. Paget also (in 1834) say, "Mr. Youell has known this to have been shot here." Following these two authorities, this species has been retained in all the successive lists since that time, but no specimen had ever been produced to substantiate its claim to the position until the one about to be mentioned. As this species was undoubtedly more frequent on the east coast many years ago, of course it is quite possible that both Hunt and Youell may have had sufficient grounds for their remarks but no precise evidence was adduced to verify their statements.
>
> Since that time the roseate tern is said to have been seen on the Norfolk coast more than once, the most precise account being perhaps that of Mr. Booth, who states ("*Rough Notes*," pt.xi.) that one of these birds "flapped slowly past the punt on Breydon mudflats, on the 26th May, 1871," but both barrels being empty at the time, the bird was out of shot before another cartridge could be inserted. All doubt was however removed in 1880, when an adult male was shot at Hunstanton by Mr. George Hunt, on the 12th July.'

This last mentioned specimen was presented to the Castle Museum, Norwich prior to 26th March 1889, on which date Thomas Southwell read a paper to the Norfolk and Norwich Naturalists' Society on the subject of 'Some Recent Additions to the Norfolk and Norwich Museum' where he stated:

> 'Amongst the more noteworthy additions to the British Birds, Lord Lilford has presented a unique Norfolk-killed specimen of the Roseate Tern (*Sterna*

dougallii), shot at Hunstanton on July 12th, 1880.'

Interestingly, Morris's *British Birds* (1857) refers to a specimen shot at Yarmouth in 1846.

Arctic Tern
Sterna paradisaea
An adult was shot at Yarmouth on 30th May 1869, originally part of the Gurney collection and the specimen (Accession no. NWHCM: 1923.74.119), now in the skin collection at the Castle Museum, Norwich, is the first dated record for this species.

Not mentioned by either Sheppard and Whitear (1826) or the Pagets (1834) the earliest reference we can find is by the Rev. Richard Lubbock in *Observations on the Fauna of Norfolk* (1845), new edition by Southwell 1879: 170 where he just comments:

> 'The Gull-billed *(S. anglica)* and the Arctic Tern *(S. arctica)* have both occurred in Norfolk.'

Gurney and Fisher write in 'An Account of the Birds found in Norfolk' published in the *Zoologist* 1846: 1382-1383:

> 'The Arctic Tern is not uncommon in early spring and autumn, on its passage to and from its breeding places in more northern localities.'

Babington (1886-1888) mentions a specimen from Yarmouth recorded in the *Catalogue of British Birds in the collection of the British Museum* produced by George Robert Gray in January 1863 page 241. This would certainly pre-date the 1869 record above, if authentic.

Interestingly, there is a record of one at the Castle Museum, Norwich, (Accession no. NWH-CM: 1835.54.6) which was a gift from Mr. J. Reynolds of Thetford in 1836. No further details are available.

Common Murre (Guillemot)
Uria aalge
The earliest dated reference we can find is by Sir Thomas Brown (1605-1682) in a letter to Merrett dated 8th May 1669 in *Notes and Letters on the Natural History of Norfolk* 1902: 84-85:

> '...that fowle wch some call willick wee meet with sometimes. The last I met with was taken on the sea shoare. the head and body black the brest inclining to black headed and billed like a crowe, leggs set very backward wings short leggs set very backward that it move overland very badly only. it may bee a kind of cornix marina.'

Thomas Southwell qualifies "Willick" in a footnote:

> 'A local name for the Guillemot.'

Common Murre (Guillemot) (Bridled)
Uria aalge
Interestingly, while in Stevenson's time the Common Guillemot was considered common off our coast in lesser or greater numbers especially in the winter months but dependent on weather patterns, the 'bridled' form was not recognised until 9th October 1847.

Thomas Southwell writes in Henry Stevenson's *The Birds of Norfolk* Vol. lll. 1890: 279:

> 'The curious variety known as the RINGED GUILLEMOT has been procured on the coast of Norfolk several times. The first example recorded was killed at Yarmouth on the 9th October, 1847. Messrs. Gurney and Fisher, in announcing it as "new to the Norfolk List," say ("*Zoologist,*" p. 1965), "It was noticed that the mark on each cheek which forms the 'bridle' is not merely a line, but an indentation or groove in the feathers throughout its length".'

Thick-billed Murre (Brunnich's Guillemot)
Uria lomvia
An adult in full breeding plumage was found at Cley by Chris Lansdell on 24th July 2008.

Chris Lansdell writes:

> '24th July 2008 dawned bright with a light easterly breeze and with the day to myself I decided to head the short distance up to Cley.
> Having spent a very pleasant hour or two in North Hide, seeing a good selection of waders including White-rumped Sandpiper, Pectoral Sandpiper, two Curlew Sandpipers and the summering group of five Spoonbills, I decided to leave the hide and take a look at the sea off Cley. There wasn't a great deal happening (just a few Gannets, three Arctic Skuas and a trickle of Common Scoter) so I started looking at a few auks loafing on the sea close in. Having identified both Guillemot and Razorbill, about the sixth bird I looked at had a strikingly obvious white gular stripe and raised alarm bells immediately. During the following 15 minutes or so I watched it (at a range of only 50 yards) and noted the following details:
> An obviously bulky and squat auk (surprisingly so to me) showing black, overall, plumage tones rather than the brownish tinged plumage of Guillemot. Also looking quite short bodied and lacking the longish tail of Razorbill. Short and quite stubby bill in comparison to the longer, more narrow and pointed bill of Guillemot but lacking the striking deep and 'grotesque' bill of a Razorbill. The most obvious feature was a white line extending from the gape to approximately two thirds of the way to the eye and angled slightly downwards. This feature was extremely obvious at the range the bird was viewed at and was what initially rang all the alarm bells for me. The whole of the head, upper breast, mantle, back and wings were uniform blackish with a narrow white line on the wing caused by white tips to secondaries. The underparts were clean white with no dark markings at all. The white breast extended upwards ending in an upside down V shape as in Razorbill but completely unlike Guillemot. I was aware that one species of Guillemot shows this pattern and the other shows a more rounded top to the

breast pattern but wasn't sure which way round it was so carefully noted what this bird showed.

I had been able to clinch everything on it – it was indeed a Brunnich's Guillemot in full summer plumage.

I was well aware that juvenile and first-winter Razorbills can show a superficially similar shaped bill to Brunnich's Guillemot but for an adult in full summer plumage this was obviously irrelevant.

The bird was not seen to flap, fly or dive at all during the viewing period. It was simply drifting very slowly eastwards.

I had been chatting with Tony Gray in the hide earlier and when he ambled up the beach I eagerly waved him over and got him onto the bird. Despite his incredulity he too was 100% happy it was a Brunnich's. At one point we just looked at each other until big grins appeared on both our faces! We then left and half ran back to coastguards to double-check literature before the news was rung out. We returned to the area behind North Hide as quickly as we could but could not relocate the bird. It had been drifting very slowly east. I then walked up as far as Arnold's Marsh scanning the sea but could not find it again despite my best efforts. Tony went on to Salthouse to look for the bird, where it was reported about two hours later by Trevor Davies and Mike Sidwell albeit at c300 yards range.

It was reported again off Sheringham the following day by Phil Vines and John Miller.'

Razorbill

Alca torda

The earliest dated reference we can find is in 'Extracts from the Calendar of the Rev. William Whitear 1809-1826' published in the *Transactions of the Norfolk and Norwich Naturalists' Society* 1881-1882: 259 where he writes:

'About the 18th of July an Auk, which I suppose to be the Razor-bill, was washed ashore alive at Yarmouth. The following is a description of it, taken July 26th 1816:- One channel in the upper mandible, but not white; none in the lower; the channel close to the feathers, mouth yellow; head black, with a rusty tinge; a very narrow line of dull white from bill to eye; throat, back, and tail black; a few white feathers among the black ones below and behind the eye; lesser coverts dusky; secondaries very dark, but not black, and tipped with white; quills not grown; breast, belly, and vent white; irides hazel; legs and feet black; very impatient of water, and got out of a tub of water, when put into it, with great haste.

August 14th, Mr. Youell informs me that the above bird is in high health, and ate one day a fish which weighed three pounds. It still continues its dislike to water, and never offers to drink. The white feathers about the auriculars and throat seem daily increasing.'

Recorded by Sheppard and Whitear in *A Catalogue of the Norfolk and Suffolk Birds with Remarks* (1826) but not commented on, the Pagets *Sketch of the Natural History of Yarmouth and its Neighbourhood* 1834:12 decribed the species as an '…occasional visitant'.

Black Guillemot
Cepphus grylle
Thomas Southwell writes in Henry Stevenson's *The Birds of Norfolk* Vol. lll. 1890: 280:

> 'The first example of this species known to have occurred on the Norfolk coast, is I believe, one which Mr. Dowell tells me was brought to him on the 16th November, 1850, by Mr. Brereton: it was an immature bird, and had been shot at Blakeney by Mr.Loades, a shore gunner there, who noticed it in company with some ducks.'

Little Auk
Alle alle
The earliest dated reference we can find is by Sir Thomas Browne (1605-1682) in *Notes and Letters on the Natural History of* Norfolk 1902: 76-77 in a letter to Merrett dated February 6th [1668-9]:

> 'I present you with a draught of a water-fowl not comon & none of our fowlers can name it the bill could not bee exactly expressed by a coale or black chalk, whereby the little incuruitie of the upper bill & recurvitie of the lower is not discerned. the wings are very short, & it is finne footed. the bill is strong & sharp, if you name it not I am uncertain what to call it pray consider this Anatula or mergus melanoleucus rostro acuto.'

In a later letter to Merrett he writes:

> 'I pray consider whether that waterbird whose draught I sent in the last box & thought it might bee named Anatula or mergus melanoleucos may not bee some gallinula. it hath some resemblance with gallina hyperleucos of Johnst. Tab 32 [31] butt myne hath shorter wings by much & the bill not so long & slender & shorter leggs & lesser & so may ether be called gallina Aquatica hyperleucos nostras or hyperleucos or melanoleucos Anatula or mergus nostras.'

Thomas Southwell adds a footnote:

> 'The "draught" of this bird sent to Merrett is not forthcoming. Professor Newton has been kind enough to send me the following note on this puzzling passage. "Jonston's figure (tab. 31) of *Gallina hyperleucos*, to which Browne says it bore some resemblance, undoubtedly represents what we know as the Common Sandpiper, *Totanus hyperleucos*, or *Actitis hyperleuca*, the *Fysterlin* of the Germans of Jonston's time (p. 160), and *Fisterlein* or *Pfisterlein* of modern days. But there seems to be some strange confusion that cannot now be cleared, between this bird and Browne's *Anatula* or *mergus melanoleucos*, of which some years later, he sent a drawing, under the latter name, to Willughby, in whose work it is described and figured (Lat. Ed. p. 261, Engl. 343, tab. Lix.), for this most certainly is the Rotche or Little Auk, *Mergus alle* of modern ornithology".'

Atlantic Puffin
Fratercula arctica
The earliest dated reference we can find is by Sir Thomas Browne (1605-1682) in *Notes and Letters on the Natural History of Norfolk* 1902: 17 where he writes:

> 'Anas Arctica clusii wch though hee placeth about the faro Islands is the same wee call a puffin common about Anglisea in wales & sometimes taken upon our seas not sufficiently described by the name of puffinus the bill being so remarkably differing from other ducks & not horizontally butt meridionally formed to feed in the clefts of the rocks of insecks, shell-fish & others,'

Pallas's Sandgrouse
Syrrhaptes paradoxus
One was taken at Walpole St Peter in July 1859.

Henry Stevenson writes in *The Birds of Norfolk* Vol. l. 1866: 376-404, having commented on the irruption of this species into Europe in the summer of 1863:

> 'But few, however, of those who in 1863, took so warm an interest in the appearance of these birds on our eastern coast were probably aware that the Lynn museum contained a fine male specimen, killed in that neighbourhood in July, 1859, one of the first if not actually the the first example obtained in the United Kingdom. The occurrence of this extreme rarity was at once made known to the scientific world in a letter to the "*Ibis*" (1859, p. 472) by the Rev. F. L. Currie, who was at that time residing in the neighbourhood of Lynn, and took a lively interest in its museum collections. From this communication it appears that the above specimen, in very perfect plumage, was shot early in the month of July, in the Parish of Walpole St. Peter's, about two miles from the Wash, and, as Mr. Currie remarks, "we must congratulate ourselves upon our good fortune in securing the bird at all, considering it was shot by a labouring youth wholly unacquainted with its value, and who was quite as likely to have plucked and eaten, or thrown the prize away (the fate of many a valuable specimen), as to have placed it in the hands of the Rev. R, Hankinson, to whom the Lynn museum is indebted for this most interesting specimen, beautifully mounted by Mr. Leadbeater." It had been previously skinned, however, by a local bird-stuffer, and the carcase unfortunately was not preserved. It was solitary when shot, but at least one other, apparently of the same species, was observed in the neighbourhood about the same time, though not procured.'

The Rev. F. L. Currie mentioned above, adds writing in the *Zoologist* 1859: 6764:

> 'There is reason to believe the present specimen to be an adult male, in perfect plumage, the beautiful elongated feathers of the tail and wings happily uninjured'

Enquiries at King's Lynn Museum in 2008 failed to establish whether either of the two specimens in the museum collection is the Walpole St Peter bird.

Common Pigeon (Rock Dove/Feral Pigeon)
Columba livia
The only county record of an absolutely typical pure Common Pigeon was a bird picked up dead at Ludham on 9th December 1925.

Arthur Henry Patterson writing in the *Transactions of the Norfolk and Norwich Naturalists' Society* 1926-1927: 299-303, states:

> '1925… On December 9th a dove was picked up dead at Ludham which had been wounded on the breast. It was sent to me with a letter in which it was suggested that it might prove to be a Rock dove (*Columba livia*), an opinion with which I agreed. The bird was sent to Dr. Riviere, and was also examined by Mr. Witherby and Captain Lea Rayner. The latter, who is an expert on homing pigeons, considered it unlikely that it could be the produce of any domestic pigeon. The severe weather prevailing, with northerly snow storms, was probably responsible for its presence in Norfolk. The Yorkshire cliffs are undoubtedly its nearest breeding place.'

Although there is some concern regarding this record, Riviere (1930) considered it to be fully authentic.

B. B. Riviere writes:

> 'The first example of a genuine wild Rock-Dove, which, so far as I am aware, has ever occurred in Norfolk, was picked up dead – wounded in the breast – at Ludham on Dec. 9th, and kindly forwarded to me by Mr. A. H. Patterson. Mr. Witherby and I have compared this bird with the large series of Rock-Doves in the former's collection, and in colouring, size and type, and especially in the character of the bill, it matches them exactly, and in fact could not be picked out from amongst them. Moreover, to make doubly certain, I showed it to Captain Lea Rayner, a well-known judge of Homing Pigeons, who judges the Homer Classes at some of the leading Pigeon Shows, and he immediately expressed the opinion that it could not be the produce of any domestic Pigeons, however inbred and "run wild." It must have been a late hatched bird, as it had only moulted the five innermost primaries. Possibly the severe weather prevailing at the time, with blizzards and snow storms, may have accounted for its presence in Norfolk, the nearest breeding-place of the Rock Dove being, I believe, the cliffs of the Yorkshire coast.'

(Originally published in *British Birds* 19: 243-244)

Acquired by Norwich taxidermist F. E. Gunn, the specimen (Accession no. NWHCM: 2009.37.1) is now a study-skin in storage at the Castle Museum, Norwich.

Stock Dove
Columba oenas
The earliest dated reference we can find is by Henry Stevenson in *The Birds of Norfolk* Vol. 1. 1866: 355-359 where he writes in a footnote:

'These birds occur twice in the "Privy Purse Accoiunts" of the estranges, of Hunstanton (1519-1578), as follows: - Itm in rewarde the xvij daye of Novembre to Osbert Reds sone, for bryngyng of stockdowes. "itm ij stockdowes of gyste".'

Commenting on the fact that this species often nests on the ground in deserted rabbit burrows:

'Mr. Alfred Newton tells me that the young stock-doves, being a prerequisite of the warreners, are a source of not inconsiderable profit to them, as they sell them for from eighteen pence to two shillings (£00.15 to £00.20) a couple, and that in consequence almost every warrener keeps a "dowe-dawg," i.e. a dog regularly trained to discover the burrows in which the doves breed. Mr. Scales, of Beechamwell, adds that "when the warreners find them in a burrow, they fix sticks at the mouth of the hole in such a manner as to prevent the escape of the young, but to allow the old birds to feed them." Mr. Newton, however, informs me that this precaution is thought to be unnecessary for the more experienced warreners, from long practice, know to a day (by once seeing the nestlings) when they will be fit to take.'

Common Wood Pigeon
Columba palumbus
The first reference we can find is by James Fisher in the Foreword to Michael Seago's *Birds of Norfolk* (1967) where he writes:

'If the text of the *Blickling Homilies* be a Norfolk text, then the first Norfolk birds mentioned in writing may be their *scealfor* (great crested grebe, probably), *culfre* (woodpigeon) and *turtura* (turtle dove) of 970 or a few years before – a millennium ago.'

The first dated reference we can find is in extracts from Robert Marsham's 'Indications of Spring' published in the *Transactions of the Norfolk and Norwich Naturalist's Society* 1874-1875: 35 where he recorded in the Stratton Strawless area on 22nd January 1750:

'…I heard a ringdove coo.'

Eurasian Collared Dove
Streptopelia decaocto
A pair, first seen at Overstrand in April 1955, nested there and successfully fledged two young. At least two of these birds wintered in the area being fed on corn by a resident, and up to three more were in a garden at Cromer the same year. Also in 1955, Peter Clarke had observed a fawn-coloured dove on wires above the coast road at Cley, but disregarded it as a similar looking hybrid that had been in the area two years previously. In hindsight this was also likely to have been a Eurasian Collared Dove. None of this was known until 1957, the year after Michael Seago found two in a walled Garden at Overstrand on 3rd July 1956 (Plate 1), which were thought at the time to hail the initial colonisation of Norfolk and thus of Britain.

Michael Seago, Richard Richardson and Andrew Church write:

'On 3rd July, 1956, M.J.S. was attracted by the unfamiliar tri-syllabic cooing of two doves, one of which was seen, in the trees of a large walled garden near the sea in North Norfolk. Later, on consulting published descriptions and an illustration of the collared dove (*Streptopelia decaocto*), he found they tallied very favourably with his field notes.

In the weeks that followed either R.A.R. or A.C.C. were able to visit the site for varying periods almost daily and their observations, necessarily restricted owing to the very public nature of the site, are summarised below. Meanwhile, reports of similar birds were received from a locality a mile and a half away on the outskirts of a small coastal town, all of which proved to be '*decoacto*' and not the domesticated Barbary dove (*S. risoria*) nor any hybrid.

Intensive enquiries within the county and an appeal for information in the regional press have so far failed to produce evidence of "escapes" or liberated birds and there seems no reason to suppose that these Norfolk specimens are anything other than genuine wild colonists from the Continent.'

(Extracted from an account first published in the *Norfolk Bird Report* 1956: 21-23, which also contained details of all known, but undisclosed, breeding sites in the county by the end of 1956)

Michael Seago writes in *The Birds of Norfolk* 1999: 346-348, of which he was co-author:

'The writer of this species text found three Collared Doves on 3rd July 1956 at Overstrand in a large walled garden containing extensive lawns, shrubberies, evegreen oaks, pines, Spanish chestnuts, and also a poultry run. That summer the known pair raised three broods and five young fledged. Nearby at Cromer two pairs nested and three young flew from the nests. The following year details came to light of a pair of Collared Doves which had bred in 1955 at Cromer and reared two young.'

European Turtle Dove
Streptopelia turtur
The earliest reference we can find is by James Fisher in Michael Seago's *Birds of Norfolk* (1967) where he writes:

'If the text of the *Blickling Homilies* be a Norfolk text, then the first Norfolk birds mentioned in writing may be their *scealfor* (great crested grebe, probably), *culfre* (woodpigeon) and *turtura* (turtle dove) of 970 or e few years before – a millennium ago.'

Listed by Sheppard and Whitear in *A Catalogue of the Norfolk and Suffolk Birds, with Remarks* (1826) but not commented on and and considered '…rarely seen' by the Pagets in *Sketch of the Natural History of Yarmouth and its Neighbourhood* 1834: 7, the earliest dated reference we can find is by Henry Stevenson in *The Birds of Norfolk* Vol. l. 1866: 359-360:

'In the western parts of the county, about Feltwell and Brandon, they are now extremely plentiful, and in the vicinity of the coast abound in the extensive fir coverts about Cromer and Sheringham; yet, in 1846, the Rev. E. W. Dowell, in his MS. notes, records one shot at Roydon, and another at North Pickenham, as rarities in that part of Norfolk, and states that a specimen "shot at Brinton puzzled all who saw it for some years, as it had never been seen there before".'

Oriental (Rufous) Turtle Dove
Streptopelia orientalis
One was shot at Castle Rising on 29th January 1946 (Plate 9). It was only the second British record and the specimen (Accession no. NWHCM: 2009.90), a gift from J. Donaldson, is in the skin collection at the Castle Museum, Norwich.

An account was published in *Wild Bird Protection in Norfolk* 1946: 26-27:

'On January 9th, during a pheasant shoot at Castle Rising, a turtle dove was flushed from a covert by beaters and shot by one of the guns. It was sent to Norwich Castle Museum for identification and proved to be a specimen of the Eastern Turtle Dove (*Streptopelia orientalis*). The distinguishing features were the large size, the dark slate-blue rump, and grey instead of white under tail-coverts, tips of neck patch feathers and ends of tail feathers. The bird was badly damaged but it appeared to be completing a moult from juvenile to first winter plumage. It proved on dissection to be a female. It may have been an "escape" but a letter in the "*Eastern Daily Press*" asking for information as to any known to have been kept in aviaries met with no response.
The bird was identified by B. B. Riviere, F.R.C.S. and E. A. Ellis.'

In the above account, the 9th January date is a misprint. The specimen label at the Castle Museum, Norwich confirms the date as the 29th. Although Seago in *Birds of Norfolk* (1967) gives the date as the 9th, it is corrected in the 1977 edition.

Rose-ringed (Ring-necked) Parakeet
Psittacula krameri
The earliest dated reference we can find is by Moss Taylor in *The Birds of Norfolk* 1999: 349, of which he is co-author:

'In Europe it occurs patchily in The Netherlands, Belgium and Germany, as well as in England, which supports the largest naturalised European population. Those in Europe are assumed to have originated from escaped or released birds. It first appeared in the wild in England in 1969 and by the time that it was admitted to Category C of the British and Irish list in England in 1977, the feral population was estimated at 500-1,000 birds, mostly in Kent and the Thames Valley. On the 19th August 1998 no less than 1,507 were counted leaving a roost in Esher in Surrey.
As long ago as 1855 J. H. Gurney confirmed nesting in the wild at Northrepps and on five occasions young were successfully fledged. The only other breeding record in Norfolk concerned a pair which bred in the King's Lynn area just prior to 1974… However, it was not until 1975 that the species featured for the first time in the *Norfolk Bird Report*.'

It is very interesting, and possibly alarming, to note that figures released in 2008 show that up to 7,000 now roost at Esher in Surrey and the British population of the species is estimated at 30,000.

Great Spotted Cuckoo
Clamator glandarius
Only the second British record, a young male, was shot by Edmund 'a gunner' on the denes between Yarmouth and Caister on 18th October 1896. Formerly in the Connop collection at Rollesby Hall, this specimen was donated to the City of Birmingham Museum in 1954 and remains in storage there.

J. H. Gurney writes in the *Zoologist* 1897: 135:

> 'October (Prevailing wind South-west.) 18th. - A Greater Spotted Cuckoo, *Coccystes glandarius*, immature, with dark crown, rich buff chest, and very little crest, shot between Caister and Yarmouth golf-house. This bird (minus its tail, which was unfortunately scattered to the winds) was bought by Mr. E. C. Saunders, who forwarded the body. It was a male, with single-notched sternum, and with a simple projecting manubrium, very like our Common Cuckoo. The gizzard and oesophagus, which seemed very dilatable, contained fragments of black insects with yellow lines upon them, identified, after some trouble, by Messrs. R., McLachlan and C. O. Waterhouse as the larvae of *Pygaera bucephala*, the Buff-tip Moth. This Cuckoo had probably come over the day before, when the wind was from the north, and most likely from the same place as the Macqueen's Bustard which was shot at Humber-mouth (also on the 18th), and perhaps from the Don or Volga. Or both of them may have come on the 16th, when there was wind amounting to a gale from the north-east, and this latter supposition is more probable.'

Interestingly, when Edmund took the bird to him Saunders offered him a reward to find the missing tail feathers, and some time later Edmund returned with most of them (E A Ellis *pers comm*). Widely respected and celebrated Norfolk naturalist Ted Ellis knew Saunders well and we must presume this is true.

Common Cuckoo
Cuculus canorus
The earliest dated reference we can find is by Sir Thomas Brown (1605-1682) in *Notes and Letters on the Natural History of Norfolk* 1902: 20:

> 'Cuccowes of 2 sorts the one farre exceeding the other in bignesse. some have attempted to keepe them in warme roomes all winter butt it hath not succeeded. in their migration they range very farre northward for in summer they are to bee found as high as Island.'

Thomas Southwell adds a footnote:

> 'The circumstances which give rise to the idea that there were two kinds of Cuckoos, differing only in size, might possibly be discovered were it worth the research; possibly it would be found that the second species was of foreign origin.

Aldrovandus, as quoted by Willughby, says, "Our Bolognese Fowlers do unanimously affirm, that there are found a greater and a lesser sort of Cuckows; and besides, that the greater of the two kinds, which are distinguished one from the other by the only difference of colour: but the lesser differ from the greater in nothing else but magnitude." Perhaps it was Browne's latent respect for antiquity which led him to mention the tradition.'

Barn Owl
Tyto alba alba
Known as the White Owl by earlier writers, the first references we can find are by Sheppard and Whitear in *A Catalogue of the Norfolk and Suffolk Birds, with Remarks* 1826: 7 where they referred to it in general terms:

> 'This bird, as well as others of the genus, is destructive among rabbits, as we have been informed by a relative, who has shot it in the very act of striking them on a warren: and we have ourselves frequently seen White Owls skimming over the burrows.'

The Pagets in *Sketch of the Natural History of Yarmouth and its Neighbourhood* 1834: 4 considered it '…common'.

Dark-breasted Barn Owl
Tyto alba guttata
One, believed to be the first British record, was obtained near Norwich about 13th December 1864.

Henry Stevenson writes in *The Birds of Norfolk* Vol. l. 1866: 51-54:

> 'An extremely dark variety of this owl in Norwich museum (British series, No. 29.B), was killed near Norwich about the 13th December 1864, and is particularly interesting from its similarity, both in colour and markings, to a specimen in our Raptorial collection, presented by Professor Reinhardt. Of the latter, this gentleman writes in a letter to Mr. A. Newton (Oct. 9th, 1860), "I have ordered a stuffed *Strix flammea* to be put up in a little box, which will be dispatched to the care of Mr. Goddard, one of the first days. The bird is from Fyen (Funen), but it is, I think, no peculiar race; at least not peculiar to the said island where the bird is rare; I should rather suppose that all the examples of *S. flammea* from Sleswig Holstein and the northern parts of Germany are nearly as dark beneath as the specimens you saw in Copenhagen." I am not aware that this dark variety has received any specific distinction, but it is quite possible, as Mr. Newton is inclined to believe, that the bird in question may have come across from the Danish locality, whence Professor Reinhardt's example was procured. Supposing this to be really the case, the question naturally arises, whether barn owls from more eastern localities may not, occasionally at least, visit our coast in autumn? Of this I have no direct proof at the present time, but all I have known to be killed or wounded here, by the telegraph wires, have been invariably picked up in the three last months of the year. The Norwich specimen differs from any I have ever seen killed in this country (although the young birds of the year are

more or less dark on the under parts), in having the whole of the lower surface of the body rich reddish fawn colour; the facial disk rusty red, becoming greyish white only, near the outer edge, and the upper portions of the plumage ash grey spotted as usual, but still with a little more intermixture of the buff than in the Danish bird.'

Eurasian Scops Owl
Otus scops

The first authenticated county record was one picked up alive, but injured, near the foot of Cromer lighthouse on the morning of 27th November 1861 (Plate 6). Previously in the Henry Stevenson collection, this specimen (Accession no. NWHCM: 1935.15.11), now much faded, is on display in the bird gallery at the Castle Museum, Norwich.

Henry Stevenson writes in *The Birds of Norfolk* Vol. l. 1866: 42-43:

'On the morning of the 27th of November, 1861, an adult male was picked up at the foot of the lighthouse hill, at Cromer, by one of Mr. Gurney's keepers, who found the bird still alive, but evidently much injured from flying against the glass, attracted by the glare of the lamps during the previous night, when, half stunned, it had fallen to the ground and fluttered down the hill to the spot where it was picked up. This bird, now in Mr. Gurney's collection at Catton, had a mass of fur in the stomach about the size of a walnut, amongst which was discernible an almost perfect skeleton of a mouse, together with the heads and forceps of several earwigs, and three stout caterpillars nearly an inch in length. The head exhibited no marks of injury, and the plumage was perfect, but the flesh on the breast and the point of one wing showed symptoms of having sustained a very severe blow.'

Interestingly, the Rev. William Whitear writes in 1824 in 'Extracts from the Calendar of the Rev. William Whitear 1809-1826' published in the *Transactions of the Norfolk and Norwich Naturalists' Society* 1881-1882: 255:

'On the 17th June, 1824, a specimen of the *Strix scops* was shot by Mr. George Wigg, at Strumpshaw, in Norfolk; and is now in the collection of John Dear, Esq., of Bradiston. Mr. Brown has seen it.'

Gurney and Fisher (1846) mentioned they knew of two specimens which were said to have been killed near Norwich, which may have included this record.

Snowy Owl
Bubo scandiacus

One was shot at Felbrigg in April 1814.

Sheppard and Whitear in *A Catalogue of the Norfolk and Suffolk Birds, with Remarks* 1826: 7, state:

'A female Snowy Owl was shot at Felbrigg in Norfolk the first week in April 1814, the weight of which was 5 and a quarter pounds; length 2 feet; breadth

5 feet 4 inches. This is the first instance we have heard of the Snowy Owl being seen in England.'

The Rev. William Whitear adds in 'Extracts from the Calendar of the Rev. William Whitear 1809-1826' published in the *Transactions of the Norfolk and Norwich Naturalists' Society* 1881-1882: 260:

'A female Snowy Owl was sent by Mr. Hornby to Corbett, April 5th, 1814…'

Henry Stevenson writes in *The Birds of Norfolk* Vol. l. 1866: 57-58:

'Mr. Hunt, in his "*British Ornithology*," states that one was shot at Felbrigg during the spring of 1814, and adds – "The weather had been previously exceedingly severe during nearly three months. This specimen, we are informed by the Rev. G. Glover, was presented to Lord Stanley. It had been observed for several days standing on a heap of snow which had been blown against a fir; it had been often roused, and was at length taken with difficulty".'

Little Owl
Athene noctua
Interestingly, Peter Dolton writes in *The Birds of Norfolk* 1999: 353-354:

'The Little Owl is not a native species to Britain. Introductions commenced in 1843 though it is thought that birds released in Kent in the 1870s and in Northamptonshire in the 1880s gave rise to the successful colonisation of England. Records in Norfolk predating these could have referred to immigrants from the Continent, possibly The Netherlands.
Hunt, in *British Ornithology*, published in 1815-22, referred to a nest being taken at 'no great distance from Norwich' but the record was not included in his 'List of Norfolk Birds' of 1829. Stevenson recorded one killed at Blofield in 1824 noted by Mr.Lombe, and Paget gave two instances of specimens having been taken in Yarmouth prior to 1834 and commented that they were 'well authenticated'. An example that could refer to an immigrant from the Continent came on to a fishing smack ten miles off Yarmouth in February 1862.'

Tawny Owl
Strix aluco
Just listed as the "Brown Owl" by Sheppard and Whitear in *A Catalogue of the Norfolk and Suffolk Birds, with Remarks* (1826), but not commented on. The earliest reference we can find is by the Pagets in *Sketch of the Natural History of Yarmouth and its Neighbourhood* 1834: 4, where they also knew it as the Brown Owl, and considered it '…common'.

Long-eared Owl
Asio otus
The earliest reference we can find is by Sheppard and Whitear in *A Catalogue of the Norfolk and Suffolk Birds, with Remarks* 1826: 8 where they write:

'It is said to be common near Beccles, and to breed in that neighbourhood. A female of this species, which we killed on the 13th of March, was not so beautiful as a male killed the beginning of the same month. We have seen seven of these birds together, and on bing disturbed they would take flight high in the air, where they resembled Hawks.'

Beccles is in Suffolk but the "neighbourhood" would certainly have included Norfolk.

The Pagets in *Sketch of the Natural History of Yarmouth and its Neighbourhood* 1834: 3 considered it '…rarely seen.'

Short-eared Owl
Asio flammeus
The earliest dated reference we can find is in 'Extracts from the Calendar of the Rev. William Whitear 1809-1826' published in the *Transactions of the Norfolk and Norwich Naturalists' Society* 1881-1882: 256 where he writes:

'In the month of May, 1825, two pairs of Short-eared Owls were found sitting on their eggs, on the ground, four eggs in each nest, on the property of the Rev. Robert Hamond, at Congham, in Norfolk, 'Norwich Chronicle,' May 21.'

Sheppard and Whitear write in *A Catalogue of the Norfolk and Suffolk Birds, with Remarks* 1826: 7-8:

'These Owls visit this part of the kingdom in September and October, and remain till spring. They arrive in flocks of from ten to twenty, and frequent heaths; in which respect they differ from the Long-eared species, which is fond of the gloom of fir plantations. Montagu says, that the ears of a dead specimen are not discoverable; but in one which we have seen, the ears remained distinct from the rest of the plumage after the bird was killed, - dead or alive there was no difference.'

Boreal (Tengmalm's) Owl
Aegolius funereus
One was caught at Beechamwell, near Swaffham on 27th June 1849.

Thomas Southwell writes in Henry Stevenson's *The Birds of Norfolk* Vol. lll. 1890: 385:

'One in Mr. Dowell's collection was taken alive by a labouring man, at Beechamwell, near Swaffham, on the 27th June 1849. It was found sitting in a bush, apparently dazzled by the bright sunlight, and "mobbed" by jays, blackbirds, and a flock of smaller tormentors.'

It is worth noting that the month in which this bird was caught is considered by Yarrell (1871-1885) and Harting (1872) as January 27th, while Lubbock (1879), Gurney and Southwell (1884-1889) and Riviere (1930) considered it to be June 27th. All agree on the year.

Interestingly, Gurney and Fisher write in the *Zoologist* 1846: 1305:

'One of these Owls was taken some years since at Bradwell, in the north-eastern part of the county of Suffolk.'

Henry Stevenson writing in *Birds of Norfolk* Vol. l.1860: 60, after referring to an 1857 record at Burlingham, states:

'…but a single specimen is recorded by Messrs. Gurney and Fisher to have been taken some years since at Bradwell, in the north-eastern part of Suffolk; and may have been the bird which was formerly in the collection of Mr. Stephen Miller at Yarmouth.'

He adds in a footnote:

'This celebrated collection, to which I shall have frequent occasion to refer, was sold by auction at Yarmouth, in September 1853, subsequent to Mr. Miller's decease, but the bad state of preservation of many of the specimens, unfortunately rendered them of little value.'

Prior to the 1974 county boundary changes Bradwell was in Suffolk.

European Nightjar

Caprimulgus europaeus

The earliest dated reference we can find is by Sir Thomas Brown (1605-1682) in *Notes and Letters on the Natural History of Norfolk* 1902: 26:

'A Dorhawke or kind of Accipiter muscarius conceiued to haue its name from feeding upon flies & beetles. of a woodcock colour but paned like an Hawke a very little pointed bill. large throat. breedeth with us & layes a maruellous handsome spotted egge. Though I haue opened many I could neuer find anything considerable in their mawes. caprimulgus.'

He expands on this in a Letter to Merrett in 1668:

'A Dorhawke a bird not full so bigge as a pigeon somewhat of a woodcock colour & paned somewhat like a hawke with a bill not much bigger than that of a Titmouse & very wide throat known by the name of a dorhawke or prayer upon beetles, as though it were some kind of accipiter muscarius. in brief this accipiter cantharophagus or dorhawke is *Avis Rostratula gutturosa, quasi coaxans, scarabaeis vescens, sub vesperam volans, ouum specioisissimu excludens*. I haue had many of them & and am sorry I have not one to send you I spoake to a friend to shoote one butt I doubt they are gone ouer.'

Common Swift

Apus apus

Not mentioned by Sir Thomas Browne (1605-1682) in *Notes and Letters on the Natural History of Norfolk* (1902), although he does refer to "swifts" in the 'Fishes' section, but these are newts. Sheppard and Whitear in *A Catalogue of the Norfolk and Sufolk Birds, with Remarks* (1826) just list it as Swift and Deviling, but it is not commented on. The earliest dated reference we can find is in 'Extracts from the Calendar of the Rev. William Whitear 1809-1826' published in the *Transaction of the Norfolk and Norwich Naturalists' Society* 1881-1882: 242 where he rcorded one on 14th May 1816 in the Starston area.

The Pagets in *Sketch of the Natural History of Yarmouth and its Neighbourhood* 1834: 4 considered it '…common.'

Pallid Swift
Apus pallidus
One was found by Peter Colston flying over Burnham Overy Marshes with Common Swifts on 25th July 1993.

Peter Colston writes:

'I was stationed on the sea wall at Burnham Norton from 0930 hours on 25th July 1993 watching the rather inactive Oriental Pratincole squatting on the mud. At 1120 hours a party of Arctic Skuas arrived ahead of a black thunder-cloud. Many Swifts also moved ahead of the storm track and their numbers began building up over the fresh-marsh. It was fairly sunny in a blustery south-west wind and the last few Swifts heading inland were making slow progress. Suddenly, among the tail-enders was an amazing pale individual which shone like a beacon against the backdrop of the storm behind Scolt Head. It was very pale milky-brown with extensive white throat, pale forehead, distinctive jizz and flight. I estimated its distance at a third of a mile at a hundred feet. I watched the bird intently as it came towards me in company with 3 or 4 Common Swifts. It took a full minute to come close and gave me sufficient time to assess a mental checklist of Pallid features. When certain that the bird could only be a Pallid Swift, I shouted to nearby birders "Look at this swift!". Only three were near enough to hear. The bird slowly flapped and glided past showing all features typical of a Pallid Swift. The overall paleness (especially the head), large white throat patch, more paddle-shaped wings with slightly rounded tips were obvious as was the contrast between the slightly darker primaries and the paler inner wing.

The other observers, all unfamiliar with Pallid Swifts, remarked how obviously different the bird was in colour, shape and flight from Common Swift. Without priming them on the differences one pointed out 'blunter wing tips, pale inner wing with contrastingly darker primaries – the opposite of Common Swift'. The bird passed over the sea wall before joining large numbers of wheeling Swifts. I followed it for a further ten minutes; it was always identifiable even against the light by its slightly more robust shape, differing wing configuration, less forked tail and rather predictable flight pattern.

Pallid Swift breeds along rocky coasts, in mountain regions and in towns in southern Europe and north-west Africa. This sighting is the first recorded in Norfolk. During November 1984, a total of four, forming part of a late autumn influx of southern birds, appeared in Britain. The first British record was from Kent in 1978.'

(An account published in the *Norfolk Bird Report* 1994: 367)

Fork-tailed (Pacific) Swift
Apus pacificus
The first for Britain was found by Alan Brown and identified by Steve Gantlett at Cley on 30th May 1993 (Plate 12), following a heavy arrival of Swifts.

Steve Gantlett writes:

'At 10.45am on 30th May 1993 I arrived back at Cley Coastguards' car-park after an early morning sojourn on Blakeney Point to enjoy once again the Desert Warbler there. Alan Brown was in the car-park talking to Jackie and Dave Bridges about a strange swift he had just seen over the adjacent Cley Reserve.

I joined them and Alan explained that he had just been in the North Hide and had spent ten minutes watching an odd swift with a white rump. Mindful of the relative frequency of partial albino Common Swifts he felt quite sure it was no more than that. Jackie and Dave set out for Blakeney Point and the Desert Warbler. I was anxious to see the bird, however, and accompanied by Alan I hurried down to the North Hide in case it was still there. It was indeed flying around over the North Scrape with Common Swifts. But its very clearly demarcated white rump instantly suggested that this was more than just a Common Swift exhibiting partial albinism. It was certainly very close to the Common Swifts in size, but its wings were considerably more scythe-shaped and its tail was noticeably longer and more deeply forked. This was clearly very interesting indeed!

I called Richard Millington and suggested that he hasten to the North Hide; Alan headed back to the car-park to alert other birders. There were really only two possibilities for the bird's identity. It had to be either a White-rumped Swift or a Pacific Swift even though the former is not on the British List and the latter has not occurred naturally in Britain. It was very slightly larger than the Common Swifts so that seemed to rule out the former, but Pacific Swift should show indistinct greyish feather-edgings to the body feathers. Although I knew that these greyish scaly markings were very difficult to see they were not visible even though the bird was often no more than 80 yards away in quite good light.

Within a minute or two the bird obligingly did a fly-past just 25 yards in front of the hide. It was clear that it did have faint grey scaling on both the upperbody and the underbody. It was a Pacific Swift.

The news was on Birdline by 11am and birders from all over the country were converging on Cley Norfolk Naturalists Trust Reserve! The bird remained flying around the marsh with Common Swifts until about 4.10pm when it disappeared. By this time several hundred observers had seen it. Other less fortunate ones were still arriving from further afield well into the evening. It was not seen again.

DESCRIPTION
Size and structure Superficially similar to Common Swift, but very slightly larger and more rakish with distinctly more swept back, scythe-shaped wings, with less obvious angle at carpal joint. Tail noticeably longer, more pointed and more deeply forked than Common Swift; forked even when fanned.

Head and upperparts Dark brownish-black, with greyer head, pale throat and narrow grey tips to feathers producing scaly appearance to nape and mantle, but only visible at very close range in favourable light. Off-white rump patch quite sharply defined and wrapping around sides of tail-base, and very obvious even at ranges of up to half a mile.

Wings Dark brownish-black, darkest on underwing coverts, and very slightly paler on upperwing coverts. Undersides of remiges dark, slightly silvery, grey. Upperside of remiges similar but darker, and contrasting rather less with upperwing coverts.

Tail Dark brownish-black.

Underparts Dark greyish-black, slightly paler than upperbody, with narrow grey tips to feathers producing scaly appearance to whole underbody only visible at very close range in favourable light (but more obvious and distinct than on upperparts).

The Pacific Swift breeds from Siberia eastwards to Kamchatka and Japan and south to south-east Asia. Northern populations winter from Malaysia to Australia.

The only other European record of a Pacific Swift is an exhausted bird caught (by R. Walden) on a gas platform 28 miles off Happisburgh, Norfolk on 19th June 1981. It was flown by helicopter to Beccles, Suffolk, where it was released the same evening.'

(An account published in the *Norfolk Bird Report* 1993: 133-134)

Interestingly, the 1981 bird appears in Piotrowski's *The Birds of Suffolk* (2003) in the Systematic List as an apparently accepted Suffolk record, '…seen associating with Swifts at nearby Shadingfield the following day.'

Alpine Swift
Apus melba
One was shot near the castle at Old Buckenham in the latter part of September 1831. The specimen (Accession no. NWHCM: 1865.21) is on display in the bird gallery at the Castle Museum, Norwich.

Henry Stevenson writes in *The Birds of Norfolk* Vol. l. 1866: 346-347:

'But one specimen of the White-bellied Swift is known to have occurred in Norfolk, of which I am enabled to give the following particulars through the kindness of the Rev. Thomas Fulcher, of Old Buckenham, who has recently presented this mostinteresting bird to the Norwich Museum:- "There is a slight inaccuracy (he writes) in Yarrell's notice of it. It was shot in Old Buckenham, in a field between the old castle and New Buckenham parsonage, in the latter part of September (not 13th October), 1831. The gentleman who shot it left it, whilst still warm and bleeding, with a bird-stuffer in New Buckenham, but neither of them knew the value of it. After a few weeks it was offered to me, and I had it preserved. A friend of mine [Daniel Stock of Bungay] sent an account of it to "*Loudon's Magazine*" the same year. In February, 1833, I made a pen and ink sketch of the bird, natural size, and sent it with a full description to Professor

James Rennie, who inserted a reduced copy of the figure with my description in the "*Field Naturalist*" (vol. i., No, iv., p. 172). The following are the dimensions of this specimen as given in the above journal, although, as Mr. Fulcher remarks, "in measuring it some allowance must be made for the shrivelled state of the skin:" – "The length, from the tip of the bill to the end of the tail, is rather more than eight inches; breadth across the wings twenty inches; it is much more bulky than the common swift (*Cypselus murarius Temminck*), and must have weighed, at least, as much again. Bill nearly two-fifths of an inch long, measured from the base of the upper mandible, curved and black; the colour of the irides unknown, but I believe it was dusky. The head, back of the neck, back, wings, and tail grey brown, and the edges of the feathers of a paler colour. Round the breast is a collar of grey brown. The throat, lower part of the breast, and the body to the commencement of the under tail-coverts white; the sides dusky, with a mixture of dull white; under surface of the wings and tail, and the under tail-coverts dusky. The quill-feathers are darker than the back, and remarkably strong and pointed; the quills dusky white. The tail is more than three inches long, forked, and consists of exactly ten feathers. Legs short and strong, flesh coloured, and feathered to the toes, which are all placed forward, as in the common swift; the claws strong and brownish black".'

Little Swift

Apus affinis
One was discovered by Gary Wright at Cromer Cliffs on 12th November 2005.

Gary Wright writes:

'On 12th November, having spent the morning decorating and listening to the cricket on the radio, I decided the weather was too good to waste indoors. I would like to have spent the afternoon at Holkham Bay looking at grebes but the rest of the family fancied a walk closer to home along the clifftops between Cromer and Overstrand, with the swings of Happy Valley being a particular lure for my children. The swings won I was out-voted and I took my binoculars almost as an afterthought.

Having got the swings out of the way, we walked along the clifftops across the golf course, enjoying the late autumnal sunshine. At about 3.15 pm and halfway to Overstrand, I noticed what I thought was a hirundine hawking along the cliff-face about 150 yards ahead. Raising my binoculars and expecting to see perhaps a late Swallow, I was surprised to see it was a swift. Thoughts of Chimney Swift went briefly through my mind in view of the recent influx but as the bird banked, it revealed a big square white rump. I thought for a moment that I must have been mistaken and that it was a late House Martin but no, the underparts were all dark and it was indeed a swift. I quickly realised I was watching a Little Swift, a species I had seen abroad, and ran to get closer views.

I reached a vantage spot whereby the bird was feeding just off the cliff edge in front of me and swooping past within 10 feet in bright sunshine. When my family caught up, I got them all to note the features – even my 5 year old son could pick out the big square white rump on an otherwise dark bird with his naked eye! The bird also had a square tail, comparable to a house Martin in size and shape and had a noticeably whitish forehead and throat, especially when viewed head on. All this was obvious with the naked eye, even without binoculars. I told my children that this was a 'big one', not just a 'nice bird for Dad'.

I was anxious to get birders to the site before dark but didn't have a mobile phone with me and the nearest public phone was over half a mile away in Overstrand. I was worried about running the distance, having had major back surgery a few months previously, but after watching the bird for 5 minutes, I decided to make the dash. My back held and I remembered the Birdline number whilst my children carried on watching the bird. By the time I returned the bird appeared to have moved on so I was relieved when it was soon relocated half a mile closer to Cromer by the first visiting birders; putting on a show until darkness before roosting on the cliff face in plummeting temperatures.

The following morning, 300-400 people gathered in the dark, hoping to see the bird leave its roost at dawn. There were some anxious moments initially when it became apparent the bird was not on its ledge but fortunately it was eventually spotted clinging onto the cliff just a few feet below the crowd and almost within touching distance of increasingly desperate birders. With the weather now cold and grey, with a sharp northerly wind blowing, the bird looked a pathetic shivering creature huddled into the cliff and quite unlike the bird of the previous afternoon. At 8 am, however, it lifted off, quickly gathering itself, gained height and disappeared to the south, not to be seen again.'

(An account published in the *Norfolk Bird Report* 2005: 295-296)

This article in the *Norfolk Bird Report* 2005 gives the date of the finding of the bird as the 13th, obviously a misprint.

Common Kingfisher
Alcedo atthis
The earliest dated reference we can find is by Sir Thomas Browne in *Notes and Letters on the Natural History of Norfolk* 1902: 22:

'The number of riuulets becks & streames whose banks are beset with willowes & Alders wch giue occasion of easier fishing & slooping to the water makes that handsome coulered bird abound wch is calld Alcedo Ispida or the King fisher. they bild in holes about grauell pitts wherein is to bee found great quantitie of small fish bones. & lay very handsome round & as it were polished egges.'

European Bee-eater
Merops apiaster
The first British record was one killed at Mattishall in June 1794.

Henry Stevenson writes in *The Birds of Norfolk* Vol. l. 1866: 313-314:

'Yarrell remarks that "no specimen of the common Bee-eater, of Africa, appears to be recorded to have been killed in England till the summer of 1794, when a communication was made to the Linnean Society, and a specimen of this beautiful bird was exhibited by the president, Sir James Edward Smith, which had been shot out of a flock of about twenty, near Mattishall, in Norfolk, in the month of June by the Rev. George Smith; and a portion probably of this same flight, much diminished in numbers, was observed passing over the same spot in the month of October following".'

It has been suggested, and not unreasonably, that the correct year should be 1793 as a plate of the specimen by Lewin is dated 7th November 1793 (Yarrell 1843).

European Roller
Coracias garrulus
The first British example was one obtained at Crostwick on 14th May 1664.

Henry Stevenson writes in *The Birds of Norfolk* Vol. l. 1866: 310-313:

'The earliest record, however, of the roller in Norfolk is contained in the following remarkable note, by Sir Thomas Browne, just two hundred years ago:- "On the 14th May, 1664, a very rare bird was sent me, killed at Crostwick, which seemed to be some kind of jay. The bill was black, strong, and bigger than a jay's; somewhat yellow claws, tipped black; three before and one claw behind. The whole bird not so big as a jay. The head, neck, and throat of a violet colour; the back and upper parts of the wing of a russet yellow. The fore part of the wing azure; succeeded downward by a greenish blue, then on the flying feathers bright blue; the lower parts of the wing outwardly of a brown; inwardly of a merry blue; the belly a light faint blue; the back toward the tail a purple blue; the tail, eleven feathers of a greenish colour; the extremities of the outward feathers thereof white with an eye of green. – *Garrulus argentoratensis*".'

Sir Thomas Browne's note on the Roller is reproduced 'as accurately as possible' by Southwell in the text of *Notes and Letters on the Natural History of Norfolk* 1902: 30:

'On the xiiii of May 1664 a very rare bird was sent mee kild about crostwick wch seemed to bee some kind of Jay. the bill was black strong and bigger than a Jayes somewhat yellowe clawes tipped black. 3 before and one clawe behind the whole bird not so bigge as a Jaye [the *crossed out*]
The head neck & throat of a violet colour the back upper parts of the wing of a russet yellowe the fore & part of the wing azure succeeded downward by a greenish blewe then on the flying feathers bright blewe the lower part of the wing outwardly of a browne [the *crossed out*] inwardly of a merry blewe the belly a light faint blewe the back toward the tayle of a purple blewe the tayle eleuen fethers of a greenish coulour the extremeties of the outward fethers thereof white with an eye* of green. Garrulus Argentoratensis [*the name added in a different ink and pen*].
*Tinge, shade, particularly a slight tint. – "Imp. Dict".'

Thomas Southwell adds a footnote:

'This note is interesting as the first record of the occurrence of the Roller in

Britain, to which country it is a rare wanderer. Although it had been known on the Continent, its identity seems to have puzzled Browne, and he imagines (as did others, both before and after him,) it to be some kind of Jay; later, in his second letter to Merrett (January, 1668), he says that it answers to the description of *Garrulus argentoratensis* (the name given by Aldrovandus to whom it was known), and calls it "the Parrot-jay." This is five years after the original note was made, and we find that the words *Garrulus argentoratensis*, written by the same hand but with a different pen and ink, have been added subsequently, doubtless as a result of further information. In another letter he mentions having sent the bird to Merrett, but adds, "If you have it before I should bee content to have it againe otherwise you may please keep it."

Eurasian Hoopoe
Upupa epops
The earliest dated reference we can find is by Sir Thomas Browne (1605-1682) in *Notes and Letters on the Natural History of Norfolk* 1902: 23:

'Upupa or Hoopoebird so named from its note a gallant marked bird wch I have often seen & tis not hard to shoote them.'

Eurasian Wryneck
Jynx torquilla
The earliest dated reference we can find is by Sir Thomas Browne (1605-1682) in *Notes and Letters on the Natural History of Norfolk* 1902: 22-23:

'An Hobby bird so calld because it comes in ether with or a little before the Hobbies in the spring. of the bignesse of a Thrush coloured & paned like an hawke maruellously subiet to the vertigo & and are sometimes taken in those fitts.'

Thomas Southwell adds a footnote:

'This is evidently the Wryneck, which we now call the "Cuckoo's Mate," probably for the same reason that Browne associates it with the Hobby. It may be that the Hobby having become comparatively scarce, it was necessary to find another travelling companion for this bird, and that the Cuckoo was chosen as the most suitable. Old Norfolk names are Emmet-eater, and in one old book it is called Turkey-bird in a MS note.'

European Green Woodpecker
Picus viridis
The earliest dated reference we can find is by Sir Thomas Browne (1605-1682) in *Notes and Letters on the Natural History of Norfolk* 1902: 21, where he writes:

'Of picus martius or woodspeck many kinds. The green…'

See also the footnote reference by Southwell, in the Great Spotted Woodpecker text below.

Great Spotted Woodpecker (Northern)
Dendrocopos major major
The first proven Norfolk specimen of the Continental northern race was shot at Yarmouth in November 1881.

B. B. Riviere writes in *A History of the Birds of Norfolk* 1930: 95:

'The Northern Great Spotted Woodpecker, distinguished from the British race by its stouter bill and purer white ear-coverts and scapulars, appears to be a fairly regular winter visitor to Norfolk, though, owing to its distinctive features not having been recognised in the past, but few specimens have up till now been identified… The following authentic specimens of this race have been obtained in Norfolk, for knowledge of the first three of which I am indebted to Dr. C. B. Ticehurst, by whom they were identified: a male killed at Yarmouth in November 1881, now in the Gurney collection in the Norwich Museum;…'

Great Spotted Woodpecker
Dendrocopos major anglicus
The earliest dated reference we can find is by Sir Thomas Browne (1605-1682) in *Notes and Letters on the Natural History of Norfolk* 1902: 21, where he writes:

'Of picus martius or woodspeck many kinds. The green and Red…'

Thomas Southwell adds a footnote:

'*Picus martius* is here used, as it is by Sibbald, and all preceeding writers, in a general sense for all birds commonly called "Woodpeckers," and does not imply that the Great Black Woodpecker (*Picus niger maximus*, of Ray's Synopsis), to which species the name was restricted by Linnaeus, is found here, and Browne goes on to mention the three British Woodpeckers, the Green, the Red, by which the Great Spotted Woodpecker is intended, and Leucomelanus, or Lesser Spotted Woodpecker. He also includes the Nuthatch, which was at that time (as well as the Wryneck) called a "Woodpecker".'

Lesser Spotted Woodpecker
Dendrocopos minor
The earliest dated reference we can find is by Sir Thomes Browne (1605-1682) in *Notes and Letters on the Natural History of Norfolk* 1902: 21, where he writes:

'Of picus martius or woodspeck many kinds. The green the Red the Leucomelanus or neatly marked black & white…'

See also the footnote reference by Thomas Southwell, in the Great Spotted Woodpecker text above.

Calandra Lark
Melanocorypha calandra
One was found on Scolt Head by Jonathan Brown on 19th May 1997.

Jonathan Brown, Neil Lawton and Michael Rooney write:

'On the morning of 19th May 1997 we were carrying out breeding bird census work on Scolt Head NNR. Although working in the same general area, we were each covering different parts of the saltmarsh and sand dune habitats.

At about 11.30 am Jon noticed a scuffle between two birds; a closer look revealed that one was clearly a Skylark but the other was distinctly larger and bulkier with broader wings. The Skylark was clearly the aggressor and soon chased the other bird off although it seemed to land about 100 metres away. During the next twenty minutes Jon had three further views of the mystery bird, twice in flight and once close enough to pinpoint it on the ground, a situation not helped by the undulating terrain and patches of marram grass that prevented close range visual location from any distance. However, flight views were good and at close range enabling a number of pertinent identification features to be determined and a mobile 'phone call describing a large lark with black under-wings and a white trailing edge 'like an adult Little Gull' was enough to send Neil and Michael hurrying to join Jon.

They arrived simultaneously to find that the bird had flown into the salt-marsh. A search of the area produced nothing and with the first wisps of sea fog rolling in from the northeast, two rather worried men were heading back towards the dunes when the bird appeared from the ground a little way ahead hotly pursued by a Skylark. It flew past us calling, at about head height affording excellent flight views clearly showing the black underwings and a white trailing edge to the secondaries visible from above and below. The flight was gently undulating, the wings appearing broad and rounded. General flight impressions were of a bulkier and heavier bird than a Skylark with a noticeable heavy-headed look. The flight call was a rolling 'tchrupp', quite loud with a rather liquid feel to it. By now we had no doubts as to the bird's identity but were obviously keen to obtain views of it on the ground, although Jon had already noted the black patches on the sides of the neck and the white crescents above them giving a slight half-collared effect.

Unfortunately on this occasion the bird had flown farther than ever but it seemed to land about half a kilometre to the east. As we were about to set off in pursuit, the sea fog thickened and we had to sit it out until the next clear patch gave us a chance of relocating the bird. Despite taking every care to ensure that we saw the bird before it saw us, our next views were of it rising in flight in front of us. It circled us once, calling, before heading off even further east. This time the fog prevented us from pinpointing the landing area. More in hope than expectation we set off in pursuit once more. The fog continued to thicken and we had walked another kilometre before once again seeing and hearing the bird in flight. On this occasion it headed out into the saltmarsh and was lost to sight in the fog. We followed the flight line but could not relocate the bird in conditions of poor visibility.

It was now 1:30 pm and we had to consider whether to publicise news of the bird's presence. The pros and cons were debated and for a combination of reasons involving disturbance to breeding birds and damage to fragile habitats combined with health and safety and staffing implications, a considered professional decision was made by Michael Rooney, the Site Manager, that the best interests of the reserve would be served by withholding the news.'

(An account published in the *Norfolk Bird Club Bulletin* No 24: 4-5)

White-winged Lark
Melanocorypha leucoptera
Only the second British record, a probable first-winter male was discovered by John Lines on rough grass alongside Kings Lynn Beet Factory on 22nd October 1981.

John Lines writes:

'I am, from an ornithological standpoint a creature of habit. My birding tends to confine itself to regular, usually twice weekly, visits to local patches one of which is the Sugar-beet Factory at Kings Lynn. On this particular blustery day (22nd October 1981) I had checked two of the three lagoons and was embarking on the third when I disturbed a party of ten Skylarks which are residents of the surrounding rough ground. As they took wing I casually glanced at them soon realising one bird almost resembled a Snow Bunting.

The general pallor of the bird and the strikingly white wing pattern caused this instant reaction. I then focussed field glasses on the stranger before it settled on the ground with the other Larks. I had never seen a White-winged Lark before, but I knew it could be no other species. On the ground it was easy to compare with attendant Skylarks whose size it appeared to match. However, it had a heavier, stouter bill and no crest. There was a noticeable white superciliary eye-stripe and a dark eye. The crown was a rich rufous brown fading slightly on neck and back. The primary wing-coverts were rich brown similar to the crown, the secondary coverts being less so. The scapular feathers were pale brown having dark shafts and sub-terminal patches. The chin, breast, flanks and under-tail were striking white with rufous streaking on the sides. The dark brown tail appeared somewhat shorter than in a Skylark, but had white outer tail feathers. In flight the white secondary feathers gave the striking wing pattern while the under wing-coverts could also be seen to be white.

Having identified the bird I realised it was a little known vagrant and a highly unusual occurrence. I could vaguely recall many years ago Bryan Sage telling me of a White-winged Lark in Hertfordshire in the 1950s, but could not recall any subsequent records. I knew that each Friday afternoon would see John Moyes at nearby Wisbech Sewage Farm. I consider him one of the finest of field ornithologists and mentioned my sighting to him as we counted the waders there the following day. Subsequently John found the White-winged Lark which remained at the Beet Factory until 24th October 1981.

The record was submitted to British Birds Rarities Committee in 1982, but has only recently gained full acceptance.'

(An account published in the *Norfolk Bird Report* 1986: 416-417)

Following a review of this species by the BOURC in 1993, of the five records remaining on the British list, only two were found to be acceptable, the Norfolk record above and one near Brighton, East Sussex in 1869 (see a very interesting article by Tony Marr and Richard Porter, on behalf of the BOU Rarity Records Committee, entitled 'The White-winged Lark in Britain' in *British Birds* 88: 365-371).

Black Lark
Melanocorypha yeltoniensis
Only the third for Britain, an adult male, was found by Sean Offord at Winterton North Dunes late afternoon on 20th April 2008 (Plate 13), which remained until early next morning.

Sean Offord writes:

'Sunday 20th April 2008 was the day after my youngest son's third birthday party. The morning was drizzly and overcast, and the easterly wind, which had been blowing for three days solid, was persisting. I had been watching the European wind maps on the internet with mounting excitement, as their little arrows all pointed steadfastly west, right across the entire continent, from the steppes of Kazakhstan to the coast of Norfolk. But Winterton dunes, my local patch, had remained cold and quiet, with hardly any signs of migration.

I have lived in Winterton for four years. We moved here, in part, so that I could get back into British birding, as in the years before we had had children, my partner Jill and I had spent almost all of our holidays in the tropics (it is handy being a teacher with a very good friend in the airline business), and so I had sort of lost interest in UK birding. But the arrival of two kids put paid to my jet-setting lifestyle, and I knew I had to rekindle my interest in a local patch, or go quietly bonkers as my airline pal David continued to swan about the jungles of Peru sending me updates on his ever increasing world list.

And moving here has been a revelation for me; I have gone from being a global birder with a carbon footprint the size of a small country, to a complete obsessive about totally local birding; so much so that when my good friend and next-door neighbour Peter Cawley found a White-spotted Bluethroat less than half a mile from my house a few weeks before the day in question, whilst I was out of the county with no chance of getting back to see it, I was still able to be pleasantly cheerful and magnanimous about it all, purely because the bird had been 100 metres outside of the parish boundary! Even when Pete later took me to the site of his find, and re-enacted the moment, complete with his uncanny impersonation of the bird hopping about in a ditch, I simply smiled appreciatively and congratulated him…

Anyway, back to the day in question. Despite the drizzly conditions and easterly wind, the dunes remained quiet. The day before, Pete had said that he thought everything was being held up in Europe where weather conditions were so poor that, despite the winds, nothing was on the move.

So I was veering between the automatic expectancy that east winds during migration bring to Norfolk birders, and a state of Eeyore-like gloom and pessimism engendered by his comments when, after a day of birthday outings for the little one, we drove back into Winterton, just as the sun was coming out and the wind seemed to be dropping a touch. I thought if anything *had* made it through the European bottleneck, then now would be the time to look for it. I finally made it into the north dunes just before 4.00pm.

Deciding on where to go birding within the parish of Winterton depends very much on the weather conditions. In an easterly, the south dunes are usually a no-no because all the best cover is quite high up on ther valley bank and exposed to the wind, the valley floor usually holds about a thousand dog-walkers and their precious pets, racing up and down, dropping their little presents and chasing off pretty much every bird which dares to enter their mutty kingdom. Round the back of the Hermanus Chalets is much more sheltered, and a good bet when passerines are in the offing, but there is not much habitat to work through. Since I figured by the pleasant mood of my other half that I had got a couple of hours before having to return to family duties, I decided the time would be better spent heading into the usually quieter north dunes.

I walked north from the village and first inspected a little copse of Silver Birches right on the edge of the village, which offers some shelter in easterlies. Nothing, except a rather nice little Adder. Never mind, I thought, I will head up to an area we call The Warren, a sort of open, wetter habitat than the dunes themselves which, although you cannot actually get into it, can be overlooked and will usually hold something. But today: nothing. Normally, gloom and pessimism wins over in these circumstances, and I begin to dawdle and daydream, wandering along main paths (already well trodden that day by thousands of dogs and their owners), ignoring all the exciting habitat to left and right, until it is time to get back home. But it just so happened that a few days before I had given myself a little pep-talk about my birding habits whilst in the field. In the four years I have been living here I had yet to find anything rarer than a Firecrest or a Ring Ouzel (a fact which the other birders in the village, under Pete's wise tutelage, seemed to relish pointing out to me whenever they could manage to get it into conversation). So I had gamely decided to THINK RARE, KEEP MY CONCENTRATION, and LOOK CAREFULLY IN GOOD BIRD HIDING PLACES.

I did a big scan around with my bins in order to plan my next move. Right off in the distance, flying south along the last dune ridge before the sea, I saw a Sand Martin. Given how terrible the spring had been so far for common migrants this was pretty exciting stuff. I decided to make my way across to the ridge where I might see any other hirundines moving through, and would also have views both of the sea, in case any terns were moving past, and inland, where I might perhaps pick up a flying Ring Ouzel if I was lucky.

Slowly I made my way across the width of the north dunes and through the normally reliable totem pole bushes, which today held just a single Robin. I was getting fed up, and as I began climbing up the gentle gradient beyond the main pathway through the dunes I lapsed into a dawdling daydream. Still, it had taken at least ten minutes longer than usual…

The tail-end of a Wheatear disappearing over the brow of the slope reminded me of what I was supposed to be doing and I walked up to see if I could get a closer look. Now comes the bit you have been waiting for.

I got to the top expecting to see the Wheatear close by. Instead a slightly larger, all black bird took off from the little hollow about 15 metres in front of me and flew low, a very short way, landing just out of sight below the next small hill-brow. For a moment I was completely confused. I just could not work out what I had seen. This will seem a bizarre analogy, but at the time I thought it was like a sort of pygmy Jackdaw flying as though it was pretending to be injured. I moved carefully until I had a view into the next hollow, and there it was. Close

234

and clear in the short grass, walking quickly and easily, then standing still in glorious profile, only a few metres away. Thick set, all black with lovely irregular mottled whitish scalloping on its back, and a large stout pale bill. Suddenly the flight pattern clicked. Of course! It was a lark! I was looking at the third ever British Black Lark. And yes, it did have the build (and when it looked up, alert, the stance) of a mini-Jackdaw! I bet that is not in the field guides…

Immediately the adrenalin hit. I felt incredible elation and euphoria. I had found a massive rarity, which was completely easy to identify, and was walking about in the open on short grass instead of skulking in thick undergrowth. My type of bird! But my elation was instantly mixed with anxiety. I had my mobile phone on me, yet I knew I had hardly any battery power left. When I had set out I had seen that there were two bars of power left. Normally when I try to make a call with the battery at that level it just goes dead. My hands were fumbling as I wrestled in my coat pockets whilst trying to keep the bird in view. I dialled Pete, who was at Hickling Broad doing conservation work. Heroically my phone made it through and soon I was shout-whispering down the line like a stage villain. "Pete! I've got a Black Lark! I'm in the dunes between the totem pole bushes and the sea and I've got no battery power and I'm not kidding! Call everyone!" Pete was calm, as he always is. He congratulated me then hung up. I expected he briefly hit his head against a tree then began ringing round.

In the meantime the bird had flown a little further away. I relocated it and then told myself to keep calm and take a careful description, starting with the bare parts then moving carefully through all the feather tracts. The trouble is, I was too amazed and excited, and the bird was too obvious for this to seem important. It was a lark. It was black. What else do you want? I decided to enjoy it.

But as soon as I had decided to take this radical path a terrible thought occurred to me. What if the bird disappeared before anyone else managed to get here? What a curse that would be, to know you had seen a first for Norfolk and a third for the UK, but to have no evidence of it, only your word and your (inadequate) description. I could already see the sideways glances, hear the whispered tittering. I would have to keep quiet for ever… I needed evidence, and quick. I took a chance on the phone again and amazingly it carried on working. I called Ted Phillips (who lives in the village and is the proud owner of a x40 optical zoom camcorder) and Tim Hemmings (who comes birding here every weekend and is the equally proud owner of some sort of whacking great zoom on his DSLR camera). Ted got there first and in his excitement succeeded in filming, it later transpired, about five minutes of his own trouser leg and about four seconds of an unidentifiable flying black dot. Then Tim, and Colin Walker, another local birder (distinctive with his own x40 camcorder balanced on a two-legged broken tripod) arrived just as the bird flew over us and disappeared into an area of longer marram grass.

Thank the lord we refound it just as Andrew Grieve (OSME bigwig; visits Kazakhstan every year; Black Lark expert) arrived and promptly took a decent photo of it. It was only then, as I studied the clearly identifiable image of a Black Lark on his camera display, relief sweeping through me and tension draining away, that I finally allowed myself to believe what had happened.

The next hour or so was full of fantastic views of the bird, mixed in with periods of searching when it flew out of sight, sometimes over the sea wall.

Thankfully on each occasion it was eventually relocated. My impression was that it got progressively more flighty as more and more people arrived. Nevertheless, all those that made it before dark eventually had great views of the bird on the ground and in the air, often calling as it bounded across the dunes.

I staggered home on the Sunday evening in a state of shock. I could not quite believe that my youngest son's third birthday had been commemorated by a third for Britain. I wonder what I missed on the previous two years?'

Greater Short-toed Lark
Calandrella brachydactyla
A male was shot near the south wall of Breydon on 7th November 1889. The specimen is at the City of Birmingham Museum.

Thomas Southwell writes in Henry Stevenson's *The Birds of Norfolk* Vol. lll. 1890: 410:

'Mr. George Smith, of Yarmouth, records the occurrence of an example of this species in the *"Zoologist"* for 1890, p. 77, stated by him to have been shot near South Breydon Wall, Yarmouth, on the 7th November, 1889. It proved upon dissection to be a male. There can be no question as to the bird obtained by Mr. Smith being an example of this species, which is doubtless very likely to occur here in a state of nature, but it may be well to note that about the end of October, 1889, short-toed larks are known to have been imported into London with skylarks, and that two are recorded as presented to the Zoological Gardens on the 28th of the same month by Commander Latham; it is, therefore, not altogether impossible that the bird in question may have been an "escape".'

Bearing in mind the mention in the above account regarding the escape possibility, perhaps the the second county record of one found at Cley on 14th October 1959 by M. J. Carter and E. J. L. Welham may eventually be regarded as the first Norfolk record.

Wood Lark
Lullula arborea
The earliest dated reference we can find is by Sir Thomas Browne (1605-1682) in *Notes and Letters on the Natural History of Norfolk* 1902: 28 where he writes:

'The calandrier or great crested lark Galeteria I haue not met with here though with 3 other sorts of Larkes the ground lark [Sky Lark] woodlark & titlark [Pipit].'

Sky Lark
Alauda arvensis arvensis
Known as the Ground Lark at the time, the earliest dated reference we can find is by Sir Thomas Browne (1605-1682) in *Notes and Letters on the Natural History of Norfolk* 1902: 28 where he writes as above for Woodlark.

Interestingly, Sheppard and Whitear write in *A Catalogue of the Norfolk and Suffolk Birds, with Remarks* 1826: 22:

'It appears from the following remarks of Mr. Woolnough of Hollesley, that these birds frequently migrate into this country from the Continent in autumn, and return thither in the spring. Mr. W. thus writes:- "I have frequently seen *larks* and *rooks* come flying off the sea; not in one year only, but in many; not on one day only in the same year, but on several. I have seen them coming off the sea for many hours in the same day; - the *larks* from five and ten to forty or fifty in a flock; the *rooks*, on the same day, in companies from three to fifteen. This I once observed in November for three days in succession; the early part of that month was the general time of their coming: our fields were then covered with the *larks*, to the great destruction of the late-sown wheat. They generally remained with us till the first heavy fall of snow, and then disappeared. Early in the February following they appeared again on the coast in innumerable flocks, but disappeared as soon as the weather became fine, with light westerly wind: from which circumstance I concluded that they again crossed the sea. They appeared to me to be the same as our common Skylarks.

Those *larks* and *rooks* that I have seen coming off the sea, did not appear like birds that had flown off for pleasure; they always flew low to the water, and seemed fully intent on reaching the shore, on which they often alighted directly on reaching it".'

Sky Lark (Eastern)

Alauda arvensis dulcivox
One was found at Sheringham by Steve Votier and Kevin Shepherd on 5th October 1998.

Steve Votier and Kevin Shepherd write:

'For those fortunate enough to have been out and about on the coast between 30th September and 9th October 1998, a succession of amazing daily falls provided a spell of truly vintage Norfolk birding. As KBS and SCV struggled to find shelter in the lee of gorse patches in the gathering dawn on 5th October, the scene on the cliff-top at Sheringham was remarkable. A strong east/north-easterly, a raging sea, frequent squalls lashing horizontal rain upon us. Red-necked Grebes struggling east in the surf, a Merlin 'in-off', a host of 'tsipping' Song Thrushes above us, 'ticking' Robins all around, anxious bunches of Reed Buntings in the furrows, the occasional 'hweet' of a descending Chiffchaff, a sudden swirl of newly arrived Shorelarks… the panic and confusion of an exciting pre-dawn fall, the beginning of another magnificent day's birding!

As the light gradually became bright enough for comfortable binocular vision, a party of 15-20 Skylarks flew low left to right over a dark, bare soil field only 30-40m to the west of us. So obviously holding a single, incredibly grey individual, SCV's "is that a Short-toed Lark?" call drew attention to an extremely odd looking bird. Flight views were only brief but initial impressions were that it was too large for Short-toed – yet it was clearly far too grey to be just a pale Skylark. We are both very familiar with all the rare larks on the British List, yet absolutely nothing immediately sprang to mind. Fortunately the flock landed nearby and we were soon treated to the most marvellous views (x10 binoculars and x30 telescopes) of an incredible bird – feeding, resting and making short flights, almost always with accompanying Skylarks, at ranges down to 25 feet for more than 40 minutes.

As soon as we were able to examine it, we could scarcely believe our eyes. Basically, it was the most beautifully marked, incredibly grey lark (greyer than even the very grey forms of 'eastern' Short-toed Lark), marginally smaller than its accompanying Skylarks with a more rotund and compact structure and a most different feeding mannerism – yet its overall plumage markings matched those of Skylark.

We are both greatly inspired by migrant larks (for which the site is well known) and we must have carefully examined literally hundreds of thousands of nominate *arvensis* Skylarks over the years. Consequently we are both well aware of the enormous variation in *arvensis* at all times of the year and have also seen a number of leucistic and part-albino birds. Following more than twenty minutes of careful scrutiny, we were still asking each other "are we absolutely certain there's nothing else it can be?" and "surely it can't be just a Skylark?" But a Skylark it undoubtedly was – albeit an extremely odd one.

Differences noted from arvensis were as follows:

Overall plumage tone perhaps the most striking difference. Compared with the warm, sandy tones of typical *arvensis*, background colour of upper-parts cold grey with off-white underparts lacking buff wash. Warmest tones in plumage restricted to buffish fringes to secondaries and tertials. Overall plumage tones similar to grey ('eastern') forms of Short-toed Lark but considered to be greyer even than these. Because of extreme overall greyness of plumage, many plumage features reminiscent of 'eastern' Short-toed Lark – particularly striking an obvious grey 'shawl' created by extremely fine/near absence of streaking on nape/upper mantle, which isolated the finely streaked crown giving 'capped' appearance.

All streaking appeared neater and more distinct than *arvensis*, most notable its extremely neat, starkly contrasting, black centres to upper row of scapulars and finely streaked (black) crown. Breast streaking also rather 'tidy' looking with sharp blackish feather centres – unlike the more diffuse breast streaking of *arvensis*.

Size marginally smaller than all accompanying (party of 15-20) *arvensis*, though not considered to be smaller than smallest *arvensis* occurring at the site. Overall jizz/structure noticeably more rotund and compact than *arvensis*, partly brought about by proportionately slightly shorter tail and bill. Tail-length considered to be proportionately intermediate between *arvensis* and Short-toed Lark – certainly not as short-tailed as Woodlark or Crested Lark. Painstaking observations revealed no evidence of tail growing – bird considered to be genuinely shorter-tailed.

Feeding action noticeably different. Compared with rather shuffling feeding action of accompanying *arvensis*, bird generally 'running around a lot more' – rapid clockwork actions interrupted with measured stops to pick at ground, strangely recalling Ringed Plover. Bird often picked out from flock by this distinctive feature alone.

The subspecific status of Skylark is reviewedby Cramp (1988), Svensson (1992) and Snow & Perrins (1998). The situation is clearly complex but from these, we consider the Sheringham bird most likely to have been *Alauda arvensis dulcivox*, a form breeding in Western Siberia and North Central Asia. It is difficult to ascertain the true status of *dulcivox* in Western Europe from the literature, but very grey Skylarks generally considered to be of eastern origin appear to occur at least as regular vagrants.

In Britain, a total of five records of 'eastern' Skylarks are listed in the Handbook (Witherby et al 1938) but we can find no other documented records. To give some indication of the status of 'eastern' Skylark on the British east coast, very careful observations of migrant larks at Sheringham over the past twenty-one years have revealed a total of nine Short-toed, yet only two 'eastern' Skylarks. Paul Harvey (pers. comm.) has recorded only two strikingly grey Skylarks on Shetland during the past fifteen years, in comparison to over twenty Short-toed Larks. Interestingly Sheringham's first record (25th-26th September 1979) involved an individual which arrived and departed with an 'eastern' Short-toed Lark. Unfortunately this bird was not critically examined but was similar to the above bird.

We are conscious that observations like this may be regarded as forming another example of an ever-growing trend to encourage classification of every subtly different bird form as a new species. However it must be realised that many of the somewhat arbitrary divisions between species and subspecies were made long ago, based only on the examination of museum skins with little or no observation of differing jizz/structure and behaviour in the field. It is therefore not surprising that painstaking observations using modern optical equipment in recent years have unearthed forms remarkably different from cogeners. Hume's Yellow-browed Warbler, Eastern/Western Bonelli's Warbler and more recently, Caspian Gull all provide excellent examples. Future scrutiny of *dulcivox*, particularly on the breeding grounds, could well reveal a similar phenomenon.

In short, should another turn up, go see. Despite numerous other excitements, this was our bird of the year. We guarantee you will not be disappointed!'

(An account published in the *Norfolk Bird Club Bulletin* 34: 11-13)

Horned (Shore) Lark
Eremophila alpestris
The first British record concerned one shot at Sheringham in March 1830.

Henry Stevenson writes in *The Birds of Norfolk* Vol. l. 1866: 171-175:

'The first recorded specimen of the Shore-Lark in Norfolk, and probably the first ever recognised in England, is the one thus referred to by Yarrell:- "In the year 1831, I learned of my late friend, Mr. John Simms, then residing at Norwich, that a British killed specimen of the Shore-Lark, the *Alauda alpestris* of authors, had come into his possession. The bird was shot on the beach at Sherringham, in Norfolk, in March 1830: it was preserved by Mr. Simms, and is now in the collection of Edward Lombe, Esq., of Great Melton, near Norwich." This bird, which is also described by Messrs. Gurney and Fisher as an immature male, is still preserved in the above collection, which is now in the possession of Mrs. E. P. Clarke, of Wymondham.'

After his death the Lombe collection was donated to the Castle Museum, Norwich by his daughter Mrs. E. P. Clarke. The Horned Lark specimen (Accession no.NWHCM: 1873:

18.7.65) remains in storage there.

Interestingly, the second and third county records, at Sheringham (undated) and at Yarmouth in November 1850 were also the second and third British records.

Sand Martin
Riparia riparia
Not mentioned by Sir Thomas Browne (1605-1682) in *Notes and Letters on the Natural History of Norfolk* (1902) or, perhaps surprisingly, by Sheppard and Whitear in *A Catalogue of the Norfolk and Suffolk Birds, with Remarks* (1826). The earliest dated reference we can find is in 'Extracts from the Calendar of the Rev. William Whitear 1809-1826' published in the *Transactions of the Norfolk and Norwich Naturalists' Society* 1881-1182: 253, where he recorded one on 7th April 1820 in the Starston area.

The Pagets in *Sketch of the Natural History of Yarmouth and its Neighbourhood* 1834: 4 considered it '…common'.

Barn Swallow
Hirundo rustica
The earliest dated reference we can find is by Robert Marsham (1708-1797) in Tim Sparks and John Lines' *Chapters in the Life of Robert Marsham Esq. F.R.S. of Stratton Strawless, Norfolk* 2008: 15:

'In 1754 November I saw a Swallow on marshes at Brancaster Norfolk viz by the N. Sea.'

Common House Martin
Delichon urbicum
The earliest dated reference we can find is in 'Extracts from the Calendar of the Rev. William Whitear 1809-1826' published in the *Transactions of the Norfolk and Norwich Naturalists' Society* 1881-1882: 241 where he recorded one on May 6th 1816 in the Starston area.

Sheppard and Whitear in *A Catalogue of the Norfolk and Suffolk Birds, with Remarks* 1826: 33 comment:

'Some young Martins did not leave their nest at Starston till the 7th October, 1819; and on the 11th of the same month all the Martins had left that part of the county.'

The Pagets in *Sketch of the Natural History of Yarmouth and its Neighbourhood* 1834: 4 considered it '…common'.

Red-rumped Swallow
Cecropis daurica
A swallow was seen over Blakeney Quay by Blakeney wildfowler Jack (Joe) Johnson on 6th March 1952. He mentioned it to the Cley Reserve warden Billy Bishop that evening while they were enjoying a pint in the White Horse at Blakeney. Billy apparently identified it as a Red-rumped Swallow the following day, although *Wild Bird Protection in Norfolk* 1952: 18 gives the date it was identified by Billy as the 9th.

Billy Bishop writes in *Cley Marsh and its Birds* 1983: 50:

> 'In the case of my other 'first', I cannot claim that I found it but only that I identified it. A bird-watcher in Blakeney asked me one evening whether it was early for a swallow to be seen in Norfolk. The date was March 6th. Of course, this is extremely early but I knew the man concerned to be knowledgeable. So the following day I went to Blakeney to try to spot this early visitor. When I found it I saw to my surprise that it had a red rump. There was no doubt this was the first record for Norfolk of the red-rumped swallow from Africa. It was later filmed by Dick Bagnall-Oakeley, the well known Norfolk wildlife photographer.'

M. Meiklejohn and Richard Richardson write:

> 'On March 6th, 1952, a bird subsequently identified by W. F. Bishop and J. Johnson as a Red-rumped Swallow (*Hirundo daurica*) was seen at Cley, and later at Blakeney, Norfolk. In the days that followed its favourite haunt was the quay at Blakeney, but it frequently disappeared for some hours, even returning to Cley on several occasions. The bird was watched for many hours by a large number of observers including Dr. B. B. Riviere, R. P. Bagnall-Oakeley, G. T. Kay and P. A. D. Hollom, apart from the writers. It was last seen on March 25th.
>
> Most of its time was spent on the wing, but it often perched on electric wires and the outside twigs of small trees. In direct flight it resembled a Swallow (*H. rustica*) although the absence of a gorget was noticeable and the tail-streamers were thicker (or wider) and distinctly incurved – like the sail of a Sinhalese katamaran. With the tail closed, the streamers crossed each other; when it was spread, the lack of white spots was apparent. While feeding, the bird more closely resembled a House Martin (*Delichon urbica*) with that species' steep, fluttering climbs after high-flying insects, long glides on horizontal wings (slightly upswept at the tips) and the pale rump which at times appeared almost white. When it alighted, it jerked its tail once or twice like a Swallow, and then held its wings loosely beneath the tail. The bird was twice seen to dip down and try to drink from the glass roof of a conservatory, evidently mistaking the shining surface for water, before flying to the harbour and taking one sip of salt water. It was suspected of roosting in a barn at Blakeney, but this was not proved.
>
> The following description was made during several hours watching: crown and mantle steely blue-black; nape, neck and superciliary stripe orange-red ("Brambling-colour"); dark smudge through eye; upper rump orange-red shading to pale biscuit on the lower rump; upper and under tail-coverts black; wings and tail blackish-brown, latter with no white spots; entire under-parts pale reddish-buff; under wing-coverts the same except for blackish primary-coverts; bill dark; legs and feet perhaps rather paler than Swallow's. On March 16th P. A. D. Hollom heard it give two or three harsh, throaty twitters when it perched on a telephone-wire; otherwise no notes were heard.'

(Originally published in *British Birds* 46: 263-264)

Such was the rarity of the species in Britain (there had only been four or five previous records) that one on Lundy Island, Devon on the 27th March and on Great Saltee, County Wexford on the 10th April were considered to have been possibly the same bird (Taylor *et al* 1999).

Red-rumped Swallow at Blakeney Quay March 1952. (*Gary Wright*)

Richard's Pipit
Anthus richardi

One was taken at Yarmouth North Denes on 22nd November 1841 (Plate 9) and was in the J. H. Gurney Collection donated to the Castle Museum, Norwich. The specimen (Accession no. NWHCM: 1841.11.42) remains there in the skin collection, having been "reduced" from a mounted specimen.

The scant detail in the information concerning this record was compiled from three reference sources, Fisher (1843), Stevenson (1866) and Patterson (1905) and a visit to the Castle Museum, Norwich.

A. H. Patterson writes in his *Nature in Eastern Norfolk* 1905: 126-127:

> 'Very little seems to have been noticed respecting the habits of this species locally. The furzy Denes appear to have been its favourite haunt, where I am inclined to think the Grasshopper had attractions for it. The first recorded for Norfolk was taken on the North Denes on November 22nd, 1841…'

Interestingly, the second and third Norfolk records, in April 1842 and 24th April 1843, were also shot on Yarmouth Denes. In fact the first six county records were all shot in the Yarmouth/Breydon area - five of them by Police Sergeant Henry Barnes.

Blyth's Pipit
Anthus godlewskii

A first-winter bird was found by Tim Wright in clifftop fields between Sheringham and Weybourne on 14th October 1996, where it remained until the 16th.

Tim Wright writes:

242

'October 14th looked promising from the start. A warm south-east wind was blowing and bird-wise there was plenty of activity. Skylarks and Starlings were clearly moving in good numbers, and thrushes, Rock Pipits and finches also trickled through.

Just after mid-day, at the west edge of Sheringham Bird Observatory recording area, I flushed a large pipit from a cliff-top field along with 2 Skylarks. It immediately called a double-noted 'chup chup', sounding much like a Tawny Pipit. Luckily it landed briefly, a short distance away still in the presence of the Skylarks.

On closer examination, it looked rather like a Tawny Pipit with horizontal stance, unstreaked peachy flanks, whitish supercilium and bright pinkish-orange legs. Its bill was pointed and broad-based, and the bird was approaching a Skylark in size, but clearly smaller and more compact.

The bird suddenly disappeared from view, but luckily I relocated it feeding close by. Further plumage detail became apparent, including a neat gorget of blackish streaking across the breast and pale lores. This, together with the strength and distribution of upperpart streaking and a relatively short tail meant it couldn't be a Tawny Pipit. However, it didn't look like a Richard's Pipit either, nor did it behave and call like one.

There was certainly a need to look very closely at this surprise bird, and with it appearing settled, I was fortunate enough to do this. For an hour or more I 'grilled' it down to 8 metres with a telescope. The more detail I noted, the more the evidence was swinging towards Blyth's Pipit as the bird's identity. Apart from plumage detail, behaviour and call were significant.

The bird remained settled, and there was absolutely no-one about. It was worth trying to contact other birders even though it meant leaving the bird. Luckily I got through to Kev. Shepherd and Dave Appleton quickly, and raced back to the bird. Both were soon at the scene, seeing the bird well and being happy with its identity. By the end of the day over 60, mainly local birders, had seen the Blyth's. It remained for a further two days being appreciated by hundreds of observers.

During its stay the Blyth's Pipit favoured a small gulley between some recently sown winter cereal and a strip of set-aside in two cliff-top fields. When settled, it ran along this gulley feeding and constantly pumping its tail like a small pipit. It preferred to be close to the cover of the set-aside. Much of its time (including roosting) was spent in the Sheringham Bird Observatory recording area. From time to time it was in a field closer to Weybourne.

Some of the important identification features can be summarised as follows:-
*   Relatively short tail and legs and horizontal stance (exposed tail roughly equal to exposed tertial length) (Richard's Pipit typically has long tail and legs with upright stance) Short tail obvious in flight.
*   Broad-based, relatively short, pointed bill with straight culmen (Richard's Pipit typically has a much heavier longer bill with curved culmen) Gentler facial expression than Richard's Pipit as a result.
*   Pale lores and fairly short, whitish supercilium, most prominent behind eye (helping to distinguish from Tawny Pipit).

* Weak/broken malar, especially towards bill base. Base of malar a small area of 'open streaks' (lacking the characteristic strong malar and solid black triangular base of typical Richard's Pipit).
* Neatly streaked upperparts with appreciable contrast between dark brown mantle streaks and pale grey-brown ground colour. Streaked areas forming neat lines with similar width pale areas giving 'tramline' effect (Richard's Pipit typically has very haphazard mantle streaking with darker ground colour).
* Dark centred median and greater coverts edged and tipped whitish. Tips forming two very distinct wing bars. Median coverts all juvenile type with no contrast (moult) noted making the bird a first-winter.
* Crown also neatly streaked dark brown with pale ground colour similar to mantle (giving capped effect). Rather open faced. Dark moustachial line, small whitish crescent beneath eye and rather warm gingery ear coverts.
* Second outermost tail feathers predominantly white towards tips forming neat white triangle when tail splayed. (Typically white for most of length on Richard's Pipit which also has much darker brownish-black uppertail).
* Little contrast between peachy flanks and belly (On Richard's Pipit typically much more of a contrast between warm flank colouration and whitish belly).
* 'Chup Chup' call very different from typical House Sparrow-like notes of Richard's Pipit and similar to Red-throated Pipit but less 'hissing'.
* Running action with constant tail pumping (no side movement) like a small pipit (never strutting around like a typical Richard's Pipit). Would also freeze or disappear into short grass rather than taking flight at a distance. (Also never hovered and flicked tail prior to landing, liks Richard's Pipit or Sky Lark).
* Sometimes nervous of other birds, especially when in open; crouching, freezing and holding head low in hunched posture.

'*dauricus*' race Richard's Pipit had to be considered with the identification of this bird. Whilst some features of this race differ slightly from the usual race '*richardi*', I understand '*dauricus*' always look, behave and call like typical Richard's Pipits. This bird clearly fell into a category all of its own i.e. a separate species. This represents the first well documented, multi-observed record of Blyth's Pipit for the County, with currently only five other accepted British records.'

(An account published in the *Norfolk Bird Club Bulletin* No 22: 27-29)

This was the first Blyth's Pipit to be accepted in the British Isles which had not been trapped, photographed or found dead.

The *Birds of Norfolk* (Taylor *et al* 1999) wrongly give the dates for this record as 16th-18th October, presumed to be a misprint.

Tawny Pipit
Anthus campestris
A female was caught in a clap-net on Yarmouth North Denes on 9th October 1897. The specimen is in storage at the City of Birmingham Museum.

J. H. Gurney writing in the *Zoologist* 1898: 114 states:

'9th [October 1897]. Wind N.W. A female Tawny Pipit in somewhat faded plumage was netted on Yarmouth denes, and exhibited at the next meeting of the Norf. and Nor. Nat. Soc. by Mr. Southwell, who took the opportunity of giving a *resume* of the present status of Norfolk ornithology. It has been added to Mr. Connop's extensive collection, a catalogue of which Mr. Southwell has recently published.'

Interestingly, Thomas Southwell writes in the *Catalogue of British Birds in the collection of Mr. E. M. Connop*, which he compiled in 1898:

'Tawny Pipit, female, caught in a clap net on the North Denes, Great Yarmouth, on the 7th October 1897 (George Smith), first Norfolk specimen.'

The George Smith mentioned above was a bird dealer and taxidermist of North Denes, Great Yarmouth and it is unlikely that he captured the bird himself. It was most likely to have been taken to him by a bird trapper as something unusual. Smith would have recognised it as something out of the ordinary and passed it to the Castle Museum, Norwich, presumably to Gurney, to be identified. Where Gurney obtained the date as 9th is questionable.

J. H. Gurney and Thomas Southwell read the following to the *Norfolk and Norwich Naturalists' Society* on 31st January 1899 which was published under "Fauna and Flora of Norfolk, Birds" in the *Transactions of the Norfolk and Norwich Naturalists' Society* 1898-1899: 508:

'Tawny Pipit, a female, in rather faded plumage, now in Mr. Connop's collection, was caught in a clap-net on the North Denes, Great Yarmouth, on the 7th of October, 1897. The wind on the previous day had been from the southwest.'

This would seem to confirm that Gurney did indeed have the wrong date in the *Zoologist*.

Olive-backed Pipit
Anthus hodgsoni
One was found by Steve Joyner and Norman Williams in The Dell at Wells on 10th October 1975.

Steve Joyner writes from his notes taken at the time:

'October 1975 was arguably the best ever period for eastern and Siberian rarities in Norfolk. Unprecedented numbers of passerine vagrants were recorded, including one new bird for Britain (Yellow-browed Bunting) and three further new species for the county. During the last three weeks of the month the weather conditions were perfect with a strong easterly flow out of Siberia curving down the North Sea onto the North Norfolk coast.
As the conditions developed Norman Williams and I studied weather maps with eager anticipation, we were aware that by the 9th October the weather was ideal for an influx of eastern migrants. So, on the 10th we decided to visit the coast. On arriving at Cley West Bank we found that amazing numbers of birds were coming in off the sea. Hundreds of wildfowl and waders were coasting west-

erly close inshore, and continuous flocks of passerines were skimming low over the beach, often landing in the first available cover. Clearly this was going to be a 'dawn to dusk day'.

An initial dash along Blakeney Point was rewarded with views of many more migrants sheltering in the *suaeda* bushes, and the memorable sight of a migrating Great Grey Shrike in a flock of coasting Starlings.

With daylight limited we decided to spend the remainder of the day searching the trees in Wells Woods. As time was pressing we headed directly to The Dell area, where I flushed a small pipit from the undergrowth, as it flew up to the trees it gave a 'teez' call. Expecting to see a Tree Pipit I was immediately surprised to see a pipit facing me with heavily blotched underparts and a strong pale supercilium, clearly this was not a Tree Pipit, maybe a Red-throated Pipit? Norman now joined me and we watched the bird moving among the trees, expecting the upperparts to be heavily streaked we were totally confused to note the relatively unmarked mantle with a distinct olive tone. The bird soon became rather elusive in the trees and with light fading we left to consult the literature.

In 1975 Olive-backed Pipit was an enigmatic species and there were no illustrations in the standard bird books. The only information available at the time was

British Birds articles describing birds seen on Fair Isle. However, even without the current knowledge of diagnostic head pattern and habitat preference, we were able to confirm the identification and record the seventh British record of Olive-backed Pipit. At the time I commented to Norman that it would be a long wait before we saw another Olive-backed Pipit! Of course they are now recorded annually with numbers even reaching double figures in exceptional years.'

Tree Pipit
Anthus trivialis
From the 17th to the mid-19th century the three species of pipit recognized by the early naturalists, Tree, Meadow and Rock, were known as Tit Larks. It wasn't until 1843 that Yarrell condemned this practise on the grounds that it was popularly applied indiscriminately to all three species of pipit found in Britain (Lockwood 1984).

The earliest dated reference we can find is in 'Extracts from the Calendar of the Rev. William Whitear 1809-1826' published in the *Transactions of the Norfolk and Norwich Naturalists' Society* 1881-1882: 245 where he recorded one on 2nd May 1817 in the Starston area.

Sheppard and Whitear in *A Catalogue of the Norfolk and Suffolk Birds, with Remarks* 1826: 21 under Field Lark comment:

'A common species in the neighbourhood of Harleston during the summer; and it is also found in various parts both of Norfolk and Suffolk. This bird is subject not only to an *Hippobosca*, but likewise to a large species of *Acarus*. Five of these insects were taken off the head of a lark on the first day of its arrival.'

The Pagets in *Sketch of the Natural History of Yarmouth and its Neighbourhood* 1834: 5 considered it '…rather common.'

Meadow Pipit
Anthus pratensis
See above comments in the introduction to Tree Pipit. The earliest reference we can find for the species is below.

The Pagets in *Sketch of the Natural History of Yarmouth and its Neighbourhood* 1834: 5 considered it '…rather common.'

Red-throated Pipit
Anthus cervinus
Martin Woodcock discovered one on a small pool by the East Bank at Cley on 8th June 1954.

Martin Woodcock writes:

'On June 8th, 1954 while walking on the east bank at Cley, Norfolk, I flushed a dark-looking pipit from the edge of a small pool. It settled on a large muddy island in the pool, and I noticed at once that it had a brick-red throat. Thinking that it might be a Red-throated Pipit (*Anthus cervinus*) I sat down and made a number of sketches of it, and took full notes on its plumage at a distance of about 10 yards. These were as follows; the crown, mantle, wings and tail were dark brown, darker and without the greenish tinge of a Tree Pipit (*A. trivialis*) the back was heavily streaked, and there was a single wing-bar, formed by pale tips on the greater wing-coverts, as in a Meadow Pipit (*A. pratensis*); the primaries were dark brown or blackish, with pale edges. In flight, a narrow strip of white could be seen on either side of the tail, but this was difficult to see when the bird was at rest. There was a distinct buffish eye-stripe, and the chin, ear-coverts and throat were brick-red. The under-parts were rather dark buff, and there were several brown or black streaks on the flanks and the side of the breast. The bird gave the impression of being darker than a Meadow Pipit and possibly a little larger. Unfortunately it did not utter any note or call. It was seen later in the day by Mrs. R. F. Meiklejohn who knows the bird abroad, and W. F. Bishop, the official watcher at Cley Marsh.
What appeared to be the same bird was seen in flight two days later by myself, and A. H. Daukes. On this occasion it uttered a note like "cheeze".'

(Originally published in *British Birds* 47: 443-444)

Eurasian Rock Pipit
Anthus petrosus petrosus
See above comments in the introduction to Tree Pipit. The earliest reference we can find for the species is by the Pagets in *Sketch of the Natural History of Yarmouth and its Neighbourhood* 1834: 5 where they also knew it as Shore Pipit and Rock Lark and comment:

'…a few occasionally seen about Breydon wall.'

Scandinavian Rock Pipit
Anthus petrosus littoralis
One was obtained close to Norwich on 7th March 1864. It is in storage at the City of

Birmingham Museum.

B. B. Riviere states in *A History of the Birds of Norfolk* 1930: 37:

> 'The first example, originally in Stevenson's collection but afterwards purchased for the Connop collection, was killed close to Norwich on 7th March 1864 (*Birds of Norfolk*, vol. i,. p. 170).'

Henry Stevenson writes in *The Birds of Norfolk* Vol. l. 1866:169-171:

> 'In the month of February, 1855, a single bird (Rock Pipit) was shown to me (killed near Yarmouth during very severe weather), which corresponded with specimens procured by myself in Devonshire and Sussex; and two others in my own collection were secured at one shot, on the river's bank, near St. Martins gates, quite close to the city, on the 7th of March, 1864… The great difference observable in the plumage of some rock-pipits obtained in this country has, at various times, attracted the attention of naturalists, and the question whether two or more distinct races have not been hitherto confounded, is now occupying the attention of our leading ornithologists. Mr. Hancock, who has recently examined my two Norwich specimens, together with many others submitted for his inspection, decides that one at least of those birds, having a bright buff or cinnamon coloured breast, corresponds with the *Anthus rupestris* of Nillson; but though this is not, in his opinion, entitled to specific distinction, his decision, as affecting a Norfolk specimen, is the more interesting from the fact, that the chief home of *A. rupestris* is in Scandinavia.'

Water Pipit
Anthus spinoletta
A female was shot by M. A. Catling at Cley on 25th January 1905. The specimen is in storage at the City of Birmingham Museum.

B. B. Riviere writes in *A History of the Birds of Norfolk* 1930: 35-36:

> 'The first Water-Pipit to be obtained in Norfolk was a female, which was killed on 25th January 1905, and identified by Howard Saunders (Gurney, *Zoologist*, 1906, p. 24). This bird was shot by M. A. Catling at Cley, and was bought for the Connop collection (Pashley, *Notes on the Birds of Cley*, p. 109).'

Blue-headed Wagtail
Motacilla flava flava
One was obtained at Yarmouth about 18th April 1851.

Henry Stevenson writes in *The Birds of Norfolk* Vol. l. 1866:164-165 under the heading of Grey-headed Wagtail:

> 'I am not aware that more than three examples of this rare species have been actually identified as killed in Norfolk. Of the first (No. 92) in our museum collection, the following account is given by Messrs. Gurney and Fisher: - "A

male bird killed at Sherringham about May, 1842; another wagtail was procured at the same time, which was probably the female; but as the person who shot them only preserved the brighter-coloured specimen, the latter was unfortunately not identified." The next example, which occurred at Yarmouth about the 18th April, 1851, was also a male, and came into the possession of Mr. John Smith, of that town, who recorded its capture in the "Zoologist," p. 3174; and a female in the collection of Mr. Alfred Master, of this city, was killed on the Heigham river, a few years back, very late in the spring.'

B. B. Riviere writes in *A History of the Birds of Norfolk* 1930: 38:

'This, the Continental form of Yellow Wagtail, occurs in Norfolk as an occasional spring and autumn passage migrant. Stevenson was able to record only three examples, the earliest of which, killed at Sheringham in May 1842, has subsequently been found to belong to another subspecies (*Motacilla flava thunbergi*), under which title it will be referred to later.' (see under Grey-headed Wagtail below)

Thus Stevenson's second referenced bird in April 1851 is elevated to the first county occurrence.

Yellow Wagtail
Motacilla flava flavissima
Known as Ray's Wagtail by a number of 19th century naturalists, the earliest dated reference we can find is by Robert Marsham (1708-1797) in Tim Sparks and John Lines' *Chapters in the Life of Robert Marsham Esq. F.R.S. of Stratton Strawless, Norfolk* 2008: 16:

'I have never seen these birds in Norfolk in the winter season.'

Grey-headed Wagtail
Motacilla flava thunbergi
One was obtained at Sheringham in May 1842. The specimen (Accession no. NWHCM: 1935.15.45) is on display in the bird gallery at the Castle Museum, Norwich. It was donated to the Museum in 1935 by Gerard H. Gurney from the J. H. Gurney collection. It was the first British record.

B. B. Riviere writes in *A History of the Birds of Norfolk* 1930: 38-39:

'In connection with the single Norfolk specimen of this northern race of Yellow Wagtail, a male killed at Sheringham in May 1842, there has accumulated an unusual amount of literature, for it has since been assigned to three different subspecies, and has been described by various authors under four different names. It was first recorded in 1845 by Lubbock as *Motacilla neglecta*, and by Gurney and Fisher a year later under the same title. Stevenson mentions it under the name of *Motacilla flava*, (see Blue-headed Wagtail account above) whilst in 1875 Gurney, upon re-examining it, assigned it to the subspecies *Motacilla flava cinereocapilla* (*Norfolk and Norwich Nat. Soc. Trans*, vol. ii., p. 226). Dr. C. B. Ticehurst, however, who examined it in 1915, has identified it as an example of

Motacilla flava thunbergi, which opinion has also been confirmed by Mr. Witherby (*Brit. Birds*, vol. ix., p. 93).'

J. H. Gurney writes:

> 'About May 1st, 1842, a Wagtail was killed at Sheringham in Norfolk, and recorded by my father in *The Annals and Magazine of Natural History* for that year (p. 353) as *Motacilla neglecta*.
>
> On subsequent examination it was decided that it was referable to *Motacilla flava cinereocapilla* Savi, and was re-mentioned under that name in the *Norwich Naturalists' Soc. Trans.* (Vol. ll., p. 226).
>
> This bird has recently been submitted to a careful scrutiny by Dr. Claud Ticehurst, and compared with a series of skins, the result being that he is quite satisfied that it should be assigned to *M. f. thunbergi*, Billberg (= *M. borealis* Sundeval)'

H. F. Witherby adds:

> 'Mr. Gurney has kindly allowed me to see this bird ant it is certainly a typical adult male *M. f. thunbergi*. This being so, the inclusion of the Ashy-headed Wagtail *M. f. cinereocapilla*, in the British List, now rests solely upon the specimen obtained in May at Penzance and figured by Gould (*Birds of Great Britain*, Part xxii.). This figure is a very good one and in my opinion undoubtedly represents an adult male *M. f. cinereocapilla*.'

(Originally published in *British Birds* 9: 93)

Ashy-headed Wagtail
Motacilla flava cinereocapilla
A male was discovered by Richard Richardson and also seen by Peter Clarke at Cley on 16th May 1955. It was only the second record for Britain.

Richard Richardson and Peter Clarke write:

> 'On 16th May, 1955, during a period of moderate south-westerly winds, a *flava* wagtail with all the characteristics of a male Ashy-headed Wagtail (*Motacilla flava cinereocapilla*) appeared with two rather tawny-looking females on the coastal fresh-marshes at Cley, Norfolk.
>
> We were both familiar with the summer male Grey-headed Wagtail (*M. f. thunbergi*) from which the bird in question differed as follows: - The forehead, crown, nape *and ear-coverts* were a beautiful bright grey-blue, nearer that of *M. f. flava* and paler than that of *thunbergi*, whose very dark ear-coverts contrast markedly with the crown colour. The throat and malar region were white and there was not the slightest trace of a superciliary stripe. The bird called frequently, but the notes did not differ from those of *flavissima*.'

(Originally published in *British Birds* 48: 459)

Black-headed Wagtail
Motacilla flava feldegg
A male, first seen by Bryan Bland, was at Cley from 23rd July to 13th August 1983.

There had been some uncertainty as to who actually found this bird, and on what dates it was present. Unfortunately, Bryan Bland can recall no details of the occurrence and the bird, being a race, didn't attract the interest, at that time, a full species might have. The *Norfolk Bird Report* 1983 gives 23rd July to 11th August and Gantlett (1984) gives 23rd July to 13th August. It would appear that the record was accepted in 1999 after a request that year for information on its occurrence by the county recorder in the *Cley Bird Club Newsletter* and *Norfolk Bird Club Bulletin*. The notes, sketches and photographs received by the BBRC from Maurice Eccleshall, Kerry Harrison, Richard Millington and Eddie Myers as a result of this request, none of whom apparently saw the bird in July, were responsible for its acceptance. The BBRC's acceptance announcement in *British Birds* 93: 548 where, interestingly, it gives the dates of 30th July to 6th August (the exact dates Maurice Eccleshall was on holiday in the area), gives the names of M. Eccleshall, K. Harrison and R. Tidman *et al* against the record. The *Norfolk Bird Report* 1983, unfortunately just mentions the record with no finder's or observer's details.

The most detailed account of the bird was in Richard Millington's notes for 4th and 5th August 1983 where he wrote:

> '4th August '83…One male Black-headed Wagtail watched at ultra-close range just out in front of Bittern Hide. It fed alongside the edge of the grass and reeds, all around the edge of the scrape.
>
> Though moulting, it was still convincingly crippling; jet black head (speckled with yellow due to moult), rich bright yellow over whole of underparts including throat and chin. Dull greeny upperparts greener on rump, worn wing feathers and unevenly grown tail feathers. Structurally different to standard Yellow Wagtail, apparently 'chestier' with peaked crown and strong bill…
>
> 5th August '83…male Black-headed Wagtail still in front of hide, looking much the same – well worn and patchy, much more impressive at distance. Effects of wear, including indistinct wing-bars and pale gingery-buff primaries noted.'

(An account extracted from the unpublished files of the British Birds Rarities Committee archive)

John Williamson, writing in *The Birds of Norfolk* 1999: 393 states:

> 'Seago (1977) included a number of occurrences which have subsequently been rejected by British Birds Rarities Committee. A male at Cley from 23rd July to 11th August 1983 has recently been accepted by BBRC as showing characteristics of this race.'

Sykes's Wagtail
Motacilla flava beema
Examples of Sykes's Wagtail which breeds in north Kazakhstan and south-west Siberia have been claimed on a number of occasions in the county, both as breeders and migrants. Yellow Wagtails reportedly resembling *M. f. beema* bred at Hickling as long ago as 1894. The adults were

obtained and are on display at the Castle Museum, Norwich (Seago 1967 & 1977).

However, all past claims and published records are considered most likely to refer to the distinctly-plumaged Yellow x Blue-headed hybrid, known as 'Channel' Wagtails, which resemble *beema* more frequently than any other form (Taylor *et al* 1999; *Birding World* 2007; *Norfolk Bird Report* 2007). See the excellent article by Phillipe Dubois entitled 'Yellow, Blue-headed, 'Channel' and extra-limital Wagtails: from myth to reality' published in *Birding World* 20:104-112.

Enquiries at the Castle Museum, Norwich, in early 2009 revealed that the two 1894 Hickling specimens on display in the bird gallery are labelled respectively: Blue-headed Wagtail *Motacilla flava flava* (Accession no. NWHCM: 1927.83.1) and Yellow Wagtail *Motacilla flava rayi* (Accession no. NWHCM: 1927.83.2). They were a gift to the museum by the Hickling head keeper Jim Vincent in 1927 (D Waterhouse *in litt)*. This would indicate that the breeding adults were not Yellow Wagtails resembling *M. f. beema*, but any young may well have resembled that race.

However, further research has revealed that no young hatched. B. B. Riviere confirms the Castle Museum specimens' details in *A History of the Birds of Norfolk* 1930: 38 where he writes under Blue-headed Wagtail:

> 'Evidence of the Blue-headed Wagtail having bred in Norfolk rests solely upon that afforded by a pair of birds together with a nest containing six eggs, which were obtained by Robert [Bob] Vincent [the Hickling keeper and father of Jim Vincent] near Meadow Dyke, Hickling, on 11th June 1894. These were originally in the collection of J. A. Cotton, of Bishopstoke, Hants, and later in that of the Hon. E. S. Montagu, and through the kindness of Mr. J. Vincent, in whose possession they now are, I have recently had the opportunity of examining them. The male is a Blue-headed Wagtail in worn summer plumage, but the female is a Yellow Wagtail (*Motacilla flava rayi*), and whether the former was in fact the mate of the latter is, perhaps, open to doubt, though Vincent, I understand, satisfied himself that the birds were indeed a pair, and joint owners of the nest, before he obtained them.'

He adds in a footnote:

> 'This case of birds was presented by Mr. Vincent to the Norwich Museum in 1926.'

What this does is categorically prove that no Sykes's Wagtails bred or hatched at Hickling in 1894.

Interestingly an old name for Yellow Wagtail was Ray's Wagtail, as indicated by the museum labels and the Riviere account above.

Citrine Wagtail
Motacilla citreola

A first-winter was found by Tim Inskipp at Welney on 16th November 1980, which remained until the 17th. Following submission of details and a considerable delay, it was finally accepted in May 1997 as the first for the county, by which time a further two had already been accepted.

Tim Inskipp writes:

'The bird was first seen chasing a Meadow Pipit and then landing briefly on an earth bank behind a small pool about 30m away in front of the hide. Even on a brief view it looked an odd wagtail – rather like an immature *alba* but lacking a dark gorget and having a shorter tail. It landed behind the bank in a thick patch of Reed Sweet-grass *Glyceria maxima* where it was no longer visible. It remained there for some time but fortunately it eventually flew round again and sat for a while on a heap of earth about 50m away, allowing a reasonable view through a x20 telescope for about one minute when details were obtained.

I was then convinced it was a Citrine Wagtail because of the combination of grey upperparts, blackish wing coverts and tertials with strikingly contrasted white tips and edges, and more particularly the pale yellow of the supercilium, which was characteristically broadest over the eye, narrowing for and aft and continuing round the back of the ear coverts to join the whitish lower face. This last feature is present in all Citrines except adult males which of course have a completely yellow face. I have no evidence that this ever occurs in *flava* wagtails and it is thus emerging as a very important identification feature. The completely dark bill and grey flanks were other useful supporting characters.

The yellow on the face is characteristic of all first-winter Citrine Wagtails that I have seen from about the middle of October onwards. I assume that the totally grey and white birds that are recorded in Britain in September and early October undergo at least a head moult to produce this colour. This seems strange since they will already have had a complete post-juvenile moult in August?

The call was a typical 'dzzrp' usually given by Citrines in flight – very different from the typical *M. f. flavissima* flight call but quite similar to the calls of some races of *flava* occurring in India, a guide to identification but not diagnostic.

A detailed description and sketch were sent to the BBRC.'

(An account extracted from the unpublished files of the British Birds Rarities Committee archive)

Grey Wagtail
Motacilla cinerea
Not mentioned by Sir Thomas Browne (1605-1682) in *Notes and Letters on the Natural History of Norfolk* (1902), the earliest reference we can find is by Sheppard and Whitear in *A Catalogue of the Norfolk and Suffolk Birds, with Remarks* 1826: 21 where they comment:

'The Grey Wagtail is by no means uncommon in the autumn and winter season in the low meadows by the river Gipping in Suffolk, and likewise in the neighbourhood of Higham. It is also frequently met with in Norfolk at the same seasons. It runs upon the tops of the weeds, which are partly submerged in the ditches, and probably feeds upon the *Dytisci* and *Gyrini*, which are almost always to be found in those situations.'

White Wagtail
Motacilla alba alba
Two were obtained at Yarmouth on 24th April 1888.

Thomas Southwell writes in Henry Stevenson's *The Birds of Norfolk* Vol. lll. 1890: 378-379, initially quoting Stevenson from *The Birds of Norfolk* Vol. l (1866):

> '(Vol. i., p. 163). So lately as 1866, Mr. J. H. Gurney, jun., and myself were unable to include this species with certainty in our list of "*Norfolk Birds*," contributed to the "*Trans, of the Norfolk and Norwich Nat. Soc.*"(iv. P. 275), but on the 14th April, 1888, its claim to be admitted was placed beyond doubt by the occurrence on the golf ground, at Yarmouth, of two males, which came into the possession of Mr. George Smith, of that town.'

Although Stevenson gives the date as 14th April, George Smith into whose hands the specimens passed, gives the date as 24th April in the *Zoologist* 1888: 229.

Following on from this, in the *Catalogue of Birds and Animals contained in the Tolhouse Museum Great Yarmouth* (1908), there is listed as Case 3 (out of 398), 'White Wagtails, - two males, obtained near the Golf ground, Great Yarmouth, on 24th April 1888. First specimens for Norfolk (see *Zoologist*, June 1888).' It is presumed they were destroyed, along with the majority of the collection, by German bombing on 18th April 1941.

White (Pied) Wagtail
Motacilla alba yarrellii
Formerly known as White Wagtail, the British race is now more commonly known as Pied Wagtail. The earliest dated reference we can find is by Robert Marsham (1708-1797) in Tim Sparkes and John Lines' *Chapters in the Life of Robert Marsham Esq. F.R.S of Stratton Strawless, Norfolk* 2008: 16:

> 'In August 1763 I saw a milk white wagtail several times flying near the house & sitting on the lawn at Sr Arm Wodehouse at Kimberly.'

Bohemian Waxwing
Bombycilla garrulus
The earliest dated reference we can find is by Sir Thomas Browne (1605-1682) in *Notes and Letters on the Natural History of Norfolk* 1902: 68, where he writes in a letter to Merrett in September 1668 obviously referring to this species:

> 'Garrulus Bohemicus probably you haue a prettie handsome bird with the fine cinneberin tipps of the wings some wch I haue seen here haue the tayle tipt with yellowe wch is not in the description.'

Henry Stevenson when describing this species in *The Birds of Norfolk* Vol. l. 1866: 154-160 failed to notice this early reference. It was only later when Thomas Southwell published an edited reprint of the Sir Thomas Browne publication in 1902 that the 1868 reference was first noted.

Sheppard and Whitear's *A Catalogue of the Norfolk and Suffolk Birds: with Remarks* 1826: 11, state under Waxen Chatterer:

> 'The Waxen Chatterer, though only an occasional visitant, has not unfre-quently made its appearance in these counties, and generally from November to March. Some years since a prodigious flock of them were seen in a grove at

Bawdsey in Suffolk, by W. W. Page, esq., then resident at that place. Mr. Leathes informs us that these birds were in considerable abundance at Herringfleet in the winter of 1810.'

Black-bellied Dipper
Cinclus cinclus cinclus
One was shot near the Foundry Bridge, Norwich in November 1855. It would appear to be the first British record.

Henry Stevenson writes in *The Birds of Norfolk* Vol. l. 1860: 59-74:

'The Water Ouzel can be considered only as an accidental visitant to this county, the few specimens obtained from time to time appearing between the months of November and February (usually in severe weather), upon our inland streams, as well as in the vicinity of the coast. Whether or not the black-breasted water ouzel, the *Cinclus melanogaster*, of Gould's "Birds of Europe," is specifically distinct from the ordinary British form, with a chestnut band across the abdomen, or merely a climatical variety, undoubtedly our Norfolk specimens belong to the former type. I have at different times examined six or seven examples, all killed in this county, which with one exception to be hereafter mentioned, exhibited no trace of chestnut on the under parts, but were identical to a Lapland specimen in the Norwich Museum (No. 40.b), collected in that country by the late Mr. Wolley... Of more recent occurrences I may notice a male in my own collection, which was brought to me in the flesh, having been shot in November, 1855, whilst hovering over the river between the Foundry bridge and the ferry. It is not a little singular that a bird so accustomed to the clear running streams of the north, and the quiet haunts of the "silent angler," should be found as in this case, almost within the walls of the city, sporting over a river turbid and discoloured from the neighbouring factories, with the busy noise of traffic on every side. About the same time that this bird appeared near the city, three others were observed on more than one occasion on the Earlham river, by Mr. Fountaine of Easton, who is well acquainted with our British birds, but these suddenly disappeared, and were not seen again. Mr. Cremer, of Beeston, has one killed in that neighbourhood on the 25th of December 1860; another in the possession of Mr. Hubbard, a bird-stuffer, in Norwich, were also procured in that year; and a third, in my own collection, on the 29th of January, 1861. All of these birds were shown me in the flesh, and had black breasts like my first specimen and were in good plumage and condition.'

Interestingly, some of the more important specimens in Stevenson's collection were purchased by the Gurney family at the auctions of the collection, before and after Stevenson's death in August 1888, the first of 211 lots in September 1887 and the second of 38 lots in March 1889. In 1935 G. H. Gurney gifted a Black-bellied Dipper, collected near Norwich, to the Castle Museum, Norwich (Accession no. NWHCM 1935: 15.102), which may have been the 1855 bird. Unfortunately the specimen was destroyed in August 1956, probably due to insect infestation.

White-throated Dipper
Cinclus cinclus aquaticus/hibernicus/gularis
The earliest dated reference we can find for is in the Paget's *Sketch of the Natural History of Yarmouth and its Neighbourhood* 1834: 4:

'One shot at Burgh, November, 1816, which Mr. Youell had.'

John Youell, a nurseryman near the North Gates at Yarmouth, was a "great bird man" and his collection contained some choice specimens. He is mentioned by the Pagets as having afforded considerable assistance in the compilation of their list (Patterson 1905).

Babington (1886-1888) included this record under 'Dipper' as different from Black-bellied Dipper which he accounts for separately, as does Ticehurst (1932) who lists the specimen under 'British Dipper' as having chestnut underparts and states that it is in the Lucas collection, which was housed at Fleggburgh Hall. Its present whereabouts is unknown.

As there is apparently now no specimen to examine, there is no way of determining with any degree of certainty which of the three chestnut-breasted forms this record refers to: the Central European *C. c. aquaticus*, that from Ireland and west coast Scotland *C. c. hibernicus* or the remainder of Britain *C. c. gularis* – in fact there is so little published information on these forms, the BBRC published a request in 2006 for all suspected migrant White-throated Dipper sightings to be submitted to them for assessment - so it must remain as a chestnut-breasted form of undetermined race.
Even some Black-bellied-Dippers show a narrow chestnut band on the breast-belly interface (*British Birds* 99: 634).

While the Pagets refer to Burgh Castle as 'Burgh' in the introduction to the *Sketch*, there has always been a slight question-mark over whether the 'Burgh' mentioned for this record refers to Burgh Castle or Burgh St Margaret, also known as 'Burgh' at the time.

Winter Wren
Troglodytes troglodytes
The earliest dated reference we can find is by Sir Thomas Browne (1605-1682) in *Notes and Letters on the Natural History of Norfolk* (1902) where he mentions in his reference to 'Gold-crested Wren' (Goldcrest) that it was 'lesser than a wren.' But it is not absolutely certain that he was referring to this species. Sheppard and Whitear in *A Catalogue of the Norfolk and Suffolk Birds, with Remarks* (1826) just list Common Wren with no comments other than its other names of Jenny Wren, Kitty, Titty and Bobby Wren. But they also make reference to Wood Wren (Wood Warbler), Yellow Wren (Willow Warbler) and Golden-crested Wren (Goldcrest), so Browne may have been referring to one of these species.

With that in mind, the most reliable definite reference to the species is by the Pagets in *Sketch of the Natural History of Yarmouth and its Neighbourhood* (1834) where they refer to it as '…in plenty.'

Dunnock (Continental)
Prunella modularis modularis
A bird of the continental race was shot by B. B. Riviere at Blakeney Point on 17th October

1919.

B. B. Rivere writes:

'On October 17th, 1919, at Blakeney Point, a big migration of the usual late-autumn immigrants (Lapwings, Starlings, Sky-Larks, etc.) took place from east to west along the coastline, amongst them being a few Hedge-Sparrows. At the end of the morning there were several of these birds in the "bushes," and I shot two. One of these proved to be a typical example of the Continental form (*Prunella modularis modularis*), the other being of the British race (*P. m. occidentalis*).

I believe the Continental Hedge-Sparrow has only twice previously been identified in England, viz., at Spurn, Yorks., on September 7th, 1882, and October 9th, 1911 though it has been taken a good many times in Scottish islands.'

(Originally published in *British Birds* 13: 218)

Dunnock
Prunella modularis occidentalis

Just listed under Hedge Warbler by Sheppard and Whitear in *A Catalogue of the Norfolk and Suffolk Birds, with Remarks* (1826) but not commented on, the earliest reference we can find is by the Pagets in *Sketch of the Natural History of Yarmouth and its Neighbourhood* (1834) where they considered it '…very common.'

Alpine Accentor
Prunella collaris

One was found and identified by Kevin Shepherd on the cliff-face between Sheringham and Weybourne on 30th April 1978. It was trapped and photographed the following day and became only the second Alpine Accentor to be ringed in the British Isles (the first had been ringed at Portland, Dorset only three weeks earlier).

The following was extracted from the old Sheringham Bird Observatory Logbook:

'April 30th 1978:
Having left the Observatory hut quite late in the evening K. B. Shepherd began to walk back home to Sheringham, choosing to take the coastal footpath rather than the shorter route along the railway line. As he approached Spalla Gap he disturbed a rather dark dumpy bird from the gully, it immediately flew over the cliff and down towards the beach.

Intrigued by what he had seen he followed it down, carefully searching the cliff-face he relocated the bird crouched at the bottom of the cliff where he was able to note its bright heavily streaked chestnut flanks, two pure white wing-bars encasing a black median covert bar, yellow base to the bill and overall greyish tones to the upperparts. Having watched the bird go to roost he continued home, later confirming his initial thought that the bird was an Alpine Accentor by referring to Peterson's Field Guide.

May 1st 1978:
Just after first light the Accentor was relocated close to where it had gone to

roost the previous evening. As it became more active it began to feed along the cliff eventually entering the gully at Spalla Gap, it soon became obvious that this gully was its favourite feeding area. As the bird was quite approachable it was decided to attempt to catch the bird for ringing.

After watching the bird for a while it was decided to erect a single panel mistnet across the gully at a point where it narrowed. This done the bird was left while other nets were checked.

On returning the Accentor was still free and was eventually watched to hop under the net and perch on one of the supporting cane rods. It was then decided to attempt to walk the bird up but this also failed.

Retreating back to see what else we could do, it suddenly took flight and flew straight into the net.

The bird was then taken to the ringing hut to be processed before returning it to the gully where it remained until May 4th when it was seen by the late Jim Marsham to suddenly take flight spiralling up to great height before heading off in a south-easterly direction.'

An earlier record by Arthur Patterson of one apparently feeding amongst the weed-grown pile-stumps and stones under Gorleston Pier on 21st September 1894, allowed a very close approach (Patterson 1905). But a recent examination of his diaries, now housed within the Norfolk Record Office, Norwich, revealed that the details were too scant for the record to be considered authenticated.

European Robin (Continental)
Erithacus rubecula rubecula
The first to be identified as belonging to the continental race was obtained at Holkham in September 1905.

B. B. Riviere writes in *A History of the Birds of Norfolk* 1930: 83-84:

'The Continental Robin, which is distinguished from the British form by its paler colouring, more especially on the breast, was first identified in Norfolk in 1910 by Mr. Witherby and Dr. C. B. Ticehurst from specimens obtained by the former at Holkham in September 1905, and by the latter at Yarmouth in October and November 1910 (*Brit. Birds*, vol. iv., pp. 245, 246).'

European Robin
Erithacus rubecula merlophilus
Just listed as Red-breast by Sheppard and Whitear in *A Catalogue of the Norfolk and Suffolk Birds, with Remarks* (1826) but not commented on, the earliest reference we can find is by the Pagets in *Sketch of the Natural History of Yarmouth and its Neighbourhood* 1834: 4 where they considered it '…common.'

Thrush Nightingale
Luscinia luscinia
One trapped by Peter Clarke and his daughter Penny, a trainee ringer, at Holme on 14th May 1977, was not seen in the field before or after its capture.

Peter Clarke writes in the Norfolk Ornithologists Association's Holme Bird Observatory Log:

> 'When on a routine visit to one of the heligoland traps during the morning of the 14th May 1977 we flushed a Nightingale-like bird down the funnel of the trap and into the catching box.
>
> My interest and suspicions were immediately aroused by the dark, earthy-brown appearance of its upper plumage and tail not so bright as in a Nightingale. In the catching box the obviously mottled breast band confirmed the first recorded Thrush Nightingale for the County of Norfolk.
>
> In the hand the whole of the upperparts were dark earth-brown without a tinge of rufous. Tail feathers were a dark rufous brown with a slight tinge of rufous on the upper tail coverts. There was a mottled band across the breast. Each feather was crescentically edged with dark brown giving a mottled rather than speckled or spotted appearance. Sides of throat also slightly mottled, but throat paler and unmarked. Rest of breast and belly dull white. Under-tail coverts buffish. Leg colour was medium horn. Bill was medium horn above, paler horn below and yellowish at base. Eye dark brown with black pupil.
>
> On being released the bird dived under a bramble bush and was not seen again. Two black and white photographs taken of the bird in the hand enclosed.'

A possible earlier occurrence in the county is interesting enough to be included here.

B. B. Riviere writes in *A History of the Birds of Norfolk* 1930: 83:

> 'A specimen in an old case, presented in 1908 by Mr. Cullingford, of Durham, to Mr. L. A. C. Edwards, and labelled "Savi's Warbler, Norwich, 1845," proved upon examination to be an example of the Thrush Nightingale (L. A. C. Edwards, *Brit. Birds*, vol. v., p. 224). Its authenticity as a Norfolk-killed bird must, however, upon this evidence, remain in doubt.'

L. A. Curtis Edwards, who knew Thrush Nightingale as the Sprosser, writes this interesting account referenced above by Riviere:

> 'In view of the rejection by Dr. Hartert and others of the Sprosser obtained at Smeeth, Kent, on October 22nd, 1904, and exhibited by Mr. M. J. Nicholl at a meeting of the British Ornithologists' Club (*Bull. B.O.C.*, XV., p. 20; Saunders *BB*, 1., p. 8), I have thought it might be of interest to put on record a specimen in my possession.
>
> In December, 1908, Mr. L. Cullingford of Durham, gave me a supposed Savi's Warbler which he had found in an old case that he was breaking up. He told me that there was a label on the back of the case, giving the following data: "Savi's Warbler, Norwich, June 5th, 1845," together with some other writing that had become illegible. Unfortunately he had destroyed the label, after making a copy of it, together with the case, so that I did not see it.
>
> The specimen was in a very dilapidated condition, and its appearance was quite in accordance with its supposed age, but Mr. Cullingford succeeded in making a passable skin of it. As I had then no acquaintance with Savi's Warbler,

I accepted Mr. Cullingford's identification, and the skin lay in a cabinet drawer until August 1910, when Mr. M. J. Nicholl recognized it as a Sprosser (*Daulias philomela*). On his visit to England last summer, Mr. Nicholl brought Egyptian examples of both Savi's Warbler and the Sprosser, and after careful comparison I am quite satisfied that my bird belongs to the latter species.

Of course, the history of the specimen is incomplete, but to me, at least, it bears an air of probability, and the likelihood of its being an escape at that date is much less than in the case of an example obtained within recent years.

I see no reason why this species should not occasionally visit our country, though the validity of any modern record must be tainted by reason of the possibility of the bird having escaped from confinement.'

(Originally published in *British Birds* 5: 224-225)

Common Nightingale
Luscinia megarhynchos
The earliest dated reference we can find is in extracts from Robert Marsham's 'Indications of Spring' published in the *Transactions of the Norfolk and Norwich Naturalists' Society* 1874-1875: 33 where he recorded in the Stratton Strawless area on 9th April 1750:

'…heard a nightingale…'

Bluethroat (Red-spotted)
Luscinia svecica svecica
One was found dead on the beach at Yarmouth on 21st September 1841.

Henry Stevenson knew it as the Blue-throated Warbler and writes in *The Birds of Norfolk* Vol. l. 1866: 96-97:

'The only example of this most elegant species, known to have occurred in Norfolk, is a male bird in Mr. Gurney's collection, picked up dead on the beach at Yarmouth, on the 21st of September, 1841. The same gentleman has also another male killed about the 15th of May, 1856, near Lowestoft, in the adjoining county, it is particularly worthy of note, that both these birds, as well as the first recorded British specimen now in the museum at Newcastle-on-Tyne, belong to the form with the red spot prevailing in Scandinavia, and not the white spotted form which yearly visits Germany and Holland.'

The specimen (Accession no. NWHCM: 1923.74.3) is in storage at the Castle Museum, Norwich.

Bluethroat (White-spotted)
Luscinia svecica cyanella
A male was found at Sheringham on 30th April 1906 (Plate 7) and is on display in the bird gallery at the Castle Museum, Norwich (Accession no. NWHCM: 1948.185). It was only the third British record.

B. B. Riviere writes:

'I recently saw in the collection of Mr. F. E. Gunn, the Norwich taxidermist, a male White-spotted Bluethroat in summer plumage, labelled in the handwriting of the late T. E. Gunn: "30th April, 1906, picked up dead at Sheringham". Mr. F. E. Gunn assured me that he remembered this bird being brought in in the flesh. In reply to my query as to why it had not been recorded, Mr. Gunn told me that during the latter part of his life his father seldom recorded any rarities, more particularly if he thought there was any chance of disposing of them to a collector. This I believe to be a fact, though whether, after a period of nearly thirty years, this bird should be accepted as an authentic Norfolk specimen, is perhaps doubtful...'

(Originally published in *British Birds* 12: 360)

Interestingly, the *Transactions of the Norfolk and Norwich Naturalists' Society* 1933-1934: 480, states:

'A male , the first to be recorded in Norfolk, was watched at close quarters and identified by Mr. R.M. Garnett at Salthouse on April 7th and 8th 1930 (*British Birds* vol xxiii p. 339)'

However, Michael Seago included the 1906 record in *Birds of Norfolk* (1967 and 1977) and it is also included in Taylor (1987) and Taylor *et al* (1999).

Red-flanked Bluetail

Tarsiger cyanurus
A female or first-winter male was discovered in Yarmouth cemeteries by Peter Allard on 18th October 1994 (Plate 13).

Peter Allard writes:

'The 18th October was a day of south-easterly winds and bright sunshine. With the tide reaching full just before mid-morning Breydon Water was perhaps the first venue. There was little of interest visible from the first hide after an hour, apart from thirty one Avocets, an increase in Black-tailed Godwits and six Spotted Redshanks.
Yarmouth Cemeteries were next visited. There had been a Yellow-browed Warbler in the north side the day before but it had been very difficult to locate high up in the Holm Oaks. Was it still there I wondered? A quick look in the south side revealed very little apart from a few Goldcrests and so I entered the north side. The time was approximately 0950hrs and I was the only birder present. Walking along the main path towards a cluster of Holm Oaks two birds were on the path in front of me. Both looked like Robins as they disappeared into a small evergreen bush but something made me bring my binoculars up for a closer look. One was certainly a classic Robin with bright reddish-orange breast but the other was quite a shock. Although of Robin shape and size and brownish above it displayed noticeable orange-coloured flanks and clearly lacked a reddish breast. A whitish throat patch was just visible before it disappeared from view. With heart now thumping it recalled visions of photographs I had seen last year

of an immature or female Red-flanked Bluetail in Dorset but surely I must be dreaming. Searching somewhat impatiently for several minutes the bird eventually showed again briefly in another bush and a pale eye-ring was quite obvious, displaying drooped wings, it rather recalled a Red-breasted Flycatcher. A third brief view confirmed the orange flanks were real – it really did look like a Red-flanked Bluetail but I had yet to see its blue tail! On all three occasions the tail looked dark in the rather shaded conditions of the main path.

With this in mind, and having left another birder – who had just arrived and name unknown – to look for it I rushed to the nearest telephone which fortunately is adjacent to both cemeteries on the corner of Sandown Road. I 'phoned several birders including Andy Wallis and Dave Holman informing them that I strongly suspected that I had located a Red-flanked Bluetail in the North Cemetery. Although reasonably certain, I was erring on the side of caution which is often wise in the case of extreme rarities.

Andy Wallis was first on the scene followed by John Burrell who surprisingly was just visiting "*ad hoc*" and then an excited Dave Holman arrived "hotfoot" from Waxham Dunes. The other birder who I had left had by then tracked the bird down to an area of Sycamore trees just west of the path. John Burrell glimpsed the bird on a branch and in typical style stated "yes, almost identical to the Dorset bird" and within a minute all five of us had seen the blue in its tail. This was Norfolk's first ever Red-flanked Bluetail, a female or first winter individual, it was like a dream come true. Panic was the order of the day as Dave Holman was busy on his mobile 'phone contacting all the Birdlines etc., Jane Bamford appeared from nowhere having just glimpsed the bird herself. The next two hours were quite exciting with the Bluetail showing reasonably well and birders were arriving in all states of panic by the minute.

The bird was still present late afternoon when I returned and several hundred birders had already seen the bird with people still arriving all the time. The local press were present and talking to locals and visitors. The occasion was very well organised and by dusk most of the bird club had seen it and the cemetery staff had left the gate open to assist any latecomers. This was much appreciated by all. The bird was still present the following morning in the same area and remained until until dusk on the 20th. During its three day stay an estimated seven hundred plus birders saw this splendid individual and many photographs were taken of it. Visitors to see it, other than birders, included local doctors, teachers, barristers, councillors and members of the local constabulary! It was a good bird, generating much local interest. None were disappointed as the Bluetail performed extremely well in the main path area of the North Cemetery frequenting the evergreen bushes and sycamore trees. Occasionally it perched in the open on gravestones or on the main path.

This bird constitutes the fourteenth record of Red-flanked Bluetail in Great Britain but was only the second ever twitchable bird – the first being in Dorset last year. With Breydon a complete failure this year regarding rarities it was nice for Yarmouth Cemeteries to host, what was for me, "the bird of the year".'

(An account published in the *Norfolk Bird Club Bulletin* No. 13: 8-10)

Black Redstart

Phoenicurus ochruros gibraltariensis

One was obtained at Yarmouth on 31st October 1848.

Henry Stevenson writes in *The Birds of Norfolk* Vol. l. 1866: 99-100:

> 'Until 1848 this rare species had probably not been noticed in this county, but on the 31st of October of that year an adult female was killed near the old battery at Yarmouth, as stated by Messrs. Gurney and Fisher, in the "*Zoologist*," p. 2345.'

Further research has revealed that this specimen was in the possession of a Rev. John Henry Green, presumably the same Rev. J. Green listed in the Post Office directory for 1858 as living in Nelson Road, Great Yarmouth. Upon his death, it was purchased by the Rev. Charles John Lucas of Burgh Hall, Fleggburgh, along with another Black Redstart shot at Lowestoft. This bird, however, was undated. C. J. Lucas's collection was catalogued in 1886 in a small privately published edition titled *Collection of Birds at Burgh House collected in the counties of Norfolk and Suffolk by the Rev. C. J. Lucas 1886*, and the date was published incorrectly as 31st February 1848. This is a very scarce booklet and we know of only two copies in existence, one of which is in the Great Yarmouth Library.

Arthur Henry Patterson writing in *Nature in Eastern Norfolk* (1905) states that unfortunately C. J. Lucas failed to encase many of his specimens in a manner worthy of their value, and he was unaware that the collection had been catalogued. Lucas had apparently died by this time, but Patterson stated that the bird collection still remained in the family. The present whereabouts of the 1848 specimen is unknown.

Riviere writes in *A History of the Birds of Norfolk* (1930) that the greater part of the collection is at Burgh House, Fleggburgh the residence of Mrs. Fisher. The present whereabouts of the collection is unknown, even if it still exists.

The "old battery" referred to above is thought to be the Town Battery that was located near the Britannia Pier on the corner of Euston Road and Marine Parade, and adjacent to the Hollywood Theatre. It was the smallest and the central one of three Batteries that were positioned along Yarmouth seafront and was removed in 1858.

Black Redstart (Iberian/Moroccan)

Phoenicurus ochruros aterrimus

One showing characteristics of the Iberian/Moroccan race was found by John and Judy Geeson, Stewart Betts and Pete Milford at Burnham Overy Dunes on 6th June 1992.

John and Judy Geeson write from their notes taken at the time:

> 'On June 6th 1992, whilst birding for the day with Stewart Betts and Pete Milford, we walked out along the seawall from Burnham Overy Staithe to look for a reported male Red-backed Shrike and any other late migrants we could find in the dunes at Gun Hill. Having found the shrike very quickly, we then stumbled onto a very bright and striking male Black Redstart (*Phoenicurus ochruros*). It was immediately obvious that we had something quite different from the usual spring males, with their essentially charcoal grey body and black throat/breast – which we enjoy as passage migrants or in their few East Anglian breeding

localities (*eg* Great Yarmouth, Lowestoft). This individual was largely black – on the mantle, most of the head and underparts, with a contrasting grey cap, and an extensive white wing panel formed by pale edges to the secondaries; below the usual rusty tail (slightly darker on the central feathers), the undertail coverts were also distinctly rufous.

This was a very easy description to memorise, and after returning home in the evening and consulting the available literature, especially *Birds of the Western Palearctic* Vol. 5. Cramp *et al.* OUP (1988) we confirmed that our bird was one of the Western Mediterranean race *P. o. atterimus*. We had previously encountered Black Redstarts of this form on trips to both Spain and Morocco.

As far as we are aware, this constituted the first, and currently the only documented record of *P. o. atterimus* in the county.'

Black Redstart (Eastern)

Phoenicurus ochruros phoenicuroides
A male, showing strong characteristics of the eastern race was found by James McCallum at Wells on 9th November 2003.

James McCallum writes:

'Following a day's birdwatching Natasha Drury and I took an evening walk along Wells harbour to pick up some driftwood and my boat. Coming to a large elder bush a Robin appeared in the dense crown and then suddenly, a redstart of some kind flew to the ground then back into the bush. It landed briefly on the outside edge then disappeared around the back. Its appearance initially took me by surprise as it was quite unlike any redstarts I had seen either here or abroad. Although this initial sighting was close it was very brief. Tasha, impressed by its attractive appearance asked what it was and I must admit I was a little lost for words, despite its striking appearance. I couldn't confidently put a name to it so replied "I'm not a hundred percent sure but I think it's probably a male Black Redstart of one of the eastern races".

I was a little anxious as it had now disappeared, however, we decided to stand still and quietly wait. Then after what seemed an eternity it appeared once more, again darting out from the elder onto the ground to pick up insects before flying back to the bush once more. This time it landed on our side of the cover and we were able to get really good views. Fortunately I had my A5 sketchbook with me and over the next hour or two I made lots of sketches and looked at it in great detail before deciding to leave as the light was beginning to go and the tide rising.

It was a very handsome bird, essentially bright red orange below continuing in the same intensity right onto the under tail coverts. The tail and rump were typically bright red. Its head, back and scapulars were a lovely blue slate colour becoming slightly browner on the lowest edge of the scapulars. The face was solid black, beginning at the lores and continuing behind the eye and including the entire throat. The whole breast was also this slate blue colour but heavily marked with black crescents, which merged into its black throat. The legs and bill were blackish, the bill slightly paler than the jet black face markings. The wings were essentially dark brown with broad pale buff edges to the tertials, secondaries and greater coverts. The median coverts were black with very thin paler edges while the lesser coverts were slate coloured. There was no white on the forehead as in common male redstart and when flycatching the bright red orange colour of the underparts could clearly be seen to continue onto the underwing coverts, especially on landing.

Although there is little information in many of the reference books the description of sub-species *phoenicuroides* in both Svensson and BWP fits this bird best, this conclusion was also made by Ian Wallace and Andy Stoddart who both kindly commented on my notes, sketches and watercolours. They also, in common with the Svensson ringer's guide, both suggested that despite its bright colourful appearance the wing markings would indicate a first-winter male.

There have been around five previous records of similar birds in the UK, however, the BOU has removed this sub-species from the British list because of the discovery of supposed Common Redstarts x Black Redstart hybrids. I have seen photos of a supposed summer adult hybrid in Sweden and this individual was quite similar. However, the underparts were much more typical of a male Common Redstart and not continuous red orange as in the Wells' bird.

The occurrence of this young male together with two other first-winter males, showing similar characteristics, one in the Netherlands and one in Guernsey in late autumn 2003 would suggest that these are more likely to be eastern Black Redstarts rather than hybrids. Especially when combined with exceptional numbers of Siberian and central Asian vagrants that turned up in western Europe during the same period.

The fate of such records will ultimately fall in the hands of the relevant committees who will have to make educated decisions concerning them. For me personally the findings and decisions have little bearing on my enjoyment of two rather strikingly different and exciting looking forms of familiar birds.'

(An account published in the *Norfolk Bird Club Bulletin* No 54: 15-17, as part of an article detailing the finding of two potentially new sub-species for the county in 2003)

Common Redstart

Phoenicurus phoenicurus phoenicurus

The earliest dated reference we can find is in 'Extracts from the Calendar of the Rev. William Whitear 1809-1826' published in the *Transactions of the Norfolk and Norwich Naturalists' Society* 1881-1882: 235, where he recorded one on 1st May 1809 in the Starston area.

Sheppard and Whitear in *A Catalogue of the Norfolk and Suffolk Birds, with Remarks* 1826: 19 comment:

'Perhaps the Redstart sings earlier and later than any other diurnal songster. We have heard it singing after ten o'clock at night, and at three the following morning. A Redstart, which built in our garden in the summer of 1819, adopted part of the song of a Lesser White-throat, which much frequented the same place; and its imitation was so exact as sometimes to deceive the nicest ear. Almost all the summer warblers are, more or less mock-birds.'

The Pagets in *Sketch of the Natural History of Yarmouth and its Neighbourhood* 1834: 4

considered it '...common.'

Common (Ehrenberg's) Redstart

Phoenicurus phoenicurus samamisicus

An adult summer plumage male showing characteristics of this eastern race, known as Ehrenberg's Redstart, was seen by Graham Easy, Colin Kirtland and Bob Mansfield at Heacham on 26th October 1975. It was the first British record.

Colin Kirtland writes from his notes and recollections of the occasion:

'The open sparsely vegetated area around and to the south of the chalets at Heacham always looks promising for migrants and is indeed well worth a visit in spring and autumn. As one of our regular ports of call on our visits to the east Wash, Graham Easy, Bob Mansfield and I stopped there for a brief look on a bright October morning. We didn't expect to find much this late in the autumn although a large high over western Europe had resulted in easterly and then southerly winds for several days and I had seen the Black-throated Thrush at Holkham two days previously.

A couple of Stonechats were immediately obvious, watching from exposed perches before dropping to the ground to capture insects. A late Wheatear was a nice find but even better was a bird which we at first assumed was a male Black Redstart. With its dark grey back towards us, the most prominent feature was a striking white patch on either wing formed by white outer fringes to the secondaries and tertials. However, as it turned sideways we could see that on the underside only the throat was black; the breast and flanks were bright rufous, shading into white on the belly. It was obviously a Redstart but the extensive white wing patches could only mean that it belonged to the south-west Asian race *samamisicus*, sometimes known as Ehrenberg's Redstart, which breeds from southern Turkey eastwards to the Crimea, the Caucasus and Iran. Surprisingly it was in very smart plumage, with little evidence of the buff feather tips which are usually a feature of autumn birds. We only realised later that it was the first to be recorded in Britain.

Later that day we also saw a Lesser Grey Shrike at Holme, a bird that possibly had a similar area of origin. The annual summary of rarities in *British Birds* for that year recalls: "...October 1975 was the most magical month in the recording history of rare birds in Britain...with the beautiful woods at Holkham in Norfolk providing the best ever mainland rarity watching". Those of us fortunate enough to have experienced that autumn will certainly agree!'

Whinchat

Saxicola rubetra

Just listed but not otherwise commented on by Sheppard and Whitear in *A Catalogue of the Norfolk and Suffolk Birds, with Remarks* (1826), the earliest reference we can find is by the Pagets in *Sketch of the Natural History of Yarmouth and its Neighbourhood* 1834: 4 where they considered it:

'...common on the North-denes.'

Eurasian Stonechat
Saxicola torquatus hibernans
Listed by Sheppard and Whitear in *A Catalogue of the Norfolk and Sufolk Birds, with Remarks* (1826) but not commented on, the earliest reference we can find is by the Pagets in *Sketch of the Natural History of Yarmouth and its Neighbourhood* 1834: 4 where they considered it:

> '…common on the North-denes.'

Interestingly, Stoddart and Joyner writing in *The Birds of Blakeney Point* 2005: 176 suggest that:

> 'The origin of the European Stonechats reaching Blakeney Point is not clear and may involve both British *hibernans* (the form which also occurs in Ireland, western Btittany and western Iberia) and continental nominate birds. However, *hibernans* is not a well-differentiated form and its continued separation from *rubicola* may not be justified.'

Eurasian Stonechat (Continental)
Saxicola torquatus rubicola
Although suspected of occurring, the first mention of this Continental race being recorded in the county was in the *Norfolk Bird Report* 2005 where it just states:

> '…individuals considered to be continental *S. T. rubicola* Cley April 10th and Scolt Head May 12th-end June.'

Siberian Stonechat
Saxicola torquatus maurus
A male identified by Richard Richardson was at Cley on 6th May 1972. It showed strong characters of the race *stejnegeri* and was also the first British occurrence of a Siberian Stonechat in spring. A colour sketch of this bird by Richard Richardson is held in the R. A. Richardson archive in the Alexander Library at the Edward Grey Institute of Field Ornithology at Oxford, and is reproduced in *Guardian Spirit of the East Bank* (Taylor 2002).

Interestingly the *Norfolk Bird Report* 1972 noted in the Systematic List:

> 'A bird showing the characteristics of the Siberian race *maura* at Cley in May…'

The significance of this spring record was apparently not realised at the time.

An earlier record of one shot at Cley on 2nd September 1904 was long-accepted as the first British record of Siberian Stonechat. H. N. Pashley writes in *Notes on the Birds of Cley Norfolk* 1925: 114:

> 'Indian Stonechat I received the only British specimen (a male) on September 2nd, 1904 from Mr. E. C. Arnold, and set it up for him. Mr. Howard Saunders saw it in my shop but thought it was only a melanistic Stonechat; when he compared it with skins in the National Museum found he had made a mistake.'

However, the specimen, held at the Castle Museum, Norwich, was re-examined in the mid-1970s when it was decided that it was probably an old male of one of the two western European races, and it was subsequently removed from the British List in 1977.

Isabelline Wheatear
Oenanthe isabellina

Peter Allard found one at Winterton North Dunes on 28th May 1977. It was only the second British record - the first having been shot in Cumbria in 1887.

Peter Allard writes from his notes taken at the time:

'I was up very early on the morning of May 28th 1977 and faced a real dilemma. With warm easterly winds still prevailing and the knowledge that an adult summer-plumaged White-winged Black Tern had been present at Hardley Floods since the 26th, do I visit one of my regular birding patches at Winterton Dunes or visit Hardley Floods and see the tern? White-winged Black Tern would have been a new species for me; however, Adrian Boote had visited Winterton Dunes two days earlier and found a Dotterel together with a nice selection of migrants. The decision was extremely difficult, but right at the last moment I decided to go for Winterton Dunes hoping perhaps, to find a rarity of my own. I little realized then that I had made the correct decision.

Arriving early, the weather was already warm and the wind was still from the east. I soon relocated Adrian's Dotterel, a brightly coloured individual in the main dunes system and having watched this bird feeding for some time, I moved inland from the main path to look around one of the flight pools on the Winterton Poor's Land. A fine singing Whinchat was soon found and close by were a party of four late Redwings, presumably held up by the easterlies. Heading back to the main path across the Poor's Land, a sandy waste area left to its own devices and rarely grazed, I glimpsed a very sandy and plain-looking wheatear perched on a bramble bush. Immediately noticeable was the virtual lack of any head pattern and two slightly paler areas on the mantle which formed a rather obscure 'V', both features not readily attributable to Northern Wheatear. Closer views were obtained, but it soon took flight revealing a white rump as it flew and landed on a bush further away. I was then fortunate to observe it for something like 30 minutes at varying distances as it fed on the ground with what was described in my notebook as an incredible running-hop gait, which the bird did through the short grass, covering up to five feet at a time. It constantly flicked its tail up and down and was heard to call on a number of occasions. This note was described as a soft 'cheep', sometimes virtually inaudible, uttered mainly from the tops of low bushes, usually gorse and bramble, and other vantage points. I had already concluded that it was one of the rarer wheatears, but was unsure which species I was watching. The black bill was considered slightly longer and slightly heavier than on Northern Wheatear and when it stood still on the ground, it had a very upright stance giving the impression that it was also long-legged. When feeding and running through the short sandy area, it brought back memories of the Cream-coloured Courser at nearby Caister in 1969 which fed in a similar fashion. My notebook was becoming quite full with details and sketches, some five pages in total and I had already noted that the tail pattern of this bird differed from that of Northern Wheatear, a female of which was fortunately close by, albeit rather briefly. The head pattern of this bird was very plain indeed with an indistinct blackish loral stripe and a thin paler supercilium, both of which only very marginally extended to the rear of the eye.

Fortunately, I then saw Alan Laurie, a fellow birder in the distance. Alan soon became aware of my calling and came across to the Poor's Land. The wheatear was soon relocated, and Alan had excellent views with both binoculars and telescope. As luck had it, Alan actually had a field guide with him, although carrying bird identification books around was not generally encouraged by the birding fraternity. We both agreed on the wheatear's identification, it was almost certainly an Isabelline, a new bird for Norfolk and there was now an urgent need to spread the news as quickly as possible. However, little did I realize at the time, there had only been one previous Isabelline Wheatear recorded in Great Britain. We watched for a little longer during which time, it was additionally heard to utter a louder double call note, described in my notes as 'wheet-whit'. Feeling the bird would not move too far away, we both hastily departed the area and quickly walked back to the village. A number of rather frantic phone calls were made to various local birders, but it proved very difficult to get through to anyone on a Saturday morning. Most people were out birding! Michael Seago agreed to come over, but could not leave straight away, Terry Boulton could not be contacted at all and Giles Dunmore was out on Blakeney Point for the day. Anyhow, I had to return home for several hours and in doing this, I was able to read up that there had only been one previous record of Isabelline Wheatear in Great Britain and that was of a bird shot in Cumberland (now Cumbria) on November 1887. Nerves certainly got the better of me and immediately there was this great urge to return to Winterton Dunes, some ten miles away. I had by then managed to contact Terry Boulton who said he would see me there as soon as possible. We arrived back at Winterton in the afternoon and after a complete search of the Poor's Land and failing to relocate the Isabelline Wheatear, panic crept in. However, after approximately an hour, it was very fortunately relocated close by the main track leading northwards, feeding on an area of burnt heather. Here it occasionally fed alongside a female Northern Wheatear which gave us a good size comparison. The Isabelline Wheatear was noted as slightly proportionally larger with larger head and body and from a distance, against the burnt heather, reminded us of a small sandy-coloured thrush. Again, its upright stance, its characteristic running gait and tail-wagging features were all very obvious in the excellent light conditions. After nearly an hour, it flew low west and back to the adjacent Poor's Land where we had to leave it and return home. It was later learned that in our absence Michael Seago did in fact have a look for it briefly at midday, but had failed to locate it and had already left before we had returned.

Many phone calls were made during the evening and several observers were very keen to come over to Winterton Dunes early the next morning. By then, the weather had turned cooler and despite an extensive search by half-a-dozen birders, there was unfortunately no further sign of it. Two Northern Wheatears, a couple of Whinchats, a Fieldfare and four Redwings were the best of many hours searching every likely area.

Details of the Isabelline Wheatear were quickly sent to the British Birds Records Committee and after what seemed a considerable period of waiting, the record was eventually accepted. Unknown to me at the time, the record then had to go to the BOU as the species was still in category 'B', the previous record in Cumberland being over 50 years ago. A very welcome letter came in March 1979 from Robert Hudson of the British Ornithologists' Union and it read 'I am happy to tell you that your Isabelline Wheatear has been accepted and promotes the species to category 'A' on the British list'. This was wonderful news and justification that regular working of a local patch can occasionally pay dividends.

Several years later, in view of Isabelline Wheatear's continued great rarity in this country and with a better understanding of the identification features, the record was re-circulated by the British Birds Records Committee. The identification was sound and, although Isabelline Wheatear has since occurred in this country on several occasions in the autumn, the Winterton record remains the only spring occurrence and the first to be identified in the field in Great Britain.'

Northern Wheatear
Oenanthe oenanthe oenanthe
The earliest dated reference we can find is by Sir Thomas Browne (1605-1682) in *Notes and Letters on the Natural History of Norfolk* 1902: 26-27:

> 'Auis Trogloditica or Chock a small bird mixed of black & white & breeding in cony borrouges whereof the warrens are full from April to September. at which time they leaue the country. they are taken with an Hobby and a net and are a very good dish.'

Thomas Southwell adds a footnote:

> 'The Wheatear is here referred to; the name *trogloditica* would seem to be more appropriate in this country, having reference to its habits of nesting in "Coney boroughs," than that of *aenanthe*, as applied to it by those who knew it as frequenting the Continental vineyards. A name still, or recently in use in West Norfolk, is Cony-chuck.'

Greenland Wheatear
Oenanthe oenanthe leucorhoa
First described in 1789, the earliest dated reference we can find for this race is by William Rowan in the *Annotated List of Birds of Blakeney Point* 1918: 13 where he writes:

> 'Rare. Taken twice by Mr. E. C. Arnold (7th September 1907; 20th September 1909). It has rarely been observed in other years.'

Interestingly, Henry Nash Pashley the noted Cley naturalist, collector and taxidermist writes in *Notes on the Birds of Cley Norfolk* (1925), published posthumously after his death in 1924, from his diaries and notes, recorded one shot in the Cley/Blakeney area and brought to him on 18th September 1909.

In his list of the birds of Cley, included in the book, he states:

> 'Often taken on autumn migration.'

It would seem that at that time they were not encountered in spring, which nowadays is their main passage period in Norfolk. But it may be the case that they were simply overlooked during those months as very few birds were shot in spring following the bird protection laws. These laws excluded the autumn migration period when, after the beginning of August, almost anything could be shot, hence all the gentleman-gunners at Cley and district would shoot at any small bird hoping that it might be something rare.

Pied Wheatear
Oenanthe pleschanka

Amazingly, Peter Allard found Norfolk's first Pied Wheatear, a first-summer male, at Winterton North Dunes on 28th May 1978, at the same location and on the same date that he had found the county's first Isabelline Wheatear the previous year.

Peter Allard writes from his notes taken at the time:

'Having been fortunate in finding the Isabelline Wheatear at Winterton Dunes on May 28th last year, I doubted luck would be so kind on a repeat visit on the same date the following year. The visit to Winterton and Horsey the previous day (May 27th) provided few clues, with very little of note and virtually no movement of birds. A female Kentish Plover at Breydon later in the day provided some hope however. An evening out with Adrian Boote and his wife was enjoyable and as we socialized, a chance remark was made of what sort of rare wheatear we would find the next morning. Little did we realize how true this was to be!

Starting out very early, the weather was not too kind with full cloud cover and a persistent sea mist rolling in from time to time backed by a cool east-north-east breeze. However, hopes were always high in late spring. As was usual for us, we took slightly different paths through the dunes, Adrian deciding to take the inland route and I the more coastal path. Virtually nothing had been noted in the first 45 minutes or so apart from a Tree Pipit when at approximately 0645hrs just as I was approaching the toad pool area, I noticed a small vivid black-and-white bird sitting on the top of a small mound right in front of me. Lifting my binoculars, I could hardly believe what I was looking at – it just had to be a male Pied Wheatear, a new species for the county list. Was I dreaming this? No. Taking a deep breath and controlling my excitement, I tried to call Adrian over, but he was nowhere to be seen in the mist. However, after some ten minutes of frantic calling, Adrian appeared out of nowhere and wondered what all the fuss was about. Had I fallen over and hurt myself? I asked him to take a deep breath and view what was perched on the adjacent mound. He uttered nothing which is unusual for him. Adrian for once was speechless. We both viewed this eastern rarity with some disbelief and rather glazed eyes until we realized it was true. It was a male Pied Wheatear, possibly a first-summer individual and just as the sea mist and the skies cleared, it amazingly began to sing. The bird remained in the same general area for several hours, but had ceased singing by about 0900hrs. The whole early episode was clouded in excitement, but it was soon realized that the news had to be spread quickly. My notes unfortunately do not recall how we managed to spread the word, but I have a vague recollection that I ran the mile or so back into Winterton village to phone the news and returned in a time an

Olympic sprinter would have been proud of.

Anyhow, Terry Boulton was one of the first on the scene followed by a procession other birders later in the day including Giles Dunmore, Michael Seago and Dave Holman. By now, however, the weather had warmed up considerably and the sun was shining, although a few clouds remained. Dave took several photographs of the bird and the one in my notebook, which he kindly gave to me, is a constant reminder of what a truly remarkable bird this was. Two other birders, Dennis Herrieven and Richard Preston found the Pied Wheatear independently later that morning, certainly making their annual weekend trip from Wymondham very worthwhile.

It was a very striking individual to say the least with a full black face and throat, the black extending over onto the mantle which then faded a little to a dark brown colouration. The whole of the underparts were white, which contrasted well with the mantle, and the white head and nape had a greyish pattern on the crown. The tail was longer than Northern Wheatear's with much more conspicuous white on the outer feathers, the narrow central bar was brownish with the thin terminal band blackish. It was seen to chase Northern Wheatears on several occasions displaying an aggressive streak, often arching its wings when the black underwing coverts were particularly impressive. The bird frequented the rhododendrons and other small bushes after the initial sighting, often looking very shrike-like as it perched on the highest branch looking for insects. It would then swoop down to feed on its prey, often depressing its tail on the ground until it returned to the top branch again to continue this characteristic feeding habit. It frequently called, especially earlier in the day, a very wagtail-like call, sometimes like a Pied Wagtail, the next perhaps more likened to a Yellow. The song was very audible and lark-like consisting of several syllables followed by a more Robin-like warble. It sang regularly from the top of bushes and sandy mounds up until about 0900hrs when singing ceased. Also heard were an occasional soft 'tick' and a harsher 'tack' with a softer Stonechat-like 'buzz' note heard on at least two occasions. The Pied Wheatear remained in the same general area certainly up until early evening when it was last seen, apparently perching on the rusty posts and fence at the base of the sandhills a little to the south of where it was initially found.

The Pied Wheatear was looked for the following day by a number of birders, including Moss Taylor, but sadly there was no sign of it and it had presumably left overnight following clear skies.

What an immature male Pied Wheatear was doing in east Norfolk in late May is anyone's guess, but it was clearly way off course, the nearest breeding grounds being in south-east Europe and south-central Asia. This was only the sixth British record and the first ever in spring. *British Birds* noted in their 'Report on Rare Birds in 1978' that this and the Isabelline Wheatear record on the same date in 1977 provided just reward for the perseverance of two or three observers with their 'home patch'. The sequel to this is that on May 28th 1979 when expectations were extremely high and binoculars at the ready, the best sighting during the entire day's birding at Winterton and Horsey was 54 Wood Pigeons flying east out to sea until lost to sight. That's birding!'

First-summer male Pied Wheatear at Winterton North Dunes May 1978. (*Norman Arlott*)

Black-eared Wheatear
Oenanthe hispanica hispanica
An adult of the race *hispanica* was found by Peter Thompson at Salthouse on 30th August 1965. It remained in the area until 14th September.

Richard Richardson writes in his diary:

'30th August: During this afternoon Peter Thompson found a magnificent male Western Black-eared Wheatear, black-throated form, on the marshes east of Gramborough Hill, Salthouse, and took great pains to round up other interested people. Quite a number of us had quite good views of it in the evening before the light failed, and here is a summary of today's impressions: Size as a Common Wheatear, though fluffed-out appearance made it look larger at first glance. Very pale sandy buff in varying shades, with black face (like a male Redstart). Plumage description from 100 yards' range: Crown, nape and mantle bright apricot-buff fading to white on supercilium, and forehead. Wings brownish, doubtless due to broad brown edges of new feathers; rump white, underparts pale pinkish-buff but whiter on the fluffy flank feathers. Tail looked black when closed and white patterning was not seen in the rather distant views obtained. Feeding habits and movements as Common Wheatear. No notes heard.'

Moss Taylor writes in *Guardian Spirit of the East Bank* 2005: 132:

'This is a day that Peter Thompson is never likely to forget. He had to help his mother in the family-run hotel at Cromer during the morning and after finishing work decided to walk to Cley along the coastal footpath. He only came across two other Wheatears during the entire six miles walk! After finding the Black-eared Wheatear he then had to walk to Walsey Hills before finding another birdwatcher who was interested in seeing it! Fortunately it was John Crudass, a future RSPB staff member, and he drove Peter back to Salthouse where the identification was confirmed. They returned to the East Bank "to round up other interested people", as Richard put it. It was the first record for Norfolk and the bird remained in the area for a fortnight.'

Desert Wheatear
Oenanthe deserti
An adult male was shot by M. A. Catling between Cley and Blakeney Point on 31st October 1907.

J.H. Gurney writes in the *Zoologist* 1908: 132:

'31st [October 1907]. –S.W. 2. The Desert Wheatear is a bird which we have been expecting for some time, but it does not appear to have been identified in Norfolk or Suffolk until to-day, when I am informed of one being shot near the sea. This is a large example, a male bird, and apparently an old one from its plumage, measuring, after it was stuffed, 6.3 in. from tip of tail to tip of beak; throat richly mottled with black, on the back a delicate buff tint. This is only the second occurrence of the Desert-Wheatear in England.'

H. N. Pashley writes in *Notes on the Birds of Cley Norfolk* 1925: 114:

'Male taken here October 31st 1907 by Mr. Catling (first for Norfolk). Exhibited at the B.O. Club, now in Connop collection.'

Formerly in the Connop Collection at Rollesby Hall, this specimen is now in storage at the City of Birmingham Museum. It is described by Rowan in the *Annotated Checklist of Birds of Blakeney Point* (1918), as of the western variety, which is the North African race *O. d.homochroa*, (although it is listed therein under the heading of *O. d. deserti*) and considered as such by Taylor *et al* (1999). Doubt was cast by Stoddart and Joyner (2005) who consider it most likely to have originated from one of the more migratory eastern forms *deserti* or *atrogularis*.

Rufous-tailed Rock Thrush (Rock Thrush)
Monticola saxatilis
A male was found by Mr and Mrs A. G. Kneen at Salthouse Heath on 9th May 1969.

The following account was compiled from notes sent to the Norfolk Bird Report Editorial Committee by Miss E. M. Love, Mr E. W. Forty and Dr D. McNeil. From these notes, it is presumed that these observers were completely unaware of the bird's presence:

'Mr and Mrs E. Forty, Miss E. Love, Mr L. Hills and Dr D. McNeil arrived at Salthouse Heath at about 4-30pm on 9th May 1969, to look for a Red-backed Shrike. Shortly afterwards Dr McNeil said that he thought he had seen a Redstart at the edge of a patch of burnt gorse. They approached more closely and Mr Forty said that he thought he could see a Red-backed Shrike, but noted that he caught a flash of orange- red when it flew up to a low bush. Miss Love, catching a quick glimpse of the bird remarked that it looked blue and Dr McNeil questioned why it didn't have a red back. It then flew away with a dipping flight, its brilliant tail showing white at the base and its back was blue. Dr McNeil identified it as a Rock Thrush as soon as it flew. In size it was larger than a Wheatear and its posture when perched on a bush was more horizontal than a Song Thrush. On the ground it was slightly more upright than a nearby Blackbird. In total the bird was visible for approximately 30 seconds, during which time a good description was obtained.'

Despite an extensive search the following day by many observers, there was no sign of this colourful vagrant.

Scaly (White's) Thrush
Zoothera dauma
A male was shot by a Mr. Borrett at Hickling on 10th October 1871 (Plate 7). The specimen (Accession no. NWHCM: 1889.30) remains on display in the Bird Gallery at the Castle Museum, Norwich.

Thomas Southwell writes in Henry Stevenson's *The Birds of Norfolk* Vol. lll. 1890: 377:

'An example of this beautiful thrush was killed on the 10th October, 1871, by Mr. Borrett, in the parish of Hickling. It was presented by him to the late Mr. Sotherton N. Mickelthwaite, and preserved by Mr. Gunn, who recorded the occurrence ("*Zoologist*," s.s., p. 2848). This specimen, the seventh known to have been killed in Britain, proved by dissection to be a male, and after Mr. Mickelthwaite's death was acquired for the Norwich Museum, where it now is. Mr. Borrett confirms the statement of the other fortunate observers of this rare bird, that its appearance on the wing was so like that of a woodcock as to lead them to mistake it for one.'

T. E. Gunn writes in the *Zoologist* 1871: 2848:

'On the evening of the 10th instant I received a beautiful specimen of this very rare species from the Rev. S. Micklethwaite, of Hickling, who, in reply to my communication, informed me it had just been killed by Mr. F. Borrett in a marsh in that parish. This is the first instance on record of the occurrence of White's thrush in this county: it therefore affords me great pleasure in placing this *rara avis* as an additional species to our rich list of Norfolk birds, In examining the bird I made the following notes:-
 Inches
 Total length from tip of beak to end of tail 12 and 5 eighths
 Tip to tip of fully extended wings 20 and a half
 Wing from carpal joint to tip 6 and 3 quarters
 Tail 5
 Beak: length along ridge of upper mandible 1 and 1 sixteenth

"Beak: width at base1 quarter
Tibia 2 and 3 eighths
Tarsus1 and 9 sixteenths
Outer toe and claw 15 sixteenths
Middle toe and claw 1 and 7 eighths
Inner toe and claw 13 sixteenths
Hinder toe and claw 1 and 1 eighth
Weight, 6 and a quarter ounces.

On dissection it proved to be a male, in good condition, and rather fat. I had the breast cooked, and found the flesh firm and the flavour not unlike that of the woodcock. Its stomach was filled with the remains of some small ground-beetles and some fibrous matter, apparently roots of grass.'

Siberian Thrush

Zoothera sibirica
A male seen briefly by Peter Wilkinson in Yarmouth cemeteries on 25th December 1977 was only the second British record.

Peter Wilkinson writes:

'Whilst bird-watching in the Kitchener Road cemeteries, Great Yarmouth, Norfolk at midday on the 25th December 1977, my attention was drawn to a blackbird-like bird with a very conspicuous and brilliant white stripe over the eye feeding with redwings and one blackbird on an open patch of short grass. My first impression was that this was a freak blackbird, but the very conspicuous white stripe was on both sides of the head and that there were several other differences as I watched the bird from 30 yards or so from behind a tree. Firstly the bird was slightly smaller than the other blackbird close by and was closer to the size of the many redwings which were in the vicinity and that the underparts from the legs to the undertail coverts was a dirty-white colouration with one or two very small blackish spots close to the black tail. The overall colouration of the bird was slaty-black with the head area jet black. The very conspicuous white stripe above the eye began in front of the dark eye and ran almost to the nape, but did not join. It took flight on two occasions flying silently up into cover in the adjacent sycamores whilst the rest of the thrushes were still feeding. In flight the most conspicuous and obvious detail was the vivid white underwings with a blackish narrow stripe in the middle, but it was the white which caught the eye and there was a very small amount of white on the end of its black tail which was quite obvious when it alighted on a branch before disappearing into cover.

Additional details which I noted at the time were a smaller blackish bill than the blackbird and palish legs. It fed with typical thrush-like posture and had slightly drooped wings. I watched this particular bird for some 10 minutes before it was disturbed by a man taking his dog for a walk and it disappeared into the sycamores and was not seen again. The visibility was very good three eighths cloud with a force 3 westerly wind. From a number of reference books quoted, I have no doubt in my mind that this bird was a male Siberian thrush, despite there having been only two previous records for the British Isles.'

(An account sent by Peter Wilkinson to the County Recorder at the time of this occurrence)

Male Siberian Thrush at Great Yarmouth cemeteries December 1977. (*Norman Arlott*)

Grey-cheeked Thrush
Catharus minimus
A juvenile was trapped by Bridget Griffin and Dave Leech at Croxton, near Thetford on 10th November 2004 (Plate 14). It was described in the systematic list of the *Norfolk Bird Report* 2004, as 'undoubtedly the most bizarre "find" of the year'.

Dave Leech writes:

'Just before 7.30 am on the 10th November, Bridget Griffin and I set out to ring at a feeding station set up by our colleague Jez Blackburn at Croxton, a small village just outside Thetford in south-west Norfolk. Jez rings at the site fairly regularly throughout the winter period but had chosen to take a short holiday in the US, an irony which would become more apparent as the day progressed. It's an interesting area; a small patch of scrub on the edge of the Raker family farm that attracts a large number of finches, including Bramblings and tits, thanks in no small part to the cropping regime on the surrounding farmland, which lies fallow over the winter months.

We put up our two 40 foot nets with our usual mix of optimism and fatigue, struggling slightly to find the guy ropes in poor light at an unfamiliar site. By 7.45 am there were plenty of thrushes moving about and it looked as if our efforts might be rewarded. Ten minutes later a mixed group of Fieldfare and Redwing, no more than 50 birds, dropped into the hawthorn bushes to the east of the nets, only to be flushed shortly afterwards by a passing truck. With high hopes of a net full of Scandinavian-ringed birds, we walked around the corner only to find an assortment of tits, a Bullfinch and a Great Spotted Woodpecker. I elected to begin extracting the Great Spot, which was in the bottom shelf, and it was only when I raised my head that I realised we had actually caught a thrush, which was now resting only a few inches from my nose. I would like to take this opportunity to apologise to the residents of Croxton for any offence my language might have cause at this point but it's not often you see a bird in a net that you can't immediately identify.

Bridget had already started moving towards the bird, having also noticed that something was not quite right. For a start it was incredibly small, the size of a Nightingale or perhaps slightly larger. The markings on the head and breast, meanwhile, were not hugely dissimilar to a Song Thrush. Everything pointed towards a *Catharus* thrush, but inland? In the east of England? And more to the point, if it was, was it Grey-cheeked or Swainson's? Neither of us had seen either species before and we don't make a point of taking our North American passerine guide with us while ringing in the Thetford area. We were going to need some serious gen.

As luck would have it, several colleagues in possession of just such gen live within five minutes of the site, and so it was that Dawn Balmer, Stuart Newson and Mark Grantham were roused courtesy of their mobile phones and arrived at the site shortly afterwards, armed to the teeth with a variety of literature. In the meantime, Bridget had bravely taken responsibility for extracting the bird while I looked on with trembling hands, sweating profusely and offering extremely helpful pieces of advice such as "Don't let it go" and "Be very careful".

Once in the hand, a brief examination of the underwing confirmed the bird's genus, a striking pale bar running along the underside of the primaries and secondaries. The crown, mantle and upperwing were uniformly dark, muddy brown with an olive-grey tinge to the back and rump and a warmer, slightly rufous tone to the tail. The undertail and belly were white with black tear-drop flecking on the upper breast and lower throat becoming denser to form clearly defined submoustachial stripes. The face was a similar muddy brown colour to the crown, with slightly paler supercilium and off-white moustachial stripes. The lores were slightly darker than the rest of the face, the orbital ring was narrow and pale and the bill was dark with a flesh-coloured base to the lower mandible. It was a juvenile bird, as evidenced by the six retained old greater coverts, which were slightly greyer than their newer counterparts. The wing measured 104mm (maximum chord) and the bird weighed 30.4g.

So what was it? Well, Veery and Hermit Thrush could be excluded straight away by the general colouration and lack of rufous tones, particularly on the tail, and the lack of a wide sandy orbital ring and lores also indicated that it wasn't Swainson's Thrush. Finally, Bicknell's Thrush could be eliminated on the basis of biometrics, as the maximum wing chord cited for this species is 98mm, leaving Grey-cheeked Thrush as the only remaining candidate. Some confusion was temporarily caused by information about the relative length of the first primary and the extent of the emargination contained in an American banding guide, which suggested that the wing formula was close to Swainson's. However, photographs of skins on the University of Puget Sound website viewed later that morning indicated that the book was in fact incorrect and that the wing formula supported our original identification.

After the size of the leg had been measured with callipers, a B ring, the same size as that used for Greenfinch, was fitted. The bird was released and flew immediately into a tall bush, calling once and quickly dropping out of sight. Once access permission had been arranged with the landowner, the news was released. Unfortunately, despite much searching, the thrush was not seen again, although it was heard to call once at 11.00 am. The lure of a Pine Grosbeak further up the East coast quickly proved too much for many birders and the crowds had dispersed by early afternoon.

Interestingly, the only other east coast record of Grey-cheeked Thrush was from an equally unlikely site, having been found dead by a schoolboy in a patch of scrub hear Horden, Co Durham and presented to his supply teacher. Fortunately for all concerned, the teacher showed the bird to none other than Eric Meek, the current chairman of the BOU Records Committee, on a training course shortly afterwards. Just goes to show – you've got to keep your eyes and mind open when birding, even when you're away from the established hotspots!'

(An account published in the *Norfolk Bird Report* 2004: 286-287)

Ring Ouzel
Turdus torquatus
The earliest dated reference we can find is by Robert Marsham of Stratton Strawless in a letter to celebrated naturalist Gilbert White of Selborne dated 24th July 1790, published in the *Transactions of the Norfolk and Norwich Naturalists' Society* 1876: 146 where he writes:

> 'I find a memorandum of mine of so old a date as September 14th 1772 *i shot a ring-Ouzel*. This was the first my father had seen. This shows they are strangers in Norfolk. But I have seen of them twice since, in severe frost.'

Common Blackbird
Turdus merula
The earliest dated reference we can find is in Henry Stevenson's *The Birds of Norfolk* Vol. ll. 1870: 275, where he writes in the account for Woodcock:

> 'The rough marine herbage also on the Blakeney "meals" forms a like resting place for a time, as well as for the large flights of blackbirds, that make their appearance on our coast in October so regularly that the gunners in those parts are accustomed to search for woodcocks when the blackbirds are over.'

He adds a footnote:

> 'The following extract from the "Household Book" of the L'Estranges, of Hunstanton, seems in a remarkable manner to confirm the joint arrival of these two species, thus recorded as far back as 1522. "Itm. pd to Stephyn Percy for ij woodcocks and iiij blackbirds, iiij pence." This is the only instance in which the blackbird is mentioned in these accounts, and being entered in the thirty-ninth week after the eighth of February, the date would fall about the first week in

November.'

Black-throated Thrush
Turdusatrogularis
A first-winter was found at Holkham on 21st October 1975 by Winifred Flower, Bridget Wardleworth and Don Wright. It remained until the 24th and was remarkably tolerant of admirers who surrounded its favourite bramble patch.

Winifred Flower writes, initially in a letter to Ian Wallace the Chairman of the Rarities Committee:

'I don't know what happens when the Advisory Chairman of the Rarities Committee sees a rare bird. Does he write it up? Or just pass it? Or does the original finder still do so? So, instead of sending notes to Nick Dymond, I enclose mine to you. I was with Bridget Wardleworth, who had come to pick blackberries. Although she's not a birdwatcher she has a keen eye, and noticed the bird a few seconds ahead of me, and we had just met D. G. Wright of Preston, of whom I know nothing.

So please throw my notes away if they are not wanted. Do you disagree with bits? Richard [Richardson?] said he thought the bird exactly like the Shetland female, but didn't say if you thought it an adult female. Knowing far less than either of you, I thought it might be immature female because of :-
the lack of coloration of the throat band,
the lack of suffusion of colour on the sides of breast,
the heaviness of the streaks,
the lack of any yellow at the base of bill.
But (my sources are only the Shetland female's photo, the *Handbook*, and a few words in other reference books) apparently there is considerable variation, and this may have been an individual veering toward the greyer and streakiest...'

She continues with an account of the occasion:

'Among numerous Blackbirds (*T. merula*) and Redwings (*T. musicus*) remaining to feed in large bramble thickets, after a huge migration of *Turdidae* along the N. Norfolk coast, Bridget Wardleworth, D. G. Wright and W.U.F. noticed an unusual thrush before noon on 21st October 1975. The bird was perched on a pine about 35ft. away in poor, grey light. The first impression was of a very upright, slightly stocky and rather long-tailed thrush, entirely grey and white.

From the crown to tail the dorsal plumage was ash-grey, with a faint pale eyebrow, and a dark line across the lores continued slightly behind the eye. The off-white breast, flanks and abdomen bore long, pale grey streaks, boldest on the flanks. The crissum was off-white. The throat was white, broken by the grey-black moustachial stripes. Below this, partially dark feathers formed an ill-defined cross band. The bill was dark grey, paler below and basally, the gape yellow-orange, legs and eyes dark. The bird flew down into the brambles, rising after some minutes to perch briefly in another pine or elder, sometimes cocking its tail on landing, and preening occasionally. This behaviour continued during about one and three quarter hours watching, and on 22nd October.

As the sun slowly struggled out, the colours changed. The white throat appeared cream, the breast palest buff and the upperparts took on more grey-brown tones. The changes with alterations in light seemed unusually marked. Really good light on the 22nd brought out the browner shades, the pale rufous on the underwing, and the characteristic dark and pale patches on the upper surface. The ventral streaking seemed to stand out less on this day, but varied greatly according to the degree to which the feathers were puffed out. Contracted, they converged; fluffed up, a pale central area was conspicuous and the streaks appeared more irregular.

Frequently Blackbird calls were heard, but with so many *turdids* moving and feeding in the bushes, no sound could definitely be traced to *T. ruficollis*.'

(An account extracted from the unpublished files in the British Birds Rarities Committee archive)

Interestingly, George Dormer writes:

'The rarity – be it American or Siberian – is always sought with a zeal and determination peculiar to the avid birdwatcher. Rare warblers and pipits are encountered with some regularity, but the vagrant thrush or lark is distinctly rarer. It was not therefore surprising that the rumour of a Black-throated Thrush seen in Holkham Wood on 21st October, 1975, heralded a mini invasion of 'twitchers' from all parts of the country. Many visitors were understandably disappointed when it left the area after only three days. That was the fifth accepted record of the species in this country, and only the thirteenth record of an Asiatic thrush of the genus '*Turdus*' since the first bird recorded was trapped in Sussex in 1868.'

(Extracted from an account published in the *Norfolk Bird Report* 1976: 99-100, which dealt mainly with the finding of Norfolk's second record of the species at Coltishall in February 1976)

Fieldfare
Turdus pilaris
The earliest dated reference we can find is by Sir Thomas Browne (1605-1682) in *Notes and Letters on the Natural History of Norfolk* 1902: 3 where he mentions "felfars" when commenting on migration. We can reasonably assume he was referring to the Fieldfare, as it was also known as Felfer, Felfoot, Fellfor, Felt, Felter, Feltifer and Feltiflier. Felfar is assumed to be no more than a misspelling or corruption of one of these names.

Interestingly, Sheppard and Whitear referred to this species in *A Catalogue of the Norfolk and Suffolk Birds, with Remarks* (1826) as the Meslin-Bird.

Song Thrush (Continental)
Turdus philomelos philomelos
The first confirmed specimen of a bird of the nominate continental race was shot at Holkham in late September 1905.

B. B. Riviere writes in *A History of the Birds of Norfolk* 1930: 72-73:

'The autumn arrival of Song Thrushes upon the Norfolk coast from the Continent appears to have been observed as early as the seventeenth century by Sir Thomas Browne, and has since been well described by both Stevenson and by Southwell. It was not, however, until Dr. Hartert, in 1909, called attention to the difference in plumage between the Continental and British races of the Song Thrush that the two forms were recognised, and the first Norfolk specimens of the Continental race, shot at Holkham at the end of September 1905, were recorded by Mr. Witherby in 1911. Although the paler and more olive colouring of the Continental as compared with our native Song Thrush renders the two as a rule distinguishable in the field, this is of course only the case when they can be seen at fairly close range, and to differentiate between the migratory movements of the two races is a matter of great difficulty.'

Song Thrush
Turdus philomelos clarkei
Sir Thomas Browne (1605-1682) mentions "thrushes" when commenting on migration and on occasions when comparing its size to another species in *Notes and Letters on the Natural History of Norfolk* (1902). However, apart from Fieldfare no other thrush is specifically named.

The earliest dated reference we can find is by Robert Marsham of Stratton Strawless in "Indications of Spring", extracts of which were published in the *Transactions of the Norfolk and Norwich Naturalists' Society* 1874-1875: 31-45 where he writes in January 1750:

'Some told me that they heard thrushes sing on ye 2nd; but I did not see a snowdrop, till ye 15th, nor hear a thrush 'till ye 17th…'

Although listed by Sheppard and Whitear in *A Catalogue of the Norfolk and Suffolk Birds, with Remarks* (1826) the species was not commented on. The Pagets in *Sketch of the Natural History of Yarmouth and its Neighbourhood* 1834: 4 considered it '…common.'

Redwing
Turdus iliacus iliacus
The earliest dated reference we can find is by Robert Marsham of Stratton Strawless in a letter to celebrated naturalist Gilbert White of Selborne dated 12th February 1792, published in the *Transactions of the Norfolk and Norwich Naturalists' Society* 1826: 165 where he writes:

'I have observed nothing remarkable in this winter but a greater number of red-wing Thrush than usual…'

Redwing
Turdus iliacus coburni
Although suspected in the past, the first confirmed county record of this Iceland and Faroe Islands race was a dead bird carrying an Icelandic ring found by Mr. John Stelzer at Kelling on 12th November 2008.

Andrew Cannon writes:

'The corpse of the bird was very thoughtfully left on Mr. Stelzer's doorstep by his neighbour's cat Minnie on 12th November 2008. Mr. Stelzer kindly took the trouble to put the ring through my door, knowing me to be a local ringer. Observing the ring to be from Iceland, rather than one of mine, I went round to his house and retrieved the corpse. I photographed the bird and the ring and forwarded the photographs and the finding details to the BTO ringing office at Thetford.

Information received from the Iceland Institute of Natural History shows that the bird was ringed, aged at least two years, on 28th March 2007 at Hofn, Hornafjordur, Austur-Skaftafells in south-east Iceland. It is apparently only the second Icelandic-ringed *coburni* Redwing recovered in England and is the first confirmed record for Norfolk. Redwings have been rather scarce here so far this autumn so this bird was probably by itself rather than associating with a large flock of nominates.'

Up to late November 2008 there had been fewer than 25 British records of Icelandic-ringed Redwings and these are concentrated along the north and west coasts. It is thought that most birds follow the west coast down to the wintering areas and so avoid most of England which is why this is a very odd recovery for Norfolk (Mark Grantham, BTO Ringing Unit *in litt*).

Mistle Thrush
Turdus viscivorus
The earliest reference we can find is by Sheppard and Whitear in *A Catalogue of the Norfolk and Suffolk Birds, with Remarks* 1826: 15 where they write:

> 'The Missel Thrush sings its loud note till the beginning of May, after which time it is not often heard. We have once, and only once, heard it run through a great variety of the most melodious notes, at a time when the male was wooing the female. The young have somewhat the appearance of hawks.'

The Pagets in *Sketch of the Natural History of Yarmouth and its Neighbourhood* 1834: 4 considered it '…common'

Cetti's Warbler
Cettia cetti
One was found dead by Mr. P. Chambers, on his lawn at Mariners Lane in Norwich City Centre on 28th June 1973 and later identified by John Goldsmith. It carried a Belgian ring on its leg and was ringed as a juvenile at Hensies, Hainaut, Belgium on 23rd August 1970. It was the first foreign-ringed Cetti's Warbler to be recovered in Britain.

John Goldsmith writes from his recollections of the occasion:

> 'Although this was the first confirmed record for the county, I suspect there were previous ones. I saw (and had rejected) what was almost certainly one in the Yare Valley near Norwich in the 1963/64 winter while Ted Ellis wrote a perfect description of one (also rejected) seen at Wheatfen I think in the late 1950s/early 1960s. I was familiar with the species having twitched them at Stodmarsh, Kent and felt along with Rod Martins, Barry Jarvis and others that they really should

be around the Broads.

I had a phone call to the old Natural History Department of Norwich Castle Museum from a lady living on the slope just down from Ber Street in Norwich City Centre. This was my 'home area' having been born and brought up at the top of Bracondale. We used to get a lot of 'little brown bird' calls in the days before the RSPB office arrived, so I was not unduly surprised with this one which had apparently hit a window and died. I was unable to identify the bird from the caller's description other than it was probably a warbler – but rather too far into the breeding season to be a Whitethroat or similar on migration. Anyway, it was later, after lunch before I managed to get a few free minutes and walk down to her residence on Mariners Lane. By now the bird had been consigned to the dustbin – so I emptied the contents and sifted through - I've never been one to take "no" for an answer!

I found it slightly dishevelled and not immediately obvious what it was, but I remembered the ten tail feather diagnostic (having a ringing licence) – and BINGO! My excitement, I recall, was not matched by the lady of the house with her bin contents all over the floor! I sprinted back to the Castle and phoned Michael Seago, breathless, to tell him the news!'

Zitting Cisticola (Fan-tailed Warbler)
Cisticola juncidis
The first British record was observed by Nick Dymond at Cley in full song-flight over a small pool near the East Bank on the morning of 24th August 1976. After a short period of observation, it ceased singing and flew purposefully west. What was presumably the same bird was relocated on 29th August at Holme where it remained in a small area of hawthorn, sedge and reeds close to the car park until 5th September.

Nick Dymond writes:

'Just after 06.00 GMT on 24th August 1976, I was walking along East Bank at Cley, Norfolk, when suddenly I heard a loud, penetrating and repetitive 'tsip-tsip-tsip…' call, which rang bells in my not-long-woken mind. I spotted the source of the call, some 30 m ahead and to my left, over a small reed-fringed pool not far from the bank: it was a tiny, fluttering bird which appeared to be suspended on a yo-yo some 4-6 m over the reeds. By now, it had dawned on me that it was a Fan-tailed Warbler *Cisticola juncidis* in full song-flight: a species with which I had become very familiar during visits to the Camargue in southern France and to the Gambia. I moved along the bank, level with the bird; after perhaps a minute, it dropped into the sparse, short reeds at the back of the pool, about 20 m from me, and landed on a bent reed, about 15 cm above the mud, completely visible, with its upperside towards me. It had pale brown upperparts, strongly streaked darker, without any bold white or buff supercilium. Its tail and rump looked rather rufous, particularly as it landed; its tail was very short and rounded. The warbler was turning its head from side to side, showing its thin bill and pale throat. There were several Bearded Tits *Panurus biarmicus* and a begging juvenile Reed Warbler *Acrocephalus scirpaceus* close by, affording good size comparisons: the stranger was markedly smaller than either of the local species. I turned away to test the dampness of the grass and, in that brief moment, the warbler vanished.

Feeling somewhat bemused, I ambled towards a spot near the north drain, where an Aquatic Warbler *A. paludicola* had been seen the previous evening, and stood watching and listening; I then heard again the distinctive 'tsip' call-notes, this time more spaced out. I could not see the bird and was certain that it was perched in the vegetation. As I hurried 60 m along the bank, the Fan-tailed Warbler suddenly appeared over the grass and reed area in front of me, doing its characteristic yo-yo flight and uttering its monotonous song. It was facing away from me, and was some 6-10 m above the reeds about 35 m from the bank. With the sun behind me, I could clearly see the rufous rump and uppertail; the short, rounded wings; and, as the bird reached the top of each rise, the half-fanned tail, which appeared dark underneath, with white at the sides. After a seemingly lengthy display of its characters – at least a minute – it suddenly ceased singing and flew purposefully away from me, towards the west, at a height of about 12 m. I watched it through my binoculars until the speck vanished, which in the early morning haze I estimated to have been about 500-600 m. After it had gone, I compared it with a Blue Tit *Parus caeruleus* which seemed similar in body size and wing length, but had a bigger, rounder head and much longer tail.

Despite continuous searching for the rest of the day, by myself and at least a dozen other birdwatchers, the bird was not relocated at Cley. It or another, however, was seen at Holme, Norfolk (35 km west), from 29th August to 15th September 1976 (see note by Peter R. Clarke, below).

A Fan-tailed Warbler was observed at Cape Clear Island, Co. Cork, on 23rd April 1962 (*Brit. Birds* 65: 501-510), but the record described here is the first for Britain. I. J. Ferguson-Lees and Dr. J. T. R. Sharrock (*Brit. Birds* 70: 152-159) predicted that Fan-tailed Warblers would soon colonise and breed in Britain.'

(Originally published in *British Birds* 71: 275-276)

The bird located at Holme is thought to be the same as the Cley individual, so for completeness we have included that account.

Peter Clarke writes:

'At about midday on 29th August 1976, I was standing outside the bird observatory's ringing laboratory at Holme-next-Sea, Norfolk, when I heard a penetrating, sharp, treble call-note which was quite new to me. Despite a frantic search of the sky, I could not locate the bird responsible and sadly concluded that some obscure bunting or finch had eluded me.

About an hour later, I. Moore came running to tell me that a Fan-tailed Warbler had been seen, in an area of small hawthorns *Crataegus* at the rear of the reserve car-park, by himself and J. Campton, M. Dale, P. Lee, O. Marks, G. Parker and G. W. Want. JC, who had first identified the bird, had had numerous sightings of the species a few weeks previously in southern France. By the time of my arrival, the warbler had disappeared, but halfway back to the ringing laboratory someone shouted, 'There it is!' and, with some astonishment, I heard and saw a small bird flying past giving exactly the same call-note that had puzzled me earlier in the day; it kept flying eastwards until lost to sight.

The following description was compiled on the spot by JC:

Attention drawn by high, jerky song flight, diminutive size and fanning of very short tail. After song flight lasting about 30 seconds, landed in top of small hawthorn bush and observed down to 10 m for 15-20 seconds: streaked upperparts, lack of prominent eye-stripe and very short tail. For next ten minutes, observed flying and uttering typical, evenly-spaced, mono-syllabic call-note 'zip, zip' or 'zeep, zeep'.

The following additional notes were later received from IM:

'High, jerky flight with regular "zip, zip" monosyllabic call and fanning of distinctly short tail at each bound of flight'; and 'from about 20 m for about 10-15 seconds, obvious field marks… small size, short tail and streaked brown upperparts with no prominent eye-stripe.'

The bird was rediscovered in the original area the next day and remained there until 5th September. The favoured marshy habitat was at sea-level and comprised sedge *Juncus* interspersed with common reeds *Phragmites australis* and stunted hawthorn bushes. The bird was sighted daily during its stay, although for long periods it could not be located. The best chances of seeing it were between 07.00 and 09.00 GMT and again around noon. Despite being in the area daily, I failed to obtain any close views of the bird at rest and my only non-flight sighting was for only a few seconds at over 200m through 10 X 50 binoculars: when perched halfway up a bent reed stem, it was very similar in shape and colour (but not in size) to a juvenile Whinchat *Saxicola rubetra*: the underparts were unstreaked and the head appeared to have a darkish cap. The song was difficult to describe, but was a rasping 'dzeep, dzeep, dzeep' rather than 'zip, zip, zip' or 'chip, chip, chip'. The irruption into song flight was often preceded by a single sharp 'tew'.

In view of the statement by I. J. Ferguson-Lees and Dr. J. T. R. Sharrock (*Brit. Birds* 70: 157) that 'There is some evidence that autumn wanderer's, possibly including birds of the year, sing and even build nest frameworks in areas remote from those in which breeding has occurred', it is interesting that the individual at Holme was once seen carrying what appeared to be nesting material.'

(Originally published in *British Birds* 71: 276-277)

Pallas's Grasshopper Warbler
Locustella certhiola
One was seen extremely well by Graham Smith after being flushed along the West Bank at Cley on 13th September 1976.

Graham Smith writes from his notes and recollections of the occasion:

'During mid-September 1976 I spent several days in north Norfolk on a combined birdwatching, cycling and walking holiday. It was the first time I had visited the county and, fortuitously, it coincided with a period of light south-easterly winds and occasional showers. To someone used to slogging the Essex marshes in search of a few migrants it came as a remarkable experience. One morning, for instance I walked between Burnham Overy Staithe and Gun Hill. There was a juvenile Red-backed Shrike sitting on a bush at the start of the walk and a Barred Warbler and a Wryneck in another bush at the point where the track reached the dunes while numerous Pied Flycatchers, Redstarts, Whinchats and other migrants were flitting along the wires between the two. Heaven indeed!

On 13th September I was walking along the seawall near the coastguard station at Cley when I flushed what I momentarily took to be a Sedge Warbler. I had it in clear view for several seconds as it flew about 60m, and it was immediately obvious to me that it was no ordinary Sedge Warbler. Its fanned tail was long, broad and rounded, like a *Locustella* warbler's, and appeared uniform dark grey in colour with obvious, though not pronounced, greyish-white tips to each feather. The tips made each feather look neatly rounded rather than pointed or ragged as on many autumn Sedge Warblers. The rump was dark dull brick-red, with darker edgings to some of the feathers, which created an effect that was neither barred nor spotted but best described as "rumpled". It contrasted markedly with the tail, but not with the back or mantle, which had a similar ground cover, heavily overlaid with dark greyish-brown streaks.

After a twenty minute wait I relocated the warbler, which was creeping about at the base of a small patch of Phragmites, and was able to watch it for a further two minutes or so. Since it was performing a kind of side-step through the stems most of the best views were head on. The head pattern resembled that of a Sedge Warbler but was darker and the supercilium was pure white and noticeably thinner, not broadening over the eye. The feature that really demanded attention, however, was its satiny white under-parts, which contrasted strikingly with the very dark upper-parts and was further emphasised by the ear-coverts which, unlike a Sedge Warbler, were dark and streaked like the crown. There was also a buffish suffusion along the flanks and across the breast, which was densely overlaid with blackish-brown spots and semi-streaks to form a distinct gorget. This combination reminded me of certain pale juvenile Whinchats. The bill appeared dark grey and the legs flesh pink.

I waited a further ten minutes then tried to flush it, without success. I realised by then that I must have been looking at one of the rarer *Locustella* warblers. Its size and well defined supercilium seemed to eliminate Lanceolated Warbler; the colour of the rump and shape and pattern of the tail were equally clearly not those of a Moustached Warbler. A combination of these features also ruled out Grasshopper Warbler, or at least any I had seen previously.

From the literature available to me in Norfolk I tentatively identified it as a Pallas's Grasshopper Warbler. It may seem remarkable – given the situation in Norfolk nowadays – but I met no other birdwatchers that day to speak to: indeed, I saw very few on any day of the five or six days I was in the county. I did mention it to a couple of people on the final day of my stay but they did not seem very interested in looking for it! I also thought of putting the details in the log book at Nancy's (of blessed memory) but wanted to confirm it in my own mind first. This I did, when I reached home, by consulting The Handbook and various field guides. Books are books, however, and there is nothing quite like seeing birds in the field. A couple of years later I was fortunate enough to visit the village of Bratsk in Siberia, where this species proved to be common (and remarkably obliging), and this allayed any lingering doubts I may have had as to my bird's identification.

At the request of the Rarities Committee, P. R. Colston examined skins at the British Museum (Tring): the colour of the under-parts of the Norfolk individual fell within the range of variation of Pallas's Grasshopper Warbler. This record was only the fourth of this Asiatic warbler in Britain & Ireland, the previous three being at Rockabill Lighthouse, Co. Dublin in September 1908 and on Fair Isle, Shetland in October 1949 (*Brit. Birds* 43: 49-51) and October 1956 (*Brit. Birds* 50: 395-396). A fifth occurred only a week after the one in Norfolk: for the third time on Fair Isle, on 20th-24th September 1976.'

Lanceolated Warbler
Locustella lanceolata
A first-winter was trapped by Dave Riley, Kevin Shepherd and Steve Votier at Dead Man's Wood, Sheringham on 29th September 1993.

Kevin Shepherd and Steve Votier write:

'Like so many early mornings during the exceptional autumn of 1993, it was most exciting to watch Dead Man's Wood at Sheringham again working like a dream during the first glimmer of dawn twilight on 29th September. A substantial landfall of migrants freshly in from northern Europe was in progress with numerous small dark silhouettes shooting in from a great height into the isolated oasis of habitat amidst a desert of agricultural fields. Most were 'tsipping' Song Thrushes, but the occasional 'tick' of a Robin and a soft 'hweet' of a Chiffchaff indicated that a variety of species were involved.

Expecting such an arrival in promising meteorological conditions, we had erected a full complement of mist-nets much earlier by torchlight. Everything was ready and waiting for another great day! Separating to cover the site more effectively, SCV departed for a clifftop seawatch leaving KBS in charge of nets. We were entertaining a fellow ringer from the north-west, Dave Riley about to enjoy the delights of a Norfolk 'fall' on his first visit.

As expected, first net-round was extremely hectic and included a pleasant surprise: a 'Locustella' warbler extracted by DR. It was caught in the bottom panel of a net running through a narrow belt of rough grass fringing the seaward edge of the Wood. He naturally assumed it was a Grasshopper Warbler, but commented on its smallness before it was quickly bagged. KBS and DR then returned to the ringing laboratory to find an excited SCV announcing the presence of a Hoopoe well settled on the clifftop. He was keen to rejoin it, but paused to have a quick look at the *Locustella*. He too was immediately impressed by its small size and very streaky overall appearance. To find out just how small it really was we instantly took a wing length and briefly consulted Svenson (1992) to find it well outside the range of Grasshopper Warbler and well within the range of Lanceolated Warbler!

With the emotion and confusion surrounding our misidentification of the Paddyfield Warbler at the site only five days previously still fresh in our minds, there was great pressure to make sure we got this one absolutely spot-on! We divided the workload, SCV carefully processing the *Locustella* whilst KBS and

DR dealt with the remainder of the catch. The Hoopoe became irrelevant as all fell silent. The anticipated outcome seemed pure fantasy, but as DR released the last Robin SCV confidently declared "It's a definite Lancey!" Struggling to maintain composure, we stared in total disbelief. One of Europe's most sought after vagrants was before our very eyes – here in Norfolk for the first time.

Being familiar with the species extremely skulking habits, it was obvious that were we to release it in the Wood, it would never be seen again. We therefore decided to release it in a large area of suitable habitat on the clifftop where at least there was an outside chance that others would see it. Upon release it disappeared completely and we were convinced it had gone for ever. Miraculously however as soon as the first birders arrived it reappeared right beside the clifftop footpath near to where it was to remain faithful for the rest of the day. Although at times very skulking, it performed splendidly when observers remained patient. Everyone who arrived in time saw it well. It stayed until dusk when it was seen to go to roost, but after a starlit night there was no sign of it the following morning despite an extensive search.

Description: A streaked *Locustella* warbler showing the diagnostic features of the genus. Long under-tail-coverts almost reaching the tip of the tail. Very pale and convex second primary accentuating the rounded looking wings. Large bright pink legs and feet. Long, broad and well graduated tail. Very similar in appearance to Grasshopper Warbler, but it could be separated by a combination of plumage and structural features. Size: A very small warbler, smaller than a Grasshopper Warbler. Wing length only 56mm, a full 5mm shorter than the smallest Grasshopper Warbler recorded in Svensson (1992). This feature was also apparent in the field, the bird looking tiny as it scurried about, mouse-like, in the grass. Structure: wings appeared very short in comparison to the tail, much more so than usually shown by the genus. Plumage: Generally much more heavily marked than the other streaked *Locustella* warblers. The most relevant features are shown in the illustration.'

(An account published in the *Norfolk Bird Report* 1993: 135-136, which also included details of the only four previous British occurrences south of Fair Isle)

Common Grasshopper Warbler

Locustella naevia

The earliest dated reference we can find is in 'Extracts from the Calandar of the Rev. William Whitear 1809-1826' published in the *Transactions of the Norfolk and Norwich Naturalists' Society* 1881-1882: 254 where he recorded one on 27th April 1821 in the Starston area:

'…saw a Grasshopper Warbler in the hedge of the Beck meadow.'

Sheppard and Whitear in *A Catalogue of the Norfolk and Suffolk Birds, with Remarks* 1826: 16 comment:

'We have met with this species both in Norfolk and Suffolk. Montagu does not mention, as Bewick has done, the spots upon the throat and neck. Its plumage is very glossy, having a silvery tinge upon it, particularly the under part. It very much resembles a Lark in its general figure, but the hind claw is not long enough for it to rank in that genus.'

The Pagets in *Sketch of the Natural History of Yarmouth and its Neighbourhood* 1834: 5 considered it '…occasionally met with, but rare.'

River Warbler
Locustella fluviatilis
A singing male was found by Paul Pratley in a rye field adjacent to hawthorn and elder hedge-rows at Roydon Common on 29th May 1981.

Paul Pratley writes:

> 'Whilst taking part in the B.T.O. Nightjar survey on the evening of 29th May I heard an unfamiliar song resembling a cricket at Roydon Common. I soon observed a bird about the size of a Reed Warbler with a continual buzzing song. Unfortunately, it was not until late the following day that I obtained confirmation of my observation and the stranger was identified as a River Warbler. Over a series of visits detailed field notes were obtained.
>
> The most noticeable features included uniform dull brown upperparts although a rufous tinge was seen on the rump in good light. A creamy orbital ring extended into a fine whitish supercilium running a short distance each side of the eye. From a distance the underparts appeared uniform grey, but with good views the finely streaked breast was much greyer than the belly.
>
> Probably hundreds of ardent watchers sought this River Warbler, whilst thousands viewed it on television. It sang mostly either from a hedge (of hawthorn and elder) or from a nearby rye field, often skulking high up in the hedge and some distance from any standing or running water. Disturbed, it often flew with noticeable undulating flight, the long wings and tail suggesting a small Cuckoo.
>
> The very distinctive song was described as an extended 'ziz ziz ziz' slower than a Grasshopper Warbler and containing two notes repeated very quickly. Often continuing up to a minute, at other times it lasted only one or two seconds. The song contained a metallic note interspersed with 'ziz ziz' notes. At close quarters a 'prrr' was often heard prior to the commencement of the song.
>
> This occurrence was only the fifth for Britain and the first on the mainland. Previous records are from Fair Isle on 24th/25th Sept 1961, 16th Sept 1969 and 23rd/25th May 1981 (died) and also Bardsey on 17th Sept 1969.
>
> Most of the River Warblers in the world breed in Russia where they are known as river crickets. The species also breeds in Poland, Hungary, East Germany and Austria. They occur in riverside meadows with long grass and some bushes. During migration River Warblers may be found in cornfields and other dry areas for they have to cross much arid country to reach wintering grounds in south-east Africa. In winter quarters they are most often found in reedbeds and in bushes beside rivers and lakes.'

(An account published in the *Norfolk Bird Report* 1981: 89-90)

Savi's Warbler
Locustella luscinioides

The first British specimen was taken at Limpenhoe in May 1819 and was examined by Temminck who thought it was a variety of Reed Warbler, as the species had not yet been described at the time. Following the recognition of a specimen collected in the Cambridgeshire Fens in 1840, the Norfolk bird was finally correctly identified as a Savi's Warbler. The specimen (Accession no. NWHCM: 1827.35.2) was a gift to the Castle Museum, Norwich from the Rev. James Brown in 1827. It was mounted, but has been made into a skin, and remains in the skin collection at the museum.

Henry Stevenson writes in *The Birds of Norfolk* Vol. l. 1866: 110-115:

> 'At least six well authenticated specimens of this very rare British warbler are now ascertained to have been procured in Norfolk, of which the first, though long overlooked, was for many years the only one known to science. This bird (No. 63b), in the museum collection, was obtained by the late Rev. Jas. Brown, at Limpenhoe, in the early part of the present century, during the month of May, and the following interesting account of it was kindly sent to me by Mr. Brown, in 1856, on his hearing that I had lately received one from Surlingham broad. He says – "Its singular note had been observed at Limpenhoe by Sir Wm. Hooker, myself, and another ornithological friend, whilst investigating the natural history of that district, but for a considerable time not a sight of the bird could be obtained. We called it the 'reel' bird, on account of the resemblance of its monotonous note to the continuous whirr of the reel, at that time used by the hand-spinners of wool. At length it was discovered uttering its singular song (if so it may be called), from the top of an alder bush that grew in the midst of a large patch of sedge, into which it fell like a stone as soon as it was approached. After, however, much patience and caution, it again re-ascended the alder and was shot. It was a very shy bird, and in its habits seems to resemble the grasshopper lark (warbler), creeping among the sedge in search probably of insects and small mollusks. It was submitted to the inspection of the celebrated ornithologist, Temminck, whilst he was in London at the sale of Mr. Bullock's museum."

He adds a footnote here:

> 'This remarkable sale took place in the spring of 1819. The bird in question was therefore very probably killed in that year, at all events it could not have been obtained later.'

He then continues:

> "He was puzzled, and requested permission to take it with him to the continent, to compare it with specimens in his own splendid collection. He returned it with his opinion that it was a variety of the reed wren, and as such it is noticed in their '*Catalogue*' by Messrs. Sheppard and Whitear".'

Aquatic Warbler
Acrocephalus paludicola
An immature male was shot by T. E. Gunn in the Sandhills at Blakeney Point on 8th September 1896.

J. H. Gurney jnr. writes in the *Zoologist* 1897: 133, giving the apparently wrong date of Sept 9th:

> 'September 9th. S.S.W., rather strong. An Aquatic Warbler, Acrocephalus aquaticus, Gm., in immature but very good plumage, with the lines on the back more pronounced than the streaks of buff on the crown, shot at the foot of Blakeney sandhills by Mr. Gunn, was a male, and contained the remains of earwigs and a beetle, no doubt foraged in the Chenodium bushes. It is the fifth for England, and is a good deal like one shot by Mr. Edward Hart, at Christchurch in Hampshire.'

Andy Stoddart and Steve Joyner write in *The Birds of Blakeney Point* 2005: 184:

> 'A male Aquatic Warbler, undated, from the Sandhills and received from the Gunn collection is in the Castle Museum, Norwich, and is presumably this bird.'

B.B. Riviere in *A History of the Birds of Norfolk* 1930: 66-67, also gives the date as 9th September, presumably quoting Gurney. But interestingly writes:

> 'As long ago as 1872, twenty-four years before the first Aquatic Warbler was recorded for Norfolk, J. H. Gurney, in a note in the '*Norfolk and Norwich Nat. Soc. Trans.*' (1871-1872, p. 62), expressed the belief that this species probably occurred in the county from time to time, though unrecognised, and he pointed out, what is undoubtedly a fact, that the figure of the Sedge Warbler in John 'Hunt's *British Birds*' was obviously painted from an Aquatic Warbler which , in view of Hunt's association with Norwich, was probably a Norfolk bird.'

The specimen (Accession no. NWHCM: 1948.184.4) remains in storage at the Castle Museum, Norwich.

Sedge Warbler
Acrocephalus schoenobaenus
The earliest dated reference we can find is in 'Extracts from the Calendar of the Rev. William Whitear 1809-1826' published in the *Transactions of the Norfolk and Norwich Naturalists' Society* 1881-1882: 255 where he recorded one on 26th April 1823 in the Starston area.

Sheppard and Whitear in *A Catalogue of the Norfolk and Suffolk Birds, with Remarks* 1826: 17, who also knew it by the name of Reed Bird write:

> 'The legs and feet of the Sedge Warbler are remarkably large in proportion to the size of the body; the bill is also larger than is usual in birds of this genus. The disproportion of these parts has been noticed by Ray and White, but seems not

to have been remarked by other authors.'

The Pagets in *Sketch of the Natural History of Yarmouth and its Neighbourhood* 1834: 5 considered it '…not uncommon.'

Paddyfield Warbler
Acrocephalus agricola
One was found at Sheringham by Kevin Shepherd on 24th September 1993. Initial identification difficulties proved somewhat interesting.

Mark Golley writes:

"Well it's me who has drawn the short straw on this one." 'No these weren't my words on being approached to write this feature (honest!) but they were my utterances on taking yet another trip across from the "trial boardwalk" on Cley NNT to the workshop and back. As a little treat and a break from the 'work' I called up Dougal McNeil at Blakeney Point to see what had arrived on such a pleasant September afternoon. I was gobsmacked to hear from him that there was a 'Blyth's Reed' at Sheringham! What happened to the grapevine?

Regaining my composure and finishing my work I hastily made my way to the, now, famous location of Dead Man's Wood. Scurrying along the path I announced my arrival with an uncharacteristic full blown, expletive-filled statement regarding the decided lack of news coming my way. Anyway I calmed down as the bird showed… And well, I was a little taken aback with my first views. I frowned, pondered what was before me, kept quiet and snuck up to a telescope. Up popped the bird again, and in the full glory of a Nikon EDll was a Blyth's… hold on! The first instincts, the initial nagging doubts recurred tenfold. Musings, mutterings and mumblings were gently passing my lips and I casually sauntered over to the learned crowd of Richard Millington, Ron Johns, Duncan Macdonald and Simon Harrap. Thankfully it was a crowd of 'fellow believers' – this bird was not a Blyth's Reed Warbler – the prominent head pattern, cold tea toned upper parts contrasting with the warmer, gingery rump, the short wings, the overall 'feel' of the bird just smacked of Norfolk's first Paddyfield Warbler. Much debate ensued as to the identity of the bird – it had been trapped earlier – so a lot of people took a lot of convincing as to the true identity of the bird. Some local observers were 'fresh' from the first Fagbury Cliff Blyth's Reed of the previous Sunday and were heard to comment how much better this 'Blyth's Reed' looked! Eventually those listening to the pros and cons of both species were left to make up their own minds. The bird performed exceptionally well to all comers (and did they come) for the entire afternoon and evening and the debate raged on and on and on. And occasionally you could see why – at certain angles the head pattern seemed to vanish and the bird could take on a whole new appearance, but it was never really the appearance of Blyth's Reed Warbler. As darkness fell, many people were rooted in the Paddyfield camp.

Kevin Shepherd and Steve Votier went back to the plethora of literature, the calculator and the wads of notes. Their night's work showed that there *was* much overlap between the two species and that some of the measurements were inconclusive either way, but there were pro Paddyfield points from the measurements… now we were getting somewhere. Eventually everything was falling into place and by the end of the weekend everyone had to admit it *was* a Paddyfield Warbler. The bird thought better of it and with a starry, moonlit Friday night it left for who knows where.

This bird, as well as generating much (heated) healthy debate, draws attention to the fact that whether in the hand or in the field, birds, even now, with the wealth of ID information at grasp can be fiendishly hard to get right.'

(An account published in the *Norfok Bird Club Bulletin* No 7: 12-13)

Interestingly Kevin Shepherd and Steve Votier write:

'On September 24th KBS found a very strange looking acrocephalus warbler in Dead Man's Wood Sheringham. Initial brief views strongly suggested Paddyfield Warbler, but more careful scrutiny revealed a number of apparently anomalous features. He called SV and the bird was promptly trapped. Following careful examination in the hand and reference to Svensson's 'Identification Guide to European Passerines' (1992) and Lewington's 'Field Guide to the Rarer Birds of Britain & Europe' (1991) the bird was clearly either Paddyfield Warbler or Blyth's Reed Warbler. More features seemed to point to the latter and the bird was identified as a Blyth's Reed.

After arrangements were made with Young's Farm for access to the site the news was released. A significant portion of the large number of birders who arrived were seriously questioning the identification, suggesting that the bird showed a number of features more akin to Paddyfield Warbler rather than to Blyth's Reed Warbler. All credit must be given to Clive Byers and Craig Robson who following careful scrutiny of all features, stated categorically that the vagrant was indeed a Paddyfield Warbler. Fortunately it had been photographed in the hand and a detailed description with thorough biometrics taken to enable any doubts to be totally eradicated. The bird performed well to all comers for the entire afternoon and evening. But following a moonlit night searches next morning were unsuccessful.

Main points used to confirm the identification were as follows: Short wings (wing length 61.5mm) with a very short primary extension, the primaries being equal to approximately only a quarter of the length of the exposed tertials or only extending just beyond the longest uppertail coverts. Tertials with contrastingly darker centres. Striking head pattern consisting of broad white supercilium, widest in front of the eye, with a subtly darker upper border – both these features varied in appearance according to light conditions and the bird's posture. Distinct paler grey patch on sides of neck forming a 'shawl' effect. Sandy/olive upperparts, slightly warmer on the rump and uppertail coverts (although this individual atypically for Paddyfield showed no rufous tones). Very long tail, being distinctly rounded (the difference between the shortest and longest tail feathers was 8.45mm). Tail frequently cocked almost Wren-like in the field. Wing formula and biometrics: Primaries emarginated on the 3rd, 4th and 5th (slightly); 2nd primary = primary no 6; notch on the 2nd primary = 3,8mm <secondaries; 1st primary = 3.45mm> primary coverts and bill to skull = 15.8mm.

This is the first record for Norfolk although long predicted given the increase in records during recent years. There are 21 previous occurrences in Britain. Paddyfield Warblers breed in southern Russia and Asia, wintering in south-east Asia and India.'

(An account published in the *Norfolk Bird Report* 1993: 134)

Blyth's Reed Warbler
Acrocephalus dumetorum
A first-winter was found by Mark Golley and Richard Millington at Warham Green on 25th September 1996.

Mark Golley and Richard Millington write:

'During the early morning of Wednesday 25th September 1996, whilst checking the overgrown pit at Warham Green, near Wells, we found and positively identified Norfolk's first Blyth's Reed Warbler. Naturally, we immediately broadcast the news via Birdline but, judging by the incredulous reaction from many birders, by unequivocally claiming a Blyth's Reed in the field we were apparently committing a most audacious, perhaps even heretical act…

Had it been ringed? No. It was, however, showing well and calling, so there was no doubt in our minds (or that of Neil Alford, whom we met on site) that it was a classic first-winter Blyth's Reed Warbler. Indeed, we could not envisage that trapping the bird could add anything to the identification process, since even the primary emarginations had been clinched!

As the bird remained faithful to its chosen locale for three days, many birders were able to share the experience of watching a vagrant Blyth's Reed Warbler in Britain without a shiny new ring on one leg being the prime identification feature (no disrespect to ringers, without whom most British records of this species would not exist).

From the very first glimpse, it appeared suspiciously unfamiliar, being structurally rather dissimilar to Reed Warbler (relatively frail and short-winged, with a low forecrown and sharply tapering bill), while the characteristic face pattern (especially the prominent pale super-loral stripe) and the diagnostic call confirmed that it was indeed a Blyth's Reed Warbler.

Subsequent, prolonged observations at various ranges and in different light enabled visitors to evaluate the relative importance of a number of in-field characters for themselves. To us, the initial impression always held good, with good views providing a range of additional clues.

The overall colour of the upperparts seemed ever changing, sometimes pale and at other times dark, but never did it appear cold grey or show any rich rufous hue; rather it was generally a neutral, dusty pinkish-brown, with a dull, slightly olive wash on the crown and mantle, but distinctly warmer tawny-brown on the remiges, retrices and uppertail-coverts. The underparts were essentially greyish-white, with an ochre wash invading the rear flanks and a slight touch of yellow on the breast, but contrasting white throat and undertail coverts.

Most important, however, were the characteristic face-pattern and subtle wing contrasts. The rather 'open' face (recalling that of a *hippolais* warbler, but with a short dark loral line) was dominated by a broad creamy-white supercilium reaching to the eye and continuing some way beyond as a pale grey smudge, and a fairly obvious off-white eye-ring (on Reed Warbler, the pale eye-ring is normally the most prominent facial feature). Apart from the rather dark tertials showing paler fringes and the primaries darkening towards the tip, the wings showed very little contrast, with all the flight feathers and major coverts being essentially grey with browner fringes. The largest alula feather could be seen to be grey on the inner web and wholly olive-brown on the outer web (on Reed Warbler it is normally largely dark on both webs, with a narrow brown fringe).

The fresh plumage and warm tones indicated that it was a first-winter, while the close views it afforded allowed the diagnostic emarginations (halfway down the third and nearer the tip of the fourth primaries) to be seen in the field, although counting the primary tips proved to be almost impossible, due to the outer primaries lacking contrastingly pale tips.

The bare-parts colouration also supported the identification. The two-tone bill was mostly dark brown on the upper mandible and fleshy orange on the lower mandible (with the merest smear of dark subterminally on the lower edge of the latter), while the legs and feet were essentially grey, being paler grey on the front of the ankle and leg, although brownish-grey on the upper tarsus and toes, pink on the rear of the leg and dull yellow on the soles of the feet.

The characteristic 'jizz' seemed to be a cumulative effect of the long, sloping forehead and tapered bill (giving a 'snouty' look), undeniably short wings (usully held slightly drooped, with the rump exposed) and somewhat pot-bellied stance; the so called 'banana' posture was often evident, as a result of the habitually up-tilted head and tail. Interestingly, although the tail was normally held relatively proud, it was never truly cocked up and never appeared large; indeed, the bird actually looked quite short-tailed.

It was generally quite confiding and a good deal less shy than Reed Warblers normally are. It preferred warm sunlit spots, where it was not particularly skulking. During its first day, the Warham Blyth's Reed Warbler often flicked its wings nervously whilst also flicking and slightly fanning its tail, but this habit was observed less often later in its stay. Insects were plainly its main prey item (especially flies, which it would both assiduously stalk and sally out of cover for), while it ignored the plentiful berries on offer.

Travellers to India in winter will be familiar with the distinctive contact call of Blyth's Reed Warbler, which often is a soft, course "teck" (similar to, but not as clipped or metallic as, Lesser Whitethroat), often delivered in a short series. This was the only call uttered; it was given frequently, usually prior to some change in its routine, such as moving off to another set of bushes.

Even BWP states that some Blyth's Reed Warblers cannot be told from Reed Warbler, so we would not be so bold as to presume that birders should identify every vagrant Blyth's Reed in Britain, but the purpose of this account is to offer hope that at least some may be confidently identified in the field. The identification of this increasingly regular visitor is not a process of elimination; there are a good number of positive features to look (and listen) for which, in combination, should render most Blyth's Reed Warblers eminently identifiable. As always, inviting as many witnesses as possible will help, while good photographs might be needed to silence any remaining cynics.

TOP 10 BLYTH'S REED WARBLER IDENTIFICATION CHECKLIST
British birders encountering a potential vagrant Blyth's Reed Warbler might check for the following features (in this approximate order of importance);
Short primary projection
Sloping forecrown and tapered bill
Sylvia-like call
Prominent fore-supercilium
Emarginations on third and fourth primaries
Greyish-toned legs
Lack of contrast in wing feathers
Lack of contrastingly ginger rump
'Banana' posture
Tail flicking
Any bird showing the full suite of characters will surely be one!'

(An account published in the *Norfolk Bird Club Bulletin* No 22: 25-27)

An earlier offshore record, previously claimed for Norfolk, was found dead on the Dudgeon light-vessel 19 miles north of Wells on the night of 20th-21st October 1912 (*Transactions of the Norfolk and Norwich Naturalists' Society* 1914-1915: 76). It remained a county record for over 80 years. It was included by Riviere in *A History of the Birds of Norfolk* (1930), where on page xxxiii, he includes a 'sketch map to illustrate Norfolk Coast and Coastal Lights'. It was also included by Seago in *Birds of Norfolk* (1967 and 1977) where in the 1977 edition he gives the light-vessel's position as 18 miles north of Sheringham. The species was deleted from the Norfolk List in 1993 (*Norfolk Bird Report* 1992), on the grounds that the occurrence was too far offshore to be regarded as a valid county record (Taylor *et al* 1999).

Marsh Warbler
Acrocephalus palustris
A male shot at Blakeney Point on 10th October 1923 was the first fully accepted record. The specimen (Accession no. NWHCM: 1932.9) remains at the Castle Museum, Norwich.

Andy Stoddart and Steve Joyner write in *The Birds of Blakeney Point* 2005: 185-186:

'The only record concerns a male shot on 10th October 1923 in the Sandhills and donated by Riviere to the Castle Museum, Norwich where it still resides in the 'British Bird Gallery' public display area (*British Birds* 17: 26). This bird was identified by Harry Witherby and Norman Ticehurst and was the first record for Norfolk

The specimen was examined during the preparation of this book and found to be intermediate in measurements between Marsh and Reed Warblers in respect of wing length (69mm), the position of the notch on the second primary (10mm from tip) and the notch/wing ratio (0.15).

It does, however, fall conclusively within the range for Marsh Warbler given by Svensson (1992) according to the 'Walinder Method' (bill length to skull minus the product of bill width at the nostrils and tarsus width). In the case of this bird the measurements are 14mm – (2mm x 3.5mm) = 7. Furthermore the visible primary projection equals the length of the exposed tertials and the overall tone of the bird looks pale olive-toned with no rufous hue, even on the rump.'

The wind was westerly on the day it was shot, but there had been a gale from the north-east on October 4th (*British Birds* 17: 267). The *British Birds* page referenced by Stoddart and Joyner above is obviously a misprint and should read 267 not 26.

Eurasian Reed Warbler

Acrocephalus scirpaceus
The earliest reference we can find is by Sheppard and Whitear in *A Catalogue of the Norfolk and Suffolk Birds, with Remarks* 1826: 17-18 where they write:

> 'The Reed Wren frequents the reeds on the river Gipping, and we have seen it at Higham: it is also found in other parts of these counties. A bird, which appears to be a variety of this species, was shot about the middle of May by the Rev. James Brown of Norwich, in the marshes below that city. This bird had no *vibrissae*.' (It turned out that this bird was in fact Norfolk's first Savi's Warbler).

The Pagets were apparently unaware of this species as it isn't mentioned in *Sketch of the Natural History of Yarmouth and its Neighbourhood* (1834).

Great Reed Warbler

Acrocephalus arundinaceus
The first three referenced occurrences were all sight records, a pair seen on the River Bure near Yarmouth on 8th July 1886 by the Rev. M. C. Bird, another seen at Horning on 1st August 1906 by the same observer (Gurney *Zoologist* 1907: 132) and one seen near Horning on 21st July 1919 by Mr. E. Campbell (Gurney *Zoologist* 1913: 175). Unfortunately all lacked adequate detail to be fully acceptable as a first for the county.

Therefore the first fully authenticated and acceptable record was one found at Cantley Beet Factory by John F. W. Bruhn on 18th June 1969, it remained until the 30th.

John Bruhn writes from his notes and recollections of the occasion:

> 'With reference to the Great Reed Warbler, there is an entry – scarcely field notes – where I describe the bird as extremely elusive. My main activity in May/ June 1969 was with Grey Heron pulli and Sand Martins at colonies particularly at Sparham pits. Evidently I was at Cantley on the 18th June 1969 to try for whatever was there and the Great Reed Warbler notes, such as they are, are with my ringing log. What emerges is that I set up before dawn in the reed beds, toured the site and only THEN heard the Great Reed Warbler, which I tried to track down from cover to cover before eventually catching a glimpse of it. The only details are of its skulking behaviour and of its song, contrasting with Reed Warbler's, and with quite long periods during which the bird moved, only to strike up again some distance away. There is also a note of its size, but no plumage detail. Though there is no mention of this, it is likely that I did not have binoculars with me, something I frequently did for security reasons when heron

and Sand Martin ringing. On one Shetland trip they were left behind in a Bonxie colony while ringing young and we only realised they'd been left behind after getting the ferry back to the mainland!

Leaving the nets up at Cantley was not an option and I ended up with just one Reed Warbler ringed before packing up to start a day's work. My recollection of hearing the bird from the railway crossing seems to relate to my return to the car, and still hearing it at a distance. So it was a great relief to know that my phone-call to Michael Seago had been followed up and my identification confirmed.'

Peter Allard adds:

'In those days access to the site was through Limpenhoe village and along a cinder track to the railway line where a small car park was regularly used by birdwatchers, ringers and anglers. John's identification was confirmed when Barry Jarvis saw the bird the following day. It was subsequently heard singing and seen very well, although it continued to be elusive at times, by a succession of visitors who included me, Moss Taylor, Michael Seago (who tape-recorded its song), Terry Boulton, Frank Pitts and Ted Phillips. Finder John Bruhn visited the site again on July 2nd but by then the bird had departed after an exciting 13 day stay and was one of the highlights of the 1969 summer.'

Interestingly, Jim Vincent writes in *Wild Bird Protection in Norfolk* 1941: 14:

'On May 16th one of the reed-cutters reported that he had seen "a reed-warbler as big as a mavis [Song Thrush]" in the reeds quite close to him and that it was unusually noisy. Two other men who were cleaning out a dyke 100 yards away from him also heard this strange bird singing. All three are good observers and know all the local species. I explored the area three days later, but neither saw nor heard the bird, but from its description, I believe it to have been a great reed warbler.'

Booted Warbler
Hippolais caligata
One was found by Giles Dunmore and Steve Joyner at Titchwell on 18th September 1982.

Steve Joyner writes:

'Following a night of light S.S.E. winds, G. E. Dunmore and I headed for the north Norfolk coast on the 18th September 1982 anticipating a fall of Continental night-migrants. We visited Titchwell and on returning from sea-watching flushed a small pale warbler from sueda bordering the western edge of the R.S.P.B. Reserve. Brief views were obtained as the bird fed in low cover. Initially we noted a warbler of Willow/Chiffchaff size with pale greyish upper-parts, short wings showing a paler panel, thin off-white supercilium, uniform whitish underparts and pale pinkish bill. The bird then moved into an area between the dunes and the brackish lagoon and was lost to view. Realising we had seen something new we first thought the bird was a dull Bonelli's Warbler.

Later we returned to find the warbler had been relocated and was being watched and its identity discussed by a group of birders. After obtaining good views all agreed the visitor was a Booted Warbler. During its four-day stay it remained in the same area, frequently being observed in low cover on the banks edging the lagoon. This is the first accepted record for Norfolk and the seventeenth for Britain.

For the benefit of observers faced with the problem of identifying any unfamiliar small, pale, warbler suspected of being a Booted Warbler, I have listed the features noted on the Titchwell bird:

Hippolais warbler characteristics including short under-tail coverts giving a rather rounded body shape, relatively large broad-based bill accentuated by pale colouring, square-ended tail and rounded head with high crown. The Titchwell bird showed short wings and relatively short primary extension beyond the bunched secondaries/tertials. Flying, it revealed a different 'jizz' compared with Willow/Chiffchaff appearing dumpy with broad, rounded, wings and shortish fairly broad tail.

Overall paleness of plumage, lacking any green or yellow tones. The Titchwell visitor showed pale grey-brown upperparts and slightly browner wings and tail. Autumn Booted Warblers observed on Scilly have been generally less grey and more sandy brown on upperparts. Underparts were off-white with slight buff wash on lower flanks.

Rather nondescript appearance, lacking any distinctive plumage features, particularly the plain-faced appearance with only a thin off-white supercilium extending from in front of the eye to the rear of the ear-coverts and an indistinct eye-stripe only behind the eye. Three features were, however, noted: slightly darker brown marking above the eye; pale edges to the tertials and secondaries forming a pale panel on the closed wing, and a narrow off-white margin to the outer-tail feathers noticeable when the tail was fanned in flight.

Behaviour and habitat preference of migrants appears to be a useful guide. The Scilly birds and the Titchwell example preferred feeding slowly and quietly either in low vegetation or on the ground rather than in nearby trees and bushes.'

(An account published in the *Norfolk Bird Report* 1983: 366-367)

Sykes's Warbler

Hippolais rama
One was discovered by Rob Lee at Sheringham on 23rd August 2002.

Rob Lee writes:

'The 23rd August 2002 got off to a bad start, when almost immediately upon my arrival at work Paul Lee telephoned to say that he was watching a Bee-eater perched on wires by the roadside on our local patch between Sheringham and Weybourne, a spot I had driven past not 40 minutes earlier. The subsequent pager reports, as it was tracked along the coast, only added to my frustration and it was not until the afternoon that I could console myself with a belated stroll around the area. At about 2.00 pm I was on the NT footpath over the railway by the old barn scanning around when a bird in a nearby elder caught my eye. As I lifted my binoculars I caught a glimpse of something grey and white as it disappeared back into cover. Moving close, the bird soon showed itself again and it was clearly something of interest. Regretting the decision to leave my telescope in the car I attempted to make the most of binocular views. Although there was nothing else for comparison, the bird appeared about Willow/Chiffchaff size and was basically grey above and white below. At about 15 metres range I could see its bill had a yellow lower mandible and, as the bird stretched up and cocked its head, that it was broad based. It was clearly a *Hippolais* Warbler and one of the rarer ones at that. I was favouring Booted Warbler, as the supercilium extended a short way past the eye, something I have not noticed on Olivaceous Warbler. However, at the same time it didn't look like a classic Booted either. The bird was showing really well as it fed in the elders, mostly in the upper half, working its way up to the top before flying into the next one and occasionally showing white outer tail feathers as it did so. It was calling frequently, a Lesser Whitethroat like "tuc", and flicking its tail about but never 'pumping' it downwards. I realised I needed other people to see this bird, and as most of the other group members would be working, Giles Dunmore was the obvious choice. I phoned him to say that I was watching a Booted/Olivaceous Warbler. Unfortunately by the time he arrived the bird had gone to ground and we spent the next 2.5 hours looking for it in vain. Deciding to give up, Giles headed home and I consulted the *Collins Field Guide* back at the car. After reading the accounts of Booted and Olivaceous Warblers I felt I could safely eliminate Olivaceous on tail movements alone. I noted the differences in primary projection between the two species and also the similarity of the *rama* illustration to my bird.

Deciding on one last look I headed back to the barn, this time with my 'scope. As I approached I could hear what I thought was the bird calling again and sure enough there it was back in the elders. Looking through my 'scope I could see the short primary projection (about 0.33 of exposed tertial length) and lack of pale edged secondaries, definitely eliminating Olivaceous Warbler. I immediately contacted the other group members and news was released to the national bird networks. Richard Millington was one of the first to arrive and after some initial confusion was the first to suggest that the bird could be a Sykes's Warbler (*rama*), a recent split from Booted Warbler. Ignorant of the features of that species, I discussed with him what to look for and he suggested checking the shape and colouration of the bill. Through my 'scope I could see that it was longish with a fine tip and the lower mandible was yellow with no hint of a darker smudge or tip. Other details noted were the clean white underparts without any buff suffusion to the breast/flanks. The upperparts were a uniform greyish tone, tinged brown, with concolourous tertials that showed only slightly paler fringes. The supercilium was whitish and ended squarely just beyond the eye. The upper edge of the supercilium also showed a thin dark line to it that I had not been able to see through my binoculars. After watching for a while longer I left for home (by then 6.30 pm), while the debate as to the birds identity carried on. Although I had only ever seen one Booted Warbler before, I had seen many photos of the species as well as some video footage and I was struck by how different "my" bird was to the expected appearance of *caligata*. Even its behaviour was unusual in that it spent all of its time in bushes as opposed to foraging about in weeds of which there were plenty in the area. Later that evening I read the relevant article by Svensson in *Birding World* and after that there was no doubt in my mind at all that I had seen a Sykes's Warbler. All that remained now was the matter of getting the record accepted by the Rarities Committee!'

(An account published in the *Norfolk Bird Report* 2003: 279-280.)

Icterine Warbler
Hippolais icterina
One was shot at Blakeney by F. D. Power, the gentleman-gunner from London, on 11th September 1884.

F. D. Power writes in the *Transactions of the Norfolk and Norwich Naturalists' Society* 1884-1885: 36-43:

> 'September 3rd-19th, 1884
> September 11th. …When dusk, I flushed a greenish Warbler out of a bed of thistles, damaging it so much with large shot as to spoil it as a specimen: this was unfortunately the Icterine Warbler referred to above, Although very immature and much mutilated, thanks to Messrs Gurney and Dresser it was identified, and shown at the Zoological Society at the same time as the Barred Warbler. This, also, is new to the Norfolk list. All the upper parts, including tail, were dingy green; under parts yellowish, brighter at the sides; iris, dark brown; base of lower mandible, yellowish; rest, horn colour; legs, bluish-grey. Length five and five eighths inches; stretch of wing eight and one quarter inches; wing from flexure three and one eighths inches; tarsus seven eighths of an inch. Sex unascertainable. In general form and colour, the bird might pass for a large Willow or Wood Warbler; but the shape of the bill, approaching in character that of the Reed Warbler, and the blue legs, would at once differentiate it from them.'

The present whereabouts of the specimen is unknown.

F. D. Power was a London doctor and together with his brother G. E. Power, also a doctor, were ardent collectors of rare birds. Henry Nash Pashley, the noted Cley taxidermist was heavily influenced by these two gentlemen to take up professional taxidermy in the mid 1880s, and they were the first to give him regular employment in preparing birds for their collection.

Melodious Warbler
Hippolais polyglotta
An adult was trapped and photographed by Richard Richardson at Cley on 7th June 1957. Interestingly another was trapped and photographed at the same locality on 5th September the same year. They remained the only two county records until another was found and photographed at Blakeney Point on 24th September 2008.

Richard Richardson writes:

> 'While it is futile to speculate on all the exciting birds one has missed by narrow margins of time and distance, the following experience brings home forcibly the element of luck which is ever attendant on the bird-watcher.
> At mid-day on 7th June 1957 I was just leaving the East Bank when some

visitors asked to see the Walsey Hills trap, which I had left only a short while before. As we approached, a small olive-coloured bird was glimpsed flitting ahead of us into the trap. I pulled the cord to admit it to the glass-backed catching box where the first impression was of a 'Reed Warbler with the plumage of a Willow Warbler'. On checking the wing formula, however, I found that I was holding the first Melodious Warbler to be seen in Norfolk.

It spent the afternoon among the foreign birds in my garden aviary taking small mealworms from a dish and being much admired by the many people who came to see it.

Oddly enough just three months later, on 5th September, a second bird was caught by B. R. Spence in the same place at the same time of day and there can be little doubt that neither of these extremely skulking individuals would have been detected, and certainly not identified, had it not been for the trap. As it was, they immediately disappeared into the bushes when released and were never seen again.'

(An account published in Moss Taylor's *Guardian Spirit of the East Bank* 2005: 187)

A very interesting article by Moss Taylor entitled 'Melodious Warbler - A Norfolk Enigma' was published in the *Norfolk Bird Club Bulletin* 55: 15-20. It covers comprehensively the above occurrences, and includes a detailed description and measurements of the September bird.

Eurasian Blackcap
Sylvia atricapilla
Known as the Mock Nightingale, the earliest dated reference we can find is in extracts from Robert Marsham's 'Indications of Spring' published in the *Transactions of the Norfolk and Norwich Naturalists' Society* 1874-1875: 35 where he recorded on the 2nd April 1750:

'…I heard a mock nightingale.'

Sheppard and Whitear in *A Catalogue of the Norfolk and Suffolk Birds, with Remarks* 1826: 18 write:

'The Black-cap may with propriety be called the English Mocking-bird. We have heard it sing the notes of the Blackbird, Thrush, Nightingale, Redstart and Sedge Warbler; and besides its own perculiar whistle, which is most delightful, it frequently makes a noise resembling that of a pair of shears used in clipping a fence, which also is the noise made by the young of this species.'

Garden Warbler
Sylvia borin
Known as Greater Pettychaps the earliest reference we can find is by Sheppard and Whitear in *A Catalogue of the Norfolk and Suffolk Birds, with Remarks* 1826: 18-19 where they write:

'This species of Warbler has been found in the neighbourhood of Ipswich, and we have received its eggs from Diss… Its generals habits are similar to the Yellow Wren [Willow Warbler]; for, like that bird, it seems constantly in motion, hopping about from bough to bough in search of insects, and singing at intervals'

Barred Warbler
Sylvia nisoria
A first-winter female was shot by F. D. Power, the gentleman-gunner from London, at Blakeney on 4th September 1884.

Andy Stoddart and Steve Joyner write in *The Birds of Blakeney Point* 2005: 188-189:

> 'The first for Norfolk, and only the third for Britain, was shot by Fred Power on 4th September 1884. His notes (Power, 1885) contain the following:-
>
> 'September 4th. Wind N.E. and strong. Very wet; strong wind and stinging rain throughout... Many small migrants at the sandhills, principally Garden Warblers, Redstarts and Wheatears; but also two Wrynecks and some Greater Whitethroats. One immature Pied Flycatcher shot and another seen. On this day, the Barred Warbler was obtained. It was solitary; in colour and flight not unlike a Spotted Flycatcher, and made no note. It is a female, and bird of the year... This was exhibited together with another immature bird obtained at Spurn, in Yorkshire, at the end of August, by Mr. Dresser, to the Zoological Society, November 4th. The species is moreover new to the Norfolk list'.'

The present whereabouts of the specimen is unknown.

Lesser Whitethroat
Sylvia curruca curruca
The earliest dated reference we can find is by Sheppard and Whitear in *A Catalogue of the Norfolk and Suffolk Birds, with Remarks* 1826: 19 where they write:

> 'We have noticed the Lesser White-throat more than once at Starston, and we have also procured its eggs at the same place. It appears to be not uncommon in the neighbourhood of Diss, at which place we have seen several nests belonging to this species. In the month of July 1820, we observed a Lesser White-throat very busy in picking the *Aphis lanigera* from the apple-trees.'

Steppe Lesser Whitethroat
Sylvia curruca halimodendri
One, potentially the first British record of this Steppe race, was trapped, ringed and photographed at Winterton by Dave Parsons, Kevan Brett, Tony Leggett and Gary Trett on 30th September 2007.

Dave Parsons writes:

> 'Bird ringing operations are carried out on most weekends by the East Norfolk Ringing Group (ENRG) during the autumn on the land owned by Burnley Hall estates at Winterton, Norfolk. The main ringing site is the significant patch of birch and willow scrub situated on the private land either side of the Somerton Holmes track, just inland from the well known concrete blocks on the coastal heath.
>
> On Sunday 30th September 2007, ringing had commenced as usual at

304

dawn with a number of rides being operated by the four ringers on duty, Kevan Brett, Tony Leggett, our trainee Gary Trett and myself. Each ride had a tape lure playing a medley of common warbler, thrush and tit songs and calls. The weather was cloudy with a light breeze from the east. A steady flow of both resident and common migratory species were being trapped, with the latter mostly consisting of Chiffchaffs, Blackcaps and a few other warbler species, including a couple of nominate race Lesser Whitethroats. All birds were bagged and brought back to the central car park for ringing and processing, with an eventual approximate total of 70 being obtained.

Around 1100 hrs, the number of birds being caught had dropped to such a low level that the decision to pack in was universal, and in any case, we had all run out of coffee. The last net round was made with all nets being furled or taken down. I extracted a Lesser Whitethroat from the middle shelf of the birch ride adjacent to the car park, and without even looking at it, bagged it and continued the demobilisation.

Arriving at the ringing station, I passed the bag to Gary, with the immortal words, "There's a Lesser Whitethroat, get it ringed". As Gary is sufficiently experienced to get most things done, we left him to do that while we packed up around him. It was only when he read out the weight of the bird, at least 2g less than usual, that we queried what he had observed. The wing length was also shorter than the nominate race and so both Kevan and I inspected the bird.

While checking the measurements, some slight plumage differences between this bird and the previously trapped first-year nominate race birds were apparent. The bird was sandier on the wings, mantle and nape and where any grey feathering existed on the head, it was admixed with sandy colouration. The rump and tail feathers were also paler brown. Where whitish feather tips were evident on nominate race birds, the bird under investigation exhibited buffish edges on the tertials, greater coverts and secondaries. Underparts appeared basically as the nominate race. Structurally, the bird was obviously considerably smaller in the hand. Additional wing measurements were taken and noted.

None of those present were familiar with any eastern races of Lesser Whitethroat, though we had long thought that anything unusual likely to be trapped there of that species would be either *blythi* or *althaea* which we understood to be structurally larger and more like the nominate race. Fortunately Kevan had taken a series of photographs of nominate Lesser Whitethroat earlier in the day. Although light conditions were now different, some photographs were taken in similar poses to try and show correlation or otherwise.

The bird was released and not seen again.

The photographs were later shown to some of the more worldly-wise members of the Great Yarmouth Bird Club, notably Andrew Grieve who immediately and quite excitedly raised the prospect of *halimodendri*, which to be honest, I had never heard of. The details were passed on to the the relevant authorities and we await their findings with interest. This applies, particularly to Gary, who may have one ringing tick on his list that will never be overhauled by the rest of us. Any future Lesser Whitethroats will no doubt be scrupulously examined.'

There are two earlier claims of birds showing characteristics of this race which were reported in the *Norfolk Bird Report* 2003. One was seen at California on 21st October and another was seen and photographed at Paston on the 24th and 25th. To our knowledge neither has yet been submitted to BBRC. However, should one or the other, or both, ever gain acceptance they would supersede the above record.

Birds considered to have shown characteristics of the Siberian race *C. c. blythi* have been recorded in the county on several occasions. The first was trapped and ringed at Blakeney Point on 26th August 1954 and was reported in the *Norfolk Bird Report* 1954 as '…had the wing formula of the Siberian race *C. c. blythi.*'

Siberian populations described as *blythi*, possess on average only very slightly browner upperparts than European *curruca* and usually less pointed wing shape, but many are inseparable. In the south of the range *blythi* apparently freely intergrades with *halimodendri*, the two being largely inseparable on plumage and wing structure (Shirihai *et al* 2001).

A paper dealing with the eastern races of Lesser Whitethroat is in preparation and will be published in due course which, hopefully, will go some way to clearing up many of the problems associated with attempting to accurately identify them.

Asian Desert Warbler
Sylvia nana
One was discovered by Mark Golley at the Hood on Blakeney Point on 27th May 1993 (Plate 14). It remained until 1st June.

Mark Golley writes:

'Rain, rain, rain and more rain. That's all that seemed to be happening on May 27th. I had woken up to the sound of rain and that's what we got until about 4pm After closing the Cley visitor centre a little earlier than usual, I splashed my way out to Daukes Hide, only to be waylaid by a worryingly rare looking 'acro' in the bushes behind the hide. After 25 or 30 minutes the bird seemed to have melted into oblivion, so I sat down in the hide, only to be told of two Icterine Warblers on the 'Point'. I decided to cut my losses, pull on the wellies and head shingle-wards.

By about 6.15pm I had reached the hood, with nothing for company except a headful of songs by Neil Young and dreams of finding a Black Lark. How an idle mind works overtime! As I cut across the middle of the Hood, a small, pale passerine flicked across the path in front of me, some 20 yards away. Instantly I thought it had to be rare! I picked up my bins but within a split second the bird had dropped to the ground, but in doing so revealed some telling features – very pale upperparts, contrasting with orangey uppertail and central tail feathers and a glimpse of pale yellowy legs. It was a Desert Warbler! I could not believe my luck. I immediately alerted Blakeney Point staff over my radio, and tried to raise Bernard Bishop, but to no avail. An agonising wait for the observers to arrive was made easier on my nerves by enjoying some superb views of a Norfolk first, and I had it all to myself…

Eventually after some 15 or 20 minutes I could share the bird, which was still behaving impeccably, and during the late evening the familiar Cley contingent were enjoying crippling views, along with a few faces hotfoot from east and west Norfolk.

The bird presented few identification problems. A small rotund little *sylvia* showing a milky tea coloured head and mantle, which could look greyish or orangey tinged depending on the light. The wings were quite heavily abraded – in particular the scapulars and tertials. The general tone of the wings was warm buffy brown, with dark primary coverts and alula. The orange centred tail was also heavily worn – roughly one or two each of the relevant feathers were present! There were just enough to see the orange, edged black feathers and white outers. The underparts were entirely creamy off white.

The bare parts showed a vivid, piercing lemon yellow iris, straw yellow legs and feet and a fleshy pink bill with dark culmen and tip to the upper mandible.

The bird was heard subsinging later on the first evening and by the next day was in full song and song-flighting and nest building!! It remained at Blakeney Point until 1st June.

This constitutes the tenth British record and the first ever recorded in spring. This is most interesting as the other nine records fall in the period October to December, with October having the lion's share with six. So this bird was certainly highly unusual with its timing.'

(An account published in the *Norfolk Bird Club Bulletin* No 5: 7-8)

Common Whitethroat
Sylvia communis communis
The earliest dated reference we can find is in 'Extracts from the Calendar of the Rev. William Whitear 1809-1826' published in the *Transactions of the Norfolk and Norwich Naturalists' Society* 1881-1882: 241 where he recorded one on 23rd April 1816 in the Starston area.

Also known to Sheppard and Whitear as the Hay-jack in *A Catalogue of the Norfolk and Suffolk Birds, with* Remarks (1826) but only listed and not commented on.

The Pagets in *Sketch of the Natural History of Yarmouth and its Neighbourhood* 1834: 5 considered it:

'…more or less common'.

Common Whitethroat (Eastern)
Sylvia communis icterops
One showing good characteristics of the eastern race '*icterops*' was found by Richard Porter at Blakeney Point on 29th April 2003.

James McCallum writes:

'The 29th April 2003 was dominated by southerly gales and heavy rain showers. The afternoon saw more sunny spells and the wind easing. A good number of migrants were evident on Blakeney Point with Wryneck, Lesser Whitethroat, 2 Blackcaps, 6 Willow Warblers and 18 Wheatears all around the Lifeboat House. However, in the windy conditions everything remained elusive.

The 30th April saw much warmer sunny spells and a warm, moderate southerly breeze. Migrants were readily evident in the sheltered bushes outside the lifeboat house. In the early morning I saw a Lesser and Common Whitethroat head high across the estuary towards the mainland whilst in the bushes I counted 4 Whitethroats, 2-3 Lesser Whitethroats, 2 Blackcaps, 31 Willow Warblers, 4 Chiffchaffs, a female Blackbird and 30 Wheatears. The *sylvia* warblers were showing well so I sat watching and sketching them until I received a radio call to meet Dave Wood, fellow warden, who had just arrived with some supplies.

In the meantime, at around 10am, Tony Marr and Richard Porter had arrived at 'The Lupins' and began watching the migrants. Richard Porter noticed a *sylvia* moving through some low brambles and its identity puzzled him. At first he thought it was a Common Whitethroat, and then Lesser Whitethroat and even Spectacled Warbler went through his mind. He alerted Tony Marr and the bird began to give much better views. The bright orange-flesh legs immediately ruled out Lesser Whitethroat and the size, structure and wing pattern were clearly wrong for Spectacled Warbler.

They both agreed that it was indeed a Whitethroat with unusual plumage. Richard Porter then realised that it showed the characteristics of the *icterops* race of Common Whitethroat, which he knew well from Turkey and the Middle East. So they decided to telephone us at the Lifeboat House where we were unloading supplies. Dave had taken the call and relayed the message to me. Initially we just looked at each other and decided that it didn't sound very exciting but thought we'd better show some interest and set off to have a look.

We were directed to the bramble it was frequenting, when suddenly it popped up in our 'scopes. At first it was head on and the initial impression was very much like a Lesser Whitethroat in colouration and tone, then it turned side on revealing rufous coverts, sandy edged tertials, pale grey flanks and pale legs. It was in fact a very striking bird; its distinctive appearance surprised us both.

Richard and Tony were pleased by our surprised reaction and the four of us began to make detailed notes and sketches.

I remarked that it shared the overall colour and tone of a Lesser Whitethroat, wings and legs of a Common Whitethroat and head markings reminiscent of male Spectacled Warbler; an initial impression very similar to that of Richard's.

We spent around an hour taking notes together then, Richard and Tony set off to look for migrants. I remained to make further watercolours with Dave double checking the colour and tones of the sketches.

The bird showed well in the morning and midday sunshine, breaking into sub song, which along with its plumage suggested that it was an adult male. In the afternoon the weather deteriorated and it became much more elusive. Although news of its discovery was immediately released no-one came up to see it, most birdwatchers probably reacting similarly to mine and Dave's initial thoughts. This was a shame as despite only being a sub-species its appearance was surprisingly striking, and for me it was almost like seeing a new species of *sylvia* Warbler.'

(An account published in the *Norfolk Bird Club Bulletin* No 54: 12-15, as part of an article detailing the finding of two potentially new sub-species for the county in 2003, which contained a description)

Dartford Warbler
Sylvia undata
One was obtained at Yarmouth some time before 1846.

Peter Allard writes in *The Birds of Great Yarmouth* 1990: 106:

> 'Messrs. Gurney and Fisher writing in 1846 mention one shot at Yarmouth. No date was given but it was an addition to the Norfolk List.'

Gurney and Fisher write in 'An Account of the birds found in Norfolk, with notices of some of the rarer species which have occurred in the adjoining counties' in the *Zoologist* 1846: 1309:

> 'With the exception of a single specimen, killed on the Denes, near Yarmouth, we know of no instance of the occurrence of the Dartford Warbler in Norfolk.'

It is probably safe to assume that the bird was killed sometime between 1834 and 1846 as the Pagets (1834) fail to mention it.

Interestingly Henry Stevenson writes in *The Birds of Norfolk* Vol. l. 1866: 133-134:

> 'But two specimens of this warbler have been recorded as killed in this county, and in both instances on the Denes near Yarmouth. The first was obtained some years since, as noticed by Messrs. Gurney and Fisher; and the last a young male, was caught by a dog in a furze bush, on the 25th February, 1859. This bird was sent to a bird-stuffer in this city, together with a stoat killed at the same time, and was intended to be placed in the mouth of "the varmint," when fortunately it was recognised as a rarity. The above Norfolk specimens are preserved in Mr. Gurney's collection at Catton. Mr. Hunt, in his "List" of Norfolk Birds, has the following note on this species:- "A pair of these elegant little birds were shot in the month of June, 1828; they are the only specimens ever found in this part of the kingdom, and are now in the possession of Mr. Crickmore, of Beccles." No locality being named in this instance, it is most probable, I think, that these specimens were obtained in the neighbourhood of the town where Mr. Crickmore resided, and would therefore be the first recorded instances of the Dartford warbler appearing in the Eastern Counties; but as Beccles is situated on the borders of the two counties, they are quite as likely to have been killed on the Norfolk as on the Suffolk side of it,'

The 1859 specimen (Accession no. NWHCM: 15.935.44) is on display in the bird gallery at the Castle Museum, Norwich.

Marmora's Warbler
Sylvia sarda sarda
One was found by Neil Lawton at Scolt Head on 12th May 2001.

Neil Lawton writes:

> 'During the mid morning of May 12th, Norman Williams and I set out

from the Ternery on Scolt Head NNR to look for migrants, we left Jon Brown 'guarding' the nesting terns. In a light east wind and bright sunny conditions, we soon began to find small numbers of common migrants including Wheatears, Whinchats and a Pied Flycatcher. As we approached a scrub-covered dune ridge at the western end of the island, I took the sheltered west facing side and NW the more exposed east side. Walking along the edge of the *Suaeda* bordering the dunes, I soon heard a harsh 'tak', from a bird low down in the *Suaeda* just a few feet away. The call was unfamiliar to me and had a chat like quality about it, so I retreated a few feet away and waited to see what appeared, when suddenly a small blue/grey bird with a long tail flew up and quickly disappeared in to nearby brambles. After a few seconds it reappeared in the brambles, it was a striking bird, small, with a long tail, short wings, with a steep forehead, spiky narrow bill, bright ruby red eye and eye ring and uniform blue-grey plumage. I immediately identified it as either a Dartford Warbler or Marmora's Warbler, this bird had fairly uniform pencil grey underparts. The realisation then began to set in that this bird had to be a Marmora's Warbler, a species new to me and the county. I quickly phoned JB, who I got to check the identification in the Collins Field Guide, his description left me in no doubt. At this point I noticed Michael Rooney landing a boat nearby and after a little frantic waving I attracted his attention and was quickly joined by him. He was more than a little surprised when I told him what I had just found. We both soon enjoyed good views of the bird, he agreeing immediately with the identification. After a short while I left to find NW, who arrived at the bird, along with JB and all four of us enjoyed excellent views both through binoculars and telescope. The bird showed well over the next hour singing and feeding from *Suaeda* and scrub down to a few feet.

It was a small, short winged bird with long narrow tail, fine bill, long legs and distinctive steep forehead. The upper parts including most of the head and tail was uniform pastel blue-grey. The wings were also blue-grey but had a warm brown wash and browner fringes to the feathers. The lores, small area of ear coverts just behind the eye and a small area just below the eye were darker blackish-grey which created a darker facial mask. The underparts were unstreaked, uniform lead-grey with slightly darker undertail coverts, a slightly paler belly patch and throat, but there was little contrast on the rest of the underparts or upper parts. The bill was relatively long and fine, with a dark tip and upper mandible and the rest was pinkish-yellow. Legs were long and thin pale pinkish-yellow and the eye and eye ring was vivid scarlet red which stood out markedly against the grey-blue head and darker facial mask.

It was an active and inquisitive bird, always on the move and frequently perching on the top of bushes looking around or singing and often down to just a metre or two. When perched on tops of bushes its legs were often splayed with a foot on different branches or twigs. The tail was often held at 45 degrees and constantly moved from side to side and up and down. When not perched out in the open it would often feed very low down in the Suaeda unseen. It was seen to feed on a number of small flying insects which it caught like a flycatcher. The bird was frequently heard singing, the song always delivered from a prominent perch. Song was a soft scratchy sweet warble, which was always finished with a trill. Call was a loud harsh 'tak' which was more like that of a chat rather than a *Sylvia* warbler and demanded attention.

After around an hour the bird became increasingly active flying up to 50 metres to the west landing in a nearby area of *Suaeda* and singing as soon as it landed. It did this a further four or five times, eventually flying far out on to the saltmarsh and despite extensive searching on and off during the rest of the day and next day could not be relocated. It was presumed like many migrants on Scolt Head, that it had filtered westwards and off the island.

On the afternoon of 18th May I was returning to my hut at the Ternery when I heard a bird calling and singing from brambles nearby, which I immediately recognised as the Marmora's Warbler. I soon located the bird in brambles, and watched it for around an hour. The bird remained in the same general area for the rest of the day, often showing well, but could not be relocated next day, nor over subsequent days. The bird had clearly remained on the island during the missing days, presumably hidden in *Suaeda* at the Ternery.

By coincidence on the day the bird was first discovered, MESR received his latest copy of British Birds which contains an excellent and thorough article on identification of Marmora's Warbler and separation of the two races. This article clearly identified this bird as belonging to the nominate race *Sylvia sarda sarda* based on bill and leg colour, the fairly uniform plumage colour (especially underparts), call and song.

There can be few other birds on the British list with such a restricted range and not surprisingly there had only been three previous records at: Mickleden Clough, Langsett, South Yorkshire 15th May until 22nd July 1982, Spurn, Humberside 8th-9th June 1992 and St Abb's Head, Borders 23rd-27th May 1993. Interestingly these three records also referred to males (are males easier to locate because they sing). This was therefore the fourth British record and the first for the county. There was a further British record later the same spring when a singing male was present at Sizewell, Suffolk 29th May 2001, it is of course always possible that this was the same bird relocating south.'

(An account published in the *Norfolk Bird Club Bulletin* No 46: 4-6, which included a more detailed description)

Ruppell's Warbler
Sylvia rueppelli
A female was found by Gary Hibberd in dense sea buckthorn scrub at Holme Dunes on 31st August 1992. It was the first British mainland occurrence.

Gary Hibberd writes:

'On August 31st I was bird-watching in the Forestry, an area of scrub in the dune habitat at Holme Dunes Nature Reserve. I was exploring one of several rides running through clumps of sea buckthorn and elder when a pale warbler caught my eye. Views were brief but the general shape and long tail made it clear I was looking at a *Sylvia* warbler. It seemed a very long half-hour before the bird reappeared in a bramble close-by, but with the light behind me I was able to obtain good views. The most striking features were its overall paleness, very distinctive whitish edges to all the flight feathers, pale pinkish-orange legs and red iris surrounded by an indistinct eye-ring. The bird soon disappeared and armed with what I thought were sufficient details I went to alert Reserve staff and check field guides.

Back at the Firs the two guides available were The Shell Guide to the Birds of Britain and Ireland and The Macmillan Field Guide to Bird Identification. After a hurried read I concluded that the bird was a young female Subalpine Warbler. After viewing the stranger Bill Boyd rang Richard Millington to relay the news onto Birdline. Richard thought the colouration of the upperparts slightly odd for a Subalpine Warbler and with this in mind RGM and Steve Gantlett soon arrived. On observing the bird Richard was certain it was in fact a Ruppell's Warbler. Such a confident statement led to a certain amount of panic, but it became clear that certain elements of the bird's plumage had to be checked more thoroughly to eliminate Sardinian Warbler. By this time Subalpine Warbler had been totally removed from everyone's thoughts. The bird in question was too large and far too grey. Lars Johnsson's guide to Birds of the Mediterranean and Alps was consulted and realisation dawned. The plate of female Ruppell's Warbler seemed perfect. Debate followed and the same conclusion was made. Holme was playing host to a Ruppell's Warbler – only the fourth record for Britain and Ireland.

DESCRIPTION

Slightly larger than Lesser Whitethroat and much paler. The overall appearance was of a small Barred Warbler.Head and upperparts were cold bluish-grey. Wings dark ash-grey strikingly edged buffish white, broader on the tertials, the tips of the primaries were neatly edged white and the secondaries more buff-white. Greater covert centres were the same colour as the uppeparts; these too were broadly edged whitish. The largest feather of the alula was black with a fine white edge. Tail was a dark ash-grey startlingly rommed in white. Underparts were clean whitish, the belly and flanks showing a greyish cast. The upper breast revealed a pinkish tinge at times, but this was possibly due to berry staining. The throat was white and at some angles a cleaner white sub-moustachial was noted. The ear-coverts were well demarcated from the throat. The bill was longish and at times appeared slightly decurved at the tip, it was dark grey with a paler bluish-grey base. In good light the iris was a distinctive brownish-red. An indistinct brownish-orange eye ring was easier to discern in photographs. Legs were pinkish-straw or orange. After an inspection of skins Ian Lewington decided that the bird was an adult female possibly in its second calendar year (Birding World 5: 9).

Being the first mainland occurrence it was certain to be a popular bird. Identification agreed, the next task was to organise viewing. There was only room for thirty people at a time to view the bird so a queuing system was organised just south of the ride. Apart from some 150 people beaten by failing light on the first day, most observers had good views and deservingly so. Many queued for up to four hours! Fortunately from the Reserve's point of view the bird was very loyal to the one sheltered site, only briefly leaving this area on the first day. But with clear skies and light winds on the night of September 4th it departed.

Considering the huge numbers of visitors involved and the fragile habitat in this part of the Reserve, damage was light. This was due mainly to the sedentary behaviour of the bird, but intensive wardening – including temporarily roped-off-areas – and the patient behaviour of birders were important factors. Over the five-day period NNT staff and volunteers collected £2700 in permit fees and £115 in donations. The whole event was very enjoyable.'

(An account published in the *Norfolk Bird Report* 1992: 436-437, which included highlights of the year at Holme and thanks to the volunteers)

Subalpine Warbler (Western)
Sylvia cantillans cantillans
The first record for England was found by Peter Hayman at Cley on 11th June 1951.

Peter Hayman writes:

'At 3 p.m. on June 11th, 1951 as I was about to enter Cley Bird Observatory, a small warbler flew past me and dived into some barbed wire. The bird was flushed easily, and upon alighting in a bush near by was recognised as a male Subalpine Warbler. I drove the bird, with ease, into the Heligoland trap, but unfortunately the trap was unmanaged and under repair, the catching-box door being closed and the swing door to the catching chamber missing. Despite my efforts to catch the bird it flew past me out of the trap. The following description was obtained whilst the bird was in a bush sheltered from a strong east wind. Bill dark, yellowish at base; eye noticeably red in the field, and at under three feet range in the trap it appeared *very* red. The whole of the upper-parts blue-grey, deepest on the head. Wings grey-brown, primaries darker, secondaries edged light buff. Tail decidedly browner than the upper-parts, outer tail-feathers white, faintly tinged buff. A thin, but quite distinct white moustachial stripe from the base of the bill, separated the grey of the upper-parts from the pink of the under-parts. The pink of the under-parts was deepest on the throat and faded out on the flanks. Under tail-coverts white, faintly washed dirty yellow. Feet bright yellow-flesh. The bird was left at 4.30 p.m. and at 5.30 p.m. it was flushed by P.J.H. and R. A. Richardson, who confirmed the above description. All other efforts to trap the bird failed, and it was last seen by R.A.R. at 7.0 p.m. This is the first record for England and Norfolk.'

(Originally published in *British Birds* 45: 262)

Male Subalpine Warbler by Heligoland trap at Cley Bird Observatory June 1951. (*Norman Arlott*)

Subalpine Warbler (Eastern)
Sylvia cantillans albistriata
One was found by Mark Cavanagh, Mark Eldridge and Andy Stoddart at Blakeney Point on 20th May 1990.

Andy Stoddart writes from his notes taken at the time:

'Mid-May 1990 on Blakeney Point had seen some welcome hot southeasterly conditions, producing on 14th fine male of Bluethroat and Red-backed Shrike. The conditions were still favourable on 20th May when I set out once more with my companions. Migrants were very few, as is typical for the second half of the month, with only a Whinchat, 2 Willow Warblers and a Sedge Warbler in the bushes by the day's close. However, 'bird of the day' had been seen early when I was called over in the Marrams to see a male Subalpine Warbler *Sylvia cantillans*. My notebook from that day reads as follows:-

Typically, small, dumpy and compact, rounded, almost 'phylloscopine' and fairly short-tailed for a *Sylvia*. Very dark-looking in flight. Upperparts darkish grey with bluey tone and darker tertials, prominently fringed pale grey. White submoustachials very broad and prominent. Throat and upper breast very dark browny-pink, pinker at sides of upper breast. Flanks and rest of underparts whitish. White outers to darker tail when cocked or opened. Iris and eye ring red. Legs pale orange. Call a harsh 'chit.

On the basis that the upperparts were dark grey, that the pinkish under-parts colour was noticeably dark and of limited extent, confined to a well-defined patch on the throat and upper breast, and that the submoustachials were very prominent, we tentatively assigned the bird to *albistriata*, the form which breeds in the Balkans, Greece and western Turkey.

The publication of Shirihai *et al.* (2001) has now thrown more light on the identification of this form and confirms the importance of the features described above. However, in the interests of caution, we listed the bird in Stoddart and Joyner (2005) as being of an '*albistriata*-type'.'

Sardinian Warbler

Sylvia melanocephala

A male trapped at Waxham by Ted Lloyd Williams on 28th April 1973 was only the fifth British record. It remained next day but was at times difficult to locate.

Ted Lloyd Williams had been ringing birds since 1971 and obtained his C permit in July 1972. Up to the time he caught this bird he had ringed over 2,000 birds of more than 50 species and since August 1972 he had been ringing birds during migration periods at Waxham.

On 28th April 1973 it was cloudy with a force 2 southerly wind and at 10 o'clock he trapped a small warbler. His first impression was satisfaction at catching his first Blackcap of 1973. However, on closer examination two main features were evident; these were that the black cap extended below the eyes and the eye had a scarlet red eye-ring. Systematic analysis was carried out which included a detailed description and measurements.

Bill blackish-brown. Lores, forehead, crown and ear coverts glossy black. Eyes muddy brown with scarlet red eye-ring. Nape, mantle and back dark grey. Uppertail coverts and rump grey, tail brownish-grey with the three outer feathers tipped white. Belly dirty white, flanks light grey, breast whitish grey hint, throat pure white, chin white. Primary and secondary coverts dark grey, primaries, secondaries and tertials greyish-brown. Scapulars brownish-grey, median lesser coverts dark grey and alula brown-edged whitish-grey.

On release the bird flew to a neighbouring tree and while perched on the lowest branch it called with the typical text book staccato call. On 29th April John Goldsmith of the Castle Museum, Norwich and several other people saw the bird and confirmed Ted's identification as an adult male Sardinian Warbler.

(An account compiled from the unpublished files in the British Birds Rarities Committee archive)

Greenish Warbler

Phylloscopus trochiloides viridanus

One was found by Peter Browne and Arnold Hichon at Blakeney Point on 6th September 1951.

Peter Browne and Arnold Hichon write:

'On September 6th, 1951, there were some 20 Willow-Warblers (*Phylloscopus trochilus*) in a small clump of coniferous and deciduous trees near the western end of Blakeney Point, Norfolk. We watched them for about an hour (1400-1500 hours G.M.T.) and, after a while, noticed that one had a pale wing-bar. It fed on outer branches and we had it under intermittent observation for ten minutes. The range was *c.*12 yards, binoculars 7 x 50 and 8 x 30, sky overcast, light fair and "all-round."

The bird disappeared several times, but was picked out again immediately it came back into view, for it "looked different" from the Willow-Warblers: in general it was paler and browner. The size was about as Willow-Warbler. It was certainly not "distinctly larger" (as K. Williamson describes Eversman's Warblers (*Ph. Borealis*) seen at Fair Isle in 1950 (*antea*, vol. xliv, p. 212), leg colour pinkish-brown (as Willow-Warbler again), behaviour similar too, possibly slightly more active. The differences in appearance, compared with Willow-Warblers present, were as follows:-

Single wing-bar, easily visible through binoculars on both wings, but not long or bright. Colour not determined, except it was pale.

Superciliary stripe narrower than Willow-Warbler, but nevertheless brighter, paler, contrasting markedly with dark eye-stripe, and altogether more prominent.

Underparts paler than the Willow-Warbler, almost whitish on belly, otherwise washed very pale yellow, and tinged brown or grey-brown on sides of breast. This latter feature noticed independently by each of us.

We watched the trees carefully for about half-an-hour the next day (*c*.1400 hours G.M.T.) but could not find the bird.'

(Originally published in *British Birds* 45: 413-414)

Two-barred Greenish Warbler

Phylloscopus trochiloides plumbeitarsus

The only record of this eastern race was found by John Kemp in The Dell at Wells on 15th October 1996.

John Kemp writes:

'After a day's birding on the north Norfolk coast on 15th October to watch Blyth's Pipit and Isabelline Shrike, I decided to finish off at Wells Woods, one of my favourite autumn sites. Arriving at 3pm and soon plunging into the depths of birch and bramble scrub, I discovered little in the way of either birds or birders. Shortly after reaching the Dell however I saw a small warbler facing me from the edge of a sallow bush. My initial impression was that it must be a Yellow-browed Warbler as it showed a long prominent supercilium and two wing-bars. As it moved around feeding I realised that it lacked the prominent cream-coloured tertial edgings so typical of Yellow-browed and also that it was 'one size' larger and its movements were less hyper-active than is typical for a Yellow-browed Warbler. The bird was just 15 feet away and in excellent light when another piece of the puzzle emerged: the legs were grey. All this occurred within 20 seconds. Frustratingly, the bird then moved deeper into the sallow complex and was soon out of sight.

A fruitless hour followed. As I searched I puzzled on the bird's identity eliminating Yellow-browed Warbler and both Greenish and Arctic Warbler on the features I had seen (the greater covert-bar was far too bold for either of the latter two species and the leg colour was wrong). The only other candidate seemed to be Two-barred Greenish Warbler, a bird I had only seen on Scilly in 1987. That evening I spoke to Dave Holman and Richard Millington and mentioned the possibility of my having seen a Two-barred Greenish, but was reluctant to claim this potential second record for Britain on a 20 second view. Nevertheless after an evening researching the literature and my own notes on the 1987 bird I became increasingly confident of its identity.

It was with great delight therefore that I learned of its relocation next morning when it gave prolonged views to Richard Millington, Mark Golley and local birders Andrew Bloomfield, Dave Foster and James McCallum. Identity was confirmed. As the day progressed it was seen by many visiting observers, but became more erratic in its appearance. On my return that afternoon it was a full two hours before I achieved a final two minutes viewing.'

(Extracted from an account published in the *Norfolk Bird Report* 1996: 246-247, which was part of an edited article detailing the occurrences of the three eastern vagrants new to the county that year)

Arctic Warbler
Phylloscopus borealis
One was obtained at Blakeney Point by E. C. Arnold on 4th September 1922 (Plate 8).

E. C. Arnold writes:

'On September 4th, 1922, near Blakeney, I shot a small warbler in the scrub, a single slight wing-bar extending over three feathers only, having caught my eye at a distance of nearly twenty yards. This bird was kindly identified by Mr. Witherby, and as I expected, turned out to be an Eversmann's Warbler (*Phylloscopus b. borealis*). It is a typical specimen. The first primary is no longer than the wing-coverts; the second comes between the 5th and 6th; the 3rd to 5th are emarginated on the outer webs and not the 6th; the wing measures 63mm; the eye-stripe is long and conspicuous, and the beak larger than that of an ordinary Willow-Wren. The wind was north-west with fog and fine rain in the morning. This is the first record for England, the three previous occurrences of the bird having been in the Orkneys and Shetlands.'

(Originally published in *British Birds* 16: 162)

Andy Stoddart and Steve Joyner in *The Birds of Blakeney Point* 2005: 192-193 write:

'The first 'Eversmann's Warbler' for England was shot by Arnold at the Marrams on 4th September 1922 and is quoted in Seago (1977) and Taylor *et al* (1999) as being held at the Castle Museum, Norwich. Unfortunately, the specimen could not be found by the Museum when searched for during the preparation of this book. It was correctly listed by Riviere (1930) as the first for England but is incorrectly described as the first for Britain in Taylor *et al* (1999) as there are earlier records from Sule Skerry Lighthouse, Orkney on 5th September 1902 and Fair Isle, Shetland on 28th September 1908'

Enquiries in 2008 revealed that this specimen (Accession no. NWHCM: 1966.479) is in storage at the Castle Museum, Norwich. The label on the case reads 'Eversmann's Warbler.

Phylloscopus borealis borealis. From near Blakeney, Norfolk. Sept. 4th 1922. E. C. Arnold. Pres. by Eastbourne College, Sussex.' The reverse of the label reads 'See *British Birds* XVI., p. 162. (The first for England – only three all told). Mounted by Bates of Eastbourne.'

Pallas's Leaf Warbler
Phylloscopus proregulus
The first British record was shot by Edward Ramm at Cley on 31st October 1896.

Andy Stoddart and Steve Joyner write in *The Birds of Blakeney Point* 2005: 193-194, firstly quoting H. E. Dresser 1897: 193-194:

> 'One of the most interesting additions that has of late been made to the avifauna of the British Islands is certainly that of a Pallas's Willow Warbler (*Phylloscopus proregulus*), a single example of which was shot at Cley-next-the-Sea, Norfolk on the 31st October 1896 by Mr. Ramm who forwarded it to Mr. Thomas Southwell and informed the gentleman that he "found it amongst the long grass on the bank or sea-wall, not far from the sea at Cley, a locality which has produced many rare migrants, and at first took it for a Goldcrest, but on approaching to within two or three yards, the bird being very tame, he thought he recognised a Yellow-browed Warbler, a species he had seen before, and therefore secured it." Mr Southwell identified it correctly as Pallas's Willow Warbler, but forwarded it to me for confirmation, and at his request I exhibited it at a meeting of the Zoological Society on the 1st December last. On comparing the bird with those in my collection from Siberia and the Himalayas it agrees most closely with a fully adult bird from Siberia; and I may here state that it is an adult female in very fresh plumage and is quite as bright in tinge of colour as any Siberian specimen I have seen.'

They go on to say:

> 'According to Bishop (1996), Arnold had neglected to obtain the bird believing it to be nothing out of the ordinary, only for it to be diligently pursued by Ramm's dog 'Duchess' and secured by Ramm himself. Other accounts cite Pinchen as the unfortunate companion (Wallace, 2004). An entertaining account of this event by Clifford Borrer is contained in the 16th September 1955 issue of *Shooting Times & Country Magazine* recently reprinted (*Birding World* 13: 126-127).
>
> The bird was subsequently sold to Ernest Connop for either £40 or £50 (accounts vary) and passed into his collection at Rollesby Hall before being sold to W. R. Lysaght of Chepstow who in turn donated it to the City of Birmingham Museum, where it now resides. This transaction gives a clear idea of the amount of money at stake on such occasions - £50 in 1896 would today be worth almost £4,000!
>
> The bird is described by Borrer as having been 'in a great tuft of grass' and 'in a corner of the sea-bank' adjacent to an old railway carriage then on Cley beach. Rowan describes it as having been shot 'against the Railway Hut' which formed the edge of his recording area and therefore includes it in his list of Blakeney Point birds. Although the species' precise location is not known to the authors,

the record is included here on the basis of its inclusion by Rowan.

In addition to being the first for Britain, this was only the third Pallas's Warbler to be recorded in Europe, the first having been secured in Heligoland, Germany on 6th October 1845, with a further bird observed there on 29th October 1875. Dresser's ageing of the Blakeney Point bird as an adult seems to modern eyes somewhat surprising as the overwhelming majority of Pallas's Warblers (and indeed all vagrants) are now known to be young birds.'

The specimen remains in storage at the City of Birmingham Museum.

The article by Clifford Borrer, mentioned above, is so interesting and entertaining we feel it should be reprinted here. Clifford Borrer writes:

THE PALLAS'S WARBLER IN NORFOLK - A NEW BRITISH BIRD

'In the days, not so very long ago, when many naturalists shot and collected birds, parts of the east coast of England were renowned for what was known to esoteric gunners as 'bush-shooting.' The four-mile stretch of Blakeney Point in Norfolk, covered as it is with shrubby sea-blite; the marsh-heads at North Cotes in Lincolnshire and parts of the Suffolk coast between Leiston shore and Orford Ness; were among the localities which were quite famous for the number and variety of small migratory birds which visited them. The ranks of warblers, pipits and buntings were eagerly scanned by skilled naturalists who wanted specimens of uncommon species.

'Heligoland traps' had not been thought of. The only way to identify a doubtful bird was to 'secure' it – as the expression was. 'Favourable' conditions for bush-shooting consisted of the stormiest weather possible, combined with an east or north-east wind. With streams of rain driving down his neck or beating in his face, his legs encased in long, heavy thigh-boots, and a sou'-wester hat pulled half over his eyes, a collector needed to be keen of sight and enthusiastic indeed to become a successful bush-shooter. He certainly deserved such luck as occasionally came his way.

The late Mr Arnold, who wrote a book about bush-shooting, used to reckon that perhaps one bird in five hundred seen might be a desirable specimen. He was certainly the most noted of all bush-shooters, but I have heard other collectors estimate that one good bird to a thousand ordinary ones in the bushes would be nearer the mark.

I have, myself, done plenty of bush-shooting in my time, and can assure any of my readers, who may be disposed to regard it as poor sport, that in its way it was extremely interesting and even exciting, and demanded considerable patience and skill. The bushes might be full of birds driven to shelter by wind and rain, but only a momentary glimpse was likely to be obtained of any individual as it darted from one clump of bushes to another. Some of the naturalists brought boys to beat for them, but it was a risky game, for excitement rose to fever heat when a first-class rarity had been detected and was being closely followed.

Every sort of device was tried to induce the birds to show themselves, including the dragging of chains and ropes through the bushes. But the only effective method was the use of a suitable dog, and thus was evolved what was termed by the local gunners, a 'bush-dog.'

SNAP-SHOT SHOOTING

It was not much use turning just any kind of dog into the bushes, and allowing it to rush backwards and forwards in pursuit of the rabbits which abounded there. Such pranks would merely cause the avine quarry to skulk all the closer, or slip back behind the line, which necessitated the shooters going over the ground again. The shooting was almost entirely of the snap-shot variety, and what was needed was a close-ranging animal which would move from side to side in front of the guns, causing the birds to flutter forward above the shrubs, or to fly out on the flanks affording the wing-gunners a clear shot. The best bush-dogs were of the springer spaniel type, but some amateurs preferred clumbers. It was important that the colour of the animal should be white.

There are people living in Cley village who yet speak, almost with reverence, of some of these canine paragons, particularly of Prince, a bush-dog belonging to the late veteran gunner, Bob Pinchen. After being for many years one of the most successful killers of rare birds, Bob was appointed warden and watcher on Blakeney Point. He was never tired of extolling the qualities of Prince, which animal (according to his master) would retrieve a good warbler or bunting with particular care and without ruffling a feather, as if recognising a valuable specimen. A bush-dog, which would search for and bring to hand a small bird, was a great asset to a collector.

Another noted Cley gunner was Edward Ramm, who was generally regarded as the most successful of the professional fraternity. The two men were keen rivals in pursuit of rarities. Ramm possessed a brown Sussex spaniel called Duchess which he regarded as superior to Prince in every way – except as to colour. Serous discussions often raged in the bars of The George, or The Dun Cow, respecting the merits of these animals. Bob would remark, casting disparaging glances at Duchess as she reposed at her master's feet "Duchess ain't the colour for a bush-dog. Duchess is too long in the leg. Duchess will get mistook for a hare one of these days, etc." Ramm, regarding Prince with tolerant disapproval, as the latter lay stretched on the sandy floor before the fire, would proceed to cast aspersions on poor Prince's honesty, protesting that the animal had robbed many a gunner by picking up and taking to his own master some rarity shot by another professional.

SAGACITY OF BUSH DOGS

As pint followed pint down the throats of the worthy gunners, all sorts of stories were recounted concerning the sagacity of bush-dogs. For example, the following is the version which Ramm always gave of how he got the rarest bird ever obtained at Cley.

It was the last day of October in the year of Grace 1896. The wind had been due east nearly all month, and he and Bob with their two dogs were sheltering one afternoon from a furious squall of rain beneath the lee of an ancient railway carriage which formerly stood on Cley beach. Suddenly Ramm observed Duchess prick up her ears as a tiny feathered wanderer flitted past and sought the shelter of a nearby corner of the sea-bank.

Bob remarked it was only a 'titty-wren' – the local name for a common goldcrest – but the super-intelligent Duchess followed the feathered waif out into the storm, and stood pointing at a great tuft of grass in which it had sought shelter. Ramm had seen just enough of the bird as it passed to recognise it as a warbler of some kind – certainly not a 'titty'. Duchess kept looking over her shoulder at him with such reproachful glances, that the gunner felt sure the bird was "summat out of the ordinary" as he used to express it. Awaiting the next lull, he sallied out into the teeth of the gale and kicked the grass, where-upon out darted the little stranger, affording the easiest possible chance.

FIRST BRITISH SPECIMEN

When Ramm picked up the bird he saw at once it was something he had never encountered before, for it had a lemon-coloured rump. When skinned and dispatched to London, it was recognised by the Museum authorities as the first British and second European example of an oriental rarity known as Pallas's barred willow-warbler. Ramm always maintained that it was largely due to the cleverness and sagacity of Duchess that he obtained this rich prize, and valuable it certainly was in those far-off days. The late Mr E. M. Connop gave hime fifty pounds for it.

"That's what I call a bush-dog" was how the story usually concluded, "and I'm blowed if my missus didn't buy Duchess a pound of tender steak all for her four-legged self!"

Bush-shooting is now a thing of the past, and a gunner who at one time could often make ten or fifteen pounds out of a good bird would be likely to find himself mulcted of 'five fivers' by the local magistrates, if he ventured to slay a bluethroat or a barred-warbler today. Gone for ever are those old-time gentleman-gunners, skilled alike with pen and gun who have left us so many amusing records of their exploits as bird collectors. With them have departed the professional fowlers who could pick out a solitary rarity from among the hordes of 'commoners' on a migration morning; while their faithful well-trained bush-dogs are as extinct as the wolf in Scotland.

Clifford Borrer (nom de plume *Sea Pie*), Norfolk.'

Birding World editors' comment:

'This article, first published in *The Shooting Times & Country Magazine* September 16th 1955, was recently unearthed by Rodney Sewell, the current landlord of The George & Dragon in Cley. Many contemporary birders will have noticed Prince's grave in the Blakeney Point plantation, but may not have realised its ornithological significance.'

(An account published in *Birding World* 13: 126-127)

Yellow-browed Warbler
Phylloscopus inornatus
One was shot at Cley on 1st October 1894. The specimen is in storage at the City of Birmingham Museum.

J. E. Harting writes in the *Zoologist* 1894: 459-60:

'The attention which of late years has been paid to the smaller migratory birds during their autumnal migration has led to the discovery that several species which have been long regarded as rare stragglers to England are most likely annual summer visitors; their small size and unobtrusive colouring causing them to be generally overlooked. Amongst these may be named the Marsh Warbler, *Acrocephalus palustris*, the Barred Warbler, *Sylvia nisoria*, the Icterine Warbler, *Hypolais icterina*, and the Yellow-browed Warbler, *Phylloscopus superciliosus*. The last-named species has been met with in two localities during the past autumn, and it will be well to place the fact on record in the pages of 'The Zoologist' for future reference. On Oct. 8th, Mr. Swailes, an observant nurseryman, at Beverley, hearing the note of a small warbler which was unfamiliar to him, shot the bird, and sent it for identification to Mr. F. Boyes, who pronounced it to be *Phylloscopus supercilosus*, and on communicating this information, Mr. Swailes found and shot two others in the same locality. Mr. Boyes having reported this interesting occurrence in 'The Field' of Oct. 27th, Mr. J. H. Gurney, in the succeeding issue (Nov. 3rd), announced that on Oct. 1st one of these little birds was shot on the coast of Norfolk by a labouring man, who fired at it merely for the purpose of unloading his gun! As ten instances of the occurrence of this species in the British Islands have now been made known, its claim to be regarded as a British bird, which for a quarter of a century remained doubtful, may now be said to be established. In appearance it might be mistaken for a Goldcrest, *Regulus cristatus*, but, as observed by Mr. Caton Haigh (Zool. 1892, p. 413), may be detected by "its quick and even flight and brighter colour." Moreover, there is a double bar of pale yellow across the wing-coverts and a white superciliary streak, which suggests the specific name. Its true home is apparently in Siberia, where Mr. Seebohm found it breeding, in the forest between the Yenesei and the Koorayika. The nest, a semi-domed one, was on the ground in a tuft of grass, composed of dry grass and moss, lined with reindeer-hair, the eggs resembling those of the Willow Warbler, *Phylloscopus trochilus*.'

H. N. Pashley, the noted Cley naturalist and taxidermist, writes in *Notes on the Birds of Cley Norfolk* 1925: 36:

'1894 Oct 1st – The first Yellow-browed Warbler for Norfolk was taken on this date. The bird was shot with a 10-bore gun and very large shot. Its head was nearly severed and the rump and intestines almost entirely shot away, so the sex could not be determined. I have known several good and rare birds shot in the same way as this. The man who shot it fired off his battered old muzzle loader at the first bird he saw rather than take it home loaded. It was such a weapon as few people would care to fire off. This bird is in Mr. Connop's Museum.'

Interestingly he notes on page 109 of the same publication:

'The first taken here was the fourth for the British Isles, a male, on October 1st, 1894...'

Hume's Leaf Warbler
Phylloscopus humei

The first was found by Richard Richardson frequenting a small wood by Snipe's Marsh at Cley on 3rd December 1967 which remained until 7th January 1968. It was initially identified as a Yellow-browed Warbler. Fortunately its call was recorded by Enid Stanford. These recordings were held by Andy Stoddart in 1996, who arranged for sonograms to be made from them when the British Birds Rarities Committee was investigating claims of *humei*. In 1998, following advances in warbler identification, especially the importance of vocalisation, the record was reviewed and recognised as the second British record of a Hume's Leaf Warbler, known at the time as Hume's Yellow-browed Warbler.

Dave Holman writes from his notes and recollections of that period, and combining information very helpfully provided by John Marchant, Robert Hudson and Giles Dunmore:

'Back in the autumn of 1967 most of my contemporaries and I had only recently become familiar with Yellow-browed Warbler. I had only seen my first in October and November of 1967 so a slightly different individual found at Cley in December of the same year by the late Richard Richardson didn't ring too many alarm bells for me at least. My brief notes only drew attention to the call a whistled "Seeeoo" compared to the coal tit like "Wheesp" of a Yellow-browed Warbler at Holkham a month earlier. I also noted less bright upperparts with slightly less prominent supercilium but that was about the extent of my rather woeful notes. When *humei* was recognised as a full species, not just a race of *inornatus* in 1997 this individual assumed greater importance. Fortunately the late Enid Stanford had made sound recordings from which sonograms were produced. Meagre notes from G. Dunmore and me were submitted to the BBRC but without any doubt it was Enid's sound recordings that allowed the record to be accepted and published in 1998, over thirty years after the original sighting, as the first for Norfolk and only the second for the UK.'

As stated by Dave, the importance of the sound recordings made by Enid Stanford at the time of this occurrence cannot be over-stressed. Without those recordings this record would *not* have gained acceptance!

Radde's Warbler
Phylloscopus schwarzi

The second British record was found by Barry R. Spence and Ray Harris on Blakeney Point on 3rd October 1961.

Barry Spence relates that he regularly travelled from his home in Leicestershire to ring birds in Norfolk with Richard A. Richardson.

On the date in question he walked to Blakeney Point from Cley to meet up with R.A.R., who had travelled to Morston on his motorbike and then crossed over to the Point by boat. During a trapping session they caught an Icterine Warbler and a few other migrants. While walking back off the Point with Ray Harris they flushed a bird at the Hood. It flew off high heading a long way inland over the estuary before turning back and landing in cover at the Hood. B.R.S. then trapped the bird but didn't know what it was. They took it back to Cley and contacted R.A.R. who kept it overnight in his outdoor aviary, later making contact with H. G.

Alexander and Kenneth Williamson.

The bird was identified next morning as the first Radde's Bush Warbler for Norfolk and only the second for Britain. It was ringed and taken back to the Point for release. Both H. G. Alexander and his brother W. B. Alexander were present to see it released, along with other dignitaries.

Richard Richardson writes in the *Norfolk Bird Report* 1961: 390:

> '*October:* The 3rd was probably our most exciting day of the year; it most certainly produced the rarest bird, for shortly after ringing an icterine warbler among the tree-lupins on Blakeney Point a strange, large, dark olive leaf warbler was mist-netted in the *Suaeda* bushes at The Hood which proved to be a first winter male Radde's bush warbler.'

Richard Richardson, Barry Spence, H. G. Alexander and Kenneth Williamson write:

> 'On the evening of 3rd October 1961, while working through the *Suaeda* bushes at The Hood, Blakeney Point, Norfolk, B.R.S. and R. Harris discovered a large, dark olive warbler, about the size of an Icterine (*Hippolais icterina*). The bird was easily captured in a mist-net and proved to be quite unfamiliar. The failing light made an accurate appraisal impossible and so it was decided to take it back to Cley where, after being weighed, it was put to roost in a dark box. The following morning it was minutely examined by R.A.R., B.R.S., H.G.A. and P. R. Clarke and found to be a first-winter male Radde's Bush Warbler *Phylloscopus schwarzi*). This identification was later confirmed by K.W.
>
> We were particularly struck by the length of the claws and they had a clinging quality which reminded us of a young Swallow (*Hirundo rustica*) in the hand. To enable as many interested people as possible to see the bird, it was released in R.A.R's planted garden aviary till the afternoon. It was then ringed, returned to Blakeney Point and watched among tree-lupins in the sand dunes. It was last seen there at dusk on the following day, 5th October.
>
> In the field it appeared a large, dark, oily-olive leaf warbler with rather short rounded wings, a longish tail, a dark crown and a heavy blackish line through the eye contrasting markedly with a very conspicuous, long, narrow supercilium off buffish-white which tapered to the nape. This and the short, stout bill gave the head a bold and almost shrike-like appearance. The under-parts showed as pale yellowish, clouded on the breast and flanks with olive, and the vent was a quite distinctive shade of warm buff. The straw-yellow legs looked fairly long. When feeding, it adopted a rather *Sylvia*-like posture, keeping low in the bushes or marram grass and frequently hopping on the sand; it persistently flicked its wings and dipped its tail in typical *Phylloscopus* manner. In the aviary it took earwigs offered in a china dish and minute flies which it caught in flight or picked off the wire netting, from the perches and from a plate-glass window, but it ignored mealworms and elderberries. It drank freely from an earthenware flower-pot saucer and bathed once. The only note heard at any time was a single or double chat-like *chik* of alarm.
>
> There is only one previous British record of this central and east Siberian species and that was a bird killed at North Coates, Lincolnshire, on 1st October 1989.'

(Originally published in *British Birds* 55: 166-168, which included a summary of the detailed description)

Dusky Warbler
Phylloscopus fuscatus
One was discovered by Moss Taylor and Michael Bowtell, and identified later by Enid Allsopp and Howard Medhurst, at Holkham Meals on 26th October 1968.

Moss Taylor writes from his notes and recollections:

'Living and working in Essex at the time, I spent as many weekends as possible birding in north Norfolk, often with my friend from school days, Mike Bowtell. On Saturday 26th October 1968 we drove up to Cley, where after a morning seawatching, we moved on to the woods at Wells and Holkham, drawn by the report of a Radde's Warbler there the previous weekend. In fact conditions were ideal for new arrivals with an overcast sky and an easterly wind. This was confirmed as we walked through the pines from Wells car park, with hundreds of Blackbirds grounded in the woods and frequent parties of Fieldfares and Redwings arriving from the north.

Between the dell and the pool, our attention was attracted by a persistent and harsh call, being repeated at frequent intervals from some dense undergrowth below the silver birches. Notes taken at the time described it as a loud 'tchet', not unlike a subdued call of a Stonechat, or the churr of a Wren when it was repeated in quick succession. We were able to watch the bird, in reasonable light, down to about ten yards and I wrote the following description on returning home after the weekend, from field notes that I made at the time: "General size, shape and behaviour as other *phylloscopi*. Probably appearing a little longer than a Willow Warbler due to a rather longer, graduated tail, which it flicked nervously on calling. General impression was of a uniform grey-brown bird with no trace of yellow or green in the plumage. Upperparts uniform earthy brown with no suggestion at all of a wing bar. Tail coloured as back and wings. Head displayed a fairly prominent, pale buff supercilium, below a darker brown crown. Distinct black line passing from bill, through the eye and extending almost to nape, where it became rather wider. Throat paler than rest of underparts, which were fairly dark brown but paler than the upperparts. Bill fine and horn coloured. Legs dark brown with a suggestion of dark orange around the feet."

As far as we were concerned, we were looking at the Radde's Warbler that had been found the previous weekend and we left the bird where we had found it, feeling very pleased with ourselves having added a new species to our life list. As we were walking back to the car, we met Keith and Enid Allsopp, and Howard Medhurst and told them about the bird, who apparently relocated it with little difficulty in view of its persistent call.

In those days, the standard field guide was Peterson's Birds of Britain and Europe, but the then current edition simply included the two species under Accidentals at the back of the book, giving a very short description of each and certainly no pictures. I can well remember going through the descriptions in Peterson with Mike, and we both expressed some surprise that our bird showed more of the features of Dusky rather than a Radde's Warbler. However, at that time it was virtually unknown for both species to be seen in the same autumn, let alone at the same location within a few days of each other.

It was only later that I learnt that our 'Radde's Warbler' had been re-identified as a Dusky Warbler, by amongst others Ron Johns. It was also joined by a second Dusky Warbler the following weekend! Having seen a number Dusky Warblers since then, I realise how lucky we were to have such good, close views of a normally very skulking species. On reflection, the total lack of any yellow in the plumage, the fine horn coloured bill, dark brown legs and call note were actually all characteristic of Dusky rather than Radde's Warbler, but at the time we were unaware of this.'

Western Bonelli's Warbler
Phylloscopus bonelli
Peter Clarke discovered one at Holme on 7th August 1970, which remained until the 13th.

Peter Clarke writes in the Norfolk Ornithologists Association's Holme Bird Observatory Log:

'A leaf warbler with whitish underparts was seen fleetingly on the 7th August in the Corsican pines at Holme Bird Observatory. Next day, better and longer views were had of the bird and despite the apparent lack of any rump patch it seemed reasonably certain that the bird was a Bonelli's Warbler.

When coming out into the open (which it did not do very often) the bird was extremely active and never still for a moment while feeding at varying heights from the roof of the Heligoland trap down to ground level, where it hopped about amongst the sea buckthorn scrub.

The white underparts were striking with a greyish suffusion on the sides of the upper breast. Prominent feature of the upperparts was the apple green patch on the closed wing. Mantle greyish, olive brown. Poorly defined eye-stripe. Legs dark. Although brief views were had of the bird's rump, no light patch could be seen at 30 yards.

The bird did not call in the first 4 days of its stay. A single, plaintive, rising call-note was heard frequently on the last 3 days.

Also present were Mr. O. Laugharne, Mr. R. A. Richardson, Keith and Enid Allsop and others.'

Western/Eastern Bonelli's Warbler
Phylloscopus bonelli/orientalis
When the two races of Bonelli's Warbler were split into separate species Western Bonelli's Warbler *P. bonelli* and Eastern Bonelli's Warbler *P. orientalis* in 1997, four earlier county records could not be specifically assigned and remain Bonelli's Warbler sp. The first was found at Holkham by Ian (D.I.M.) Wallace on 22nd August 1971, the second at Holkham by K. V. Pritchard and C. Mason on 5th-14th September 1976, the third at Wells by Giles Dunmore on 12th/13th September 1982 and the fourth at Blakeney Point by Giles Dunmore, Pete Feakes and Norman Williams on 14th May 1988. Should any of these four be specifically assigned in the future, which seems unlikely, it could become the first Eastern Bonelli's Warbler for Norfolk.

Wood Warbler

Phylloscopus sibilatrix

Known as the "Wood Wren" to Sheppard and Whitear (1826) and though listed it was not commented on by them. The Pagets (1834) do not mention it at all, and Lubbock in *Observations of the Fauna of Norfolk* (1845) new edition by Southwell (1879) mentions it in passing, linking it equally with Willow Warbler as '…not uncommon', and considered the Chiffchaff the rarest of the three species. This is questioned by Thomas Southwell in a footnote who considered Wood Warbler '…much the rarest of the three'.

Common Chiffchaff

Phylloscopus collybita collybita

The earliest dated reference we can find is in 'Extracts from the Calendar of the Rev. William Whitear 1809-1826' published in the *Transactions of the Norfolk and Norwich Naturalists' Society* 1881-1882: 241 where he recorded one on 27h March 1815 in the Starston area.

Known as the Lesser Pettychaps it is just listed by Sheppard and Whitear in *A Catalogue of the Norfolk and Suffolk Birds, with Remarks* (1826) but not commented on.

The Pagets in *Sketch of the Natural History of Yarmouth and its Neighbourhood* 1834: 5 considered it

'…more or less common'.

Scandinavian Chiffchaff

Phylloscopus collybita abietinus

Birds showing the characteristics of this race from Scandinavia, north-eastern Europe and western Russia have been recorded in the county almost annually since 1964. The first, in 1964, was just recorded in the *Norfolk Bird Report* 1964: 203 as:

'North: Cley, a bird of the Scandinavian race *abietinus* at Walsey Hills, Jan. 18th- March 1st (grey and white type).'

Siberian Chiffchaff

Phylloscopus collybita tristis

Birds showing the characteristics of this race from Siberia have been recorded in the county almost annually since 1966. However, due to their accurate identification being fraught with difficulty few, if any, can really be considered to have been fully authenticated prior to at least 1994 (see the very informative article by Andy Stoddart entitled 'Siberian Chiffchaffs in Norfolk' in the *Norfolk Bird Report* 1994: 364 and '*Tristis* Chiffchaffs in Norfolk' in the *Norfolk Bird Club Bulletin* 16: 9-11).

Interestingly, Moss Taylor gives two records of Siberian Chiffchaff in *The Birds of Sheringham* 1987: 52, the first being 26th/27th October 1976. Peter Allard is more circumspect in *The Birds of Great Yarmouth* 1990: 108 where he gives eight records suspected of being of this race, the first on 10th November 1975. Andrew Bloomfield gives up to 21 records of this race in *Birds of the Holkham Area* 1993: 111, the first dated being an incredible 20 on 15th October 1982. Mark Golley in *The Cley Year* (1997) lists the race as occurring and Andy Stoddart and Steve Joyner give six records of this race in *The Birds of Blakeney Point* 2005: 198, the first being on

27th October 1987.

Siberian Chiffchaff was added to the list of races considered by the County Records Committee in 1994, and in that year the first authenticated county occurrences were recorded when one was found in Norwich by J. G. Brown on 28th September which remained until 1st October, and another was trapped, ringed and photographed by D. H. Sadler and Kevin Shepherd at Sheringham on 4th November.

Interestingly, this race was considered in the 1998 review of the Chiffchaff complex but it was decided to leave it within the Common Chiffchaff species for the time being, until more research on this race had been carried out. It seems a good candidate for a future split.

Iberian Chiffchaff
Phylloscopus ibericus
Following a review of the Chiffchaff complex the BBRC announced in 1997 in *British Birds* 90: 70-71 that it recognised four species of Chiffchaff: Common, Iberian, Canary Island and Mountain. With the submission of a claim for an Iberian Chiffchaff at the Brent Reservoirs, Greater London for 1972 the BOURC announced in 1998 in *British Birds* 91: 89 that it followed suit and accepted the four species of Chiffchaff recommended by BBRC. The Greater London record became the first Chiffchaff species other than Common to be accepted in Britain.

The first county record, a singing male, was found by Dave Andrews and Ollie Richings at Colney, very close to Norwich University Hospital on 21st April 2007, and it remained faithful to its two favoured oak trees until 17th May.

Will Soar writes:

'At about 5.45pm on Saturday 21st April 2007, I received a phone call from Dave Andrews, who was birding around the University of East Anglia campus, Colney Norwich, Norfolk, with Ollie Richings, stating that they had found an interesting *Phylloscopus* warbler. From recordings on Dave's mobile phone, they had tentatively identified it as a possible Iberian Chiffchaff *P. ibericus*. I hurried to the spot, of course, and was on site (an area of mixed trees and scrub beside a main road) within ten minutes. The bird was still singing when I arrived, and it sounded just as I expected an Iberian Chiffchaff to sound.

The constantly repeated song phrase consisted of three sections. The first was reminiscent of the "chiff" note of Common Chiffchaff *P. collybita collybita*, but perhaps more like "tiff-tiff-tiff-" and repeated from three to six times. This was followed by two higher pitched notes, rather like "weet-weet", followed by a final section of a rattle of five or more lower notes.

In the fading light of this first evening, most of the subtle plumage and structural differences from Common Chiffchaff were not discernible. Over the next few days, however, we were able to observe the bird extensively, noting all of the key features of Iberian Chiffchaff.

The bird was very similar to Common Chiffchaff in appearance, but its primary projection was noticeably longer, and its tail also appeared slightly longer. The upperparts were brownish-grey, with an olive tinge to the lower mantle, rump and uppertail-coverts. A blackish eye-stripe contrasted strongly with a very obvious pale supercilium, which was pale yellow in front of the eye, merging into buffish-white above and behind the eye. The throat was very pale yellow, becoming brighter yellow around the sides of the breast, especially towards the alula area, where it contrasted with a white belly. There was a faint yellow wash on the rear flanks and around the vent area. The bill was quite long and fine, and mostly pale, being blackish on the distal third of the upper mandible and on rather less of the distal portion of the lower mandible. The legs were paler than is usual in Common Chiffchaff. In some lights, they even appeared to approach the pinkish-brown tone that is normal for Willow Warbler, but this was particularly difficult to see, as the bird moved around in variable light, mostly quite high up in its favoured oak trees.

We listened to the bird sing for about two hours on the first evening, and during this time it sang just like an Iberian Chiffchaff. At some points, however, during our use of playback, it gave some song phrases that vaguely resembled Common Chiffchaff, but with much less change in pitch. We later decided that this was likely to have been due to the bird's excitement at having 'found a rival' (and we later found references to and examples of, this more mixed song that belonged to confirmed Iberian Chiffchaffs).

During these first couple of hours of observation, the bird reacted strongly to our playback of Iberian Chiffchaff song: on each of the several occasions that we started our playback, it flew directly towards us, often landing within a few feet of us calling "piu" and shivering its wings, rather like a Wood Warbler. In contrast, it showed no response at all to our playbacks of Common Chiffchaff song. This reaction, along with song and call details, led us to phone out the news of the bird as 'a possible Iberian Chiffchaff'. The identification was confirmed the next morning, when many visiting birders were able to enjoy good views of the bird still singing almost constantly. Sonograms made from sound recordings that we had taken further confirmed that it was indeed an Iberian Chiffchaff. Over the following days, it remained consistently in the same two oak trees, occasionally flying about 30 yards into some scrub, where it gave very good views.

Many thanks go to Dave Andrew and Ollie Richings for their discovery.'

(Originally published in *Birding World* 20: 154-155)

Willow Warbler
Phylloscopus trochilus trochilus
The earliest dated reference we can find is in 'Extracts from the Calendar of the Rev. William Whitear 1809-1826' published in the *Transactions of the Norfolk and Norwich Naturalists' Society* 1881-1882: 241 where he recorded one on 18th April 1816 in the Starston area.

Known to Sheppard and Whitear in *A Catalogue of the Norfolk and Suffolk Birds, with Remarks* (1826) as the Yellow Wren and Oven Bird where it is listed but not commented on.

The Pagets who also knew it as Yellow Wren in *Sketch of the Natural History of Yarmouth and its Neighbourhood* 1834: 5 considered it '…more or less common'.

Northern Willow Warbler
Phylloscopus trochilus acredula
The earliest dated reference we can find in by H. N. Pashley in *Notes on the Birds of Cley Norfolk* 1925: where he writes:

> '1901 – October…At the end of this month a Northern Willow-Warbler was shot. I sent it to Mr. Howard Saunders for identification and it is now in the Connop collection.'

And on page 109 he adds:

> 'First specimen for Cley was taken end of 1901 (Connop collection). Have received several others since.'

The specimen, a male, is in storage at the City of Birmingham Museum.

Goldcrest
Regulus regulus
The earliest dated reference we can find is by Sir Thomas Browne (1605-1682) in *Notes and Letters on the Natural History of Norfolk* 1902: 29 where he writes:

> 'Great varieties of finches and other small birds whereof one very small called a whine bird marked with fine yellow spots & lesser than a wren.'

Thomas Southwell adds in a footnote:

> 'In his fifth letter to Merrett Browne says, "I confess for such little birds I am much unsatisfied on the names given to many by countrymen and uncertain what to give them myself." This is painfully apparent in the cases of the two birds here referred to as the "Whinne-bird" and the "Chipper." From the description of the former, "marked with fine yellow spots and lesser than a wren," also with a "shining yellow spot on the back of the head," it seems likely that the Gold-crested Wren is intended.'

The "Chipper" is thought to be the Siskin, as will be seen in that account.

Firecrest
Regulus ignicapilla
One was caught in the rigging of a ship five miles off the Norfolk coast in October 1836, and was the first British record.

Henry Stevenson writes in *The Birds of Norfolk* Vol. l. 1866: 138-139, under the heading of Fire-crested Regulus:

> 'I know of but two recorded instances in which examples of this rare species have been actually obtained in this county. The first was the one referred to by Yarrell as "caught on the rigging of a ship five miles off the coast of Norfolk, in the early part of October 1836;" the second was procured at Yarmouth, in

November, 1843. Of the latter Mr. W. R. Fisher remarks, in the "Zoologist," p. 451, "It was taken, I believe, among some gold-crests, which appear annually about that time in considerable numbers. The dark bands on the cheek, and the white line over the eye, are in this bird very conspicuous, but the colour of the crest is much less vivid than in many of the gold-crests, whence I conclude that it was a young male".'

The 1836 bird became the first for Britain, after J. H. Gurney considered an 1832 record in Cambridgeshire to have been misidentified and the report deemed unreliable (Palmer 2000). However, it could be considered as an 'offshore' record. The 1843 occurrence is certainly the first recorded on Norfolk's and Britain's mainland.

The Rev. Richard Lubbock writes in *Observations on the Fauna of Norfolk* (1845) new edition by Southwell 1879: 55:

> 'The Fire-crested Regulus (*Regulus ignicapillus*) is mentioned by Mr. Yarrell as having been taken on the rigging of a vessel off this coast… Mr. Fisher of Yarmouth gave a man a commission to get him all the Gold-crests he could (with a view to obtaining this first species). When about thirty had been brought, a Fire-crested Wren appeared amongst the victims.'

Thomas Southwell adds in a footnote, initially referring to the first record:

> 'This specimen is, I believe in the collection of Mr. John Hancock, of Newcastle. Mr. Fisher's specimen was procured at Yarmouth in November, 1843.'

John Hancock (1808-1890) is considered the father of modern taxidermy and the Hancock Museum at Newcastle-upon-Tyne is named after him and his brother Albany. The museum contains many specimens from their collections, but due to it being closed for three years (from 2006) for refurbishment and extensions, we have been unable to ascertain whether the 1843 specimen is still in existence.

Spotted Flycatcher
Muscicapa striata

The earliest dated reference we can find is by Sir Thomas Browne (1605-1682) in *Notes and Letters on the Natural History of Norfolk* 1902: 73 where he writes in his fourth letter to Merrett in December 1668:

> 'Haue you an Apiaster a small bird called a Beebird'

and in his fifth letter to Merrett dated February 6th 1669 he writes:

> 'That which is knowne by the name of a bee-bird is a little dark gray bird I hope to get one for you.'

Thomas Southwell adds in a footnote:

> 'Probably the Spotted Flycatcher is here referred to, the prefix not being used

in a technical sense; it is known here as the Beam-bird, either of which names may be a corruption of the other. Another Norfolk name for this bird is the Wall-bird.'

Red-breasted Flycatcher

Ficedula parva

A first-winter female was shot by F. M. Ogilvie at Cley on 13th September 1890.

Gurney and Southwell write in the *Transactions of the Norfolk and Norwich Naturalists' Society* 1893-1894: 643:

> 'Yet another rare migrant has to be added to those already recorded from Cley; on the 13th September, 1890, Mr. Ogilvie shot a female Red-breasted Flycatcher there. The plumage resembled that of an immature bird, but Mr. Gunn, from an examination of its ovary, considers it adult.'

F. M. Ogilvie writes in the *Transactions of the Norfolk and Norwich Naturalists' Society* 1893-1894: 197-199:

> 'The fact that this bird is new to the Norfolk list is perhaps sufficient apology for the following short paper. It has seemed best to commence with a description of the specimen and then add such notes as might be of interest to the Norfolk and Norwich Naturalists' Society.
> Red-breasted Flycatcher, female adult. September 13th 1890.'

He goes on with a description, discuses the dissection of the specimen and the stomach contents, and continues:

> 'These notes were taken a few hours after death. Mr. T. E. Gunn, F.L.S., dissected the bird before me, and I am also indebted to him for verifying my description and measurements and for other assistance.
> This Flycatcher I shot on the beach at Cley-next-the-Sea, September 13th, 1890. I flushed it two or three times from "the Scrub" (as the Sea-blite which covers the beach there is called) before I was able to secure it, following it for about five minutes. It uttered no note during this time. Its flight was graceful and buoyant, and always at some height from the ground, differing in this from the other birds I saw in the scrub, chiefly warblers (Willow Wrens, Chiffchaffs, &c.) which flew very low, and were flushed with some difficulty from their hiding places.
> During the week ending September 13th the weather was very fine, with hot sun and light wind, mostly from the west and north-west; on the 13th wind was east at daylight, then north-east, going round to south in the afternoon…
> It is of course, possible that the specimen may be a bird of the second year, as the difference between a second year's bird and one of greater age seems hardly perceptible, but I cannot believe it is a bird of the year. Both at the British Museum and Zoological Society, where I exhibited this specimen, it was held to be undoubtedly adult; and, backed by such strong authority as this, I have less hesitation in putting forward my own view so confidently.'

Interestingly, Thomas Southwell comments in the same volume of *Transactions of the Norfolk and Norwich Naturalists' Society* page 202:

'I regret that in the "Birds of Norfolk" I referred to this bird as an immature female, it was so reported to me, and on the only brief opportunity I had of seeing the bird I did not examine it with a view to determining its age. Mr. Ogilvie (see page 199) tells me it is certainly in mature plumage; and I take this opportunity of correcting my former statement, the only excuse for which is, that I had to stop the press to enable me to include it at the very last moment; but I ought not to have committed myself to the statement without verification.'

This bird remains on display in the Ogilvie Bird Collection at Ipswich Museum, mounted in Case 29, with one Spotted Flycatcher and five Pied Flycatcher, all shot at Cley by Ogilvie in the Septembers of 1890 and 1891. "The whole case is intended to represent a portion of the 'scrab'-covered beach at Blakeney; the 'scrab' consists of the sea-blite (*Suaeda fruiticosa*), and in this covert all the birds were flushed and shot. All the materials in the case were brought from the spot, and the scene represents very well the general appearance of the beach. – F.M.O." (Christopher Frost's *The Ogilvie Bird Collection* 1989: 48).

Collared Flycatcher
Ficedula albicollis
A male was found by Jack Reynolds and trapped and ringed by Peter Clarke at Holme on 4th May 1969. It remained until the 6th.

Peter Clarke writes in the Norfolk Ornithologists Association's Holme Bird Observatory Log:

'A Collared Flycatcher at Holme Bird Observatory from the 4th May until the 6th May 1969 was first seen by Mr. J. Reynolds at 8am.
Its main habitat was a small dune area of sparsely planted sea buckthorn bushes beside one of the heligoland traps.
It would usually perch on the smaller bushes 2 to 3 ft high, making frequent sallies to the ground after insects. On several occasions flights took place with a female Redstart and a cock Pied Flycatcher which arrived on the 6th.
In the field it was a strikingly black and white flycatcher, with jet black crown and white underparts. There was a broad white collar from the throat round the nape where it was broadest. The white patches on the forehead and wings were much more extensive than in a cock Pied Flycatcher. The mantle was blackish and the primaries brownish. A greyish white band across the rump was palest in the centre. Tail, legs and bill black.
The bird was mist-netted quite easily at 6.50pm and released after a few minutes. In the hand, only the right hand outer tail feather showed about half an inch of whitish on the outer web. The two outer tail feathers were brown, the rest black. Primary coverts were brown, edged with paler brown. The inner secondaries inner webs were black.
During its 3 day stay the bird was seen by scores of people and many photographs were taken in the field. A daily 12 hour watch was kept in order to control visitors. On the 6th May the bird spent much more time in the tops of the highest pine trees. It could not be found on the 7th after a couple of birdwatchers had

without any authority, been through all the trees and bushes at dawn.'

Eurasian Pied Flycatcher
Ficedula hypoleuca
The earliest reference we can find is by Sheppard and Whitear in *A Catalogue of the Norfolk and Suffolk Birds, with Remarks* 1826: 14-15 where they write:

> 'We have seen a specimen of this bird, which was killed near Cromer. Two others were caught by Mr. Downes in his garden at Gunton in Suffolk; and a fourth was shot at Keswick near Norwich.'

The Pagets (1834) considered it '…occasionally, but rarely met with.'

Bearded Reedling (Tit)
Panurus biarmicus
The earliest dated reference we can find is by Thomas Southwell in a footnote in Sir Thomas Browne's (1605-1682) *Notes and Letters on the Natural History of Norfolk* 1902: 26-27:

> '… it is singular that he [Sir Thomas Browne] omits all mention of another bird, and that an essentially Norfolk species which would have been new to the *Pinax* – the Bearded Titmouse, afterwards known to Edwards as the Lesser Butcher Bird. Browne certainly sent a drawing of this bird to Ray, who in his "Collection of English words not generally used" (1647), as pointed out by Mr. Gurney, mentions it as "little Bird of tawny colour on the back, and a blew head, yellow bill, black legs, shot in an Osier yard, called by Sr. Tho. for distinction sake silerella," the drawing of which he acknowledges he had received. Pennant, 1768 ("Brit. Zool.," i. p. 165), follows Edwards ("Nat. Hist. of Birds,") &c., 1745), who classes it with the Laniidae, and it was finally established as the only representative of a new genus under the name of *Panurus biarmicus*. The local name is Reed Pheasant, but Browne's name of Silerella seems an exceedingly appropriate one.'

Northern Long-tailed Bushtit (Tit)
Aegithalos caudatus caudatus
The first confirmed record was one identified by Keith Herber at Brancaster Thompson Farms on 1st November 2003. The *Norfolk Bird Report* 2003 incorrectly gives this record as 19th November.

Keith Herber writes from his notes and recollections of the occasion:

> 'The North Norfolk Farmland Study and Ringing Group have collated data on birds for the Thompson Brancaster Farm management group for nearly 10 years, the information being derived from our ringing/re-trap database, observations made during ringing or field visits or whilst travelling through the area, supplemented by data from various BTO and Norfolk Bird Atlas surveys. The data in the form of quarterly and annual reports is used by farm management, through their Consultants to support in the first case their application for High Level Stewardship and secondly helps with its ongoing monitoring, leading to "farming with conservation in mind" as the ultimate target.

We consider the above a worthwhile application of our ringing, bird watching and conservation skills and gives purpose to our aims in both ringing and ornithological terms and is one of the reasons we go to Sussex Farm Wood on a regular basis throughout the year (weather permitting of course).

Most ringing sessions take place on a Saturday, to enable those who work during the week to get out and join us, particularly our trainee ringers.

Although a Yellow-browed Warbler had been trapped and ringed at the end of September, October had been a disappointing month for movement through the site, which can be described generally as an area of extensive high bramble, elderberry and some raspberry interspersed by a mixture of sycamore, oaks and elms planted by the landowner some years previously. The area is referred to as the "plantation" and may have been the kitchen garden for a nearby (now derelict) property prior to the re-planting. Birdwise, during the month we had recorded a trickle of Goldcrests through the site, while small numbers of Redwing were usually found early morning, one or two Bramblings were also about and a few lingering Blackcaps trapped and ringed, so nothing really to set the pulses racing, but then it is one our study sites on the farm complex and even the common species are important. It is also worth mentioning that numbers of Long-tailed Tits on the site had been at a low ebb, with generally only one or two resident birds recorded on most visits during October, all of which were ringed birds, although two new (un-ringed) birds were located on 28th October, a prelude of things to come??

Our usual practice on a Saturday is to have the nets open before first light, but during the second half of October catches were low so 1st November saw a change in strategy with a lunchtime start, prompted by the possibility of roosting Redwings using the site.

Two trainee ringers and I opened the nets at around 1.00-1.15 pm, and we were immediately hit by a mixed tit/crest flock (40-50+ birds) amongst which were 25 Long-tailed Tits, 14 Goldcrests and three Treecreepers so my trainees got plenty of practice in honing their extraction skills. With all the birds safely in bird bags we retired to the ringing table a short distance from the "plantation" where we began to process the birds. Processing generally involves identifying the species, ringing the bird, determining its age and sex and taking various biometrics before release. As a trainer my role was to oversee the processing operations to ensure each bird is properly and safely handled and that the data collected is accurate and properly recorded, giving advice when needed.

Part way through processing, Barry Sutherns, one of the trainees, gave me the wing length for a Long-tailed Tit he was dealing with, and called out "wing length 65mm". I immediately said "no way, recheck the wing length please", which he did and came up with the same measurement. At that time I was also acting as scribe, entering up the data onto our field sheets, on looking up I saw that the bird he was holding had what I could only describe as a "brilliant" white head, and the penny dropped as I said "you've not ringed it yet have you?" His answer was immediate, "well yes it's ringed". I cannot quite remember the rest of our conversation …… but as soon as he had finished processing the bird (under various threats of what might happen if he let it go) the bird was passed to me for checking and yes it was clearly a Northern Long-tailed Tit *Aegithalos caudatus caudatus*, and on checking the wing length it was 65mm therefore probably a male, our resident birds usually have wing lengths in the range 59 to 63mm. From notes made at the time we recorded that it had an all white head, almost pure white including the nape, white underparts with no flecking or pink on breast, outer webs of secondaries notably white, we also recorded that it had no obvious white on its tertials which we thought at the time would possibly rule out subspecies *sebiricus*. Unfortunately none of us had brought cameras or had mobile phones with camera facilities.

As mentioned earlier few Long-tailed Tits and Goldcrests were recorded in the weeks preceeding this find, so we concluded this bird was a very recent arrival possibly along with the Goldcrests. It may also be of interest that some of the Long-tailed Tits and Goldcrests ringed on 1st November were re-trapped over the following weeks, but not our "white-headed" friend. In fact several birds from the flock were still present (based on re-trap data) into February 2004, but were not re-trapped subsequently.

Interestingly, my wife and I were birding in Suffolk towards the end of January 2004, where we met up with Adam Rowlands (Site Agent RSPB Minsmere) to look for the reported Northern Long-tailed Tits on Westleton Heath, and were rewarded with fairly good views, which certainly supported the earlier identification of our lone Sussex Farm bird.

Following on from the Northern Long-tailed Tit, we trapped and ringed two Northern Bullfinches on 11th November at the same site.'

Some, at least, out of a party of ten, thought to be of this race, were seen by Billy Bishop at Cley on 2nd October 1961.

Billy Bishop writes in *Cley Marsh and its Birds* 1983: 124:

> 'I once saw a party with white heads in the reeds on Cley Reserve, thought to be of the northern race, in October 1961.'

In addition, two were seen at Blakeney on 21st-22nd October and 9th-10th November the same year. 11-13 were at Blakeney on 8th December 1966, three at Winterton on 20th April 1975, 2 at Fritton on 24th March 1978, one at Hopton on 10th November 1980 and one at Trimingham on 7th September 2003.

However, although all showed characteristics of this race and were recorded as such in the relevant *Norfolk Bird Report*, none was fully authenticated.

Long-tailed Bushtit (Tit)
Aegithalos caudatus rosaceus
The earliest reference we can find is by Sheppard and Whitear in *A Catalogue of the Norfolk and Suffolk Birds, with Remarks* 1826: 23-24 where they write:

> 'In this part of the kingdom the Long-tailed Titmouse is known by the name of Pudding-poke, without doubt from the circumstance of its building its nest in the form of that household article. We have more than once this spring observed an old bird of this species sitting in its nest, with its head partly out of the hole in the side of the nest, and its tail turned over its head, and projecting about an inch and a half.'

Blue Tit (Continental)

Cyanistes caeruleus caeruleus
B. B. Riviere writes in *A History of the Birds of Norfolk* 1930: 43-44:

'That the Blue Tit was a migrant to Norfolk has long been suspected, its frequent appearance upon the coastline in autumn and the fact that it has occurred both in spring and autumn at Norfolk light-stations – Cockle Light-vessel, 14th March 1883,… also Lynn Well Light-vessel, 20th September 1925 and 1st October 1926… being strongly suggestive of an immigration from the Continent. The only specimen of the Continental Blue Tit which has so far been identified in England, however, is one which I recorded as belonging to this race (Brit. Birds, vol. xix., p. 240), which was obtained at Cley in October 1921.'

The note in *British Birds* reads:

'The arrival of Blue Tits upon our east coast from the Continent in autumn has long been suspected, and in Norfolk their frequent appearance upon the coast-line at this time of year – one actually flew on board the Lynn Wells Light Vesssel on September 20th this year – and their occasional presence amongst westerly moving flocks of other autumn migrants, has certainly suggested an immigration from overseas. I am now able to record a specimen of the Conti-nental form of Blue Tit (*Parus c. caeruleus*), the first for England – though one has occurred in Scotland – which was killed at Cley in October 1921. This bird, which is a female, has a wing measurement of 64 mm., which is the minimum for the Continental race, but its colouring, when compared with the large series in Mr. Witherby's collection, differs from all British Blue Tits, and exactly resembles *Parus c. caeruleus*.'

(Originally published in *British Birds* 19: 240-241)

Blue Tit

Cyanistes caeruleus obscurus
The earliest dated reference we can find is by Robert Marsham (1708-1797) in a notation written in the margin of the Coal Tit account in his personal copy of either Willughby & Ray's *The Ornithology* (1768) or Gilbert White's *The Natural History of Selborne* (1789) published in Tim Sparks and John Lines's *Chapters in the Life of Robert Marsham Esq. F.R.S. of Stratton Strawless, Norfolk* 2008: 16 where he writes:

'N.B. There is a Titmouse with a blew head like this.'

Sheppard and Whitear, also knew it as Betty Tit and Jenny Tit in *A Catalogue of the Norfolk and Suffolk Birds, with Remarks* 1826: 23 where they write:

'In winter the Blue Titmouse frequents the sheds in which turnips are kept, for the sake of feeding on the maggots which are frequently found in that root, and many of which are exposed when the tops of the turnips are cut off previous to their being given to the cattle.'

Great Tit (Continental)

Parus major major

B. B. Riviere writes in *A History of the Birds of Norfolk* 1930: 43:

'Long before the difference between the Continental and British forms of this species were recognised, the Great Tit was known to be a migrant to Norfolk. Gurney and Fisher having, as early as 1848, recorded what appeared to be a return migratory movement at Yarmouth in February..., whilst the British Association Reports contain records of specimens taken at the Cockle Light-ship on 24th March 1883..., and at Happisburgh Lightship on 7th November 1887...

Norfolk examples of the Continental race were first identified by Dr. C. B. Ticehurst in 1910, when an unusually large immigration of Great Tits occurred on the Norfolk and Suffolk coasts in October and the first week of November..., a flock of twenty being seen actually arriving from the sea on Yarmouth Denes on 1st November..., whilst they were reported from several of the Norfolk light-stations in October.'

C. B. Ticehurst writes:

'During the middle of October both Blue and Great Tits were, I am informed, unusually plentiful in the gardens around Yarmouth, and on November 1st, a flock of about twenty Great Tits was seen by Mr. Quinton, a bird-catcher, arriving over the sea from the N.E. on to the Yarmouth North Denes. On the next two days, he caught several there, and I received four from him.

On examining all these Great Tits, I find they belong to the continental form *Parus major major*. The occurrence of this sub-species in Britain has long been suspected and doubtless birds seen in the Shetlands (*Ann. Scot. Nat. Hist.,*1907, p. 50) and in Caithness (*t.c.*. 1904, p. 188) belonged to this form, but, so far as I am aware, this is the first time that it has been positively proved to have occurred in the British Isles.'

(Originally published in *British Birds* 9: 247)

Great Tit

Parus major newtoni

The earliest reference we can find is by Sheppard and Whitear in *A Catalogue of the Norfolk and Suffolk Birds, with Remarks* 1826: 23 where they write:

'This species has an astonishing variety of notes. When disturbed on its nest it will make a hissing noise, and boom with its wings like a Blue Titmouse. We have seen such a number of the Great Titmouse in a large plantation of evergreens at Campsey Ash, that the place resounded with the noise of their beaks rapping against the bark of the yew-trees. The large hind toe and crooked claw of this kind, and of others of the genus, are doubtless of service in enabling these birds to hang in a variety of attitudes while searching for their food.'

Coal Tit (Continental)
Periparus ater ater
One was killed at Northrepps on 15th January 1866.

Henry Stevenson writes in the *Transactions of the Norfolk and Norwich Naturalists' Society* 1872-1873: 116.

> 'That the Continental Coal Tit occurs in this country was ascertained by the authors, through examination of two Norfolk killed specimens, in the collection of Mr. J. H. Gurney, jun., one procured at Northrepps in January, 1866, and the other at Lakenham, near Norwich, in the spring of the same year. This discovery adds a new species to the Norfolk list.'

B. B. Riviere gives the date of the Northrepps bird as January 15th in *A History of the Birds of Norfolk* 1930: 44.

Coal Tit
Periparus ater britannicus
Although listed by Sheppard and Whitear (1826) under Colemouse it is not commented on. The earliest reference we can find is by the Pagets in *Sketch of the Natural History of Yarmouth and its Neighbourhood* 1834: 5 where under the name of Cole Titmouse they considered it '…common.'

Willow Tit
Poecile montana kleinschmidti
Because of the similarity between Marsh and Willow Tits it was not realised until 1897 that the Willow Tit existed as a separate species in Britain. The first Norfolk record, however, was one killed at Loddon in January 1893 which was identified retrospectively.

S. H. Long and B. B. Riviere writing in the *Transactions of the Norfolk and Norwich Naturalists' Society* 1913-1914: 788, state:

> 'A specimen of the British Willow Titmouse was obtained by Capt. A. E.Hamerton at Loddon in January 1893…'

Interestingly C. B. Ticehurst writes:

> 'On August 9th, 1912, I obtained a specimen of the Willow-Tit (*Parus. a. kleinschmidti*) in an alder car on the Norfolk side of the Waveney near Beccles. This is, I believe, the first recorded occurrence of what is probably an overlooked bird in Norfolk.'

This is followed by the following in square brackets by H. F. Witherby:

> '[I have in my collection a female Willow-Tit obtained at Loddon, Norfolk, in January, 1893, by my friend Capt. A. E. Hamerton, who gave it to me about two years ago, but I have omitted to record it.]'

(Originally published in *British Birds* 6: 218-219)

Willow Tit (Continental)
Poecile montana borealis
The British Willow Tit *P. m. kleinschmidti* is highly sedentary and although there was no evidence that Willow Tits were involved in the irruptions from the Continent in 1957 and 1959, two birds showing the characteristics of the northern race *P. m. borealis* have been recorded in Norfolk. One was at Sandringham on 23rd November 1980 and another at East Ruston on 21st November 1996; while a palish individual was present in Yarmouth cemeteries on 26th October 1960, a site at which the species has been recorded on only one other occasion (Taylor *et al* 1999).

Marsh Tit
Poecile palustris
Just listed by Sheppard and Whitear in *A Catalogue of the Norfolk and Suffolk Birds, with Remarks* (1826) but not commented on, the earliest reference we can find is by the Pagets in *Sketch of the Natural History of Yarmouth and its Neighbourhood* 1834: 5 where they considered it

'…common about Belton, Filby, and other marshes.'

Red-breasted Nuthatch
Sitta canadensis
The first for Britain and Ireland was discovered by Jean and Roy Aley at Holkham Meals on 13th October 1989.

Jean and Roy Aley, who were on their last full day of a visit to North Norfolk from Orpington with friends from Orpington Field Club, write:

'At 13.30 GMT on 13th October 1989, at Holkham Meals, Norfolk, we were watching a group of tits *Parus* and Goldcrests *Regulus regulus* when we noticed an unusual nuthatch *Sitta* feeding on a grassy footpath some 6m ahead of us. We watched it for several seconds before it flew into an adjacent pine for a moment, and then away through the trees.

The bird was the shape of a European Nuthatch *Sitta europaea*, with a short tail and fine bill, but was clearly smaller: at the time we estimated it to be 4.5 inches (11 cm) long. The upperparts, excluding the head, were blue-grey and all the underparts pinky-buff. The head showed a black eyestripe with a clear white supercilium and black crown. The shape and plumage were clearly those of a nuthatch, but *europaea* was ruled out by size and head pattern. We had no means of identifying the bird at the time, although, subsequently, we looked at a European field guide and had to consider Corsican Nuthatch *S. whiteheadi*; our bird, however was pinker below, and did not seem to fit in other respects, either.

We looked for it again, with a local birder, but could not relocate it; we soon found out, of course, that it was identified the next day as a Red-breasted Nuthatch *S. canadensis*. It stayed until at least 6th May 1990.'

(Originally published in *British Birds* 88: 150)

An account was published in the *Norfolk Bird Report* 1989: 412-413, as follows:

'A small Nuthatch tentatively identified as a Corsican and showing a black crown and white supercilium was reported by Mr. and Mrs. R. Aley from the west end of Holkham Meals on the evening of 13th October 1989. It was feeding on a grassy path 20 feet ahead of the highly surprised observers. It quickly flew into an adjacent pine and then away through the trees.

At 8 am the following morning only a handful of birders was present and nobody had encountered the bird; in fact some were already leaving! After an hour a strange call was heard from the tops of pines at the so-called 'crossroads' near the Royal Summer-House. It was a fairly quiet nasal trumpet-like call noted as 'neh, neh, neh, neh'. Paul Varney commented to the four people present that Red-breasted Nuthatch (which has a similar head pattern to Corsican) is described in the *National Geographic Society Field Guide* as having a call 'like a toy tin horn'. This fitted the call fairly accurately. The bird was not seen, however, and the calling ceased. A short while later Peter Hayman heard the call and thought he saw the bird in flight, thus initiating a detailed search through a nearby tit flock. At 09.40 am the observers were near the summer-house when a bird appeared on a pine trunk 20 yards away. It displayed a strikingly white super-cilium with contrasting black eyestripe and complete black crown and nape. Upperparts were typical nuthatch blue-grey and underparts rusty orange-brown. This combination of plumage feathers and the bird's small size confirmed its identity as a Red-breasted Nuthatch, *Sitta canadensis*, a first for Britain and Ireland.

Peter Hayman and Allan Lewis both obtained brief views. Although the bird had been in view for less than a minute all were in agreement concerning identification. Despite intensive searching by others it could not be found in the immediate area of the first sighting. It was then relocated by call ten minutes later about 400 yards away.

The bird continued to be elusive; some observers had a three-hour wait before it showed again. Rob Morris then arrived equipped with a tape of the species calling. When this was played the bird responded immediately, calling back and flying out of the canopy to alight in elder bushes only fifteen feet ahead and giving breathtaking views. It then performed excellently in the vicinity of the main path for a quarter of an hour before returning to the pine tops where it was difficult to see for the remainder of the day. It was feeding, clinging to the under-sides of pine cones and also investigating the main track itself.

The small size of the bird was especially apparent in flight when it was judged to be about the size of a Blue Tit. The pure black crown (with no grey tones), the underpart colour intensity (compared with skins) and the response to tape are suggestive of an adult male.

And so to the bird: a charming highly active little nuthatch displaying very sharp plumage features and an extremely distinctive call. It is very small and very mobile and Holkham Meals is extremely large. Normally it was best searched for around the summer-house and often in association with a tit flock. Once the tits were located ears strained for the usually quiet but distinctive high-pitched call. But catching the call offered no guarantee of seeing the bird: it normally travelled with a sociable band of tits and Goldcrests. On many occasions a group of observers would be enjoying views of the Nuthatch while others were finding Marsh, Coal and Long-tailed Tits, Goldcrests and even Chiffchaffs and a Lesser

Spotted Woodpecker.

Then it was gone! Occasionally the tit flock was located but not a sound from the Nuthatch, yet casually raised binoculars could focus immediately on the elusive prize – before it again vanished.

It seemed a creature of varying habits. Although often roving with the tit flock it occasionally lingered in favoured spots. On fine days it would feed along the sunny edges of the pines steadily moving with the tits, but generally remaining in view for moments. It often behaved like a typical nuthatch moving up and down trunks and along branches of large pines. Pines were generally favoured although in its first days it was found on track-side sycamores and even small elder bushes. Less typically it fed in exposed sprays of pine needles in both large trees and rather small ones, delicately picking at the base of the needles.

Throughout its stay the Nuthatch showed a definite variation in its calls. The most typical was a nasal 'beep, beep' usually uttered in flight or when agitated. Another shorter, fainter, version of this call was often heard when the bird was feeding with the tit flock. From time to time the calls merged into a rapid series of short musical notes rising in pitch towards the end. After the news was announced on Birdline Information Service an estimated 2,000 birders assembled for the grandstand viewing on Sunday 15th October. The quarry initially wandered widely being first located only just short of the far western end of the pines. Most viewing has been in the area of the summer-house (where it has come to drink) and the nearby crossroads, but many have stumbled across it well to the east of Meals House. One fortunate observer saw it as he stepped out of his car in Lady Anne's Drive! Another couple, on 15th October having seen it near the summer-house decided to visit the Dell at the Wells end and stumbled across the bird again there. For the remainder of the year this highly unlikely New World vagrant continued to either delight or frustrate an endless procession of birders.

The Red-breasted Nuthatch is plentiful in the evergreen forests of North America. In most winters part of the population migrates east and south depending on the conifer seed crop. The species has been seen to fly 60 miles offshore in the Gulf of St Lawrence. Numbers of Red-breasted Nuthatches passing through Cape May Bird Observatory this September were exceptionally high with a peak day-count of 120 on 30th September which was ten times higher than recent autumn maxima. The species, given very low trans-Atlantic vagrancy potential, is at least as surprising a find as previous British records of Varied Thrush or Golden-winged Warbler.

If accepted this will be the second record of Red-breasted Nuthatch for the Western Palearctic, the first being of an adult male on the Western Islands (Iceland) on 21st May 1970.

This summary has been compiled from extensive accounts kindly provided by A. I. Bloomfield, D. Hatton, D. Holman and P. Varney. Acknowledgements are also due to P. Colston, A. Desrochers, S. Whitehouse; finders Mr. & Mrs. R. Aley for additional information; and the anonymous observer who provided the Nuthatch with ample drinking water.'

Eurasian Nuthatch
Sitta europaea
The earliest dated reference we can find is by Sir Thomas Browne (1605-1682) in *Notes and*

Letters on the Natural History of Norfolk 1902: 21 where he writes:

> 'Of picus martius or woodspeck many kinds. The green the Red the luecomelanus or neatly marked black & white & the cinerous or dunne calld [coloured] little bird calld a nuthack.'

See a footnote by Thomas Southwell in the Great Spotted Woodpecker account.

Wallcreeper
Trichodroma muraria
The first British record was of one shot at Stratton Strawless on 30th October 1792.

Thomas Southwell writes in Henry Stevenson's *The Birds of Norfolk* Vol. lll. 1890: 380-382:

> 'The record of the occurrence of this species in the county of Norfolk is not a little singular. In the year 1875 Mr. H. P. Marsham, of Rippon Hall, near Norwich, was good enough to place in my hands, as secretary of the Norfolk and Norwich Naturalists' Society, a series of letters written to his great grand-father, Robert Marsham, F.R.S., of Stratton, by Gilbert White, and to this correspondence we owe the knowledge of the fact that on the 30th October, 1792, a wall-creeper was shot at Stratton Strawless, near Mr. Marsham's house. The corresponding letters from Marsham to White were in the possession of the late Professor Bell, and by a mutual exchange the complete series was published both in the "*Trans. of the Norfolk and Norwich Nat. Soc.*" (ii., pp. 133-195) and in Professor Bell's edition of the "*Natural History of Selbourne.*" The first mention of the bird occurs in a letter from Marsham to White, dated October 30, 1792, in which he says,
> "My man has just now shot me a bird, which was flying about my house; i am confident i have never seen its likeness before. But on application to Mr. Willughby, i conclude it is a wall creeper or spider catcher. I find he had not seen it in England".'

Southwell adds a footnote here regarding the previous sentence as follows:

> 'This is quoted from Ray's translation. The actual words are, "They say it is to be found in England; but we have not as yet had the hap to meet with it" (p.143).
> Professor Newton tells me that the author referred to is Merrett, and that in his "Pinax" (1667) the wall creeper is included as a British bird.'

He continues:

> 'White was much interested by the information, and sent him a translation of Scopoli's description of the bird, which induced Marsham to send in return a coloured drawing of two quill-feathers, of which he says,
> "A young lady drew them for me, and they appear to me to be very exact copies and charmingly executed."
> Professor Bell was kind enough to lend this drawing to Professor Newton,

who found it to represent probably the fifth and seventh primaries of the wing of a female or young male of Tichodroma muraria, "leaving no doubt," as to the correctness of the determination of the specimen by Marsham and White." In his reply White remarks,

"You will have the satisfaction of introducing a new bird of which future ornithologists will say – "found at Stratton, in Norfolk, by that painful and accurate Naturalist, Robert Marsham, Esq."

I may be excused for adding the concluding remarks with regard to the coloured sketch sent him, which will be found reproduced on plate v., as they are so characteristic of this estimable man, and were written only five months before his death:

"I am much delighted with the exact copies [of the two quills] sent me in the frank, and so charmingly executed by the fair unknown, whose soft hand has directed her pencil in a most elegant manner, and given the specimens a truly delicate and feathery appearance. Had she condescended to have drawn the whole bird, I should have been doubly gratified! It is natural to young ladies to wish to captivate men; but she will smile to find her present conquest is a very old man."

To which Marsham replies, "I am glad you liked the drawing of the two feathers; I hinted my wish for the whole bird; but she lent a deaf ear: and in that manner, all young Women have treated me (when i ask favours) since i was turned of 40".'

Interestingly, J. H. Gurney jun. adds in the *Zoologist* 1875: 4695:

'With reference to the extremely interesting note in Zoologist (S. S. 4664) as to the occurrence of a British specimen of the "wall-creeper," allow me to add that Stratton Strawless Hall, where the bird was obtained, is situated in Norfolk about seven miles north of Norwich. It was an ancient mansion, which subsequently to 1792 has been entirely rebuilt.'

Eurasian Treecreeper (Northern)
Certhia familiaris familiaris
Birds showing the characteristics of the nominate northern race *C. f. familiaris* have been recorded in the county on four occasions and appeared in the *Norfolk Bird Report* as such. The first was found by F. M. Ellis at Weybourne on 4th November 1978, the second by Bill Boyd at Holme on 2nd November 1987, the third by Andrew Grieve at Hemsby on 1st October 2004 and the fourth by M. Nash at Gramborough Hill, Salthouse on 4th October 2007. None was trapped enabling an in-the-hand detailed examination to take place therefore, none can be considered authenticated. To gain acceptance as a fully authenticated county record, any future individual would need to be bearing a northern European ring or be trapped and critically examined in the hand.

Eurasian Treecreeper
Certhia familiaris britannica
Although listed by Sheppard and Whitear in *A Catalogue of the Norfolk and Suffolk Birds, with Remarks* (1826) as Common Creeper it was not commented on by them. The earliest reference we can find is by the Pagets in *Sketch of the Natural History of Yarmouth and its Neighbourhood*

1834: 7 where they considered it '...rather rare'.

Eurasian Penduline Tit
Remiz pendulinus
A calling male was discovered by Dave Hewitt at Hickling Broad close to Rush Hills Scrape on 4th April 1987.

Steve Gantlett writes:
'A singing Penduline Tit was found at Hickling Broad on 4th April 1987 by one lucky observer, David Hewitt. Thirty or so birders were soon on the scene, but there were no further sightings that day. It was cold and windy – hardly ideal conditions for finding a tiny marsh bird in one of the country's most extensive reed beds.

Early next day conditions had improved, but it was late morning before the prize was relocated at least half a mile from the original site. During that afternoon over a hundred birders were able to enjoy watching Norfolk's first (and Britain's twelfth) Penduline Tit. It remained in the area until at least 10th April, but throughout its stay it remained elusive and many observers went away disappointed.

Hickling Broad is a National Nature Reserve of over 1,300 acres. The very nature of its habitats: extensive reed-marsh, carr and open water, makes access very difficult. Fortunately for bird-watchers the Penduline Tit chose to frequent the south edge of the Broad, where access and viewing along Weaver's Way is by way of a raised bank public footpath. This Penduline Tit was an adult male and was frequently heard calling and performing its brief and subdued twittering song. It was extremely active appearing almost anywhere along the south side of the Broad. It was frequently observed feeding on seed-heads of lesser reedmace, the drifting white downy plumes on the breeze revealing to more than one observer the bird's presence. This enchanting vagrant also spent much time moving around scattered clumps of willows in the marsh, constantly jerking its tail from side to side in characteristic fashion.

It was a tiny bird, about the size and shape of a Blue Tit. The general effect was suggestive of a diminutive and pale male Red-backed Shrike. *Twitching* magazine has provided the following description: 'Head pale grey with a broad black mask widening from the forehead through and behind the dark eye. Bill dark, fine and pointed. Mantle and wing-coverts rich dark chestnut. Wings and tail dark grey extensively edged pale greyish-white especially on tertials. Underparts pale pinkish-buff, whiter on chin and throat. Legs and feet blackish. The call: a high pitched plaintive '*tsee*'.

The first British record was at Spurn in 1966 followed by occurrences in Scilly, Kent (1980 and 1983/4), Gwynedd, Humberside (2 together), Essex and Northants. At first sight it might appear that a Penduline Tit is an unlikely species to occur in Britain. But there is considerable evidence of a northerly and westerly spread within Europe. It is also a bird which wanders in winter and at times (like Bearded Tits) exhibits eruptive behaviour. Despite its tiny size it is capable of travelling considerable distances – up to 500 miles. As an example of rapid range expansion, the first and very characteristic 'cock's nest' was found in Holland in 1962 (the bird itself was never actually seen). Within two decades, observations in that country had become so widespread that the species was removed from Dutch Rarities Reports.'

(An account published in the *Norfolk Bird Report* 1987: 100-101)

Eurasian Golden Oriole
Oriolus oriolus
The earliest dated reference Henry Stevenson could find in either published or manuscript notes is given in *The Birds of Norfolk* Vol. l. 1866: 86-88, as follows:

> 'Mr Hunt, in his "List of Norfolk Birds," says – "I have three specimens killed in different parts of this county; and recently (April 1824), a fine male specimen was shot at Hethersett, which is now in the possession of J. Postle, Esq., of Colney." Of this bird, which is also referred to by the late Mr. Lombe in his MS. notes, the Rev. Edwd. Postle, of Yelverton, kindly sent me the following particulars only a few weeks before his death:-
>
> "It is now in the possession of my sister at Thorpe, and was shot by my father at Hethersett. He only saw the male bird and had the good fortune to secure it by means of a crow keeper's gun. It was reported that the female had been seen with it, and Mr. Lombe for several days had the place watched by his keeper, but it was never reported to him as seen. The male was very tame, as he allowed my father to go some little distance for the weapon which brought him to death".'

Sheppard and Whitear write in *A Catalogue of the Norfolk and Suffolk Birds, with Remarks* 1826: 12:

> 'And we have been informed that a pair of these birds built a nest in the garden of the Rev. Mr. Lucas, of Ormesby in Norfolk.'

Isabelline Shrike
Lanius isabellinus
A first-winter was found by Steve Joyner and Rod Martins frequenting bushes and bramble scrub at Overy Dunes on 12th October 1975, it remained until the 13th.
The implications of this find would only become apparent years later.

Steve Joyner writes from his notes taken at the time:

> 'During October 1975 Holkham Meals had a distinctly Siberian feel. Up to ten Yellow-browed Warblers could be seen flitting through the trees and the rarer Pallas's, Radde's and Dusky Warblers were all found in the birch and sallow scrub on the southern edge of the pines. Small influxes of these charismatic birds are now a regular autumn feature, but in 1975 they were relatively little known eastern vagrants and any encounter with them was a rare and exciting experience. Autumn 1975 was clearly developing into something special, so Norman Williams and I decided we must take every opportunity to visit the coast.
> On the 12th October after a pleasant walk through the trees we reached the extreme western edge of the pine belt at Holkham, where an excited Rodney

Martins informed me that he had just seen an odd shrike. A brief search relocated the bird perched on one of the outermost pine trees, it was immediately obvious we were watching an unfamiliar shrike. Overall it was strikingly pale with grey brown upperparts, pale bordered dark mask behind the eye, and an off-white bar at the base of the primaries. The underparts were greyish white with fine vermiculations across the breast indicating a first-winter bird. However the most distinctive feature was revealed in flight, when the strong contrast between the pale upperparts and bright red tail was striking. These features readily identified the bird as an Isabelline Shrike, showing characteristics of the race *phoenicuroides*.

Although the bird remained in the area for two days it was rather elusive, only occasionally being seen in the Overy Dunes area. At the time this constitiuted the sixth record for Britain.'

At the time of its discovery this bird was the second accepted record for the county, after the first at Walcott in 1961 of what was then known as Red-tailed Shrike, a race of Red-backed Shrike. Following a review of the records of Isabelline Shrike by British Birds Records Committee the Mundesley record was considered no longer acceptable as Isabelline, thus promoting the Overy Dunes bird to the first for Norfolk.

Isabelline (Turkestan) Shrike
Lanius isabellinus phoenicuroides

The first fully authenticated and accepted record of this race for the county was an adult male found in song at Snettisham by David Snelling, Andy Bunting, Neil Lawton and Bill Boyd on 2nd May 1995.

Neil Lawton writes from his notes and recollections of the occasion:

'On the afternoon of 2nd May, after visiting Holme Dunes, David Snelling decided to visit Snettisham Coastal Park, and a few hours later he reappeared at Holme to tell us about an odd bird which he had seen. He described it as a shrike with a prominent bright red tail, a neat black mask and striking white wing flashes when it flew. After looking through various field guides including *Rare Birds* by Alstrom and Colston he tentatively identified it as a male Isabelline Shrike. It was decided that Andy Bunting who was working at Holme at the time should go with him to check it out. After a further hour AB called and told us that the bird was definitely a male Isabelline Shrike. Bill Boyd and I headed off, but even at this point we were both sceptical and I was at best expecting a male Red-backed Shrike or at worst a Redstart. After a rapid car journey and a quick walk we reached DS and AB and immediately saw the bird perched on nearby sea-buckthorn, all doubt now disappeared as we stood watching a singing male Isabelline Shrike of the race *phoenicuroides* commonly known as Turkestan Shrike and the first positively identified bird of this race, although some of the more tricky-to-identify autumn birds may have also involved this race.

It had a reddish-chestnut crown which contrasted with the greyer-brown mantle, a narrow whitish supercilium and a combination of black lores and ear coverts, which produced a well defined black mask that was continuous from the base of the bill and through the eye, resulting in a bold and conspicuous head pattern. White at the base of the primaries produced a white triangle on the wing which was in contrast to the rest of the greyish-brown wings. It had a bright rufous tail, upper tail coverts and lower rump, with a grey upper rump which was paler than the rest of the mantle. Underparts were creamy white with a pinkish flush along the flanks. Bare parts were largely black, with a typically stout shrike bill. The song was scratchy and subdued.

After ruling out Brown Shrike which AB had already done and a description taken, we headed off to find a phone and release the news. The bird showed well up to dark and was seen by around forty observers. Despite much searching next day the bird was not seen again. According to one local dog walker it had been present since the previous day, which coincided with a large influx of summer migrants along the coast.

At the time it was the fifth county record of Isabelline Shrike and the first definitely attributed to the race *phoenicuroides*.'

This bird was the second British record assigned to the race *phoenicuroides* (*British Birds* 100: 92-94).

Red-backed Shrike
Lanius collurio
The earliest dated reference we can find is by Sir Thomas Browne (1605-1682) in *Notes and Letters on the Natural History of Norfolk* 1902: 25-26 where he writes:

'A small bird of prey calld a birdcatcher about the bignesse of a Thrush and linnet coloured with a longish white bill & sharpe of a very fierce & wild nature though kept in a cage & fed with flesh. a kind of Lanius.'

Thomas Southwell adds in a footnote:

'The Red-backed Shrike, *Lanius collurio*, is the only species of Lanius mentioned by Browne'.

Lesser Grey Shrike
Lanius minor
One was obtained at Yarmouth in spring 1869. Originally in the Gurney Collection it was donated by Gerard H. Gurney to the Castle Museum, Norwich (Accession no. NWHCM: 1935.15.93). It remains in the skin collection having been reduced from a mounted specimen.

Murray A. Mathew writes in the *Zoologist* 1870: 2060:

'I have lately received specimens of the lesser grey shrike (*Lanius minor* of Temminck), with a black band on the forehead and rose-tinted under-parts, - the shore lark (apparently young birds of the year), and Temminck's stint, all obtained recently in the neighbourhood of Great Yarmouth.'

Henry Stevenson writes in the *Zoologist* 1870: 2139:

'With reference to the Rev. M. A. Mathew's statement in the last number of the 'Zoologist' (S. S. 2060) that he received an example of Lanius minor, recently obtained in the neighbourhood of Yarmouth, I may add that, from enquiries made on the spot, I feel justified in adding this species to the Norfolk list, through the occurrence of Mr. Mathew's specimen. The bird in question appears to have been shot in the spring of 1869 (the exact date I cannot now ascertain), in a garden at the north end of the town, and was purchased and mounted by Mr. Carter, a local birdstuffer, who subsequently sold it to Mr. Mathew. It is quite evident, however, from the price asked for it, that its specific rarity was unknown until its distinctive markings were recognised by its present owner.'

Great Grey Shrike

Lanius excubitor

The earliest dated reference we can find is in 'Extracts from the Calendar of the Rev. Willian Whitear 1809-1826' published in the *Transactions of the Norfolk and Norwich Naturalists' Society* 1881-1882: 261 where he recorded:

'I saw a Stork at Mr. Harvey's of Yarmouth, killed at the same time as Mr. Hunt's. The same person had a Cinerous Shrike, killed February 1819.'

Sheppard and Whitear write in *A Catalogue of the Norfolk and Suffolk Birds with Remarks* 1826: 13, under Great Cinereous Shrike:

'In the autumn of 1819 four of these birds were sent to Mr. Hunt, which had been killed in Norfolk. Early in December 1819, a Cinereous Shrike frequented a thick thorn hedge, near Mr. Hoy's house at Higham, but was so shy that it could not be approached within gun-shot. On examining the hedge Mr. Hoy found three frogs, and as many mice, spitted on the thorns. He therefore set six very small steel traps, each baited with a mouse. On the following day two of the traps were found sprung, and the baits gone. By watching in concealment Mr. H. soon afterwards observed the Shrike to dart down upon a bait, and rise perpendicularly, but not quick enough to escape, as it was caught by its toes. The bird was carried alive to the house, and placed in a room in which a thorn bush was fixed, and some mice given to it: one of which it was observed through a hole to spit upon a thorn with the greatest quickness and adroitness.'

Woodchat Shrike

Lanius senator senator/rutilana

One shot by James Adams at Bradwell in April 1829, was the first British record.

The Paget's in *Sketch of the Natural History of Yarmouth and its Neighbourhood* 1834: 4 state:

'A specimen, shot at Bradwell, April, 1829, by Mr. Adams, a farmer in that village, and in whose possession it now is.'

Interestingly, Lombe gives May 1829 in his MS notes in Bewick and in Montagu's *Dictionary* (Babington 1884-1886)

No trace of the specimen has been found.

Prior to the 1974 county boundary changes Bradwell was in Suffolk.

The above account does seem a little sketchy to be considered as the first Norfolk occurrence.

Before the 1974 boundary changes the first fully authenticated Woodchat Shrike record for Norfolk, and perhaps the one that should remain so, was a male shot at Yarmouth on 29th April 1859, which is on display at the Castle Museum, Norwich.

Henry Stevenson writes in the *Zoologist* 1859: 6602, dated 15th June 1859:

> 'On the 29th April a male Woodchat was shot at Yarmouth: this bird had very nearly completed its spring moult, but from the appearance of the old feathers still remaining in the tail, had probably but just attained its adult plumage: the chestnut patch on the back of the neck and the tints of back and wings were somewhat lighter than in some older specimens. The Woodchat is a rare visitant to this eastern district, not more than one or two examples having been previously met with.'

He added in the *Zoologist* 1866: 64 that the specimen was '…now in the possession of Mr. J. H. Gurney…'

Woodchat Shrike (Balearic)
Lanius senator badius
A male of this distinctive Balearic race was discovered by Andrew Goodall at Great Cressingham on 2nd July 1995, which stayed until the 6th. It was only the second British record.

> 'On the evening of 2nd July 1995, Andrew Goodall was approaching the crossroads on the Peddars Way footpath at Great Cressingham when he noticed a bird perched prominently on top of a thin hawthorn whip. Visibility was initially poor, owing to heavy black rain clouds, and allowed only silhouetted views. Even in rather poor light, the combination of its pied appearance and posture suggested it was something unusual.
>
> Having made several trips to Menorca, AG soon recognised the bird as a Woodchat Shrike, a species he had often encountered there. In order to gain better views, he walked past the bird and looked back, the light now to his advantage. With improved views, AG ascertained that, like the Menorcan birds, this individual lacked a white patch to the bases of the primaries. The bird remained in the area until 6th July, during which time it was photographed (see *Birding World* 8: 248).'

(Originally published in *British Birds* 98: 32-42)

Eurasian Jay (Continental)
Garrulus glandarius glandarius
Three were shot in Norfolk in January and February 1918.

B. B. Riviere writes:

'I have for some time suspected that the Continental Jay (*Garrulus g. glandarius*) must occur in Norfolk during winter because, though not a very common bird in the nesting season (which is hardly surprising, considering the extent of game preservation), Jays are remarkably abundant in Norfolk during the winter months, it being no uncommon thing to see as many as fifteen or twenty put out of one small wood by the beaters, when covert-shooting. During the past winter I have had the opportunity of examining a good many Norfolk-killed specimens, and have been struck by the greyness of the back of some of them.

I therefore recently sent five skins, which had been shot in Norfolk during January and February, 1918, to Dr. Hartert at Tring.

He has very kindly compared them with the series in the Tring Museum, and reports that three of them are undoubtedly of the Continental race (*Garrulus g. glandarius*) the remaining two being British (*Garrulus g. rufitergum*). I believe the only other counties from which the Continental Jay has up to now been recorded are Kent and Sussex.'

(Originally published in *British Birds* 11: 259)

Eurasian Jay
Garrulus glandarius rufitergum
The earliest reference we can find is by Sir Thomas Browne (1605-1682) in *Notes and Letters on the Natural History of Norfolk* (1902) where he writes, when describing the Roller, that it appears to be some kind of Jay and gives comparisons to the Jay when detailing its description. Obviously the Jay was well known to him even though he does not mention it in its own right.

The earliest dated reference we can find is in extracts from Robert Marsham's 'Indications of Spring' published in the *Transactions of the Norfolk and Norwich Naturalists' Society* 1874-1875: 33 where he recorded at Stratton Strawless on 7th April 1773:

'I have heard a wind jay in Stratton mimic an owl and kite so well that I thought these birds were singing till I saw the jay.'

Eurasian Magpie
Pica pica
The earliest reference we can find is by Thomas Southwell in *Notes and Letters* [of Sir Thomas Browne 1605-1682] *on the Natural History of Norfolk* 1902: 27 where he adds in a footnote regarding the Corvids in the text:

'Although the Magpie must have been well known to Browne I find no mention of it in these notes.'

Sheppard and Whitear in *A Catalogue of the Norfolk and Suffolk Birds, with Remarks* (1826) comment on the species but give no Norfolk reference, and the Pagets in *Sketch of the History of Yarmouth and its* Neighbourhood 1834: 6 considered it '…not uncommon in some places.'

Spotted Nutcracker
Nucifraga caryocatactes
One was shot at Rollesby on 30th October 1844 (Plate 8), a year of marked immigration of this

species into Western Europe.

Henry Stevenson writes in *The Birds of Norfolk* Vol. l. 1866: 281-285:

> 'Three specimens of this rare and most accidental visitant to our shores have been killed in Norfolk up to the present time, of which the first was obtained at Rollesby, near Yarmouth, on the 30th October 1844. This bird, in the possession of Mr. J. H. Gurney, was described in the *"Zoologist"* for 1845 (p. 824), by Mr. W. R. Fisher, as having a long pointed beak, the upper mandible slightly projecting, with the tip horn coloured and the rest black. It had been seen about the same spot for a week before it was shot, and the contents of the stomach consisted entirely of Coleopterous insects.'

The cased specimen is in storage at the Castle Museum, Norwich (Accession no. NWHCM: 1935.15.41) and was a gift to the museum from Mr. Gerard H. Gurney in 1935. Taxidermy was by Thomas Knight of 9, London Road, Norwich.

Western Jackdaw (Scandinavian)
Corvus monedula monedula
Birds of the nominate Scandinavian race are presumed to appear regularly in the county, but the first confirmed record was of a bird recovered at Kilverston in April 1951 which had been ringed at Humulu, Denmark on 11th June 1950. One of only four ringed Jackdaws known to have moved between Norfolk and the Continent up to 1999 (Taylor *et al* 1999).

Western Jackdaw
Corvus monedula spermologus
The earliest reference we can find is by Sir Thomas Browne (1605-1682) in *Notes and Letters on the Natural History of Norfolk* 1902: 27 where he writes:

> 'Among the many monedulas or Jackdawes I could neuer in these parts obserue the pyrrhocorax or cornish chough with red leggs & bill to bee commonly seen in Cornwall.'

Western Jackdaw (Eastern)
Corvus monedula soemeringii
Birds showing characteristics of the eastern race are scarce but regular in most years, and are probably overlooked. Records come not just from well-watched coastal areas, such as Cley, but also from inland (Taylor *et al* 1999).

The first mention in any *Norfolk Bird Report* was in 1995 where it states:

> 'During Dec. several birds showing characteristics of one of the eastern races, probably *C. c. soemeringii*, reported as follows Cley 10th-31st and 2 Easton/ Bawburgh 17th-31st.'

Rook
Corvus frugilegus
The earliest dated reference we can find is by Sir Thomas Browne (1605-1682) in *Notes and Letters on the Natural History of Norfolk* 1902: 27:

'Spermologus. Rookes wch by reason of the great quantities of corn fields & Rookes grouse are in great plenty the yong ones are commonly eaten sometimes sold in norwich market & many are killd for their Liuers in order to cure the Rickets.'

Carrion Crow
Corvus corone
The earliest dated reference we can find is by Sir Thomas Brown (1605-1682) in *Notes and Letters on the Natural History of Norfolk* 1902: 27 where he writes:

'Crowes as euerywhere ...'

Hooded Crow
Corvus cornix
Known to some of the earlier writers as the Royston Crow, the earliest dated reference we can find is by Sir Thomas Brown (1605-1682) in *Notes and Letters on the Natural History of Norfolk* 1902: 27:

'Crowes as euerywhere and also the coruus variegates or pyed crowe with dunne & black interchangeability they come in the winter & depart in the summer & seeme to bee the same wch clusius discribeth in the faro Islands from whence perhaps these come. and I have seen them very common in Ireland, butt not known in many parts of England.'

Northern Raven
Corvus corax
The earliest dated reference we can find is by Sir Thomas Browne (1605-1682) in *Notes and letters on the Natural History of Norfolk* 1902: 27:

'Coruus maior Rauens in good plenty about the citty wch makes so few Kites to be seen hereabout. they build in woods very early & lay egges in februarie.'

Common Starling
Sturnus vulgaris
The earliest dated reference we can find is by Sir Thomas Browne (1605-1682) in *Notes and Letters on the Natural History of Norfolk* 1902: 28:

'Stares or starlings in great numbers. most remarkable in their numerous flocks wch I haue obserued about the Autumne when they roost at night in the marshes in safe places upon reeds & alders. wch to obserue I went to the marshes about sunne set. where standing by their vsuall place of resort I obserued very many flocks flying from all quarters. wch in lesse than an howers space came all in & settled in innumerable numbers in a small compasse.'

Rosy Starling
Sturnus roseus
The first, shot at Rougham in June 1747 was the second British record.

J. H. Gurney writes in the *Transactions of the Norfolk and Norwich Naturalists' Society* 1874-1875: 225:

'Perhaps it may be worth notice that there is a record of the occurrence of the rose-coloured pastor in Norfolk, as far back as 1747 in *Edwards' Natural History* (vol. iv, p. 222, supplementary matter). It was shot at Rougham by Mr. Roger North, as it was feeding among blackbirds. Edwards records another killed at Norwood, from which he did not, erroneously stated by Yarrell, take his picture. Which of them has the honour of being the first British specimen cannot now be ascertained.'

Interestingly, the Norwood, Greater London, occurrence mentioned above was obtained in 1742 and became the first British record.

House Sparrow
Passer domesticus
The earliest dated reference we can find is in Henry Stevenson's *The Birds of Norfolk* Vol. l. 1866: 209-214, where he writes:

'The late Bishop Stanley, in his "Familiar History of Birds" (p. 89), alluding to the range of the sparrow, in all countries, extending with "the tillage of the soil," says, "From certain entries in the Hunstanton Household Book, from 1519-1578, in which sparrows (or as they are there written *spowes* or *sparrouse*) are frequently recorded, it would appear that these birds took their place in the larders of the nobility as delicacies with other game, from which we may infer that they were at that time as rare in Norfolk as they still are in some parts of Russia, owing probably to the same cause, viz., the limited state of tillage and growth of corn." That the sparrow was probably scarce in that part of Norfolk (Hunstanton, near Lynn) in those days is most probable, and for the cause alleged by our late Diocesan, but at the same time he was in error in supposing that the term *spowes*, so frequently met with in the L'Estrange "accounts," referred to our *Passer domesticus*. The term *spowe* invariably occurs in connection with knots, ring-dotterels, redshanks, and other grallatorial species, common enough then, as indeed they still are, upon the Hunstanton beach, and under this name, as I shall hereafter be able to show, the *Whimbrel* was invariably designated in those old records. Once only, in the same "accounts," is the word *sparrouse* used, as "Itm xij. sparrouse of gyste" (articles given in lieu of rent), and these being thus entered alone, were in all probability real sparrows, brought as a delicacy by some poor retainer.'

Eurasian Tree Sparrow
Passer montanus
The earliest reference we can find is by Sheppard and Whitear in *A Catalogue of the Norfolk and Suffolk Birds, with Remarks* 1826: 26 where they write:

'We have received a specimen of the Tree-Sparrow from the Rev. H. Tilney of Hockwold, at which place it breeds. Mr. Scales pointed out to us this species at Beechamwell, and favoured us with its eggs.'

The Pagets who also knew it as the Mountain Sparrow in *Sketch of the Natural History of Yarmouth and its Neighbourhood* 1834: 6 considered it '…common in lanes, &c. and not unfrequently seen about the town.'

Interestingly, Henry Stevenson writes in *Birds of Norfolk* Vol. l. 1860: 208:

'I have long imagined that some, at least, of our winter specimens, particularly in localities where they are never seen at other seasons, might be migratory arrivals, but it was not till very recently that I met with the following proof, as it were, of my former impression in the same paper, by Mr. Ed. Blyth, in the "Field Naturalist" (vol. i., p. 467), to which I before alluded in my remarks on the migration of the redbreast and the golden-crested wren. Mr. Blyth's informant, who at that time (Oct. 8th, 1833), had just returned in a coasting vessel from Aberdeen to London, says, - "A flock of tree-sparrows settled on the ship, and others of this species continued to arrive during the whole day, as the vessel passed the Norfolk and Suffolk coast, particularly when off Hasboro', Yarmouth, and Harwich…".'

Rock Sparrow
Petronia petronia
One was found by Richard Millington at Cley on 14th June 1981.

Richard Millington writes:

'In Norfolk, 14th June 1981 was clear and sunny with a very warm force 5 south-westerly wind. There was plenty of visible migration in progress at Cley during the morning. Starlings were passing west at the rate of about 2,000 per hour; Lapwings, Turtle Doves and Linnets were also passing west along the coast.

At 8.00am I was walking from the North Hide at Cley towards the Coastguards' car-park. I noticed a small bird feeding in company with several Linnets under the Eye Field fence. It was a sparrow-like, brown bird with a boldly striped head, but it was no species familiar to me. I briefly considered if it could be some sort of American sparrow, but my first thought was to get Steve Gantlett onto the bird. Steve was on the shingle ridge just ahead of me, but I soon caught his attention and he came back to join me near the fence. "What does Rock Sparrow look like?" I asked him as he arrived; I had never seen Rock Sparrow abroad, but Steve had. Almost immediately the bird flew up onto the fence, revealing a shortish dark tail tipped with prominent white spots. This highly distinctive feature cemented our already firming suspicions that the bird was indeed a Rock Sparrow, a south European species new to the British List.

We watched the bird at ranges of about 50-100m for another ten minutes as it fed along the ruts in the turfed gravel strip between the beach and the field. It alighted on the fence a few times and we both compiled detailed descriptions. When the bird looked up, face-on, I noticed it did have a small oblong, pale yellow patch on the centre of the upper breast, which completed the set of clinching features. Steve promptly left to alert other observers. Meanwhile, Mark Eldridge and Chris Jones were walking along the beach from the east and they joined me, still watching the bird. John McLoughlin scurried along from the Beach Shelter and was fortunate enough to arrive in time too. But at 8.30am, for no apparent reason, the bird flew up and headed strongly westward across the Eye Field. We tried to indicate this to the small crowd of approaching twitchers, but they failed to realise that the bird was actually flying past them and away. It was never seen again, despite much searching, and it remains the sole British record of Rock Sparrow.'

(Accounts were published in *British Birds* 76: 245-247 and in the *Norfolk Bird Report* 1984: 105-106)

Rock Sparrow on Cley beach by Eye Field June 1981. (*Robert Gillmor*)

Chaffinch
Fringilla coelebs
Not mentioned by Sir Thomas Browne (1605-1682) in *Notes and Letters on the Natural History of Norfolk* (1902) although he does mention 'Great varietie of finches and other small birds', and just listed by Sheppard and Whitear in *A Catalogue of the Norfolk and Suffolk Birds, with Remarks* (1826) without comment. The earliest reference we can find is by the Pagets in *Sketch of the Natural History of Yarmouth and its Neighbourhood* 1834: 6 as '…very common.'

Brambling
Fringilla montifringilla
The earliest dated reference we can find is by Sheppard and Whitear in *A Catalogue of the Norfolk and Suffolk Birds, with Remarks* 1826: 26-27 where they write:

> 'This winter bird of passage sometimes makes its appearance in very large flocks. At Beechamwell, Mr. Scales considered them of service to his land, from their devouring in great abundance the seeds of the Knot-grass (*polygonum aviculare*). In the severe winter of 1819-20 large flocks of these birds were observed at Stratton Strawless feeding on the Beech-mast.'

European Serin
Serinus serinus
One was seen in Opollo Gardens on Yarmouth North Denes on 13th June 1885 and obtained the following day.

Robert William Chase writes in the *Zoologist* 1886: 27-28:

> 'On May 16th I received, in the flesh, from Mr.G.Smith, of Yarmouth, a male Woodchat, *Lanius rufus*, I hear that several others were obtained on the East Coast further north. From the same source I also had a Serin Finch, *Serinus hortulanus*, shot in the Apollo Gardens, Yarmouth, June 14th. Unfortunately the specimen was so riddled with shot that proper identification of the sex was impossible, but from the plumage it was no doubt a male. This, I believe, is the first occurrence of this species in Norfolk, and will be a welcome addition to the already rich avifauna of that county.'

Robert William Chase was born in Birmingham in 1852, he was a true Victorian naturalist, keen, informed and with a vast personal knowledge of his chosen subject. Unfortunately, as with many of those men, his knowledge was largely empirical and died with him in 1927. During his lifetime he amassed a collection of 15,000 individual specimens of British birds, their nestlings, nests and eggs, believed to be the largest collection of its kind and the nestling collection is virtually unique. The Chase collection is housed at Birmingham Museum and consists of a total of 320 cases of which 81 were displayed by the Museum in the 'Chase Bird Exhibition' from 29th August -9th October 1977 (Birmingham Museums & Art Gallery Press Release).
The Serin was still at the City of Birmingham Museum when enquiries were made in 1988.

European Greenfinch
Carduelis chloris
Listed by Sheppard and Whitear in *A Catalogue of the Norfolk and Suffolk Birds, with Remarks*

(1826) as Green Grosbeak but not commented on, the earliest reference we can find is by the Pagets in *Sketch of the Natural History of Yarmouth and its Neighbourhood* 1834: 6 where they considered it '…very common.'

European Goldfinch
Carduelis carduelis
The earliest dated reference we can find is by Sir Thomas Browne (1605-1682) in *Notes and Letters on the Natural History of Norfolk* 1902: 29:

> 'A kind of Anthus Goldfinch or fooles coat commonly calld a drawe water. finely marked with red & yellowe & a white bill. wch they take with trap cages in Norwich gardens & fastning a chaine about them tyed to a box of water it makes a shift with bill and legge to draw up the water unto it from the little pot hanging by the chaine about a foote belowe.'

Eurasian Siskin
Carduelis spinus
The earliest reference we can find is by Sir Thomas Browne (1605-1682) in *Notes and Letters on the Natural History of Norfolk* (1902) where he writes:

> 'Great varietie of finches and other small birds whereof one very small one calld a whinne bird [Goldcrest] marked with fine yellow spots & and lesser than a wren . There is also a small bird called a chipper somewhat resembling the former wch comes in the spring & feeds on the first buddings of birches & and other early trees.'

Thomas Southwell adds in a footnote:

> 'The Chipper, he says, "comes in the spring and feeds upon the first buddings of birches and other early trees;" he also calls it *"Betulae carptor,"* and says that he sends a drawing to Merrett; a third mention is as follows: "That which I called a *Betulae cerptor*, and should rather have called it *Alni carptor*… it feeds upon alder buds, nucaments, or seeds, which grow plentifully here; they fly in little flocks." I can only suggest this bird may be the Siskin, which fairly answers the description… One would however have thought that the Siskin would have been well known to Browne, as it evidently was to Turner, Willughby, and Ray. Merrett mentions it under Turner's name of "Lutolea".'

The earliest dated reference, we can find, however, is in 'Extracts from the Calendar of the Rev. William Whitear 1809-1826' published in the *Transactions of the Norfolk and Norwich Naturalists' Society* 1881-1882: 251 where he recorded on 22nd November 1819:

> 'Mr. Brown killed a Siskin in front of my house; 24th, he killed three others out of a small flock which were feeding on the seeds of the Alders. I afterwards saw two other small flocks of these birds busily engaged on the same Alders.'

Common Linnet
Carduelis cannabina

Although listed by Sheppard and Whitear in *A Catalogue of the Norfolk and Suffolk Birds, with Remarks* (1826) it is not commented on by them. The earliest reference we can find is by the Pagets in *Sketch of the Natural History of Yarmouth and its Neighbourhood* 1834: 6 where they considered it '…common.'

Twite
Carduelis flavirostris

The earliest dated reference we can find is in 'Extracts from the Calendar of the Rev William Whitear 1809-1826' published in the *Transactions of the Norfolk and Norwich Naturalists' Society* 1881-1882: 251 where he recorded on 14th December 1819 at Breydon:

> 'I killed some Dunlins in different satates of plumage, and two Twites out of a small flock – there was no pink colour on the rumps of these birds. They are called French Linnets at Yarmouth.'

Sheppard and Whitear write in *A Catalogue of the Norfolk and Suffolk Birds, with Remarks* 1826: 27-28:

> 'This is a winter bird of passage…Twites are found in the salt-marshes near Yarmouth; and we have seen a flock of them at Shotley Point in Suffolk. A Twite was killed on the 23rd of May; so that a few may perhaps breed in this country. Mr. Scales informs us that this species of Finch visits Beechamwell very early in the spring, and feeds upon the seeds of the Alder as they drop from the cones.'

Common (Mealy) Redpoll
Carduelis flammea

Not mentioned by Sheppard and Whitear (1826), the Pagets (1834) or Lubbock (1845), the earliest dated reference we can find is by Henry Stevenson in *The Birds of Norfolk* Vol. l. 1866: 228-29:

> 'The Mealy Redpole can scarcely be called an annual winter visitant, although flocks of more or less extent may be met with in several consecutive seasons; but now and then, from some cause not easily explainable, their total absence is remarked upon by our bird-catchers, and as I have frequently experienced when most wanting a specimen to supply some loss in my aviary, not a bird has been netted the whole winter through. Their appearance and numbers also, as with the more common species, cannot always be accounted for by the severity of the weather (in this country at least), either at the time of, or subsequent to, their arrival on our coasts. In 1847 and 1855, the latter a very sharpe winter, they were extremely plentiful; and in 1861, from the middle of October to the close of the year, probably the largest flocks ever noticed in this district, were distributed throughout the county. Hundreds of them were netted by the bird-catchers, being far more plentiful than the lesser species, and many still retained the rich flame-coloured tints of the breeding season. Yet the weather throughout this period was not unusually severe; and in the previous winter of 1860-1, hardly a bird was taken, though remarkable for its intense frosts; and again in 1863 and

64 they were equally scarce, with an almost equal degree of cold. I am not aware that the nest of this species has ever been found in Norfolk; but Mr. Alfred Newton has recorded in the "Zoologist" (p. 2382) the occurrence of a male specimen, in full breeding plumage, at Riddlesworth, in July, 1848, which he had "no doubt had bred there"; I was also assured by one of our Norwich bird-catchers, that in the spring of 1862, after the large influx of the previous autumn, he observed a flock of twenty or thirty as late as the middle of April.'

Lesser Redpoll
Carduelis cabaret

Although listed by Sheppard and Whitear in *A Catalogue of the Norfolk and Suffolk Birds, with Remarks* (1826) it was not commented on. The earliest reference we can find is by the Pagets in *Sketch of the Natural History of Yarmouth and its Neighbourhood* 1834: 6 where they considered it '…occasionally met with.'

Arctic (Greenland) Redpoll
Carduelis hornemanni hornemanni

One showing the characteristics of this nominate race, which breeds in north Greenland and adjacent parts of Canada, was found at Wells on 28th September 1966, a date which coincided with a big arrival of Redwings and Bramblings with Siskins, Song Thrushes and Redpolls at Cley. It remained until 10th October during which time it was filmed by Dick Bagnall-Oakeley who saw the bird three times and who described it as:

'Conspicuously larger than other redpolls which were filmed drinking with it (size probably accentuated by its paleness). White underparts and white unstreaked rump – this pure white extending well up the back. Conspicuous white patches (bars) in wing. Very bright crimson poll.'

(An account extracted from the unpublished files in the British Birds Rarities Committeed archive)

No further details are available in the *Norfolk Bird Report* 1966 where it is not even mentioned in the annual summary!

Arctic (Coues's) Redpoll
Carduelis hornemanni exilipes

Formerly known as Coues's Redpoll, two females of this, almost circumpolar, race which breeds in the northern tundras of North America, Asia and northern Europe, were taken on the North Denes at Yarmouth on 26th October 1910.

C. B. Ticehurst writes in the *Transactions of the Norfolk and Norwich Naturalists' Society* 1925-1926: 263:

'Coue's Redpoll (*Acanthis hornemanni exilipes*) has, so far as I can make out, never been recorded from Norfolk, though it must occur in every large visitation of Mealy Redpolls. I obtained one (a female) in the big Redpoll year of 1910 which was taken among many Mealy Redpolls on the North Denes at Yarmouth on October 26th, just about the same date that Dr. W. Eagle Clarke obtained three in Fair Isle.'

Interestingly, C. B. Ticehurst writes in *The History of the Birds of Suffolk* 1932: 76:

> 'Coues' Redpoll has not so far been distinguished within our boundary, but doubtless it occurred in 1910 amongst the numbers of Mealy Redpolls as I picked out two from a bird-catchers "store" on 26th October, which were taken just over our boundary, on the Norfolk side of Yarmouth. This paler, less spotted species with a small fine bill is probably commoner in England during "Redpoll years" than records of it indicate.'

C. B. Ticehurst's collection is now in the Natural History Museum at Tring in Hertfordshire. Enquries at the museum in early 2009 revealed that they have two specimens from Great Yarmouth collected in 1910. They are BMNH 1941.5.30.6337, a juvenile female and BMNH 1941.5.30.6339, a female, both taken on Yarmouth North Denes on 26th October 1910 and formerly in the Ticehurst collection. Both specimens are labelled as *exilipes* (N Cleere *in litt*).

Two-barred Crossbill
Loxia leucoptera
A male was shot at Burgh Castle on 1st September 1889.

J. H. Gurney writes in the *Zoologist* 1890: 57:

> 'On Sept. 1st a male Two-barred Crossbill was shot at Burgh, near Yarmouth. It is very brightly coloured, and with the lesser wing-coverts a deep plum-colour, the two alar bars well developed. From its stout bill and other marks it is evidently *Loxia bifasciata*.'

Interestingly, Thomas Southwell writes in the *Transactions of the Norfolk and Norwich Naturalists' Society* 1893-1894: 645:

> 'On the 1st September, 1889, a male example of this bird was shot at Burgh, near Great Yarmouth, although strictly speaking the spot on which it occurred was within the geographical boundary of Suffolk, I think it may fairly be claimed for this county, as it was in a tract of country known as Lothingland, running up into Norfolk, and several miles north of the southern boundary of the latter county; a flight of a few yards, too, would have carried it into undoubted Norfolk ground.'

This specimen was purchased by W. W. Spelman of Bradeston House, Brundall, and later purchased by E. M. Connop of Rollesby Hall and added to his extensive collection. Although this bird was listed when the Lysaght collection, which included the Connop collection, was donated to the City of Birmingham Museum in 1954 a search for it in February 1988 failed to locate the specimen.

The county boundary changes in 1974 brought Burgh Castle officially into Norfolk.

Red (Common) Crossbill
Loxia curvirostra
The earliest dated reference we can find is by Sir Thomas Browne (1605-1682) in *Notes and Letters on the Natural History of Norfolk* 1902: 25:

> 'Loxias or curuirostra a bird a little bigger than a Thrush of fine colours & prittie note differently from other birds, the upper & lower bill crossing each other. of a very tame nature, comes about the beginning of summer. I have known them kept in cages butt not to outliue the winter.'

Parrot Crossbill
Loxia pytyopsittacus
A male was shot at Riddlesworth prior to 1851.

Henry Stevenson in *The Bird of Norfolk* Vol. l. 1866: 239-241, writes:

> 'This rare species, by no means easily distinguished from large varieties of the common crossbill, has not hitherto been included amongst the birds of Norfolk, but since the publication of Messrs. Gurney and Fisher's "*List*" in 1846, one authentic example, at least, has occurred in this county, and entitles it to a place in the present work. This specimen, identified by Mr. Alfred Newton, was described by him in the "*Zoologist*" for 1851 (p. 3145), as killed near Riddlesworth Hall, where it is still preserved in Mr. Thornhill's collection.'

Alfred Newton writes in a note dated April 1851 in the *Zoologist* 1851: 3145, after describing one found in Suffolk:

> 'As Messers. Gurney and Fisher do not include this species in their "Account of Birds found in Norfolk," (Zool. Iv. 1312), I am glad to be able to say that at Riddlesworth Hall there is one, also a red male, which was shot in the neighbourhood, and in that county, some years since.'

Trumpeter Finch
Bucanetes githaginius
A first-summer male was found at Blakeney Point by Jason Moss on 31st May 2008 (Plate 15), quite remarkably it was the third county first to be discovered during the opening five months of that year. It remained until 4th June.

Jason Moss writes:

> '31st May 2008 will not really stick in my mind as a great day's birdwatching. The weather wasn't particularly inspiring with regards to bird migration, and I figured that the bulk of the excitement of spring passage had all but passed, having just enjoyed two days (28th-29th May) of quality spring birdwatching, with a Subalpine Warbler, my first Icterine Warbler, a Red-backed Shrike, an Osprey and good numbers of common migrants appearing on the Point throughout the two days. These were easily two of my better birding days, and one of the perks of working on Blakeney Point through the summer! 31st May, however,

had quietened down bird-wise, with a Spotted Flycatcher, 2 Garden Warblers, a Lesser Whitethroat and a few Willow Warblers and Chiffchaffs entertaining us throughout the day. In fact, the lull in the migration meant Paul Nichols, Edward Stubbings and I could get on with some real work, in the form of an Oystercatcher survey.

On completing the survey of the main dunes, finishing up at the seawatching hide, the three of us began wandering back to the Lifeboat House for some dinner and a well-earned cup of tea! However, as we made our way along beach way, a bulky, sandy-brown bird caught my eye, sitting on top of the *Suaeda* lining the track. I was struck initially by its bulk, massive bill and beady black eye, and said to Eddie and Paul "I think I've got a rosefinch, but… um…" and I was pretty much stumped at that point. It clearly wasn't a rosefinch; too pale and plain, but I had no idea what else it could have been. Luckily, Paul was fairly on the ball, and added "That's a Trumpeter Finch!" No identification issues ensued, as better views revealed a red bill and a pink rump; not many other birds fit that description! It was about 19:30 by now, and we proceeded to enjoy decent flight views, displaying its obvious bulk, although it was probably only marginally larger than a Linnet. However, it was difficult to see on the ground, and flushed easily. We followed it for a good hour or so before we finally got a view of it perched on the shingle along beach way. Good 'scope views revealed pinkish secondaries and dark primaries, on an otherwise plain sandy-brown bird. The relatively washed out pink on the wings and the pale-ish red of the bill led us to the conclusion that it was a first-summer bird.

Having enjoyed the bird for a period by ourselves, we obviously had to contemplate the organisation of a twitch. The main worry was disturbance to nesting birds along the shingle ridge and in the area that the finch was frequenting. After some discussion the next morning with Richard Porter, Simon Aspinal, Steve Joyner and James McCallum, the decision was made to put the news out to the masses. In the meantime, two incubating Oystercatchers in the vicinity were roped off, and we just waited to instruct the arriving throngs of the location of the Trumpeter Finch, and the location of the breeding birds most sensitive to disturbance. The first day went ahead without a hitch, with everyone being well behaved. However, it was difficult on the following days, as Paul, Eddy and I had several duties to complete, which meant that we couldn't 'baby-sit' the twitchers all of the time. It was quite disheartening that, on a number of occasions, we would check the twitch to find that people were standing far too close to the nesting Oystercatcher on the shingle along beach way, oblivious to the fact that they were preventing the adult from incubating its eggs, and often giving childish dirty looks when asked to move. This by no means applied to all, with most standing well back, viewing the finch from a sensible distance, and well away from the Oystercatcher nest; the Oystercatcher actually became quite accustomed to the presence of groups of people on the horizon, rapidly returning to its eggs once the disturbance had passed. The finch was extremely accommodating to all, showing well amongst the thrift heads upon which it was feeding, and dashing across the open shingle. The setting couldn't have been much better really, as the semi-desert-like environment must have been similar to that which the bird would normally be used to.

The Trumpeter Finch remained on Blakeney Point for five days, frequenting the same area, and only occasionally wandering over to Yankee Ridge, or at most to the Lifeboat House. It was extremely convenient that I was within a ten minute walk of the bird, and didn't have to suffer the hour-long slog or £8 boat trip that most others had to in order to enjoy the bird, possibly losing enthusiasm with every yard of shingle they had to tread! The inaccessibility certainly seemed to keep visitor numbers down to a low level, which was probably best for the ground-nesters on the Point, as well as our peace of mind!

I reckon that the fifth day of the Trumpeter Finch's stay was my most memorable, mainly because I found a Dusky Warbler in the garden that afternoon. Not bad for one spring on Blakeney Point, and it definitely makes up for the low wages!'

Common Rosefinch
Carpodacus erythrinus
Known then as the Scarlet Grosbeak, a female was obtained at Yarmouth on 3rd September 1892.

J. H. Gurney jun. writes in the *Zoologist* 1892; 401:

'…a Scarlet Grosbeak is stated to have been caught alive by birdcatchers at Yarmouth.'

In the *Zoologist* 1893: 150 he writes:

'In the "Zoologist," (p. 401) a Scarlet Grosbeak Pyrrhula erythrina (Pallas) is mentioned with some hesitation, as I had not then seen it. It is a female, and was caught on the Denes, between Yarmouth and Caistor, by a local bird-catcher named Jessup. It moulted all its feathers in October; and on November 16th, though still rather ragged, agreed with a skin from Asia, except that it had lost all its dark striations. When first caught, Mr. W. Lowne – to whom the bird belongs – described it to Mr. Southwell as having a streaked breast, and a greenish tinge which it lost at the moult. It has done very well since, and grown tame on soft food and gentles. The eye on Jan. 24th was dark brown, the legs and beak horn colour, and the general tone of the plumage very like that of a hen House Sparrow.'

In the *Zoologist* 1897: 130 he concludes the story of this remarkable little bird:

'June 29th. Today the Scarlet Grosbeak, believed, if there is no miscarriage of justice (see Zool. 1893, p. 150), to have been clap-netted in South Norfolk, died, after living nearly four years. It was always a very tame bird, using its wings very little, and fond of raising the feathers on the crown of the head into an approach to a crest, as it sat sedately on its perch of wood. Gatke particularly remarks on the tameness of the species.'

Formerly in J. H. Gurney's collection, and that of Mr. G. H. Gurney (Riviere 1930), the specimen (Accession no. NWHCM: 1935.15.88) is now on display in the bird gallery at the Castle Museum, Norwich.

Eurasian Bullfinch (Northern)

Pyrrhula pyrrhula pyrrhula
One was obtained on Yarmouth North Denes on 22nd January 1893.

J. H. Gurney writing in the *Transactions of the Norfolk and Norwich Naturalists' Society* 1892-1893: 421 states:

> 'An example of the Russian bullfinch, a large and brilliant race which Brehm named *Pyrrhula major*, was shot on Yarmouth North Denes by Arthur Smith, January 22nd 1893. I happened to be at his father's house the next day and saw it, being instantly struck by its great size, 5.7 inches, expanse 9.7 inches, wing 4 inches. The wing *of P. euporoea* is 3.2 inches. It is as much deserving of specific distinction as some of the foreign Hawks and Owls which have received names.'

The specimen was in the Gurney collection at the Castle Museum, Norwich (Riviere 1930), but enquiries at the museum in 2008 failed to locate it.

Eurasian Bullfinch

Pyrrhula pyrrhula pileata
The earliest dated reference we can find is by Robert Marsham (1708-1797) in Tim Sparks and John Lines' *Chapters in the Life of Robert Marsham Esq. F.R.S. of Stratton Strawless, Norfolk* 2008: 16:

> 'Examined. From bill to [tail] 6 inches from wing to wing 10.'

Hawfinch

Coccothraustes coccothraustes
The earliest dated reference we can find is by Sir Thomas Browne (1605-1682) in *Notes and Letters on the Natural History of Norfolk* 1902: 25:

> 'A kind of coccothraustes calld a coble bird bigger than a Thrush, finely coloured & shaped like a Bunting it is chiefly seen I summer about cherrie time.'

Interestingly, Sheppard and Whitear write in *A Catalogue of the Norfolk and Suffolk Birds, with Remarks* 1826: 25:

> 'The Hawfinch has occasionally been seen both in Norfolk and Suffolk, and for the most part during the winter season.'

Black-and-white Warbler

Mniotilta varia
One was discovered by M. R. McDonnell at How Hill, Ludham on 3rd December 1985 (Plate 15).

M. R. McDonnell writes:

'Working at a nature reserve in Norfolk can be very rewarding. In my case the reserve is at How Hill Environmental Centre near Ludham. Away from the busy summer months the reserve is quiet, disturbed only by children and adults on one of the many courses run by the How Hill Trust.

The 3rd December 1985 was one of the quiet days and just before dusk I decided to walk around the reedbeds; however there was no boat available to cross the river so I was restricted to the nature trail. Whilst walking along the edge of Crome's Broad I came across a mixed flock of tits and finches, mainly Long-tailed Tits. On this occasion I checked through them – something done all too infrequently – when I was startled by a glimpse of a small bird boldly patterned in zebra stripes. I quickly noted a white crown stripe bordered by two further black stripes. Centre of the belly was white contrasting with bold black streaking on the flanks. Unfortunately, after a minute the flock moved across a dyke disappearing into alder carr and I was unable to relocate them that day. Having caught only a tantalising glimpse I was unsure of the stranger's identity knowing only that I had seen nothing like it before. I returned the following morning with M. I. Eldridge. After some hours searching we were greatly relieved to relocate the bird and studied it for thirty minutes thus confirming its identity as a Black-and-white Warbler - a bird new to Norfolk.

It was a very active bird and its treecreeping habits most striking. It shuffled around trunks and branches pecking and probing into crevices, and often removing loose bark and lichen to extract prey. It was noted hanging up side down and also hovering. On occasions it worked down to the base of the alders. A particular liking was shown for searching among small twigs at the end of broken branches. During the early part of its stay in Pigeon Wood, most views were brief. However, on 12th December it was observed for over an hour feeding in an open area of alder and birch each side of the track. This provided opportunities for P. Morris to obtain his excellent photographs.

The following description was obtained by M.I.E.: Approximately Blackcap-sized warbler. Central crown stripe and supercilia white. Lateral crown stripes black. Lores dusky. Black eye-stripe extending backwards from each eye. Black beady eye bordered by whie crescent below. Ear coverts pale grey. Mantle striped black and white. Wing coverts black with white tips to median and greater coverts forming two wing-bars, the latter more prominent. Primary coverts black. Secondaries black with fine whitish fringes suggesting a grey appearance at longer ranges. Primaries black also with whitish fringes. Tertials black the uppermost feather with broad white lower edge. Tail blackish and square ended showing some white when spread. Underparts white with a few very small dark marks at the bottom of the throat forming a partial gorget but only visible at close range. A few short dark streaks marked the sides of the breast. Two long black stripes closer to the wing extended back along the flanks. Another less well marked and broken stripe disappeared under the wing. Under-tail coverts revealed small dark marks becoming larger towards the rear. Bill long and strong looking, slightly decurved at the tip. Upper mandible and tip of lower mandible blackish; remainder of lower mandible brownish. Legs dull orange-brown with yellowish feet. The call heard on several occasions in flight was a weak *si* reminiscent of a Goldcrest.

This New World visitor was found in a wooded part of the reserve owned and managed by the Broads Authority. Access is normally limited to field courses run by the How Hill Trust, but it was decided to make special staffing arrangements to allow visitors to the reserve's nature trail enclosing the area frequented by the bird. During the following eleven days and until 15th December almost 2,000 visitors came to the reserve most of whom eventually obtained excellent views of this rare American vagrant. Extraordinarily patterned it was usually in company with a Long-tailed Tit flock making its location a comparatively easy process. On wetter days it was rather a frustrating creature providing only one or two brief tantalising glimpses as it moved from tree to tree like a black-and-white striped treecreeper.

Despite appalling wet conditions at How Hill large numbers of cars and visitors caused minimal disturbance to the reserve and to neighbouring landowners. Watchers kept strictly to the path leaving virtually no litter and reflecting great credit on the bird-watching community.

Once described as the ultimate American Wood Warbler this delightful traveller was added to the British and Irish List in October 1936 when one was found dead in Shetland. Next occurrence was forty years later in Scilly. There have been less than a dozen subsequent accepted records including one on the remarkable date of 3rd March 1978 in Devon. Another individual after successfully flying the Atlantic sadly became a casualty striking a window in Falmouth.

The Black-and-white Warbler is one of the commonest, most widespread and best known American wood warblers. Breeding range extends from Hudson Bay in the north of Canada, south to Louisiana and Texas. A long distance migrant, it winters in the states bordering the Gulf of Mexico, the West Indies, Mexico and Central America south to Columbia and Venezuela. In spring it is one of the earliest warblers to arrive. This is probably related to its habit of feeding on tree trunks and branches, which it can do at a time when most other warblers would have difficulty in obtaining food.'

(An account published in the *Norfolk Bird Report* 1985: 252-253c)

Lark Sparrow
Chondestes grammacus
One in immaculate plumage was discovered by Barry Jarvis at Waxham on 15th May 1991.

Michael Seago writes:

'May 15th dawned cold and drizzly in East Norfolk. Fresh north-westerly winds ruled out the prospect of any movement of passage migrants. As Barry Jarvis was driving towards Waxham Hall he glimpsed a bunting-sized bird with a prominent black tail boldly cornered in white. Fortunately for the ornithological record he was very recently returned from the United States and instantly recognised the stranger as a Lark Sparrow. This attractive North American bunting has only been previously recorded once in Britain.

The bird, although on occasions rather elusive, remained in the vicinity of the then derelict Waxham Great Barn until May 17th enabling many birders to appreciate the unmistakable quail-like head patterning with chestnut ear-patch and striped crown as it fed on seeding grasses. On occasions observers were entertained by singing performances; the song consisting of loud introductory notes followed by trills and unmusical buzzing.

Among the host of watchers was one observer who happened to be in this country from Florida and successfully added the bird to his British List! Colour photographs of this Lark Sparrow have featured in *British Birds*, *Birding World* and *Birdwatch* magazines.

It is interesting to note that shortly before mid-May a polar weather front spanned the Atlantic, west to east, with wave depressions travelling eastwards at 50 knots. Waxham's waif could have received all the assistance from the wind it needed to cross the Atlantic.

The first occurrence of a Lark Sparrow in the Western Palearctic was at Landguard Point, Suffolk, where a smart example docked between June 30th and July 8th 1981. At the time the BOU Records Committee whilst accepting the identification declined to place the species in category A (ships in fact travel direct from Texas to Felixstowe passing within a few hundred metres of Landguard). However, following re-writing the rules regarding ship-assisted passage the bird deserves promotion.

As is so often the case the Waxham vagrant checked its calendar and vanished on the night of the 17th – much to the disappointment of many weekend watchers. But there was compensation: a male Red-breasted Flycatcher appeared in nearby stunted oaks next morning.

In North America, Lark Sparrows are found in open country from central southern Canada, across the whole of the United States (except the Atlantic coast states) south into Mexico. The species winters in the southern United States and in Mexico.'

(An account published in the *Norfolk Bird Report* 1991: 261)

White-crowned Sparrow
Zonotrichia leucophrys
An adult male was found by Richard and Sue Bending in their Cley garden on 3rd January 2008 (Plate 16). Because it was only the fourth British record and the first to stay for more than two days, it became the subject of an international twitch during the following weeks and remained until 14th March.

Richard and Sue Bending write:

'On Thursday 3rd January 2008, we noticed an unusual bird feeding among Chaffinches and Dunnocks in a sheltered part of our garden at Cley, Norfolk. It fed furtively below our bird-feeders, in an area overhung by shrubs near a beech hedge. Sparrow-sized it had a black crown with marked white stripes – reminding us of a badger's head – and a pink bill. Extensive searches through our bird books failed to identify it, so the next day we borrowed a rare bird guide from Norwich library. A picture of the White-crowned Sparrow leapt off the pages – we knew that this was the bird we had seen, and yet it seemed utterly incredible. We also feared that it would never be seen again.

However, back home, we soon caught a glimpse of the sparrow and at once sought expert advice – not hard to find in Cley. Chris Wheeler, Richard Porter and Simon Aspinall came in haste, and confirmed that we indeed had a major rarity – either a White-crowned or a White-throated Sparrow – but positive identification was not possible in the failing light. We were all excited, but aware that public disclosure would require careful planning. Meanwhile, we agreed to tell no-one else.

The same expert birders returned the next day, Saturday 5th January, and, in better light, were able to confirm that it was indeed an adult White-crowned Sparrow. Some photographs were hastily taken to document the record. This sparrow normally winters in eastern North America, and we were informed that 1995 was the last time that one had been seen in Britain. We knew that the appearance of this very rare visitor would be a major event for birders, but that presented us with a problem. We wanted to share our bird, but we knew that hundreds, perhaps thousands, of birders would want to see it. Because our small garden is completely enclosed, the sparrow was only visible without disturbance from inside the house, but it was wildly impractical to open our home to the crowds who were likely to come. Richard Porter then introduced us to Richard Millington, who has experience of such situations, and a plan was hatched. It was suggested that we might attempt to entice the bird onto our driveway, where it would be visible from the road, but would still have access to the beech hedge for shelter. So we moved all our feeders, swept up the residual seed, put fresh seed on the gravel drive, and waited….

On Sunday morning, to our delight, the sparrow hopped out onto the driveway, and it could then be seen from the road. The news was broadcast at midday on that Sunday, and very soon crowds began to gather. Fortunately, the sparrow appeared regularly enough for everyone to see it. The largest crowd amassed the following day, Monday 7th January, but the timely arrival of a very helpful traffic warden greatly eased the congestion. Despite the restricted viewing, the watchers have been very good-tempered, many of them contributing to a collection for Cley Church, which has been much appreciated. We have been very grateful indeed to Richard Porter, Richard Millington and others from Cley Bird Club, who gave us good advice and managed the whole process. It has been a good experience, and we have not once regretted putting the news out.'

Richard Porter takes up the story:

'As soon as I saw this bird I knew we had a potential nightmare on our hands, or consciences. The faint-hearted would certainly have suppressed it. The bird was in a small garden with no easy access and, given where it was, there was no way the news could be put out. We therefore scouted the environs and realised that, if we could get the bird to feed on the Bendings' gravel driveway, we might be in with a sporting chance; here it would be viewable from the Holt-Cley road, although for only about 20 people comfortably at a time. At this stage, I telephoned Richard Millington to discuss this idea and tactics. We agreed it was the only possible solution, so we set to work. First we had to have the Bendings' full support and agreement. They had never experienced the commotion of a full twitch, so we explained everything carefully and honestly. They were up for it. We then discussed it with their next-door neighbours, who were also supportive (and assured us that their aged cat, Hooligan, had never caught a bird!).

We then had to get the sparrow to move and change its habits. All the feeders in the garden were taken down, the seed scooped up from the ground, and everything moved to the gravel driveway, which lay beyond their garden fence and caravan. More seed was added to the driveway and Christmas tree branches were grouped along the wall, so the bird could have a retreat – we knew from watching it in the garden that it was very shy and nervous. Then the long wait. Nothing happened that day (Saturday), but late on the Sunday morning it put in an appearance at the seed on the drive. We decided to wait just a little longer (sorry if I'm making you nervous), to make sure it was settling in to its new feeding station, so that it would tolerate spying throngs just a few yards away. The next step was to put up notices – notably on the five-bar gate across the driveway, to advise viewing from the other side of the road. Also, a collecting bucket was organised. Being a retired man of the cloth, it was only right that Richard Bending had first call on the fund, and so 'in aid of Cley Church restoration' was decided upon.

Within an hour, the news went out. Flowers were arranged for the neighbouring couple whose house overlooked the road, and the Three Swallows pub (50 yards away) was advised to increase their stocks! During the following hours, days and weeks the twitch went well. Despite the limited viewing, and up to 300 birders gathering at a time on the peak days, not too many tempers frayed, everyone behaved well, and all said what a great little bird it was. 'Jaunty' seemed a popular description. Voluntary donations to the church restoration fund surprised us all and, by early February, had topped £4,000 (over £6.000 by late February).

There were, inevitably, occasional problems with managing the initial crowds, which tended to surge across the road each time the bird hesitantly appeared. Luckily, traffic warden Andy Barker was great at reading the mood, and both the twitchers and the motorists managed nicely. Some locals had their usual moan about birdwatchers, and the verges around the village green became a little churned up – made worse by several days of unrelenting rain. But the fact that Cley birders agreed to restore and re-seed the affected areas (whether caused by birders or not), as well as the terrific collection for the church, successfully blunted the barbs. I would like to say that my involvement in helping kick-start this mass twitch was because I wanted to see this super little bird shared by lots of birdwatchers. But the reality is that living in Cley (of all places) makes any though of suppression a very foolish thing.

I would like to thank Richard and Sue Bending for finding the bird and allowing the event to unfold, and their nextdoor neighbours, Connie & Tom Evans, for their tolerance and tea, Andy Barker of the North Norfolk Constabulary for a complete understanding of twitchers and handling the big day accordingly and Paul Laurie and Steve Gantlett for supplying the initial seed (even though Steve was in Dorset at the time!). Also the farmer whose fence needed some minor repairing, Trevor Poyser, Steve Beal and Cley birders for arranging for the restoration of the verges and the national news media for telling the story well and not sending us up (well, only slightly). And thanks also to those who helped me and Richard Millington man the site and collect for the church restoration fund, come wind and high water, including Chris Wheeler, Roger Brownsword, Trevor Davies and Martin Woodcock. Finally thanks to the several thousand twitchers who visited the site and played their part well.'

(An account published in *Birding World* 21: 14-15)

The total sum donated to Cley Church as a result of this bird's visit was £6,378. Some of which, it has been suggested, will go towards a small stained glass window in the church depicting the little lost soul that was responsible for that sum being raised.

Adult male White-crowned Sparrow near Cley Church January 2008. (*Gary Wright*)

White-throated Sparrow
Zonotrichia albicollis
A first-winter male was found by Harold Jenner at Herringfleet on 16th November 1968.

E. W. C. Jenner writes:

'H. E. Jenner heard a bird-note which he did not recognise at Herringfleet on Nov. 16th , 17th, 18th, 20th, 22nd, 23rd and 24th. He was unable to get a sight of the bird until Nov. 24th. It was thought by several observers to be a Little Bunting, but Mr. Jenner was certain the identification was incorrect.

On Dec. 22nd it was feeding on a bird table, its flight was impaired and Mr. Jenner determined to catch it alive. He prepared a suitable trap, and after some disappointment, he succeeded in taking it alive on Dec. 29th and put it in a cage. On Jan. 1st 1969 the bird died. Identification could now be done, and H. E. Jenner is quite satisfied that it is a White-throated Sparrow, N. America, accidental to Britain, and one of the rarer accidentals. NEW TO SUFFOLK. The skin has been preserved.'

(An account published in the *Lowestoft Field Club Bulletin* 1968: 75)

The finder was less than happy when as a result of the county boundary changes in 1974, the locality of this record and his home address changed from Suffolk to Norfolk!

Interestingly, the *Lowestoft Field Club Bulletin* 1969: 114 adds a little more detail to this record:

> 'The bird reported last year at Herringfleet died on Jan. 1. By dissection it was found to be a 1st winter male which had died of pneumonia. This record (which constitutes about the seventh for the British Isles) has been accepted by the Rare Birds Committee.'

Apparently Jenner sent the skin of the specimen to the BBRC via the Post Office, and it came back, after acceptance, somewhat damaged (A Easton *pers comm*). Its current whereabouts is unknown.

Harrold Jenner died on 3rd June 1990 aged 69. He was an accomplished taxidermist and his collection of birds, animals and fishes was dispersed amongst a number of friends.

Dark-eyed (Slate-coloured) Junco
Junco hyemalis

Quite amazingly, two different Dark-eyed Juncos were found in the county on 14th July 2007, at Langham by Dave Curtis and at Terrington St Clement by Rick Marsh. As the two birds were first seen virtually simultaneously we feel that both should share the 'county first' tag and the accounts of the discovery of both birds are detailed here.

A presumed first-summer was found by Dave Curtis in his garden at Langham at or soon after midday on 14th July 2007 (Plate 16).

Dave Curtis writes:

> 'The summer months can be quiet on the birding front even in north Norfolk so I fill the time with running a moth trap. I had spent Saturday morning 14th July checking its contents, the wet weather of the past few weeks ensuring that even the moth catch was poor. Alison called me to lunch at 12:10 and we sat at the table on the patio to enjoy some welcome sunshine.
>
> The view from the patio has a pear tree on the left and an apple tree further away on the right. At the time there were feeders in the pear tree and on a feeder stand between the two fruit trees. I was having trouble with Grey Squirrels so the feeders had been allowed to almost empty to try to discourage them. This meant that we had fewer birds than normal around the garden.
>
> We had just started to eat when I saw a small grey bird fly into the apple tree; as we have Blackcap breeding close to the garden I was expecting a *Sylvia* warbler as I raised my binoculars. The view that met my eyes was a major surprise – a uniform grey bird with a slightly darker mask, white belly, pink bill and orange legs!
>
> I let out an expletive then a shocked "We've got a Dark-eyed Junco in the apple tree". I moved as slowly as I could to the door and then ran inside for my camera and did the headless chicken past it several times but finally found it and got back to the garden to see that the bird had moved. We soon relocated it at the left of the apple tree and I grabbed the first shots. One shot had the bird watching the sky, probably as one of the local Sparrowhawks went over – this could have been a very brief appearance! All the while I was muttering things like "This can't be true" and trying to stop my hands from shaking. I use a Pentax

372

*istDS body and my old Sigma 400 mm lens so internal stabilisation is not an option. Amazingly, the RAW files record that I was using manual focus and still managed to get sharp shots.

The Junco dropped down to the battered yew and then to the lawn and fed briefly on some spilled seed while I continued to take pictures. Then it lifted up into the beech hedge and disappeared. I reviewed the images to see if I was dreaming but no, as far as I could see it was a Junco and the last image gives the time as 12:16. A quick look at my copy of Sibley was enough to confirm the ID. Although my initial thoughts had been adult male, when the images were transferred to a PC a slight brown wash was evident on the back and this suggested it was a 1st-summer male.

I ran for the phone and called local birders Dave and Pat Wileman and then Rare Bird Alert. Alison and I agreed that we would allow access to our back garden although the 3-day old floor in the conservatory was to be deemed 'out of bounds' to the masses. So the pager message went out at about 12:27 as I ran to my birder neighbours Keith and Sheila Edwards, their feeders being another obvious target for the bird.

The first local birders arrived very quickly and some brief views were obtained in our garden. Then Keith and Sheila alerted us to the bird in their back garden and kindly agreed to let birders in. The bird initially spent time in the flower bed making forays towards the feeder spill but it was seen to fly between the two gardens several times, treating the neighbours to a wonderful spectacle as the birders followed at speed en masse. The Junco also went missing for periods and occasionally gave more distant views in the paddock over the 6ft wall at the bottom of the garden.

Through all this my part-eaten sandwich stayed on the patio table and was eventually admired by lots of hungry birders. The local youngsters joined in the fun, asking visiting birders if they had seen their lost pet bird. "It's a Brunco".

Towards the evening the Junco spent much of its time in Keith's garden where it was prone to lurking under a peony and make brief forays out for food. I never saw it again in my garden although others were treated to a superb view on the lawn quite close to the house. It was last seen at about 20:40. Over the course of the afternoon and evening we had over 300 visitors – judging by the donations at £1 a time. Parking problems were kept to a minimum by the sterling efforts of Pat and Dave.

I re-filled and re-sited my feeders near the right hand apple tree and, therefore, further away from the house and patio to give a better field of view from both sides of the house and hopefully to cause the bird less disturbance. I also cleared the patio furniture and plant containers to make room for the expected crowds. I slept very badly that night as I was continually dreaming of the Junco and surrounding events. I was up at 05:10 next morning and watching the garden intently. The local Woodpigeons seemed to be mocking me with their call

A Dark-eyed Junco?
A Dark-eyed Junco!
A Dark-eyed Junco!!
****!!!

The Blackcap family also put in an appearance, an adult male and three female/juvenile birds.

I watched the garden intently from 05:15 to 07:15 when my phone rang. Pat asked me if any birders were in the garden and I said no, they appeared to be honouring the 08:00 opening time. She then asked me to look at the road in front of the house and there was a queue of birders waiting silently. I immediately revised opening time and got the crowd into the garden and off the street. Unfortunately there was no further sign of the bird. Spirits dropped even further with a tantalising report of a possible Dark-eyed Junco at Waxham. The last birders left the site just after lunch and we returned to some sort of normality.

This has to be the highlight of my 49 years of birdwatching and was like dreams I have had many times over the years. We had a great time meeting everyone and the whole event was very good-natured and orderly. As I had seen the 1997 bird in Chester in a back garden it was nice to be able to return the favour. The collection of £178.02 from our garden went to the RSPB and Keith donated his £171 to the Norfolk Wildlife Trust.

This was the first Dark-eyed Junco for mainland Norfolk, the previous off-shore record was of a bird caught near a gas platform on 24th May 1980. As both gardens are well-watched, our bird is unlikely to have been present for long before it was found.

DESCRIPTION

The head, upper-parts, and upper breast were blue-grey with slightly darker forehead and lores producing a mask. The back had a slight brown wash. The belly and undertail coverts were white with blue-grey edgings to the belly and rear belly, the tibial feathers were blue-grey. The flight feathers were slightly darker with a slightly browner tone, in certain lights there appeared to be very slightly paler tips to the greater and median coverts. The tail was blue-grey with white edges although this was not very noticeable on the perched bird. The bill was pink and the legs orange.

(An account published in the *Norfolk Bird Report* 2007: 168-170)

The editors, very interestingly, comment in *Birding World* 20: 297 following an article on the Dark-eyed Junco:

'Thanks to Dave's very prompt release of the news, this was the first Slate-coloured Junco to be twitchable in Britain – albeit unfortunately for only eight hours – since a first-winter which over-wintered at Chester, Cheshire, in 1997/98 (*Birding World* 11: 11). There have been 29 previous records in Britain (including singles this spring on St Kilda and in Highland) and another two in Ireland. Although records have been seasonally well-scattered, most have been in spring and this is the first to arrive in July…

Dark-eyed Junco is common and widespread throughout North America, with a total population estimated at 630 million birds. As well as inhabiting most wooded and parkland areas, the 'snowbird' is a familiar visitor to suburban bird feeders. Although a relatively short-distance migrant, the species has been recorded as a vagrant to Europe and Siberia, for which ship-assistance is surely largely responsible.

Following a turbulent taxonomic history, and reflecting the lack of genetic study, all North American juncos except for Yellow-eyed are currently lumped as a single species, Dark-eyed Junco *Junco hyemalis*. However, the species consists of five racial groupings that accord with the five species that were still recognised as recently as the 1970s, and modern reappraisals are likely to result in some being re-split as distinct species in the future. The current subspecies groups are Slate-coloured Junco (*hyemalis*), White-winged Junco (*aikeni*), Oregon Junco (*oreganus*), Gray-headed Junco (*caniceps*) and Guadelupe Junco (*insularis*).

The form which reaches Europe as a vagrant is Slate-coloured Junco *J. h. hyemalis*, which breeds from northern Alaska eastwards to Newfoundland and south to central Alberta and New England, and winters mainly south of breeding range and east of Rocky Mountains south to northern Mexico and Florida. A pink bill, white belly and white outer tail feathers are common to every Dark-eyed Junco, but in Slate-coloured, as the name suggests, the remainder of its plumage is more or less plain grey. Males tend to be purer grey (darker on the lores) than females, while immatures retain their juvenile flight feathers for their first year of life (along with most of their juvenile tail feathers and variable numbers of wing coverts).'

Unfortunately we were unable to obtain the full details of the finding of the Terrington St Clement bird, but as we understand it Rick Marsh had returned home from Wisbech at around 1145-1150 on 14th July 2007 and went into his garden, seeing the bird soon afterwards. He was unable to identify it from his *Book of British Birds*, but a neighbour was able to do so after looking at pictures on the internet. It was subsequently photographed and the BTO was informed of its presence. However, it was not seen by the BTO staff who visited on 17th July, despite being present in the garden later that afternoon. It was not seen again. Slight differences in the plumage of the two birds, apparent on photographs, confirm that two individuals were involved.

There is an earlier occurrence, of one caught exhausted on an oil supply vessel alongside the Shell Bravo gas platform 49/26T in the Lemon Bank gas field 55km east-north-east of Happisburgh on 24th May 1980. It was transported ashore by helicopter and identified at the Castle Museum, Norwich, on 28th May. Watched by over 50 birders, it was released at Holme Reserve on 31st May where it remained until at least 6th June. This record was placed in Category D of the Norfolk List (Taylor *et al* 1999).

Lapland Longspur (Bunting)

Calcarius lapponicus
One was caught alive at Postwick on 26th January 1855.

Henry Stevenson writes in *The Birds of Norfolk* Vol. l. 1866: 181-182:

'On the 26th of January, 1855, during extremely severe weather, a specimen of this very rare bunting was taken alive at Postwick, near Norwich. This bird, probably the first ever known to have occurred in this county, was brought to me soon after its capture, and proved to be a young male in winter plumage. Unlike most birds, when first confined in a cage, it seemed perfectly at home, feeding readily on the seed placed for it, and both in its gait and manner of looking up, with the neck stretched out, reminded me of the actions of a quail. In the aviary of Mr. J. H. Gurney this bird assumed full summer plumage in the following spring, and thrived so well in its new abode, that over-feeding was probably the cause of its death in May, 1856, when, for the second time, it had aquired the black head and plumage of the breeding season, and was certainly a perfect lump of fat when skinned for the purpose of preservation.'

The specimen, (Accession no. NWHCM: 1935.15.39), is on display in the bird gallery at the Castle Museum, Norwich.

Snow Bunting
Plectrophenax nivalis
Although Sir Thomas Browne (1605-1682) had knowledge of buntings he makes no mention of them in *Notes and Letters on the Natural History of Norfolk* (1902) other than as a shape comparison in his description of a Hawfinch, with no reference to species.

The earliest dated reference we can find is in 'Extracts from the Calendar of the Rev. William Whitear 1809-1826' published in the *Transactions of the Norfolk and Norwich Naturalists' Society* 1881-1882: 251 where he recorded on 14th December 1819:

> 'I saw two flocks of Snow Buntings on the shore at Caistor. They were feeding on the seeds of the Marrum. We killed five of them; some had much more white about them than others. Perhaps the whitest ones were old males, and the others young males or females. The wing of this species is very pointed, so that the bird has something the appearance of a Sandpiper in flight.'

Sheppard and Whitear in *A Catalogue of the Norfolk and Suffolk Birds, with Remarks* 1826: 24 write:

> 'Flocks of Snow Buntings visit the coast of Norfolk every winter; they are sometimes found in great abundance at Caistor near Yarmouth. – The wings of this species are long and pointed which give it a somewhat the appearance of a Sandpiper in flight. This enlarged power of wing was probably designed to enable the bird to accomplish its migration to and from the arctic circle.'

Pine Bunting
Emberiza leucocephalos
A male, probably a first-winter, was found by Ricky Fairhead and Robert Wilton at Corton, Suffolk just over the county boundary on 28th October 1995. It moved across into Hopton, Norfolk during the course of the day and was seen well in both counties.

Ricky Fairhead and Robert Wilton write:

> 'The weather during the greater part of October had been dominated by south-westerly winds resulting in an almost complete dearth of migrants. However, on the 28th light north-easterly winds offered a good chance of interesting migrants. We decided to visit Corton where a large finch flock had

become established at the Ministry of Defence complex on the county boundary.

Despite regular visits Corn Bunting had been the most notable bird this site had produced all year so 5 Twite was an event. We then noticed several Yellow-hammers on the fence and among them a stranger displaying a white facial patch. We quickly realised it was a Pine Bunting, an extremely rare vagrant to north-west Europe. After a couple of minutes viewing the prize headed off in a westerly direction escorted by 2 Yellowhammers. All three landed near the road, but a brief scan of the kale revealed nothing. We decided to spread the news.

Arriving back at mid-day the Pine Bunting was again on the perimeter fence. But as might be expected it quickly dropped into the kale just as the first birders arrived. A nail-biting 2.25 hour wait followed. Then Ian Metcalfe and John Oates spotted it amongst a group of Yellowhammers. It then crept into kale before showing at close quarters finally giving the assembled crowd excellent views.

For the remainder of the afternoon this Pine Bunting performed from time to time – mainly on the Suffolk side of the boundary. Fortunately it was later observed very well in the county of Norfolk before flying south to roost with Yellowhammers.

This Pine Bunting was a text-book individual, most probably a first-winter male. It lacked any yellow colouration and, most importantly, the fringes of the primaries were white. The latter feature excludes the possibility of a hybrid. Pine Buntings breed in similar habitat to Yellowhammers and hybridisation occurs in one area of western Siberia. In fact a hybrid appeared at Sizewell in Suffolk in April 1982. The origin of Siberian buntings is always open to debate particularly following the increase in the wild bird trade. This Pine Bunting was undoubtedly wild; the following day 3 Siberian migrants (2 Pallas's and a Radde's Warbler) appeared at Yarmouth.

The Corton Bunting becomes a county first for both Norfolk and Suffolk. Pine Buntings breed in Siberia, south of the Arctic Circle, west to the Urals and in Mongolia, favouring forest clearings in wet valleys. In winter they may be found in northern and north-eastern China, north-west India and Afganistan.'

(An account published in the *Norfolk Bird Report* 1995: 593)

Yellowhammer
Emberiza citronella
The earliest dated reference we can find is in 'Extracts from the Calendar of the Rev. Willian Whitear 1809-1826' published in the *Transaction of the Norfolk and Norwich Naturalists' Society* 1881-1882: 243 where he recorded on 29th June 1816 in the Starston area:

'…found a Yellow-hammer's nest on the ground, with four eggs in it; it was in clover.'

Listed by Sheppard and Whitear in *A Catalogue of the Norfolk and Suffolk Birds, with Remarks* (1826) but not commented on, the Pagets in *Sketch of the Natural History of Yarmouth and its Neighbourhood* 1834: 5 considered it '…common.'

Cirl Bunting
Emberiza cirlus
One was shot at an undisclosed locality in November 1849.

Henry Stevenson writes in *The Birds of Norfolk* Vol. l. 1866: 198-199:

'This rare species was not included by Messrs. Gurney and Fisher in their "Birds of Norfolk," but the appearance of a single specimen in this county in November 1849, was recorded by Mr. J. H. Gurney in the "*Zoologist*" (p.2651), though neither the exact locality nor sex is mentioned. - A correspondent in the "*Field*" (May 24, 1856) also states that a pair were killed in Norfolk in December, 1855, one of which is said to have come into the possession of the Earl of Leicester. These are probably the only instances in which this species has been identified as visiting our coast; it is probable, however, that other examples may have occurred, though passing unnoticed from their general resemblance to the yellow bunting.'

One of the 1855 specimens mentioned in the above account is a male which is cased and on display in the Bird Room at Holkham Hall, along with another shot in January 1888 (Bloomfield 1993).

Ortolan Bunting
Emberiza hortulana
The first fully authenticated Norfolk record was a bird obtained at Yarmouth in April 1866. The specimen (Accession no. NWHCM: 1901.28) is on display in the bird gallery at the Castle Museum, Norwich.

J. H. Gurney jun. writes in the *Transactions of the Norfolk and Norwich Naturalists' Society* 1871-1872: 61-62:

'Mr. Stevenson has given his reasons in the "Birds of Norfolk," (vol. i., p. 199,) for excluding the ortolan bunting; but from what has recently come to light it would seem that it may yet be entitled to a place in the rich avi-fauna of our county. Last year I bought a specimen of Mr. Gunn, (a dull-coloured one compared with the plate in Sharpe and Dresser's "Birds of Europe,") which had been netted at Yarmouth in April, 1866, and kept alive two days by a man named Harvey.'

The reference above to Stevenson excluding this species from the Norfolk List relates to an earlier specimen recorded as shot near Earlham in the summer of 1838, which is in the Connop collection at the City of Birmingham Museum. He states:

'I have had good reason to doubt the genuineness, as a local specimen, of the only Ortolan Bunting (*Emberiza hortulana*), recorded as killed in this county…'

Yellow-browed Bunting
Emberiza chrysophrys
The first British record, an immature or female, was found at Holkham Meals by Mike Parker,

Dave Holman and John Kemp on 19th October 1975.

John Kemp writes:

'October 1975 was a vintage month for Siberian vagrants at a time when far fewer observers were actively seeking migrants than nowadays. The wind had veered north-easterly on the 9th as an anticyclone became established over the Baltic. This weather system remained for most of the month and the associated easterly airstream across the whole of central Europe resulted in a most exciting period in the annals of local ornithology.

Holkham woods scored heavily in this period 'providing the best ever mainland rarity watching'. The wave of eastern birds included Dusky Warbler, 2 Radde's Warblers, 2 Pallas's Warblers (they were still major rarities), Black-throated Thrush and the county's first Olive-backed Pipit and Isabelline Shrike.

During the late afternoon of October 19th M. Parker located what he believed at the time to be a Rustic Bunting in a scrubby area near the caravan site. He found D. J. Holman and me nearby and together we soon re-located what was clearly a very unusual bunting. Fortunately the views over a period of half-an-hour were very good and at times within ten feet. This bird's most striking feature was a bold head pattern showing a white central crown stripe bordered black and yellow on the supercilium between the bill and eye. Rather smaller than a Reed Bunting, it gave a classic bunting tick call rather resembling a Robin at a distance. It was very much in the Little/Rustic Bunting mould showing whitish underparts with black breast streaking and sub-moustachial stripe, warm brown ear-coverts with a small white spot and narrow white double wing-bar formed by pale tips to greater coverts and median coverts. The question was identity. Rustic Bunting was eliminated on several points especially a lack of rufous flank streaking, but it was only after examining a selection of skins at the Castle Museum Norwich that we felt confident that our bird was a Yellow-browed Bunting.

The record was accepted by British Birds Rarities Committee and published in their *Rare Birds in Great Britain* 1975 report in *British Birds* (1976) Vol 69: 358. The delay by the BOURC to accept the record until very recently revolved round several factors including 'loss of paperwork' and 'discrepancies between descriptions'. Fortunately a Fair Isle record of 1980 added enormously to our knowledge of the identification of this species and is I believe partly responsible for the full acceptance of the Holkham bird. Further details of the Norfolk occurrence will appear in British Birds. A comprehensive account of the Fair Isle individual (which closely resembled the Holkam bird) may be found in *British Birds* Vol. 76: 217-225.

Very little is known about the Yellow-browed Bunting. Apparently only a single nest has been described. Shrub thickets and taiga forest are inhabited. It is almost certainly the most easterly distributed passerine to have occurred in this country. The wintering area is eastern China.'

(An account published in the *Norfolk Bird Report* 1989: 436)

Rustic Bunting
Emberiza rustica
A female was found at Blakeney Point by Peter Wolstenholme on 10th September 1958, it remained until the 13th.

Andy Stoddart and Steve Joyner write in *The Birds of Blakeney Point* 2005: 220.

> 'Female on 10th-13th September 1958, at the plantation, trapped and ringed and photographed on 12th. – the first for Norfolk. A photograph is in the Richard Richardson archive.'

Interestingly, the 1958 *Norfolk Bird Report* refers to this bird as "the second county record" in both the Introduction to the report and the Systematic List. Research reveals that one was claimed at Hickling Broad in 1935 by Jim Vincent the widely respected head keeper at the time and considered by many to be a very good and cautious observer. Jim wrote in the Hickling report in *Wild Bird Protection in Norfolk* 1935: 19-20:

> 'I have two birds to report which were new to me. On April 28th, after a strong northerly wind with rain, I saw a strange bunting feeding on some freshly sown grass seeds on the Lodge lawn and within eighteen paces of me. Its facial markings and wing bars and general colouration struck me at once, and after consulting the "Handbook" and Gould's plate of the bird I have little doubt but that it was a female Rustic Bunting…'

Jim Vincent also mentions in his 1935 diary that the wind for the previous two days was strong northerly.

It appears that this claim was considered unacceptable by the *Norfolk Bird Report* Records Committee some time between 1958 and 1967 as Michael Seago, editor of the NBR, in his *Birds of Norfolk* (1967) recorded the 1958 bird as the first for Norfolk. Could he have overlooked the 1935 record? The occurrence of one at Wells on 17th-22nd October 1972 was recorded in the 1972 Report as "The second county record." The 1958 bird had been officially elevated to county first although it has never been acknowledged as such in any subsequent *Norfolk Bird Report*.

Little Bunting
Emberiza pusilla
An adult female was shot at Cley on 19th October 1908.

William Rowan in *Annotated List of the Birds of Blakeney Point, Norfolk* 1918: 7, simply states:

> 'Taken once only (October 19th, 1908). This is one of six records for England.'

H. F. Witherby writes:

> 'Mr. H. N. Pashley, the well-known taxidermist of Cley-next-the-Sea,

Norfolk, has sent me an adult female example of the Little Bunting (*Emberiza pusilla*), which was brought to him on October 19th by a local gunner, who had shot the bird that day. Five examples of this bird have been previously recorded as occurring in England, thirteen in Scotland, and one in Ireland (*cf. antea*, Vol. I., pp. 249, 291, 383, 385 and above). This appears to be the first record for Norfolk…'

(Originally published in *British Birds* 2: 238)

H. N. Pashley writes in *Notes on the Birds of Cley Norfolk* 1925: 107:

'Little Bunting – 1 female (first occurrence in Norfolk) on October 19th, 1908 (Connop Museum).'

Interestingly, on page 71 he mentions 'thousands of birds of all sorts passing from the 16th to the 20th'.

The specimen remains in the former Connop Collection, in storage, at the City of Birmingham Museum.

Yellow-breasted Bunting
Emberiza aureola
The first British record was of an immature female obtained by E. C. Arnold at Blakeney Point on 21st September 1905.

An interesting account of this bird appears in Andy Stoddart and Steve Joyner's *The Birds of Blakeney Point* 2005: 221-222, in which they write:

'The first record for Norfolk and for Britain of this eastern bunting, a first winter female, was taken by Arnold at Watch House on 21st September 1905 and is now in the Castle Museum, Norwich, though not on public display. This specimen was examined during the preparation of this book. It is in remarkably good condition and mounted in a large glass case containing Sea Buckthorn and grasses, the outside rear of the case being covered with sheets from the (London) *Evening News* dated 26th May 1906. A photograph of this bird has recently been published (Palmer, 2000)
An article by Percy Trett in the *Eastern Daily Press* in March 2005, drawing on a conversation with John Gledhill and the journals of his grandfather, provides a fascinating insight into the workings of the ornithological establishment of the day:-

"One September morning, the late E. C. Arnold, the scholar naturalist, shot a small bird perched on the roof of the old Pilot House on Blakeney Point. He knew it was a bunting, but he did not recognise the species. So, that evening he skinned his prize and preserved it for when he next attended a meeting of the British Ornithologists' Club at Paganini's restaurant in London where, for the sum of 7s 6d, eminent ornithologists could sit down to an excellent dinner and could exhibit their trophies over coffee and cigars. In due course Arnold's little corpse was produced and deposited on a clean plate and a waiter summoned to take it to the chairman for inspection. John's grandfather was present and recorded that he observed a somewhat puzzled expression come over the bearded countenance of Lord Rothschild, who was presiding.

Again and again he picked it up and laid it down. He ordered another bottle of Paganini's best wine and the bird was handed around the learned gentlemen on the top table. Many a wise head was bent over it and a smile appeared on Arnold's face as Gledhill senior remarked 'You have stumped Rothschild'. Dr. Ernst Hartert, the curator of Tring Museum, was called. Hartert leant across and whispered something into Rothschild's ear. He nodded, gavelled the august meeting to silence then, holding up the specimen as though he had recognised it at a glance, announced 'Mr. Arnold is to be congratulated on adding a new species to the British List. His bird is undoubtedly a Yellow-breasted Bunting".'

Additional information regarding the cased specimen, (Accession no. NWHCM: 1966.479.299), which remains in storage at the Castle Museum, Norwich, reveals that the taxidermy is by B. Bates, 2 Bourne Street, Eastbourne and was a gift to the museum from the Headmaster and Governors of the College, Eastbourne, Sussex in 1966 (D Waterhouse *in litt*). E. C. Arnold had been an earlier Headmaster of Eastbourne College and was a well respected ornithologist and conservationist. As well as purchasing land in the Cuckmere Valley and on Pevensey Levels in Sussex, specifically to create reserves, he also acquired Salthouse Broad on the north Norfolk coast in 1932, the area which is now named after him and is known as Arnold's Marsh.

Interestingly, E. C. Arnold also shot the third Norfolk and British specimen at Blakeney Point on 4th September 1913, just a quarter-of-a-mile from where he had shot the first. The second Norfolk and British record was obtained by Pat Cringle at Wells on 5th September 1907, on the mainland opposite Blakeney Point. The specimen is in the Holkham Hall collection.

Common Reed Bunting
Emberiza schoeniclus
There is no evidence to suppose that the Reed chock mentioned by Sir Thomas Browne (1605-1682) in *Notes and Letters on the Natural History of Norfolk* (1902) is meant to be the Reed Bunting.

The earliest dated reference we can find is by Robert Marsham (1708-1797) in Tim Sparks and John Lines' *Chapters in the Life of Robert Marsham Esq. F.R.S. of Stratton Strawless, Norfolk* 2008: 17:

> 'The nest seems the most original of all birds. They nicely bind 4, 5 or 6 reeds together above high water mark in the tide river or in brooks near the heads of the reeds, & the nest hangs below the tyed parts. I have seen one between London & Greenwich & several in the little stream at Shadwell in Norfolk. They lay 4 or 5 eggs, one considerably larger than the rest.'

Sheppard and Whitear write in *A Catalogue of the Norfolk and Suffolk Birds, with Remarks* 1826: 24:

'The Reed Bunting uses the same artifice to attract attention from its nest, as the Partridge does to save its young, - limping along upon the ground, screaming, and shaking its wings.'

Black-headed Bunting
Emberiza melanocephala
A first-summer male was found by Graham White in coastal fields between Salthouse and Cley on 30th April 1979. It remained until 3rd May.

While checking the fields and hedges along the road from Walsey Hills towards Salthouse, Graham White noticed a bright yellow bird with a dark head fly into a hedge about 100 yards from him. Shortly afterwards the bird reappeared slightly closer along the hedge and he recognised it as a male Black-headed Bunting. Using 10 x 40 binoculars and 30 x telescope the following details were noted:-

A bulky bunting with a black cap that extended down over the ear coverts to the sides of the neck but not forwards onto the throat, and sharply demarcated. Throat, breast and belly were bright yellow. The back was brownish-chestnut with a chestnut smudge on the sides of the breast. Wings brownish, double barred with wide buff-white edgings. The tail was uniformly dark with no white outer feathers. Grey stout seed-eating bill. The bird uttered a 'chuup' call in flight.

He informed John Brown the warden at Walsey Hills who later saw the bird, as did many others over the following three days.

(An account compiled from the unpubished files in the British Birds Rarities Committee archive)

Corn Bunting
Emberiza calandra
The earliest dated reference we can find is in 'Extracts from the Calendar of the Rev. William Whitear 1809-1826' published in the *Transactions of the Norfolk and Norwich Naturalists' Society* 1881-1882: 244 where he recorded one on 14th July 1816 in the Starston area.

Although listed by Sheppard and Whitear in *A Catalogue of the Norfolk and Suffolk Birds, with Remarks* (1826) and known by them as Common Bunting and Clod-bird, the latter a name also given to the Wheatear, it is not commented on.

The Pagets in *Sketch of the Natural History of Yarmouth and its Neighbourhood* 1834: 5 considered it '…common.'

Rose-breasted Grosbeak
Pheucticus ludovicianus
A first-summer female was found by Les Watson in his garden at Holme on 4th May 2006. Identification was confirmed later by Jed Andrews, Sophie Barker and Prof. Fred Cooke CM.

Jed Andrews, Sophie Barker, Geoffrey Barker and David Bednall write:

'At 8am on 4th May, Holme Bird Observatory warden Jed Andrews received a report from a local resident, Les Watson, of a Rose-breasted Grosbeak *Pheucticus ludovicianus* in his garden at Holme village. Jed went straight there to try and see the bird and confirm the identification. He telephoned assistant warden Sophie Barker, who was at the Observatory, who also came to the site. Sophie had ringed the species in Canada in 2004 and went to the site with a North American field guide (Sibley 2003) and a book of cage and aviary birds (Vriends 1992) to help verify the species, aware that the possibility of an escaped weaver species would need to be eliminated. However, the bird was not seen by 10am and without an opportunity to confirm the identification, Jed and Sophie left the site but asked Les if he would kindly contact them if the bird re-appeared.

Nothing was heard until 8pm that evening when Jed received a further call to report that the bird had flown into a window at the house and been taken into care. He went to see the bird straight away, and after examining it consulted a number of other birdwatchers. Maurice Eccleshall came to see the bird and also concurred with the identification, as he had previous experience of the species on the Isles of Scilly. Maurice also consulted a friend who was an expert in cage and aviary birds to check the status of the species in Great Britain, and was advised that there was no-one known in Norfolk who kept Rose-breasted Grosbeak as a cage or aviary bird. Professor Fred Cooke also came to see the bird and, after consulting North American field guides (Sibley 2003; Stokes 1995), agreed it was a first-summer female Rose-breasted Grosbeak – the only potential confusion species, Black-headed Grosbeak, was discounted by Fred.

The bird was clearly recovering and its condition satisfactory; it was decided to keep it in care overnight and by late the next morning it appeared to have completely recovered. The BTO were consulted and they agreed the bird was unlikely to be of captive origin. Permission was given to ring it and the bird was ringed by Jed and jointly processed with Sophie. It was confirmed as a first-summer female. The evenly distributed feather-wear throughout the plumage and also in the primaries, secondaries, coverts and tail feathers were consistent with a first-summer bird. There were no abnormalities within the bird's tail, talons or beak to suggest captive origin. There was a single replaced greater covert on the left wing and a true moult limit on the right wing with two adult-type innermost greater coverts; these were darker brown and glossier than the surrounding feathers but clearly not black. The yellow/orange flush on the underwing coverts was also consistent with the bird being a female.

Of particular interest to the ringers was the rapid gain of condition in the bird. When examined on the Thursday evening there was only a small amount of fat in the clavicle pit and none at the back of the neck, although the bird was storing seed in its crop at this time. When the bird was ringed the following afternoon, it was noticed that a considerable amount of fat had been deposited not only in the pit but also under the skin of the neck, suggesting that the food has been rapidly metabolised and laid down as fat. The ringers' experience of handling migrants is that this process, and the speed with which it took place, is strongly linked to migratory behaviour. The pectoral muscles (flight muscles) were healthy.

Several photographs were taken including identification features and those to show the condition of the feet and feathers. This helped to determine that the bird had not been kept in captivity prior to being taken into care.

If accepted, this bird would be the first for Norfolk and the first in spring for Britain and Ireland.

DESCRIPTION
Overall this was a very large, bulky pale brown passerine similar in size to a Hawfinch. It had a heavy head, bulky neck, pale flesh-coloured bill and dark eyes set close to the bill.

There was a prominent supercillium, which almost met at the back of the head, and a pale sub-moustachial stripe. There was a pale median crown stripe which separated two darkish brown lateral crown stripes. The breast was buffish-white with prominent streaks over the breast and flanks. Wing and tail feathers were medium brown with white tips to the median and greater coverts, forming a double wing bar. The mantle was brown with darker streaks. The under wing coverts were yellow/orange and the legs were medium grey.'

(Extracted from an account published in the *Norfolk Ornithologists Association Report* 2006: 335-337)

An earlier claim of an adult male at Wells on 17th June 1979 was dismissed by Michael Seago as being an escape.

Category D Species

Of the species currently on Category D of the British List, just six have been accepted for Norfolk. For completeness we include the first recorded occurrences here, for the reason that this category is widely accepted as being a holding category for species which have the potential to arrive in the county naturally, and could at some stage be elevated to Category A of the Norfolk List. Several more species have been recorded in the county, some on more than one occasion, but the records were either placed in Category E or were apparently not submitted to the BBRC.

Species placed in Category D only form no part of the Norfolk List. Category E species form no part of the Norfolk List unless already included within Categories A, B or C.

Ross's Goose
Anser rossii

The first Ross's Goose to be accepted as a Category D species for Norfolk was an adult first seen at Holkham by Mark Ward on 29th September 2007. It remained into 2008.

Several earlier records have yet to be submitted to, or accepted by, the BBRC. The first to arrive, remain with and depart with Pink-footed Geese was an unringed first-winter bird first seen by Andrew Bloomfield at Wells on 3rd November 2001 and is likely to become the earliest accepted record for the county.

Andrew Bloomfield writes:

> 'Having recently discussed, with Richard Millington, the possibilities of a potentially wild Ross's Goose turning up amongst Norfolk's wintering population of Pink-footed Geese, much to my surprise on 3rd November 2001, it happened. I was driving out of Wells, mid afternoon, when I noticed a pale goose gleaming out from a group of about 2,500 Pink-feet on winter cereal. Grinding to a halt, I half expected to see the leucistic Pink-foot which had been present in the area during previous winters. To my great shock, however, it was a 'white goose' complete with black primaries. "Snow Goose" I muttered to Emma Russell who was with me – but then I noticed its size. It was small and plump with a short neck – Red-breasted Goose size perhaps. Telescope views soon confirmed my thoughts: it was a Ross's Goose. Its rather disproportionately long legs were grey (dusky-pink at close quarters), the stubby bill was pink with a greyish basal half, the lores were dark grey and there was a grey wash to its rear crown, hind-neck, mantle and tail; all the characteristics of a juvenile/first-winter bird. It bore no

rings and its plumage looked in good shape. Here was surely as good a candidate as any for being a genuinely wild bird. I watched it feeding on winter wheat and also receiving a fair number of pecks from neighbouring Pink-feet, for about 20 minutes before deciding to race back to Wells and find some other observers.

Having found Dave Foster we returned just as the flock was departing; spooked by a tractor spraying the corn. Thankfully the birds re-alighted in the next field and we soon found our quarry. After a further 20 minutes the flock again departed, this time thanks to a dog-walker. In flight the Ross's Goose certainly stood out from the flock due to its white plumage, small size, short neck and spindly narrow wings. The primaries were black, whilst a greyer tone could be seen on the primary coverts above and on its secondaries below.

It departed towards Holkham and then presumably Wells to roost (as light was by then beginning to fade). It therefore came as a surprise when on the following day it was refound in east Norfolk at Waxham. Presumably with moon-lit conditions overnight it had joined the Pinks on one of their regular nocturnal feeding jaunts. This in itself proved interesting; whilst frequently speculated, proof that the Wells Pink-feet will move so far overnight to feed had previously been lacking. The following day it was back in north Norfolk in the North Creake area, and it subsequently remained feeding always with the Wells-roosting Pinks in the Burnham Market, Overy, Holkham, Walsingham, Wighton, Docking, Stanhoe, North Creake and North Barsham area throughout the remainder of the winter. On at least two more occasions it joined the east Norfolk skeins, each visit again timed with full moon conditions. It was noted presumably returning to north Norfolk, once over Brundall and once over Holt.

During its stay it always associated with the Pink-feet and was seen feeding on grassland, winter cereals, autumn stubble (both on grass and spilt grain) and, of course, sugar beet tops. It was last reported on 6th February 2002, although several times in the last couple of weeks prior to then, the leucistic Pink-foot from previous winters re-appeared in the area and was mis-identified several times by visitors as the Ross's Goose. Interestingly the Ross's Goose departed with the first big bunch of Pink-feet to leave the area. Prior to its departure it had been seen in a flock complete with 'Lesser' type Canada, Red-breasted, 3 Barnacles, Greenland and Russian White-fronts, 4 Tundra Beans, a Greylag and a Pale-bellied Brent, a truly unbelievable scene?!'

(An account extracted from an article in *Norfolk Bird Club Bulletin* 47: 4-9, which included more details on the bird's movements, and speculation and discussion on its origins)

Falcated Duck

Anas falcata
An adult drake with Eurasian Wigeon was identified at Welney by John Kemp on 9th-10th and 27th December 1986.

John Kemp writes:

'At approximately 11:00hrs on 9th December 1986 I saw a strange duck fly past the main hide at the Wildfowl Trust's reserve at Welney on the Ouse Washes. A better view of the bird as it landed about 150yds away showed it to be a drake Falcated Teal, rather unmistakeable with its glossy green and wine-coloured head and mane, white throat, speckled breast, Teal-like undertail patch, and long curved tertials.

The bird spent much of the day within 150yds of the main hide, but in the afternoon flew off with Wigeon to the far side of the reserve where it fed while swimming in shallow water, dipping its head down to pick up vegetation in a manner similar to Gadwall and Wigeon. At a distance the bird soon merged with the thousands of Wigeon and was lost, not to be seen again until the morning of the 27th December when it was again present in its original spot for over two hours. With over twenty miles of Washland this bird has plenty of available area and will prove difficult to see unless its regular feeding site can be found. At a distance of (400yds or more) the bird looked mostly Mallard-grey with a green head and could be overlooked, rather surprising when one considers its distinctive appearance on a closer view.

Falcated Teal are Wigeon-sized ducks showing a thin wing in flight. The wing pattern is rather non-descript being mostly grey but with a very dark speculum showing a white fore-border but only an indistinct pale trailing edge. At close range the complicated head pattern is distinctive, in sunshine being glossy green with a ruby-wine loral area and crown becoming almost blackish on the mane. A large white throat area is edged with a dark band and there is a small round spot on the forehead. The breast is well marked with dark crescents but otherwise the body colour is a dull grey. The long curved tertials are distinctive with their black centers and white edges. The undertail has creamy Teal-like patches surrounded by black and with a separating white band between the black and the flanks.

On closer views it was seen walking at the water's edge with Wigeon where it appeared to be gritting, at times opening its bill in aggression if another bird came too close. The particular spot it used is regularly visited by Wigeon and other waterfowl because over the years quantities of gravely sand have been dumped there to enable wildfowl to obtain a supply of grit in this otherwise peaty area.

With the haphazard keeping of wildfowl in so many collections these days the escape possibility has to be considered, although so far all the local collectors who have been asked either do not keep the species or have not lost any. Good views of the Welney bird's legs showed that it was not carrying any rings, and its wings in flight were perfect. It certainly appeared wild, responding immediately to the Wigeons' pre-flight head jerking by stretching its neck up in the alert position, and then taking flight with Wigeon.

No captive birds are kept at Welney but during the course of most years one or two obvious escapes occur (*e.g.* Bahama Pintail, Chilean Pintail *etc*). These are attracted by the grain put out for the wild swans which also attracts wild Mallard, Pochard and Tufted Duck close in to the hides. These obvious escapes normally linger for a week or two and readily come to the feed. The Falcated Teal showed no interest in the area where the grain is fed and seemed much more alert and flighty than any known escape.

So rests the case for the Falcated Teal; the record has been submitted to BBRC.'

(Originally published in *Twitching* 1: 21-23)

Marbled Duck

Marmaronetta angustirostris

One was found by Moss Taylor at Kelling Water Meadows on 23rd April 2000. It was gone by the following morning.

Moss Taylor writes from his notes and recollections of the occasion:

'At 0715hrs on 23rd April 2000, while checking through the birds at Kelling Water Meadows, I identified a Marbled Duck which was resting on the short grass alongside the western edge of the water. It had not been there the previous day when I visited the area in the late afternoon. While not concerned at my presence (100 metres away), it was wary of a pair of Coots which were nesting nearby and at one point was driven further around the water's edge by one of the pair. My only previous experience of the species was in Morocco in 1965! Although I was aware of the possibility that it was an escape or feral bird from a wildfowl collection, a southerly wind during the previous two days suggested that it may have been a genuine vagrant. Therefore I phoned the sighting into Birdline East Anglia on arriving home and it was subsequently seen by a large number of birders and was photographed by Robin Chittenden. Apparently it remained all day but was not present the following morning.

The fact that it had almost certainly arrived and departed under cover of darkness, had remained only for a single day, was wary and showed no signs of captivity, such as leg rings, evidence of previous pinioning or undue feather wear, are all pointers in favour of it having been a genuine vagrant. In addition, its appearance coincided with the arrival of a selection of southern European species throughout Britain.

The following description based on field notes and a field sketch taken at the time of observation was submitted to the BBRC. About the size of a Teal but appeared more elongated due to longer, slightly uptilted tail. General impression was of a rather drab, pale grey-brown duck with a darker crown and upperparts. From the angle of observation, the crown appeared dark brownish-black, extending as a mask around the eye, but not reaching the base of the bill. Fairly distinct paler loral spot. Bill uniformly medium grey with a suggestion of a darker nail. Upperparts medium brown with pale buff, rounded spots on back, upperwing coverts, sides of breast and flanks. Underparts pale grey-brown with slightly darker, fine bars across breast. On being chased by the Coot, it 'scampered' across the grass with wings open, when the flight feathers could be seen to be plain grey-brown with no speculum, although the secondaries seemed somewhat paler. The colour of the legs and feet were not noted.

The identification was accepted but it was placed in Category D. Personally, I feel that its credentials were such that it may one day be accepted as a first for Britain, but then I am biased!'

White-headed Duck

Oxyura leucocephala

A male, identified the following morning by John Eaton, was found at Hardley Flood on 18th June 2002 which remained until 25th August.

John Eaton writes:

'On the evening of 18th June 2002, Pete Carr, a birder from Rockland St Mary, phoned to tell me that someone walking along the river Chet had seen a strange duck on Hardley Flood. I decided to check it out next morning, expecting to find a Ruddy Duck, or even an escaped White-cheeked Pintail, both of which had been present on the Flood during mid-May. I rode down to the Flood on my bicycle, taking only binoculars with me. About half way along the bank I saw a group of five Ruddy Ducks (3 males and 2 females), but hassling them was a larger bird. I quickly identified it as a White-headed Duck by the swollen pale-blue bill, larger size and general overall sandy colouration, plus it appeared to have a dark line across the cheeks possibly indicating a female. I needed better views and a look at a field guide. I rushed home, noted some of the important points to check, made a couple of phone calls, grabbed my telescope and quickly drove back to the Flood.

As I arrived, Pete Milford was also just arriving and together we re-found the bird and 'scoped it. We could now see it was indeed a male, either an immature or an adult moving into eclipse plumage. The body was dark sandy-brown and finely barred, the breast and rump were chestnut-brown. The crown was black and a blackish neck-band was also visible. The white cheeks were smudged with black forming a dark eye-stripe band and the bill was bright azure blue. The bird was apparently full-winged and in good condition.

It was to remain on the Flood for some weeks and was appreciated by a large number of observers. Over the weeks the bird remained on the Flood, the bill darkened to lead grey and the white face pattern became much more mottled and black. It often displayed to the female Ruddy Ducks and also chased away the males.

Hardley Flood has been a good site for rare ducks over the years, with Blue-winged Teal, Ferruginous Duck, Ring-necked Duck and Smew all having been recorded. The White-headed Duck was last seen at the site on 25th August. What was almost certainly the same bird was re-located in the midlands at Stanford Reservoir on 11th September, where it stayed until the 22nd before moving west to Blithfield Reservoir on 29th-30th September, always in the company of Ruddy Ducks.'

(An account published in *Norfolk Bird Club Bulletin* 50: 19-21)

Great White Pelican
Pelecanus onocrotalus
Three, in a very tired condition, were identified by Peter Allard at Breydon Water on 31st August 1971. They remained until 2nd September and were later reported in Essex. Three earlier claims for the county were placed in Category E.

Peter Allard writes from his notes and recollections of the occasion:

'Three adult Great White Pelicans were seen asleep at Breydon Water during the afternoon of 31st August 1971, on the mud-flats at the eastern end of the estuary. They had not been present the previous day or during that morning up until 11.00hrs and were presumed to have freshly arrived. They were apparently very tired as they slept for virtually the whole time they were under observation, apart from an occasional wing flap, which fortunately revealed the characteristic black and white underwing pattern of this species. There were no wing abrasions or any flight feathers missing and none of the three birds carried leg rings. The bill and legs were noted as pink. They were still asleep late evening and were in exactly the same location very early the following morning. All three spent the entire day just resting, apart from a brief flight around the estuary during the afternoon. At least two other observers also saw these birds, one of whom was believed to be a Mike Jenner from Belton. They were last seen on the morning of the 2nd September by Robin Harrison, one of the reserve's wardens, and by the evening they appeared to have departed.

Three Great White Pelicans, without question the same individuals, were later reported in Essex. Details of the three birds were submitted to the BBRC and they were eventually accepted into Category D.'

Greater Flamingo
Phoenicopterus ruber
One, considered to be a first-winter, was found by John Oates at Breydon on 5th October 1990 which remained until the 6th.

John Oates writes from his notes and recollections of the occasion:

'The morning of 5th October 1990 was very wet with strong south-westerly winds. The hide at Breydon Water seemed a sensible place to take shelter, especially as the tide was rising. Shortly after 8.30am I was scanning from the hide when I noticed an immature flamingo preening and feeding in shallow water about 100 yards away. This was a surprise, though the dull plumage (lacking any visible pink) made the bird look at home in the equally dull surroundings! It didn't have any leg rings.

Not knowing which species it was, I took notes and drew a few sketches hoping to confirm the identification later at home. I knew the bill pattern was important, so I made sure I noted this accurately.

The flamingo was still present when I left the hide at about 10.30am. As far as I know I was the only observer on the 5th. Later that day I arrived home and headed straight for *Flamingos* by Malcolm and Carol Ogilvie. After a short time I was happy it was a Greater Flamingo *Phoenicopterus ruber*. Realising that it might just possibly be a wild bird I reported it to Birdline East Anglia as a first-winter Greater Flamingo.

Fortunately the flamingo was still present the following day and it was seen by a number of keen Norfolk listers. It was close to the hide again and flight views revealed a striking pink underwing and a nice set of flight feathers. It was photographed both in flight and on the ground at Breydon by Robin Chittenden and moved south to Minsmere in Suffolk on the 7th and 8th. This record was placed in Category D.'

Early Norfolk records of flamingos from 1902 onwards were poorly documented and failed to eliminate other flamingo species. Eleven earlier claims for the county were placed in Category E.

Interestingly, twelve Greater Flamingos were reported circling offshore at Weybourne on 14th July 1980. Later in the afternoon twelve flew west at Sheringham, while local crab fishermen reported seeing a party of 34, about 6km offshore. Unfortunately these were never submitted to BBRC (Taylor 1987).

Category A, B and C Species Recently Removed from the Norfolk List

Prior to their relatively recent removal from the Norfolk List, the following species were considered authentic Norfolk records.

Harlequin Duck
Histrionicus histrionicus
A party of five was seen by Billy Bishop at Cley on 19th February 1947, during severe weather.

Billy Bishop writes:

> 'During the severe winter of 1947, I was crossing the Reserve and walking along the Main Drain. Despite the fact that this drain is full of sea water, it was frozen solid. Drifting snow had formed a wall on the north side and there, sitting under the edge of this bank, were five Harlequin Duck, three drakes and two ducks. I could hardly believe what I saw. But there they were, these visitors in all probability from Iceland, not more than 10 feet away from me. There were large ice floes offshore that had drifted down from the north. The general opinion was that the harlequins came this far south on one of these floes. During my war service in Iceland, I had seen many of these handsome ducks but they have never before been recorded in Norfolk and I don't think they have been since.'

(An account published in *Cley Marsh and its Birds* 1983: 49)

This record was included in *Wild Bird Protection in Norfolk* 1947, *Check-list of the Birds of Cley and Neighbouring Norfolk Parishes* (Richardson 1962), *Birds of Norfolk* (Seago 1967 and 1977) and *Cley Marsh and its Birds* (Bishop 1993 and 1996). *A Checklist of the Birds of Cley* (Gantlett 1984) included this record in square brackets, with the comment that it had never been officially accepted. It was also included in *The Birds of Norfolk* (Taylor *et al* 1999) in square brackets, with the conclusion by Michael Seago, who had discussed this sighting with Billy Bishop and was shown the brief entries in his diary, that 'Unfortunately because of the lack of a written description or any other corroboratory evidence, this record has not been accepted nationally and consequently is not now included in the accepted total of species recorded in Norfolk.' Its deletion from the Norfolk List was published in the *Norfolk Bird Report* 1992. To our knowledge this record has never been submitted to any rarity records committee.

Southwell (1890) dismissed two early 19th century records from the Yarmouth area.

Bufflehead
Bucephala albeola

The first British record was of an adult drake alleged to have been shot near Yarmouth, almost certainly Breydon Water, in about 1830. The specimen was originally kept in Stephen Miller's collection at Gorleston and then passed to Robert Rising's collection at Horsey on 22nd September 1853. This collection was auctioned on 17th September 1885 and the Bufflehead was purchased for Mr. J. J. Colman MP for 25 guineas. The specimen was presented to the Castle Museum, Norwich on 22nd September 1885 (Dr A G Irwin *in litt*).

The second county record concerned a female seen by C. T. M. Plowright and N. Tracy off Hunstanton on several dates in February 1932.

After the publication of his book *The Birds of Great Yarmouth* (1990), Peter Allard received a telephone call from Lee Evans informing him that the information regarding the Bufflehead in the book was incorrect. The bird was actually at Saffron Walden Museum and not at Norwich. Enquiries were made at both museums and both had a specimen claiming to be the same bird. Lee Evans also stated that he thought a third bird labelled as shot at Yarmouth in 1830 was at the Natural History Museum, Kensington Gardens, London (see the full story in an article by Peter Allard entitled 'The Bufflehead – a Norfolk Bird or not?' published in the *Norfolk Bird Club Bulletin* 22: 8-9).

The 1932 Hunstanton record was detailed by Dr. B. B. Riviere in the 'Ornithological Report for Norfolk 1932' in *British Birds* 26: 326, where he writes:

> 'On several dates during the month of February, on the sea off Hunstanton, Mr. C. T. M. Plowright watched through a telescope – once as close as 40 yards – a duck which he identified as a female Buffel-headed Duck. His description is as follows: "Head blackish, nape sooty. An oblong white patch on each side of the cheeks from below eye to nape. Back and mantle brown, under parts ashy white. It was feeding on small mussels in company with both Velvet and Common Scoters, compared with which its small size was very noticeable." Mr. Plowright is so good an observer that I think there can be no doubt as to the correctness of his identification, which was confirmed by Mr. N. Tracy, who also saw the bird. The only authentic Norfolk specimen of this American species is the adult drake in the Norwich Museum which was killed near Yarmouth about 1830.'

Details of the 1830 and 1932 records were sent to the BOURC and to the local rarities committee for review, and both were found unacceptable. As a consequence of this, Bufflehead was removed from the Norfolk List in 2001. An excellent article entitled 'The Bufflehead in Britain – A review' by Alan Knox on behalf of the BOURC was published in *British Birds* 94: 61-73, and reviews 16 pre-1952 Bufflehead records, and two after that date - which includes both Norfolk records - detailing rejections and acceptances.

Lady Amherst's Pheasant
Chrysolophus amherstiae

The British population has always centred on Bedfordshire following introductions made in the 1890s. However, these have dramatically decreased in recent years and only four birds remained in 2008. A Category C1 species in Britain since 1971, Lady Amherst's Pheasant was added to the county list in 1973 on the evidence of successful breeding at Guist and Quidenham. However, with no records received in 1974, and only recorded at Elsing on one date in 1975 and at Hockham on a single date in 1977, the species was unable to maintain a population in the county and removed from the Norfolk List in 1986 (Taylor *et al* 1999). It was included by Seago in *Birds of Norfolk* (1977) and its deletion from the county list was published in1993 (*Norfolk Bird Report* 1992: 498).

We have been unable to find a published, detailed reason why this species should have been deleted from the Norfolk List, having been on it for 13 years, presumably as a Category C1 species. To gain access to the Norfolk List in the first place one must assume that there was a self-sustaining population within the county at that time, or that a bird or birds from the southern British breeding population had reached Norfolk unaided, which is somewhat unlikely. Therefore we must presume that its original addition to the county list was suspect and related to birds having escaped from captivity, were bred in captivity before release or were never a self-sustaining breeding population. If that is not the case, surely it should remain in Category C, in the newly created Category C6, (naturalized species that were formerly placed in C1 but whose naturalized populations are either no longer self-sustaining or are considered extinct).

Short-billed Dowitcher
Limnodromus griseus
Prior to 1950 it was not known that two species of dowitcher existed in North America, such is their similarity, and the two were known as Red-breasted Snipe *Limnodromus griseus* on both sides of the Atlantic.

There were two records of Short-billed Dowitcher on the county list. The first was at Cley on 5th October to 3rd November 1957 (*British Birds* 54: 343-356), which regularly commuted to Salthouse. It was filmed by Dick Bagnall-Oakeley and a photograph of the bird was published in the *Norfolk Bird Report* 1957. Another was at Wisbech Sewage Farm on 28th September to October 1963 (*British Birds* 57: 267).

The 1963 record was reviewed in 1980 and it was re-identified as a Long-billed Dowitcher (*British Birds* 74: 471). The 1957 bird was one of four remaining acceptable records in the British Isles until a further review by the BOURC in April 1991 found all four to be not acceptable and Short-billed Dowitcher was deleted from the British List (*British Birds* 99: 354-360). The Norfolk record could not be re-identified as a Long-billed Dowitcher and was reclassified as a Dowitcher sp (Taylor *et al* 1999).

Short-billed Dowitcher was placed firmly back on the British List when a juvenile was located at Rosehearty in Northeast Scotland on 11th-24th September 1999, before moving to Greenabella Marsh and Greatham Creek, Cleveland on 29th September to at least 30th October.

Great Black-headed Gull
Larus ichthyaetus
One was at Cromer on 2nd-9th March 1932.

B. B. Riviere writes in Ornithological Report for Norfolk for 1932 in *British Birds* 26: 329:

'Great Black-headed Gull (*Larus ichyaetus*) – Between March 2nd and 9th Mr. Henry Cole watched almost daily a gull, feeding with Black-headed Gulls at

Cromer between the pier and sewer outlet, which he identified as belonging to the above species. His attention was first called to it as being something "out of the way" by a fisherman, C. Braconbury by name, who is a keen observer of birds. Mr. Cole described it as appearing about the size of a Herring Gull, but with a more slender neck. The black head was incomplete. "Mantle darker grey than that of a Black-headed Gull. Wings were more crossed than a Herring Gull's, and with white on primaries more pronounced than in a Black-headed Gull. Bill light orange with a bar and much thicker at the tip than a Black-headed Gull's. Legs yellow".

This is a new species for Norfolk, but from the above description by an observer of Mr. Cole's experience, one must, I think, accept this record as authentic.'

All Great Black-headed Gull records in Britain were reviewed by the BOURC, and the results published in 1993 in a very interesting article entitled 'The Great Black-headed Gull in Britain' by Keith Vinicombe and Peter J. Hopkin, which was published in *British Birds* 86: 201-205. As a result of this review only one British record remained acceptable, a bird in Devon at the end of May or the beginning of June 1859, and Great Black-headed Gull was removed from the Norfolk List. The BOURC did consider that parts of the description of the Norfolk bird were more convincing than those of the other rejected records, but, nevertheless, the possibility of a mistake could not be eliminated.

Orphean Warbler
Sylvia hortensis
One was found at Stiffkey by T. J. James and B. L. Sage on 17th August 1981.

The *Norfolk Bird Report* 1981 gave no further details of the occurrence, other than stating that it was the first county record.

Although accepted by the BBRC at the time it was officially removed from the Norfolk list in 1987 when *British Birds* 80: 561 announced in the Report on Rare Birds:

'1981 Norfolk Stiffkey, 17th August (*Brit. Birds* 75: 522), now considered not acceptable after review.'

Prior to this the *Norfolk Bird Report* 1985: 254, in a review of The County List, had mentioned that following reconsideration the record had recently been withdrawn.

Interestingly, although this species was officially on the Norfolk List for six years it was not mentioned in *The Birds of Norfolk* (1999). It was mentioned, in square brackets, in *Rare Birds of Norfolk* (1996).

Citril Finch
Serinus citronella
The only British specimen, prior to 2008, was an adult female allegedly caught on Yarmouth North Denes by bird-catcher John Quinton on 29th January 1904. It was kept alive for two days by Edward Saunders, the Yarmouth taxidermist, before being sent to John Henry Gurney in Norwich for identification. Following Gurney's examination, Howard Saunders admitted

the bird to the British List. Thomas Gunn, the famed Norwich taxidermist, prepared the bird as a mounted specimen and it soon passed into the collection of Sir Vauncey Harpur Crewe of Derbyshire. This specimen remained with him until his death, and was auctioned in 1925 or 1926 and presented to the Booth Museum, Brighton where it remained in 1999.

When researching his book *The Birds of Great Yarmouth* (1990), Peter Allard visited the Booth Museum in Brighton. The Citril Finch remained in its original case, but was not as he had expected. The bird was larger, the blackish wing-bars extending to the tertials were incorrect for Citril Finch and the bill appeared too heavy and Greenfinch-like. The Museum confirmed this was indeed the correct case. There is no evidence of the bird having been examined critically since 1905 prior to his visit.

He had considerable doubts as to its identification and photographs were circulated to local ornithologists, but for a variety of reasons they were unable to assist. Lee Evans, with his wealth of knowledge and contacts, was then approached and a photograph was forwarded to him. His reaction was that it was not a Citril Finch. He suggested a Canary of even a Greenfinch hybrid. Contact was then made with Dr. Alan Knox on behalf of the BOURC. He visited Brighton and tentatively identified the bird as a Cape Canary *Serinus conicollis*, or Yellow-crowned Canary *Serinus flavicollis* and he was able to verify that it was a Cape Canary when the specimen was taken to the Natural History Museum at Tring. It was further identified as a male on plumage characters.

Following the re-identification of this specimen, Citril Finch was deleted from the British List in 1993. A very interesting article entitled 'Removal of Citril Finch from the British and Irish List' by Alan Knox on behalf of the BOURC was published in *British Birds* 87: 471-473.

And Finally

There are a number of other species that might have been added to the Norfolk List, but for various reasons have been found to be unacceptable. A variety of reasons exist, but mainly because they were considered to have escaped from captivity or that they had been intentionally released into the wild. Others were considered to be possible fraudulent claims, whilst for some, which were shot or captured at sea and brought into Yarmouth harbour, it was impossible to be certain of the exact location of their capture, although the identification was not in doubt. A number of Category D species have for various reasons never been submitted by the observers.

Many species of presumed escaped wildfowl have been recorded in Norfolk. Of these, perhaps only Hooded Merganser and Marbled Duck could claim wild origins. There are two very old records of Hooded Merganser, one being supposedly obtained at Yarmouth in 1829 and another said to have been shot in the county in the winter of 1837/38. Riviere (1930) stated that there were sufficient reasons for doubting the authenticity of the former specimen whilst there would appear to be little or no evidence that the latter was actually obtained in Norfolk. There have been several records in recent years but none of these appears to have been submitted to the BBRC. Wood Duck is commonly kept in wildfowl collections both in this country and in Europe. The true status of the species in Norfolk is unknown, but all records to date have been treated as escapes from captivity. However, wild birds are a possibility, but Wood Duck remains in Category D of the British List.

An interesting record and one that should be mentioned is of a *Fregetta* Storm Petrel that flew past Sheringham on 10th December 2007. It is in circulation with the BBRC but as yet no decision has been made, and as no specific species (Black-bellied or White-bellied) is being claimed it could remain under consideration for some time to come. A Wilson's Storm Petrel, supposedly obtained in the North Sea, passed through the hands of George Smith, a Yarmouth bird dealer, as a Norfolk specimen some time prior to 1884. It passed into the possession of G. H. Gurney, originally having been purchased by his grandfather J. H. Gurney senior. The authenticity of this bird was never accepted by Thomas Southwell and it failed to get a mention in the third volume of *The Birds of Norfolk* which Southwell completed in 1890.

An adult Chinese Pond Heron was at Eccles on 31st October 2004 and then at East Dean, Hampshire on 13th November. It was apparently submitted to the BBRC but no decision has been published to our knowledge. The only two previous European records, in Norway in 1973 and Hungary in 2000, were placed in Category D. Sacred Ibis sightings have become more frequent in recent years, presumably due to small but increasing feral populations breeding in France, Spain and Italy. Others may possibly be escapes from wildlife parks in this country. Sacred Ibis is a future candidate for Category C status, given proof that birds are of continental origin.

Brief views of a large raptor, almost certainly a Short-toed Snake Eagle, were obtained near Acle on 26th September 1998. Although never submitted to the BBRC, it would have been the first British record. On 17th October 1907 an exhausted immature Greater Spotted Eagle was captured on a boat in the North Sea 140 miles off the Norfolk coast and was later sent to the Zoological Gardens in London. Another much better claim for this species relates to an immature seen by Jim Vincent at Hickling on 8th March 1934. His description appears to rule out White-tailed Eagle (of which he was very familiar) and having seen skins of Greater Spotted Eagle at the South Kensington Natural History Museum in London a week later, he was convinced of its identification. Possibly the same bird was seen at Waxham on the 18th. There have been frequent sightings of Saker Falcon in recent years, a Category D species in Britain. However, none of the Norfolk records appear to have been submitted to the BBRC. All have been treated as escapes or 'of unknown origin'. Genuine vagrancy is certainly possible and the first published record for Norfolk involved one which was observed flying west offshore at Sheringham on 23rd October 1990 and later coasting in at Weybourne.

There are a remarkable number of old Purple Gallinule records in the county, but all appear to relate to escapes. The most recent occurrence, at Cley from July to September 1978, was considered to belong to the Indian race. However, one recently found dead in Bedfordshire proved to be of the American race and was considered to be a wild individual. Demoiselle Crane is a highly migratory species breeding from Turkey eastwards. Very small numbers are kept in captivity and all records in this country are considered to be escapes. The Demoiselle Crane has appeared in Norfolk on a number of occasions, but a remarkable party of six, observed at Horsey on 23rd April 1967, in fields close to the coast road was never traced as having escaped from captivity.

A skua in the Castle Museum, Norwich, originally labelled as a Great Skua, was obtained at Leadenhall Market in London by J. H. Gurney junior in October 1869. The original label still reads that it came from J. Gatcombe, Yarmouth. The specimen was re-identified in 1993 as a moderately dark morph South Polar Skua and relabelled as such. It has proved to be the first occurrence of South Polar Skua in the northern hemisphere, although the exact location where it was obtained remains a mystery. It is presumed to have been shot somewhere in the North Sea and brought into Yarmouth, possibly by one of the many fishing boats operating out of the port at that time.

Laughing Dove is an abundant species resident across large parts of Africa, the Middle East and the Indian subcontinent. It has recently expanded its range into Turkey and the Balkans. It is widely kept in captivity in Britain and there are several British records. The first was at West Walton Fen from 14th-16th July 1974. It is considered that vagrancy is not impossible, but the Norfolk record, along with all British records, remains in Category E.

A Northern Mockingbird at Blakeney Point in August 1971 was considered almost certainly to have escaped from captivity. The bird was present for nine days and filmed by the then warden Ted Eales. There are two old records of Eastern Meadowlark for the county, both surprisingly obtained at South Walsham, the first in 1854 and the other in 1876. It seems more than a little odd that two Eastern Meadowlarks should be found at the same Norfolk village. It would appear that the second specimen was perhaps incorrectly labelled or more likely a fraudulent attempt to pass the specimen off as British-taken. Another was shot in Suffolk in 1860 and this specimen remains at the Castle Museum, Norwich. The BOURC considers these records, plus another in the pre-1871 period as unacceptable. Yet another American species, Yellow-headed Blackbird, has been recorded on two occasions within living memory. One at Surlingham in the mid-1960s and seen by E. A. Ellis in fields close to his house for several days, whilst another, or perhaps the same bird, was at Horstead for over a week and fed in kale fields with flocks of Common

Starlings. Unfortunately neither record was submitted to the BBRC.

The infamous Indigo Bunting at Wells, present in late October 1988, has attracted much interest and discussion over the years, particularly relating to its age, moult and origin. However, despite the species being admitted to Category A of the British List two years earlier, the Norfolk record remains held in Category E. The circumstances of its occurrence, thought by many to be credible, were not considered good enough to get it accepted as a wild bird by the BBRC. Similar circumstances surround the occurrence of the Chestnut Bunting found at Salthouse on 30th May 1998. Chestnut Bunting is a long distance migrant, but despite this and the fact that it is a relatively uncommon species in captivity, all British records remain in either Category D or E. Perhaps a more likely candidate for acceptance into Category A in the future is Red-headed Bunting, although this species was at one time a common bird in captivity. There have been at least 13 records of this central Asian species in the county, the first at Cley in June 1960. Its status has been difficult to assess, but all records are considered to relate to escapes. Interestingly, however, all except one of these occurrences have been during the spring passage period, extreme dates being 2nd May and 27th June. Included in these is one on the Corton light vessel, 10km off Hopton, in June 1964.

Many other species have been recorded in Norfolk, all of which have almost certainly escaped from captivity or are of unknown origin. There are too many to list here, but *The Birds of Norfolk* (Taylor *et al* 1999) included a selected list of the Category E species known to have occurred in the county up to the end of 1998.

Bibliography

Allard, P. R. 1990. *The Birds of Great Yarmouth.* Norfolk and Norwich Naturalists' Society.

Anon, June 1908. *Catalogue of the Birds and Animals of the Tolhouse Museum, Great Yarmouth.*

Babington, C. 1884-1886. *Catalogue of the Birds of Suffolk.* John Van Voorst, London.

Barsted, C. P. & Brown, B. J. (eds). *Lowestoft Field Club Bulletin* 1968 & 1969.

Bishop, B. 1983. *Cley Marsh and its Birds.* Boydell, Woodbridge.

Bloomfield, A. I. 1993. *Birds of the Holkham Area.* Published privately by the author.

Browne, Sir Thomas. 1605-1682. *Notes and Letters on the Natural History of Norfolk, More especially of the Birds and Fishes* with notes from Thomas Southwell 1902. Jarrold, London.

Cramp, S. (ed). 1988. *Handbook of the Birds of Europe, the Middle East and Africa. The Birds of the Western Palearctic.* Vol. V. Oxford University Press, Oxford.

Dunmore, G. E. (ed). *Norfolk Bird Report* 1998-2007.

Easy, G. M. S. (ed). *Cambridgeshire Bird Club Report* 1963-1967.

Evans, L. G. R. 1994. *Rare Birds in Britain 1800-1990.* LGRE Publications Ltd.

Evans, L. G. R. 1998. *Rare Birds in Norfolk.* LGRE Publications Inc.

Ewans, M. 1992. *The Battle for the Broads.* Terence Dalton, Lavenham.

Frost, C. 1987. *The History of British Taxidermy.* Published privately by the author.

Frost, C. 1989. *The Ogilvie Bird Collection.* Published privately by the author.

Gantlett, S.J.M. 1986. *A Checklist of the Birds of Cley.*

Golley, M. 1998. *The Cley Year – A Birder's Guide.* Hill House, Holt.

Jones, E. W. P. (ed). *Great Yarmouth Bird Club Newsletter* 1992-2001.

Lockwood, W. B. 1984. The Oxford Book of British Bird Names. Oxford University Press, Oxford.

Lubbock, R. 1845. *Observations on the Fauna of Norfolk* (new edition by T. Southwell 1879). Jarrold, Norwich.

Madge, S. & Burn, H. 1998. *Wildfowl – an identification guide to the ducks, geese and swans of the world.* Christopher Helm, London.

Moyes, J. A. W. 1984. Wisbech Sewage Farm – The End. *Norfolk Bird Report* 1983: 355-358.

Moyes, J. A. W. 1986. Wisbech Sewage Farm – the final chapter. *Norfolk Bird Report* 1985: 255.

Naylor, K. A. 1996. *Rare Birds of Norfolk.* Published privately by the author.

Norfolk Ornithologists' Association. *Holme Bird Observatory Log-book* 1969, 1970 & 1977.

Paget, C. J. & Paget, J. 1834. *Sketch of the Natural History of Great Yarmouth and its Neighbourhood.* F. Skill, Yarmouth.

Palmer, P. 2000. *First for Britain and Ireland 1600-1999.* Arlequin Press, Chelmsford.

Pashley, H. N. 1925. *Notes on the Birds of Cley, Norfolk.* H. F. & G. Witherby, London.

Patterson, A. H. 1904. *Nature in Eastern Norfolk*. Methuen, London.

Patterson, A. H. 1929. *Wild-fowlers and Poachers*. Methuen, London.

Piotrowski, S. 2003. *The Birds of Suffolk*. Christopher Helm, London.

Richardson, R. A. 1964-1967. *Personal Diary Entries*.

Riviere, B. B. 1930. *A History of the Birds of Norfolk*. Witherby, London.

Seago, M. J. (ed). *Norfolk Bird Report* 1953-1997.

Seago, M. J. 1967. *Birds of Norfolk*. Jarrold, Norwich.

Seago, M. J. 1977. *Birds of Norfolk*. (2nd edn) Jarrold, Norwich.

Sheppard, R. & Whitear, W. 1826. A Catalogue of the Norfolk and Suffolk Birds, with Remarks. *Transactions of the Linnean Society* 15: 1-62.

Shirihai, H., Gargallo, G. & Helbig, J. 2001. *Sylvia Warblers – Identification, taxonomy and phylogeny of the genus Sylvia*. Christopher Helm, London.

Snow, D. W. & Perrins, C. M. 1998. *The Birds of the Western Palearctic, Concise Edition*. Vol. 2. Oxford University Press, Oxford.

Southwell, T. 1890. *The Birds of Norfolk* Vol. 3. John Van Voorst and Gurney & Jackson, London.

Southwell, T. 1898. *Catalogue of the British Birds in the Collection of Mr. E. M. Connop Of Rollesby Hall, Norfolk*.

Southwell, T. 1902. *Notes and Letters on the Natural History of Norfolk more especially the Birds and Fishes* from the MSS. of Sir Thomas Browne (1605-1682). Jarrold, London.

Sparkes, T. & Lines, J. 2008. *Chapters in the Life of Robert Marsham Esq. F.R.S. of Stratton Strawless, Norfolk*.

Stevenson, H. 1866-90. *The Birds of Norfolk* Vols. 1-3. John Van Voorst and Gurney & Jackson, London.

Stoddart, A. M. & Joyner, S. C. 2005. *The Birds of Blakeney Point*. Wren Publishing, Sheringham.

Svensson, L. 1992. *Identification Guide to European Passerines*. 4th edition. Stockholm.

Taylor, M. 1987. *The Birds of Sheringham*. Poppyland, North Walsham

Taylor, M. 2002. *Guardian Spirit of the East Bank*. Wren Publishing, Sheringham.

Taylor, M., Seago, M., Allard, P. & Dorling, D. 1999. *The Birds of Norfolk*. Pica Press, East Sussex.

Ticehurst, C. B. 1932. *A History of the Birds of Suffolk*. Gurney and Jackson, London.

Turner, E. L. 1926. *Bird Watching on Scolt Head*. Country Life, London.

Witherby, H. F., Jourdain, F. C. R., Ticehurst, N. F. & Tucker, B. W. 1938. *The Handbook of British Birds*. Vol. 1. London.

Index